QUANTUM CHEMISTRY

Prentice-Hall Chemistry Series
Wendell M. Latimer, *Editor*

QUANTUM CHEMISTRY

by

KENNETH S. PITZER

Professor of Chemistry, University of California

PRENTICE-HALL, INC.
Englewood Cliffs, N. J.

First printing................... May, 1953
Second printing.............. August, 1954
Third printing............... March, 1958
Fourth Printing.......... February, 1960

Printed in the United States of America
74716-C

PREFACE

For a number of years the author has taught a course in Quantum Theory for students of chemistry at the University of California. The present book was planned in the light of this experience to meet the needs of the typical physical chemist. Quantum mechanics is a subject which naturally leads the investigator into advanced mathematics if he wishes to add to the theory. However, in the writer's opinion, it is both possible and desirable for the chemist to learn the fundamentals of quantum mechanics as soon as he has completed the general courses in calculus, physics and physical chemistry, and has obtained some familiarity with chemical thermodynamics and with the experimental results of atomic physics. Further mathematical techniques can readily be added later.

There are already several excellent books on quantum mechanics with full consideration of the mathematical methods. Some of these lay greater emphasis on topics of chemical interest than others. There are also excellent qualitative discussions of the applications of quantum theory to chemistry, particularly chemical bonds. In avoiding mathematics a book of the latter type necessarily omits any real treatment of the fundamentals of quantum theory. The present volume represents an attempt to combine in part the advantages of both types of books mentioned above. This is possible because the fundamental structure of quantum theory and a few illustrative applications can be presented at a lower mathematical level than would be appropriate to a complete treatment of quantum mechanics. However, the rigorous treatment of even a few topics gives the reader a foundation for the critical examination and real understanding of most of the applications of chemical interest, even if the mathematical details are omitted in many of the applications.

The text is designed to permit its use for either a semester or a year course. This flexibility is possible because the basic principles of quantum theory can be covered in less than a semester. Then the selection of chemical applications can be adjusted to the time available and the interests of the students and instructor. Indeed the selection of these applications is necessarily somewhat arbitrary both with respect to a course and with respect to a book such as this one.

There are many topics of more mathematical nature or of interest principally for reference purposes. These have been treated in the Appendices which number twenty-four in all. These appendices will aid the reader in completing his knowledge of a given topic or in the application of the principles to specific problems.

Since this is not intended to be a complete treatise, only a very limited number of specific references have been given. General references for further study are suggested at the end of each chapter and it is intended that the reader should obtain there the specific references to the original literature, together with detailed accounts of the contributions of various investigators. If in this procedure I seem to have slighted any particular investigator, I am truly sorry.

In a book of this character which includes the fields of mechanics, thermodynamics, statistical mechanics, spectroscopy, electricity and magnetism, etc., it is impossible to select a completely satisfactory set of symbols. For example T is very well established for both kinetic energy and temperature, yet we occasionally wish to express the ratio of kinetic energy to temperature. I have used broadly established symbols wherever possible but have had to make arbitrary selections in some cases. Also it seemed best at times to shift symbols for a given quantity to avoid confusion or to conform more closely with practice in another field of application.

I am indebted to my various colleagues, both past and present, on the faculty at the University of California, for innumerable discussions which have contributed to this book. I must mention in particular Professor W. D. Gwinn, who has participated in teaching the quantum theory course here recently, and Professor W. F. Libby, now at the University of Chicago, who helped organize the course originally and who has taken a continuing interest. I am happy to acknowledge with thanks the suggestions of Professors W. T. Simpson, F. A. Matsen, D. H. Templeton, J. H. Hildebrand, G. C. Pimentel, and Robert Jastrow who read all or part of the book in either the present or a preliminary mimeographed edition. And finally, I wish to acknowledge with especial appreciation the contribution of my wife, Jean Mosher Pitzer, who not only improved many of these sentences, but also gave the encouragement necessary for their writing.

Kenneth S. Pitzer

CONTENTS

vii

QUANTUM CHEMISTRY

Chapter 1

PARTICLES OR WAVES; STATIONARY STATES

1a. The nature of physical theory. At the beginning of the study of a theory which is highly abstract and mathematical, it is well to remember that the fundamental facts of physical science are experimental observations. If a theory is to deal with these experimental observations it is essential that the concepts of the theory be synonymous with measurable quantities. This was naturally attained in dealing with mechanical phenomena of ordinary scale: masses of grams, distances of meters, etc. Thus in studying the motion of a pendulum one may observe the exact position at each instant throughout the motion, in addition to the amplitude and frequency of the oscillation.

Relatively simple mathematical equations describe the behavior of a pendulum provided the amplitude is small and friction is neglected. These limitations can be removed by appropriate complications in the theory. Within the range of length, weight, etc., of practical interest the behavior of any given pendulum can be calculated to high accuracy and with a reasonable expenditure of effort. The fact that the theory of the pendulum is a fully integrated and consistent part of classical or Newtonian mechanics further simplifies this section of science. However, it should always be remembered that a theory is a condensed representation of experimental results and is necessarily valid only over the range of variables covered by experiment. One may apply the pendulum equations to a simple pendulum of length 10^{-21} cm. but one has no reason to believe the calculated results. Nor is this any significant limitation, since such a pendulum is quite outside the range of experimental feasibility.

As the frontier of science moved beyond the realm of ordinary scale mechanical phenomena, models were proposed relating the new phenomenon by analogy to things familiar.   Thus a model of elastic colliding balls of negligible volume was proposed for a gas.   The calculated pressure-volume behavior agrees with the observations on gases at low pressure.   However, such other items as the number, mass, and velocities of the balls are not observed in simple gas experiments; hence one has thereby no real knowledge of these quantities. By contrast the number, mass, and velocities of billiard balls are directly measurable.   Moreover, in applying Newtonian mechanics to the kinetic theory model of a gas, one extrapolated far beyond the established range of mass.

The successes in extrapolating Newtonian mechanics in one direction to astronomical phenomena and in the other to molecular behavior in kinetic theory led some scientists to overlook the distinctions mentioned above and to believe the unobserved details of their models.   In a number of cases new types of experiment disproved these details.   While reinterpretation or discard of the model is required in such a case, the real part of the theory, the equations that relate observable quantities, is just as valid and useful as before.

Despite the dangers in the use of models to develop physical theory, they are a great aid to human imagination.   Many persons, the writer included, tend to think first in terms of qualitative physical phenomena and to follow with the mathematics appropriate to the model so conceived.   Such individuals should not discard models but rather remind themselves frequently of the distinction between the concepts established by experiment and the parts which are only figments of imagination.

Since quantum mechanics represents a non-Newtonian behavior of mechanical systems, the human mind does not naturally conceive models following quantum behavior.   From time to time pseudo-classical models will be proposed for atomic systems, which are intended to help understanding of quantum behavior.   The limitations of such models are usually obvious but should never be overlooked.

It has been said that quantum mechanics contains the solution of all chemical problems.   Until mathematical methods advance a long way, this will remain an unverifiable assertion, even though there is no reason to doubt its truth.   Quantum mechanics does tie into a single theory a number of otherwise unrelated phenomena of very simple electronic and atomic systems which were inexplicable on any model involving Newtonian or classical mechanics. This is important in itself. In addition qualitative or semiquantitative applications of quantum mechanics frequently yield equations of a form which can be applied empirically to chemical phenomena with considerable success. These latter reasons are quite sufficient to justify the important place accorded to quantum mechanics in chemical theory.

1b. Light as a wave motion. We now take up some of the experimental phenomena which required the development of a quantum theory and which point up its principal features. The order will be dictated by convenience of presentation rather than historical sequence, although dates will be mentioned.

Newton suggested that light might be interpreted as a stream of particles. However, as the phenomena of interference were investigated (Young and Fresnel, early nineteenth century) the particle theory fell into discard. At that time a particle, by definition, was assumed to obey Newton's laws of motion, and no stream of such particles could show diffraction phenomena on passing through a grating.

Mathematical expressions had been developed for the behavior of wave motions such as sound waves or surface waves on water. These wave motions showed diffraction effects, consequently it was natural to develop a wave model for diffraction phenomena in light. Since there was no known medium in which the wave motion might be taking place, the ether was postulated. This theory was highly successful in relating the observed light intensity pattern to such quantities as the dimensions of the apparatus and the line spacing in a grating in terms of a calculated wave length of the hypothetical wave motion. However, remembering our discussion of such models, we note that the ether was still not experimentally observed and hence was strictly hypothetical.

All attempts to detect experimentally the ether or any property thereof have been unsuccessful. The famous Michelson-Morley experiment (1887) attempted to measure the velocity of a piece of laboratory apparatus with respect to the ether. Since no velocity could be detected, one was led to the conclusion that the velocity of light was the same as measured by any observer regardless of the relative motion of the observers. While this was inconsistent with the supposition of an ether pervading all space, it in no way diminished the validity of the "wave" equations for diffraction phenomena.

1c. Particle nature of light. Another difficulty with the wave theory of light arose when the photoelectric effect was discovered by Hertz in 1887. Subsequent investigators of the effect established two facts clearly:

1. When monochromatic light impinges on a metallic surface, electrons are ejected with energies ranging up to a maximum value E, given by the equation

$$E = h\nu - W \tag{1.1}$$

in which ν is the frequency of the light calculated on the wave theory, h is a fundamental physical constant, and W is an energy constant characteristic of the metal used; W has values between zero and five electron volts for most metals.

2. The energy distribution of the electrons emitted is entirely independent of the intensity of the light. In fact, by using very low light intensity and small metal particles it is possible to show that in some cases an electron is ejected before sufficient energy has been absorbed on the basis of the wave theory. This was done by E. Meyer and W. Gerlach (1914), who detected the ejection of the electron by having the metal particles suspended in an electric field and watching their motion.

These results suggested that light has characteristics belonging to a kind of non-Newtonian particles which *act like a wave motion when observed in large numbers*, i.e., all phenomena involving large numbers of these particles can be interpreted by the classical wave theory of light. However, none of the phenomena involving small numbers of them is amenable to such a treatment. In particular, an electron is ejected by one and only one light particle. Lewis named this particle the *photon* in 1926 in the course of discussions of certain logical questions which arise from the particle theory. The term *light quantum* is also used.

The second clear point of the photoelectric experiment was that the energy of the photon was $h\nu$ even though all photons had the same velocity. Obviously this was beyond classical physics. The interpretation of the photoelectric effect, including Eq. (1.1), was due to Einstein (1905). It was one of the first extensions and confirmations of the light quantum concept introduced by Planck in 1901.

Planck originally postulated the energy value $h\nu$ for ultimate units of light in order to account for the spectral distribution of blackbody radiation. However, since the interpretation of this phenomenon seems to us less simple, its discussion will be postponed to Section 7j.

Planck's constant, h, is the fundamental numerical constant of quantum theory with a value of approximately *6.62 × 10⁻²⁷ erg sec.* Values of various physical constants are tabulated in Appendix 24. Some authors use the symbol $\hbar$ for the quantity $h/2\pi$.

1d. Relativistic effects. While we shall make no attempt to give an adequate account of the theory of relativity, certain particular aspects are very important. These concern primarily the variation of mass for particles whose velocity approaches that of light.[1]

Einstein's theory of relativity is based on two postulates. First, there is no such thing as absolute motion, only motion of one object relative to another. Second, the velocity of light is finite and the same to all observers regardless of their relative motion. In addition the laws of conservation of energy and momentum were retained in the new theory. It will be noted that the postulates assume agreement with the Michelson-Morley experiment. The following equations result, wherein m is the apparent mass of the particle with velocity v, momentum p, and kinetic energy T.

$$m = m_0 \left(1 - \frac{v^2}{c^2} \right)^{-1/2} \tag{1.2}$$

$$p = mv \tag{1.3}$$

$$T = (m - m_0)c^2 = m_0c^2 \left[\left(1 - \frac{v^2}{c^2} \right)^{-1/2} - 1 \right] \tag{1.4}$$

Here m_0 is the mass of the particle at rest, the *"rest mass,"* and c is the velocity of light, approximately 3.00×10^{10} cm./sec.

From Eqs. (1.2) to (1.4) it is apparent that the mass, momentum, and kinetic energy of a particle of finite rest mass all approach infinity as its velocity approaches that of light. Since these quantities are not infinite for a photon we conclude that the photon rest mass must be zero. Then we have for the energy of a photon

$$E = h\nu = mc^2 \tag{1.5}$$

and for the momentum and mass of a photon

$$p = mc = h\nu/c \tag{1.6}$$

$$m = h\nu/c^2 \tag{1.7}$$

[1] For an account of the theory of relativity, see, for example, Bergmann, P. G., *Introduction to the Theory of Relativity*, New York: Prentice-Hall, Inc., 1946.

It may be noted that mass itself is no longer conserved in the relativity theory. Since the proportionality constant between mass and energy, $c^2 = 9 \times 10^{20}$, is such a large number, mass appears to be conserved in reactions where the energy effects are small. However, in nuclear reactions where the energy changes are large, observable mass differences occur which agree perfectly with this idea. We can then write for the total energy of any particle (including a photon)

$$E = mc^2 = T + m_0 c^2 \tag{1.5'}$$

where the $m_0 c^2$ represents a sort of potential energy. Except for the positron-electron annihilation reaction it has not been possible to release all this rest mass potential energy. In nuclear reactions the decrease in rest mass potential energy appears as kinetic energy of the product particles together with emitted photons (γ rays).

1e. Collisional properties of photons; the Compton effect. In 1922 A. H. Compton discovered the collisional energy loss required of photons as particles of negligible rest mass. He studied the scattering of x-rays of 0.7 A wave length by various light elements whose electrons are bound to the atom with energies small with respect to the kinetic energy of the photon, and observed an energy loss (increase in wave length) of the photon exactly in agreement with a particle calculation. The calculation follows (see Fig. 1.1).

Suppose the initial energy of photon to be $h\nu_0$ and of the electron, zero. After the collision the values will be $h\nu$ and

$$m_0 c^2 \left(\frac{1}{\sqrt{1 - v^2/c^2}} - 1 \right),$$

where m_0 is the rest mass of the electron and v its velocity.

Conservation of energy gives

$$h\nu_0 = h\nu + m_0 c^2 \left(\frac{1}{\sqrt{1 - v^2/c^2}} - 1 \right) \tag{1.8}$$

Conservation of momentum along original direction of photon's path requires

$$\frac{h\nu_0}{c} = \frac{h\nu}{c} \cos \theta + \frac{m_0 v}{\sqrt{1 - v^2/c^2}} \cos \phi \tag{1.9}$$

where θ is the angle of deflection for the photon and ϕ is the angle between the path of the electron after the collision and the original direction of the photon. Similarly, conservation in the perpendicular direction requires

$$0 = -\frac{h\nu}{c}\sin\theta + \frac{m_0 v}{\sqrt{1 - v^2/c^2}}\sin\phi \qquad (1.10)$$

Transposing terms in θ in (1.9) and (1.10) to the left side, squaring, and adding to eliminate ϕ yields

$$\alpha^2 c^2\left(1 - 2\frac{\nu}{\nu_0}\cos\theta + \frac{\nu^2}{\nu_0^2}\right) = \frac{v^2}{1 - v^2/c^2} \qquad (1.11)$$

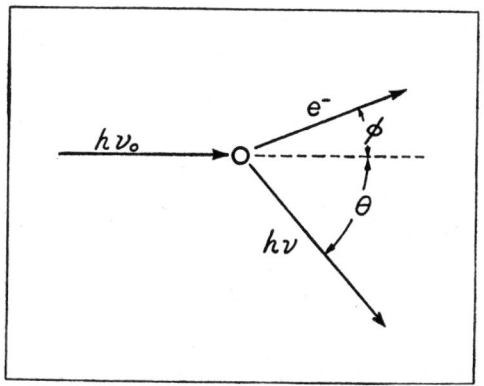

Fig. 1.1.   Coordinate system for a Compton-effect collision.

where $\alpha = h\nu_0/m_0 c^2$ is the ratio of the initial photon energy to the rest mass energy of an electron. Cumbersome but straightforward transformations of Eq. (1.8) yield an expression which may be combined with (1.11) to eliminate v and obtain

$$\alpha\left(\frac{\nu}{\nu_0}\right)(1 - \cos\theta) = \frac{\nu_0 - \nu}{\nu_0} \qquad (1.12)$$

Also with the relation between wave length, frequency, and velocity,

$$\lambda = c/\nu \qquad (1.13)$$

this rearranges to

$$\Delta\lambda = \frac{h}{m_0 c}(1 - \cos\theta) = 0.0242(1 - \cos\theta) \quad \text{A} \qquad (1.14)$$

for change in wave length.

Equation (1.14) shows that the change in wave length is independent of the initial wave length providing the electron is initially at rest but free or sufficiently so as to warrant the application of the equation. One interesting consequence is that high-energy photons lose larger fractions of their energy in electron collisions than do those of lower energy. This may be attributed to the larger mass of the high-energy photons. It will apply to collisions of any particle having a velocity near c with another particle at rest, provided neither particle disintegrates.

If the electron initially is effectively free but is in motion with a momentum not negligible with respect to that of the photon, a similar calculation applies.

1f. Wave properties of ordinary particles. If photons are similar to ordinary particles we might expect electrons, protons, neutrons, atoms, molecules, and all solid bodies to possess wave properties to a certain extent since photons exhibit them. L. de Broglie (1925) first stated the relations clearly. His results are embodied partially in the fundamental equation

$$\lambda = h/p \tag{1.15}$$

This equation is a direct analogue of Eq. (1.6).

A beam of electrons can be produced by a hot filament surrounded by a positively charged metallic case with a hole or slit in it. Such a beam will have a wave length of

$$h/\sqrt{2mE} \quad \text{or} \quad 12.2/\sqrt{V} \quad \text{A}$$

according to Eq. (1.15), where V is the acceleration potential in volts. Thus if V is a few hundred or thousand volts, the wave length is of the same order of magnitude as interatomic distances in crystals. Davisson and Germer showed in 1927 that such beams produce beautiful diffraction patterns when scattered by crystals.

The patterns observed have high intensities exactly where monochromatic x-rays of the same wave length produce them. The comparison is somewhat complicated because of the larger scattering probabilities for electrons. However, the lattice spacings observed with electrons for thin layers of material and with x-rays for thick layers are exactly the same.

Electron diffraction has been most useful in the investigation of molecular structure in the gaseous state. A relatively short path through most gases at ordinary pressures leads to large scattering, whereas x-rays show little scattering under such conditions. When fast electrons impinge on a molecule consisting of two or more atoms, they are scattered either by inelastic collisions, in which large fractions of their energy are transferred to electrons in the target molecules resulting in ionization, or by elastic collisions in which the energy transferred is small because the molecules are thousands of times heavier than the projectile electron.   The elastically scattered electrons have wave lengths very nearly identical with that of the incident beam.   The scattered waves center about each of the atoms constituting the target molecule and proceed to interfere with each other and the primary beam.   If the wave length λ is of the right order of magnitude, the interference causes observable variations in the intensity of the scattered electrons along directions perpendicular to the direction of the incident beam, forming rings in the perpendicular plane.   From the spacing and relative intensities, the interatomic distances can be determined[2] in terms of the wave length λ. In practice, the wave length may be measured directly by use as a target of a thin gold film in which the interatomic distances are known, or it may be calculated from the accelerating voltage used in the beam source and the fundamental Eq. (1.15).

A considerable number of experiments testing Eq. (1.15) have been performed with atomic instead of electron beams; H, He, Li, Cd, Hg atoms and the neutron all have given satisfactory evidence of adherence to Eq. (1.15).   Thus the wave-particle duality appears to be generally valid.

1g. Wave-particle duality. We now see that some properties of both ordinary particles and light are most easily explained on a wave basis.   In other respects even light appears to be composed of discrete particles.   How is this apparent contradiction to be resolved?   The solution is due chiefly to Born (1926) who proposed that the future path of a particle is a matter of probability.   This probability is given by the wave mathematics; hence if large numbers of particles are involved, the fraction following a given path follows from the probability of that path.

One may assume that with every particle process is associated a guiding wave.   In time this wave becomes more extended in space—possibly diffracted into several or more separate regions.   The particle actually follows some particular path but this path cannot be

---

[2] For an account of the electron diffraction method as applied to molecular structure see, Brockway, L. O., *Revs. Modern Phys.*, **8**, 231 (1936).

predicted exactly. One can predict only the relative probability of various paths. If single particles are detected they will be found sometimes here, at other times elsewhere, according to the wave intensity.

All attempts to detect the waves themselves, beyond relative numbers of particles, have failed. Thus the only reason for speaking of waves is the fact that the mathematics employed in predicting these probabilities is also appropriate to real wave motions, i.e., sound. Indeed some of the results of quantum theory can be calculated from types of mathematics quite unlike that for wave motions. However, the writer believes that the wave concept assists human understanding and does no harm provided its real meaning is understood.

This wave-particle concept is put in mathematical form by defining a wave function, usually designated Ψ, which corresponds to the amplitude of a sound wave but in this case has no physical meaning itself. Then it is postulated that the probability of finding a particle at a given location is given by Ψ^2 (or $|\Psi|^2$ if Ψ is complex). This is consistent with the interpretation of light intensity as the square of the wave amplitude. Also it, of course, makes this probability necessarily positive or zero.

1h. Stationary states. Stationary states, in the sense of stationary total energy, exist for periodic motions in classical mechanics. For examples there are a frictionless pendulum and (approximately) the solar system. However, according to classical electrodynamic laws, such a state of affairs is not permitted for an atom composed of electrically charged particles. Such a system should gradually radiate its energy away. Likewise the idea that such an atom should maintain its stationary state after a collision with another atom is practically inconceivable classically. Nevertheless, the whole present picture of atoms is based on the idea that such persisting stationary energy states exist. They are peculiar even further in that they exist for only certain fixed energies, whereas the analogous classical states could exist for any energy within certain ranges.

There is still some similarity of the quantum mechanical atom to the classical expectation. An atom newly formed, with its electrons at large distances from the nucleus, will radiate much of its energy and allow the electrons to come closer to the nucleus. The peculiarities of quantum behavior lie in the stepwise nature of the radiation process and particularly in the final stationary state of lowest energy.

The most extensive experimental evidence for this concept of stationary states is the vast body of atomic spectra data. Making use of the idea of photons, we see that when an atom emits a photon it must lose a corresponding amount of energy. However, the photons emitted by a given kind of atom have only a few discrete colors with corresponding wave lengths and energies. The energy is of course $h\nu$, as discussed in Section 1c. Consequently, they must arise from changes between a relatively small number of discrete energy levels in the atoms themselves. This idea together with the equation,

$$E_2 - E_1 = h\nu = hc/\lambda \qquad (1.16)$$

was proposed by Bohr (1913), who then continued to set up a rather arbitrary model for calculating these energy levels. This latter part of the Bohr picture succeeded for the hydrogen atom but failed for all others. We shall not describe the detailed assumptions of Bohr[3] but will content ourselves at this point with the idea that for each atom there is a pattern of stationary states of various definite energies. This pattern may be worked out from the spectral data. In the simpler cases it may be calculated by methods which will be presented in later sections.

Another direct confirmation of this picture of stationary energy states for atoms is found in the experiments of Franck and Hertz (1914). Before atoms can emit energy in the form of light they must absorb the energy in some form. One method is to bombard the atoms with electrons of known energy. If the electron energy is less than that necessary for excitation to the first higher energy level, the collision must be *elastic*, and the energy given by the lightweight electron to the massive atom is negligible. With an electron energy above that of certain higher atomic energy levels, however, a transfer of energy to the atom can and does take place. The electron is observed to emerge from the collision with less kinetic energy, as required, and photons of the expected frequency begin to appear from the atoms, which fall back to their original lowest energy states after having been excited.

[3] For discussions of the old quantum theory of Bohr and others, see Pauling, L. and Wilson, E. B., Jr., *Introduction to Quantum Mechanics*, New York: McGraw-Hill Book Company, Inc., 1935, Chap. 2.

Not all the spectral lines corresponding to changes from one energy level to another actually appear in the observed spectrum.   There arise then *selection rules* which summarize the observed facts as to which lines actually appear.   These rules can also be derived from theory in the simpler cases.

The simplest atom is that of hydrogen, with a nucleus and a single electron.   Its energy level scheme is shown in various degrees of detail in Fig. 1.2.   Actually the selection rules and experimental

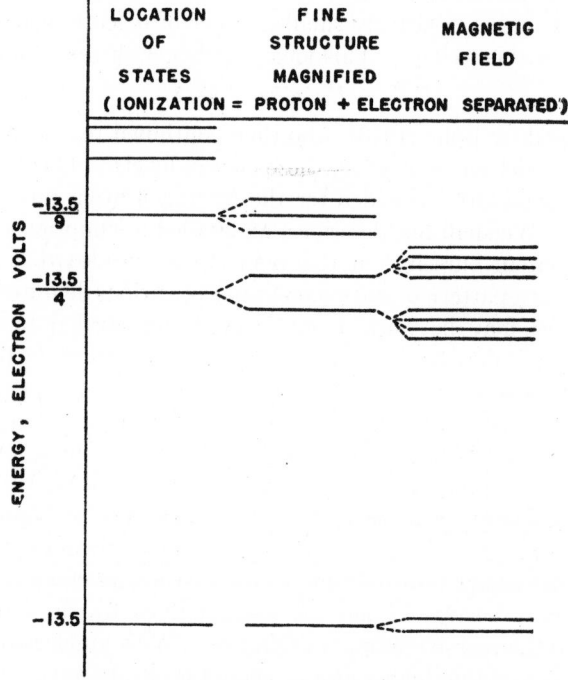

Fig. 1.2.   The energy levels of hydrogen.

difficulties are such that it would be difficult to work out this complete pattern from the observed spectra.   However, we may regard it as having been obtained in principle directly from experiments, even though actually the detailed mathematical theory was developed simultaneously.

li. Pauli exclusion principle and the periodic table; electron spin. Referring to Fig. 1.2, we see that in the most detailed pattern there are two very low energy levels followed by a group of eight at much higher energy.   Without further consideration we see at once a striking analogy to the periodic table with two elements, H and He, followed by a group of eight: Li, Be, B, C, N, O, F, and Ne.   If we examine things a little more carefully we find that the ionization potential (energy needed to remove one electron) of lithium is much smaller than for helium.   Thus if one electron in lithium is in the upper group it could be removed easily, while helium with its two electrons in the lower group would be very stable.   We postulate, then, that in many electron atoms only one electron can occupy a given "hydrogen-like" quantum state.   Pauli suggested this exclusion principle on this basis in 1925.

We may say just a bit more about the origin of the energy terms in Fig. 1.2.   It is found that an electron acts as if it were itself a small magnet with a definite magnetic moment.   This may be pictured as a small charged body spinning about its axis, and is often referred to as electron spin.   In a magnetic field the energy depends on the angle of orientation of the magnet with respect to the field. Classically this angle can have any value.   In quantum theory we are beginning to expect only discrete values, and we find them again here.   Only two angles are permitted for the orientation of an electron magnetic moment in an external field.   For this reason the lowest energy state for hydrogen appears double in a magnetic field but single otherwise.

The simplest experiment demonstrating the magnetic moment of an electron involves sending a beam of hydrogen atoms through an inhomogeneous magnetic field across their path.   An inhomogeneous field is one which is more intense near one pole than the other.   Thus if the north pole of an elementary magnet is in a more intense field than the south pole, the magnet will be drawn one way or the other depending on the orientation of the field and magnet.   For this reason a beam of hydrogen atoms is split up into two beams in such a field. Actually the proton has a magnetic moment also, but it is of a negligible order of magnitude compared with that of the electron.   This experiment (Stern and Gerlach, 1921) was actually first performed on silver atoms because they are more easily produced, but was later carried out with hydrogen atoms.

The energy states of an atom are indexed by the use of quantum numbers whose natural origin will be described later.   At this stage, we regard them merely as labels.   First comes the principal quantum number n, with values 1, 2, 3, . . . , which gives the energy of a hydrogen atom according to the formula

$$E = -13.54/n^2 \quad \text{(e.v.)} \tag{1.17}$$

Second is the angular quantum number l, which may have values 0, 1, . . . , $n - 1$, and which gives the amount of angular momentum in the motion of electron about nucleus.   (It will be shown later that this unit of angular momentum is $h/2\pi$.)   The motion of an electron around a nucleus constitutes a current of electricity in a more or less circular wire and consequently generates a magnetic moment. The orientation of this orbital magnetic moment in an applied field is given by a third quantum number m_l which can have the values $-l, \ldots -1, 0, +1, \ldots +l$.   Finally, there is the orientation of the intrinsic electron magnetic moment m_s, which can be either $+$ or $-$ and for reasons not yet apparent is given the values $+\frac{1}{2}$ and $-\frac{1}{2}$. Other essentially equivalent sets of quantum numbers can be devised but this set is convenient for most purposes.

When all four quantum numbers are given, a definite quantum state has been selected and only one electron can occupy it.   Since in the absence of a magnetic field m_s is unimportant for the energy, it is sometimes said that two electrons can occupy a state (spin ignored) provided their axes of spin are antiparallel and consequently one electron has $m_s = \frac{1}{2}$ and the other $m_s = -\frac{1}{2}$.

We shall return to the subject of atomic energy levels in a later section when additional mathematical theory has been developed.

Stationary energy states also exist for other types of periodic motion such as the rotation of molecules and the vibration of whole atoms within molecules.   These situations will also be considered in detail later.

1j. Wave-particles and the Heisenberg uncertainty principle. Having adopted the coexistence of particle and wave characteristics in all material phenomena, one is forced to wonder about the case of zero velocity particles, which corresponds to an infinite wave length.   Certainly an infinite wave length is close to no wave at all.   More particularly, we have learned to expect the particles to follow the accompanying waves and to be found in localities where the waves reinforce, and to be absent where they interfere.   Such defined regions obviously have dimensions of the order of magnitude of λ, the wave length.   The particle may be found anywhere within such regions and is found so in fact, the conformation of the density of the particle distribution to the amplitude of the wave being a statistical matter.

The simple sine or cosine wave with fixed λ does not allow one to know that the particle is definitely at any one of the infinite number of crests.   In order to locate a particle one superimposes simple sine or cosine waves with various amplitudes and wave lengths so that the total or *group* wave form has a finite group of peaks where the particle is known to be located and is zero everywhere else.   The possibility of this is well known mathematically.   The summation is known as the Fourier series or integral expansion.   In general

$$\Psi(x) = \int_0^\infty a(k) \sin 2\pi(kx - \nu t)\, dk \qquad (1.18)$$

where k is the wave number $1/\lambda$ and $a(k)$ is a weighting function. A more general formulation is

$$\Psi(x) = \int_0^\infty a(k) e^{2\pi i(kx - \nu t)}\, dk \qquad (1.19)$$

where $e^{i\theta} = \cos\theta + i\sin\theta$.

The probability of finding the particle is defined as Ψ^2. If Ψ is complex, as in Eq. (1.19), the probability function is $\Psi\Psi^*$, where Ψ^* is the complex conjugate of Ψ, i.e.,

$$\Psi^* = \int_0^\infty a(k) e^{-2\pi i(kx - \nu t)}\, dk \qquad (1.19')$$

By making $a(k)$ large over a range near some value k_0 and small elsewhere, one may obtain a result such as is shown in Fig. 1.3, where the particle is located somewhere between A and C.   The total uncertainty in the location is the distance from A to C, Δx.   Now the only way the component waves can interfere at A, reinforce at B, and interfere again at C is for the number of peaks in one component wave between A and C to be greater by one than the number of peaks in another component wave.   This difference in number of peaks in the interval means, of course, a difference in the wave number or an uncertainty in the true wave number.   Furthermore, the uncertainty in wave number, Δk, is such that over the region Δx it yields a difference in number of peaks of at least one, i.e., $\Delta k\, \Delta x \gtrsim 1$.   Since $p = hk = h/\lambda$, this leads to the expression

Ψ

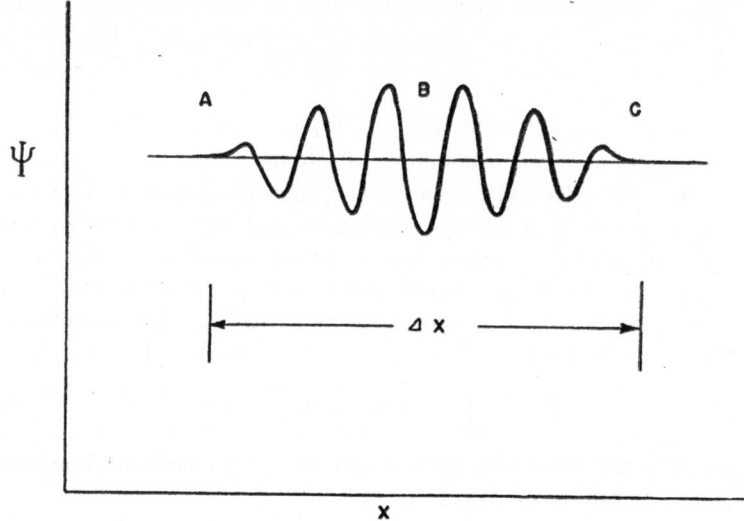

Fig. 1.3. A wave group.

$$\Delta p \, \Delta x \gtrless h \qquad (1.20)$$

which is one part of Heisenberg's uncertainty principle.

It may be desirable to present essentially the same argument in different terms. Consider the wave packet defined by superimposing with equal amplitudes waves in the range $k_0 - \delta$ to $k_0 + \delta$ for the wave number. Then Ψ becomes

$$
\begin{aligned}
\Psi &= \int_{-\delta}^{+\delta} e^{2\pi i[(k_0+y)x - \nu t]} \, dy \\
&= \frac{e^{2\pi i(k_0 x - \nu t)}\left(e^{2\pi i \delta x} - e^{-2\pi i \delta x}\right)}{2\pi i x} \\
&= \frac{e^{2\pi i(k_0 x - \nu t)} \sin 2\pi \, \delta x}{\pi x} \qquad (1.21)
\end{aligned}
$$

and the probability distribution is

$$\Psi \Psi^* = \left(\frac{\sin 2\pi \, \delta x}{\pi x}\right)^2 \qquad (1.22)$$

Normalization, i.e., dividing by

$$\left[\int_{-\infty}^{+\infty} \Psi \Psi^* \, dx\right]^{1/2} = (2\delta)^{1/2}$$

so that the total probability is unity, gives

$$\Psi = \frac{e^{2\pi i(k_0 x - \nu t)} \sin 2\pi \, \delta x}{\pi x \sqrt{2\delta}} \tag{1.23}$$

Graphical integration of $\int_{-1/2\delta}^{+1/2\delta} \Psi\Psi^* \, dx$ gives 0.87 as the chance of finding the particle within $\pm 1/2\delta$ of the point $x = 0$. In other words, the range Δx of x values which includes most chance of finding the particle is $1/\delta$ or

$$\delta \, \Delta x = 1 \tag{1.24}$$

Remembering $\delta = \Delta k$ from the statement of this example and that $\Delta p = h \, \Delta k$, one again finds

$$\Delta p \, \Delta x \cong h \tag{1.20}$$

There are several possible definitions of an uncertainty measure. The above examples have taken substantially the total range as that measure. More conventional quantities are the standard deviation or average deviation from the mean value. These quantities are smaller. It is possible to show[4] that for root mean square deviations from the mean values, the limiting minimum uncertainty is $h/4\pi$; thus

$$\Delta p_x \, \Delta x \geq h/4\pi \tag{1.25}$$

However, it is the idea rather than the exact magnitude that is important at this point. The assumption of this wave expression for the probability of particle behavior leads unequivocally to the conclusion that it is impossible to define both the location and momentum of a particle with perfect accuracy. This rather startling idea is most important for an understanding of quantal phenomena.

In Eq. (1.19) one notes that the factor νt appears in a similar way to the kx. Thus by considering Ψ as a function of t at some particular value of x, an entirely analogous situation arises, yielding the conclusion that ν and t may not be separately fixed with perfect precision. Likewise one obtains

$$\Delta \nu \, \Delta t \cong 1 \qquad E = h\nu$$
$$\Delta E \, \Delta t \cong h \tag{1.26}$$

The meaning of ν for a system other than a photon is not evident at this point. However, we shall see in Sections 2b through 2e that

[4] See, for example, Schiff, L. I., *Quantum Mechanics*, New York: McGraw-Hill Book Company, Inc., 1949, p. 54.

this same imaginary exponential expression involving the product Et in the exponent is of general validity.

These results may also be generalized to the three dimensions of ordinary space.

It is interesting to note that the uncertainty principle is consistent with relativity, whereas most of the quantum theory we are to present hereafter is not. Relativity generalizes the three space dimensions and one time dimension into a four-dimensional space time coordinate system. In this generalized system the product $\Delta p_x \cdot \Delta x$ for one of the three spacial coordinates corresponds to the product $\Delta E \, \Delta t$ for the fourth or time coordinate.

The entire subject of the uncertainty principle may also be discussed from a different point of view, namely, that of the possibilities of experimental observation together with the idea that a theory can be expected to predict only the results of possible experiments (observables). In this regard one can locate a particle only by having it scatter some other particle, which necessarily disturbs the first one. Thus one would take a different point of view if billiard balls could be located only by collisions with other billiard balls instead of collisions with photons. Quantitative calculation along these lines leads to the same equations given already.[5]

1k. Application of the uncertainty principle. The uncertainty principle underlies most of the features of the quantum theory. It has quantitative significance in its applications to thermodynamics and statistical mechanics (as shown in Chapter 7) and qualitative applications to many other problems.

Ordinarily the sum of sizes of a pair of particles is given by distance at which a sudden repulsive force arises. This is still true in quantum theory when potential energies, and thereby forces, are included. However, the uncertainty principle leads to another sort of particle size. If a particle is moving very slowly, its total momentum is small, so that the uncertainty in momentum is necessarily small. Consequently the wave function for the particle extends over considerable space, which means that the particle may interact with anything in that region. Thus a slow-moving neutron may act as if it were much larger than a fast neutron.

---

[5] See Dushman, S., *The Elements of Quantum Mechanics*, New York: John Wiley & Sons, Inc., 1938, p. 12; Born, M., *Atomic Physics*, 5th ed., London and Glasgow: Blackie and Son Ltd., 1951, p. 96.

Similarly, if a molecule exists for only a very short time, the uncertainty in time is necessarily small and the uncertainty in the energy is correspondingly large.   If this molecular lifetime (and maximum time uncertainty) is t, the range of energy indeterminateness is h/t.   By most experimental methods this indeterminateness is not noticed unless it is at least 0.01 cm.$^{-1}$ or 0.03 calorie per mole, which corresponds to a lifetime of 3.3×10^{-9} sec.

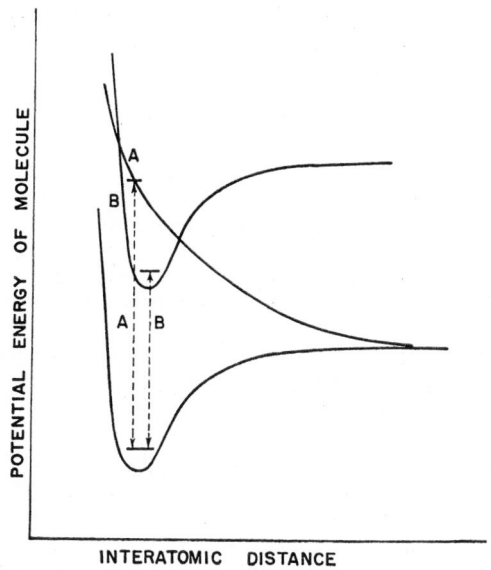

Fig. 1.4.   Potential-energy curves.

One example of this type of phenomenon arises when the excited state of a molecule contains enough energy to dissociate the molecule. If the state is repulsive (A in Fig. 1.4) so that the dissociation is virtually instantaneous, no discrete states are observed and the absorption spectrum is continuous.   One may say that the excited states are so short-lived and broad in energy as to overlap each other.

If the excited state is an attractive state (B in Fig. 1.4) but undergoes a spontaneous transition to a repulsive state within a time of the order of magnitude 10^{-11} to 10^{-10} sec., an absorption spectrum with blurred or broadened lines will arise.   This is known as *predissociation*.

GENERAL REFERENCES

Bohm, D., *Quantum Theory*, New York: Prentice-Hall, Inc., 1951, Chaps. 1–8.
Born, M., *Atomic Physics*, 5th ed., London and Glasgow: Blackie and Son Ltd., 1951.
Dushman, S., *The Elements of Quantum Mechanics*, New York: John Wiley & Sons, Inc., 1938, Chap. 10.
Heitler, W., *Elementary Wave Mechanics*, New York: Oxford University Press, 1945.
Persico, E., *Fundamentals of Quantum Mechanics*, New York: Prentice-Hall, Inc., 1950, Chaps. 1–4.

PROBLEMS

1.1 Show that the relativistic kinetic energy is $T = m^2v^2/(m + m_0)$ and that it approaches $\frac{1}{2}mv^2$ for low velocities and mc^2 for high velocities.

1.2 How does the ratio of kinetic energy to momentum, T/p, vary as the velocity increases from low values to that of light?

1.3 While the rest mass of a photon is commonly supposed to be exactly zero, most experimental phenomena are consistent with a very small value for this quantity.

(a) Derive an expression for the velocity of photons as a function of their frequency on the assumption that $h\nu = (m - m_0)c^2$.

(b) If the observed velocity of 500-kc radio waves is at least 99% of c, what is the upper limit to m_0?

1.4 If an electron of 1 A wave length is elastically scattered through an angle of 45° by a gaseous H atom initially at rest, what is the percentage change in wave length?

1.5 Calculate the wave lengths associated with (a) a proton with energy $450k$ (i.e., thermal energy at room temperature), (b) a 10^{-8} gm. particle with velocity 1 cm. per sec.

1.6 If a given state lasts only a time t_0, what is the minimum width of a spectral line arising from a transition to this state?

1.7(a) If a particle of mass m is known to be within a small space, say a cube 5×10^{-13} cm. on an edge, what is the uncertainty in its momentum?

(b) Even if the average momentum is zero, what must be the order of magnitude of the kinetic energy?

(c) Calculate this energy, in electron volts, for an electron and for a neutron. Discuss the reasonableness of postulating electrons to be particles within an atomic nucleus. Note that relativistic expressions must be used for the case of electrons.

1.8 A beam of mercury atoms is produced by collimating the atoms which escape from a vessel of mercury at 500°C. The beam travels 100 cm. from the final slit to the detector. Use the uncertainty principle to estimate the smallest spot that could possibly be obtained at the detector.

Chapter 2

THE ELEMENTS OF WAVE MECHANICS

We now come to the problem of extending these basic concepts of quantum theory into a system of mechanics which will apply to more complex problems, in particular, problems involving potential energy. This can be done only by further postulates whose real substantiation comes from the experimental verification of the calculated results. However, we shall attempt to show that these new postulates grow quite naturally out of the ideas of the first chapter.

The various presentations of quantum mechanics differ as to which postulates are regarded as fundamental and which are derived therefrom. Furthermore, one should remember that the matrix algebra formulation of quantum mechanics was discovered by Heisenberg (1925) slightly before the independent wave mechanical formulation by Schrödinger (1926). Despite these differences in expression, nonrelativistic quantum mechanics forms a unified self-consistent theory whose application to a wide variety of problems is unambiguous in principle, although sometimes involving as yet insuperable mathematical difficulties in practice.

There is no doubt that this theory is of limited scope. The very term nonrelativistic quantum mechanics indicates this. Also it appears to be incapable of dealing adequately with events which create or destroy positrons, mesons, etc. While it is desirable to produce an adequate theory in these extended regions of science, there is no likelihood that such a new theory would replace the present nonrelativistic quantum mechanics. Our present classical or Newtonian mechanics is contained both in relativity and in quantum mechanics. However, one would be most foolish to use either of the more extended theories to analyze the vibrations of a piano string or a suspension bridge.

For these reasons, one of the important subjects of this chapter is the boundary where quantum effects become negligible. The useful criteria vary with the type of phenomenon under consideration, but necessarily involve a comparison of Planck's constant with some combination of the measured properties having the same dimensions.

Many molecular (as contrasted with electronic) phenomena lie near this classical-quantum boundary. Also it is often feasible to obtain a quantitative classical treatment when the quantum treatment is too difficult mathematically. It is then very important in making comparisons with experiment to recognize the order in which the experimental results would deviate if quantum effects were present.

2a. Quantization. The natural way in which discrete quantum states arise in wave mechanics can be seen by considering a particle constrained to move on the circumference of a circle. Taking the simple wave function

$$\Psi = e^{2\pi i(kx - \nu t)} \qquad (2.1)$$

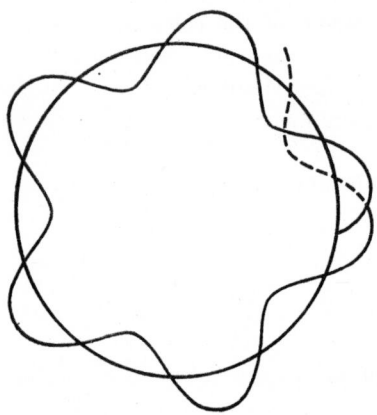

x now represents distance around the circle, so we substitute $r\phi$, where r is the constant radius and ϕ the angle.

$$\Psi = e^{2\pi i(kr\phi - \nu t)} \qquad (2.2)$$

If we plot the real (or the imaginary) part of Ψ as a function of ϕ with ν and t constant, we obtain in general a result such as is shown in Fig. 2.1, where it is obvious that Ψ takes a new value after a complete revolution (2π in ϕ). Thus a given point

Fig. 2.1.   Quantization of rotation.

on the circle gives no definite value to Ψ. This difficulty is avoided, however, if k is given a specific value so that Ψ joins on to itself; i.e., becomes *single valued*. The appropriate value is

$$kr(2\pi) = \pm n \qquad \text{(an integer)}$$
$$k = \pm n/2\pi r \qquad (2.3)$$

Since the momentum and energy are related to k we obtain

$$p = hk = \pm n(h/2\pi r) \qquad (2.4)$$
$$E = p^2/2m = n^2 h^2/8\pi^2 m r^2 \qquad (2.5)$$

Thus the very natural requirement that Ψ be *single valued* has led to the discrete set of energy levels given by Eq. (2.5) with integral values of n.

Since positive and negative values of n give different momenta (with respect to sign), we assume that each represents a possible state even though they have equal energy.   Such sets of states of equal energy are known as *degenerate states*.   The state with n zero, however, is single or nondegenerate.

2b. Momentum and energy as operators.   The basic postulates of quantum theory may be formulated in terms of the concept of mathematical operators.   An operator simply does something to the quantity operated upon.   Possible operations are: multiplication by 2, division by π, or partial differentiation with respect to x.   Multiplication of operators is not necessarily commutative; i.e., the result may depend on the order of operation.   Thus if the two operations are multiplication by x and differentiation with respect to x one finds

$$\frac{\partial}{\partial x}\left[xf(x)\right] = f(x) + xf'(x) \neq (x)\frac{\partial}{\partial x}f(x) \tag{2.6}$$

Taking the basic form for the wave expression for a free particle and the interpretation of k and ν we have

$$\Psi = e^{2\pi i(kx-\nu t)} = e^{(2\pi i/h)(p_x x - Et)} \tag{2.7}$$

Now

$$\frac{\partial \Psi}{\partial x} = \frac{2\pi i}{h} p_x \Psi$$

$$p_x \Psi = \frac{h}{2\pi i}\frac{\partial}{\partial x}\Psi \tag{2.8}$$

In accordance with this result, it is *postulated* that in wave mechanics the operator $(h/2\pi i)\,\partial/\partial x$ corresponds to the linear momentum p_x. Such an operator has meaning only when applied to a wave function. Its meaning in cases where it does not yield a number times the wave function will be discussed later.

By analogy we may write

$$p_y \Psi = \frac{h}{2\pi i}\frac{\partial}{\partial y}\Psi \tag{2.9}$$

$$p_z \Psi = \frac{h}{2\pi i}\frac{\partial}{\partial z}\Psi \tag{2.10}$$

Also from Eq. (2.7) one obtains

$$E\Psi = \frac{-h}{2\pi i} \frac{\partial}{\partial t} \Psi \qquad (2.11)$$

These are some of the basic postulates of quantum theory.

2c. Free particle. For a free particle moving only in the x direction the classical kinetic energy equation is

$$E = p^2/2m \qquad (2.12)$$

(In quantum theory, statistical mechanics, and the advanced forms of classical mechanics, momentum rather than velocity appears as the fundamental quantity.) In operator form this becomes

$$\frac{-h}{2\pi i} \frac{\partial \Psi}{\partial t} = \frac{-h^2}{8\pi^2 m} \frac{\partial^2 \Psi}{\partial x^2} \qquad (2.13)$$

(the operation $\partial/\partial x$ applied twice is, of course, $\partial^2/\partial x^2$).

One can readily verify that substitution of the wave function (2.7) into Eq. (2.13) merely gives Eq. (2.12), proving only the self-consistency of our equations.

If one seeks now further solutions of Eq. (2.13), one may first postulate that

$$\Psi(x,t) = \psi(x)g(t) \qquad (2.14)$$

Substituting into (2.13) and dividing each side by Ψ, one obtains

$$\frac{-h}{2\pi i g} \frac{dg}{dt} = \frac{-h^2}{8\pi^2 m \psi} \frac{d^2\psi}{dx^2} \qquad (2.15)$$

Now the left side is a function only of t while the right depends only on x; hence they can be equal only if each is constant. This constant we shall call E since we shall see that it is the energy. Then

$$\frac{-h}{2\pi i\, g} \frac{dg}{dt} = E \qquad (2.16)$$

$$\frac{dg}{g} = \frac{-2\pi i}{h} E\, dt \qquad (2.17)$$

$$\ln g = \frac{-2\pi i}{h} Et + \text{const.} \qquad (2.18)$$

$$g = (\text{const.})e^{-2\pi i Et/h} \qquad (2.19)$$

With one arbitrary constant this is the complete solution of the first order equation in t. Turning to the equation in x we have

$$\frac{-h^2}{8\pi^2 m\psi} \frac{d^2\psi}{dx^2} = E$$

$$\frac{d^2\psi}{dx^2} + \frac{8\pi^2 mE}{h^2} \psi = 0 \tag{2.20}$$

which is a common type of equation whose general solution is

$$\psi(x) = Ae^{+i\alpha x} + Be^{-i\alpha x} \tag{2.21}$$

$$\alpha = \frac{(8\pi^2 mE)^{1/2}}{h} = \frac{2\pi}{h} (2mE)^{1/2} \tag{2.22}$$

where A and B are the two arbitrary constants of the general solution of a second-order equation. Thus the general solution for Ψ is

$$\Psi = Ae^{i(\alpha x - 2\pi Et/h)} + Be^{i(-\alpha x - 2\pi Et/h)} \tag{2.23}$$

The first term of (2.23) may be readily identified with our original wave function (2.7) provided α is taken as the positive root in (2.22). The second term is identical except for the change in sign from α to $-\alpha$, which corresponds to a change in sign of the momentum. This can be verified by applying the momentum operator (2.8) to Eq. (2.23) with first B zero and then A zero. In other words, our general equation contains the terms corresponding to the two directions the particle can be moving.

2d. Postulates of wave mechanics. With this introductory discussion let us now state a set of basic postulates which are to cover cases where potential energy terms are present. It is not pretended that these postulates are the most general or fundamental but merely that they are convenient for the problems to be discussed and that they are consistent with other possible formulations of quantum mechanics.

1. The classical equation for the energy of simple systems

$$\sum_{i=1}^{N} \left(\frac{1}{2m_i}\right) (p_{x_i}^2 + p_{y_i}^2 + p_{z_i}^2) + V(x_1, y_1, \ldots, z_n) = E \tag{2.24}$$

shall hold provided the differential operators, Eq. (2.8) to (2.11), are used for the momenta and the energy. The left side of (2.24) is the Hamiltonian function of classical mechanics (see Appendix 11) and the corresponding operator will be called the Hamiltonian operator and designated H. In more general cases H may be a function of time in addition to the coordinates and momenta. These operators H and E have meaning, of course, only if operating on the wave function. Thus one has

$$H\Psi = E\Psi \tag{2.25}$$

which is the famous equation proposed by Schrödinger (1926).

2. The wave function Ψ must not only satisfy Eq. (2.25), but must also be single valued, finite, and continuous. These latter requirements are merely those of a physically significant function. In addition to the function Ψ itself being continuous, the first derivative must be continuous. The equation will make higher derivatives continuous except for discontinuities in the potential energy. (An apparent exception arises for an infinite discontinuity in potential energy. Such a case will be treated, Section 2h, as a limit of increasing finite discontinuities.)

3. The quantity $|\Psi|^2$ or $\Psi^*\Psi$ is a real, positive function of the coordinates of the system and possibly of time. This quantity gives the probability of finding the system in the given configuration, or in other words, the density of particles or intensity of light at that point. Ψ may be complex, in which case Ψ^* is the complex conjugate and $|\Psi|$ is the absolute magnitude.

4. In general any observable quantity has associated with it an operator. If an unspecified operator G (of which E and p are examples) when applied to Ψ gives a number, g, times Ψ, then a measurement of the quantity G will always give the result g. However, if $G\Psi$ gives a function other than a number times Ψ, then successive measurement of the quantity G on a number of independent but initially identical systems will give a distribution of values, whose average will be

$$\bar{G} = \frac{\int \Psi^* G\Psi \, dv}{\int \Psi^*\Psi \, dv} \tag{2.26}$$

where the integrations are over the entire space appropriate to Ψ.

The operator G is to be constructed from the classical expression for the observable quantity as a function of the coordinates, momenta, energy, and time. In accordance with the procedure in constructing the Schrödinger equation, the momenta and energy will be replaced by the differential operators, Eqs. (2.8) to (2.11), in forming the operator G. Thus the angular momentum of a single particle about the x axis is $(yp_z - zp_y)$ in classical mechanics. The quantum mechanical operator is therefore

$$\frac{h}{2\pi i}\left(y\frac{\partial}{\partial z} - z\frac{\partial}{\partial y}\right)$$

2e. Stationary energy states. Most systems of chemical interest are based on states of definite, stationary energy. For such states the time-dependent factor in Ψ is as shown in Eq. (2.19): $e^{-2\pi iEt/h}$. We may then write

$$\Psi(x_1,y_1, \ldots, z_n,t) = \psi(x_1,y_1, \ldots, z_n)e^{-2\pi iEt/h} \qquad (2.27)$$

The symbol E is used to represent either the number giving the energy of a stationary state or, if followed by Ψ, to represent the operator $-(h/2\pi i)\partial/\partial t$. Applying Eq. (2.25), we obtain the time-independent Schrödinger equation,

$$H\psi = E\psi \qquad (2.28)$$

where E is now a number (not an operator). The general conditions on ψ are those on Ψ.

2f. Single potential barrier problem. Limiting ourselves again to one particle in one dimension, and to stationary energy states, the Schrödinger equation becomes

$$\left[\frac{1}{2m} p_x^2 + V(x)\right]\psi = E\psi$$

$$\frac{d^2\psi}{dx^2} + \frac{8\pi^2 m}{h^2}[E - V(x)]\psi = 0 \qquad (2.29)$$

We shall next consider several problems with V constant over a range of x, and then constant at a higher value over other ranges of x. First, let us consider the situation shown in Fig. 2.2.

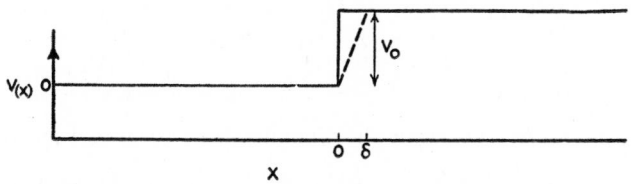

Fig. 2.2.   A single potential barrier, infinitely thick.

Suppose the particle comes up from negative x to the potential barrier at $x = 0$. In the region $x < 0$ the solution is given by Eqs. (2.21) and (2.22).

$$\psi = Ae^{i\alpha x} + Be^{-i\alpha x} \qquad (2.21)$$

$$\alpha = (2\pi/h)(2mE)^{1/2} \qquad (2.22)$$

where the first term has $p_x > 0$, and therefore represents particles moving toward the barrier, while the second term represents particles reflected back. In the region $x > 0$ two possibilities must be considered. Either E is greater than or less than V_0. If we write

$$\beta = (2\pi/h)\sqrt{2m(V_0 - E)} \tag{2.30}$$

we obtain
$$\psi = Ce^{\beta x} + De^{-\beta x} \tag{2.31}$$

but β can be either real or imaginary.

Now ψ and its derivative ψ' must be continuous at $x = 0$. However, the second derivative cannot be continuous at a point of discontinuity in $V(x)$, as can be seen from Eq. (2.29). Applying these conditions, we have

$$\psi(0) = A + B = C + D \tag{2.32}$$

$$\psi'(0) = i\alpha(A - B) = \beta(C - D) \tag{2.33}$$

$$A = C\left(\frac{i\alpha + \beta}{2i\alpha}\right) + D\left(\frac{i\alpha - \beta}{2i\alpha}\right) \tag{2.34}$$

$$B = C\left(\frac{i\alpha - \beta}{2i\alpha}\right) + D\left(\frac{i\alpha + \beta}{2i\alpha}\right) \tag{2.35}$$

If E is greater than V_0 so that β is imaginary, D must be zero because we assume that no particles are coming from positive x. Then

$$\frac{B}{A} = \left(\frac{i\alpha - \beta}{i\alpha + \beta}\right) = \left(\frac{\sqrt{E} - \sqrt{E - V_0}}{\sqrt{E} + \sqrt{E - V_0}}\right) \tag{2.36}$$

But this gives the nonclassical result that (since B is not zero) particles are reflected by the potential barrier even though they have enough energy to pass over it. The fraction reflected is

$$\frac{|B|^2}{|A|^2} = \frac{2E - V_0 - 2\sqrt{E(E - V_0)}}{2E - V_0 + 2\sqrt{E(E - V_0)}} = \frac{2 - u - 2\sqrt{1 - u}}{2 - u + 2\sqrt{1 - u}} \tag{2.37}$$

where $u = V_0/E$. On using the binomial series for $u \ll 1$ one obtains

$$\frac{|B|^2}{|A|^2} \cong \frac{u^2}{16} \tag{2.38}$$

as a first approximation. Thus with E twice V_0 about 2% of the incident particles are reflected.

The above result, Eqs. (2.36) to (2.38), is surprising and unusual in another respect. It does not contain Planck's constant, hence it would appear to be valid for all masses of particles. However, further investigation, assuming a continuous potential curve, such as the dotted line in Fig. 2.2 where the potential rises over a distance δ, yields the result that the above equations are valid when the wave length $2\pi/\alpha$ of the particles is long compared with the distance δ. If δ is large compared with the wave length $2\pi/\alpha$, the classical result is obtained that no particles are reflected. In between the results are complicated, but they do depend on Planck's constant h, and upon m and E as they appear in Eq. (2.22).

If we consider the case of $V_0 > E$, we obtain an even more surprising result. Now C must be zero because with β real, $e^{\beta x}$ would increase beyond all bounds as $x \rightarrow +\infty$. Then

$$\frac{B}{A} = \left(\frac{i\alpha + \beta}{i\alpha - \beta}\right) \tag{2.39}$$

Since β is now real,

$$|i\alpha + \beta| = |i\alpha - \beta| = \sqrt{\alpha^2 + \beta^2} \tag{2.40}$$

and $|A|^2 = |B|^2$, so that all particles are reflected at the barrier, the classical result. However,

$$(i\alpha - \beta)D = 2i\alpha A \tag{2.41}$$

$$|D|^2 = \frac{4\alpha^2}{\alpha^2 + \beta^2} |A|^2 \tag{2.42}$$

This means that D is not zero unless β and consequently V_0 are infinite. If D is not zero, then ψ is not zero for $x > 0$ and *there is a probability of finding the particle where it does not have enough energy to be.* This result is one of the basic characteristics of quantum theory; one which appears repeatedly in all potential barrier problems.

2g. Penetration of potential barriers. If the potential barrier is not infinitely thick, the result just obtained suggests that the wave function will still have a finite value at the other side of the barrier. Then the particle should have a chance of passing through. Let us investigate this next.

Consider now the potential barrier of Fig. 2.3.

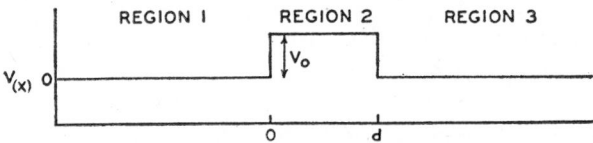

Fig. 2.3.   A single finite potential barrier.

The solutions for ψ in the three indicated regions are

$$
\begin{array}{lll}
\text{Region I} & \psi = Ae^{i\alpha x} + Be^{-i\alpha x} \\
\text{Region II} & \psi = Ce^{\beta x} + De^{-\beta x} & (2.43) \\
\text{Region III} & \psi = A'e^{i\alpha x} + B'e^{-i\alpha x}
\end{array}
$$

The continuity conditions at $x = 0$ are those of Eqs. (2.32), (2.33) above. Before writing those for $x = d$, let us note that $B' = 0$ since no particles are approaching the barrier from the right. Then at $x = d$ the continuity conditions are

$$
\begin{aligned}
\psi(d) &= Ce^{\beta d} + De^{-\beta d} = A'e^{i\alpha d} \\
\psi'(d) &= \beta(Ce^{\beta d} - De^{-\beta d}) = i\alpha A'e^{i\alpha d}
\end{aligned}
\tag{2.44}
$$

$$
C = A'\left(\frac{\beta + i\alpha}{2\beta}\right)e^{(i\alpha - \beta)d}
\tag{2.45}
$$

$$
D = A'\left(\frac{\beta - i\alpha}{2\beta}\right)e^{(i\alpha + \beta)d}
\tag{2.46}
$$

Now substituting in Eq. (2.34) one finds

$$
\begin{aligned}
A &= A'\left[\frac{\beta^2 + 2i\alpha\beta - \alpha^2}{4i\alpha\beta}e^{(i\alpha - \beta)d} + \frac{\alpha^2 + 2i\alpha\beta - \beta^2}{4i\alpha\beta}e^{(i\alpha + \beta)d}\right] \\
&= \frac{A'e^{i\alpha d}}{4i\alpha\beta}[4i\alpha\beta\cosh\beta d + 2(\alpha^2 - \beta^2)\sinh\beta d]
\end{aligned}
\tag{2.47}
$$

$$
|A|^2 = |A'|^2\left[\cosh^2\beta d + \frac{(\alpha^2 - \beta^2)^2}{4\alpha^2\beta^2}\sinh^2\beta d\right]
\tag{2.48}
$$

Thus the probability of transmission through the potential barrier, $P = |A'|^2/|A|^2$, is not zero unless βd is infinite.

In order to simplify Eq. (2.48) for estimates of order of magnitude with $\beta d \gg 1$ we note that $\cosh\beta d \cong \sinh\beta d \cong \frac{1}{2}e^{\beta d}$ and that the coefficient of the second term will not be very large if α and β are of similar magnitude. Then

$$
P \cong 4e^{-2\beta d}; \qquad \beta d = \frac{2\pi d}{h}\sqrt{2m(V_0 - E)}
\tag{2.49}
$$

This possibility of particles "penetrating" potential barriers is another fundamental peculiarity of quantum theory. It is sometimes called the *tunnel effect*. Even though the barrier may have other than rectangular shape, Eq. (2.49) may be used to estimate the order of magnitude of the possibility of penetration.

At this point we may recall that classical behavior may always be approached as $h \to 0$. Strictly, it is meant that h has become small compared with other quantities. In Eq. (2.49) we note that as $h \to 0$, $\beta d \to \infty$, and $P \to 0$.

The half time of penetration is frequently the quantity of particular interest. To obtain it one must make some estimate of the frequency, f, with which the particle collides with the barrier. Then the rate of penetration is

$$k = f \cdot P$$

and the half time is

$$t_{1/2} = \ln 2/k = 0.693/f \cdot P \qquad (2.50)$$

The phenomenon of potential barrier penetration has numerous applications in physical-chemical behavior. Radioactive disintegration by alpha particle emission is one example. The alpha particle (or its components) exist inside the nucleus but have not sufficient energy to escape over the potential barrier. However, there is an appreciable probability of the particle "leaking" through the barrier.

Although thousands of isomers are known which differ only in the geometrical arrangement of atomic nuclei, no isomers are known which arise from difference in electron location. The very much smaller mass of an electron readily accounts for this striking result.

2h. Particle in a box. Now let us turn to a third type of potential barrier problem, a particle trapped between two barriers as in Fig. 2.4. Analogous to Eq. (2.43), the solutions are

$$\begin{array}{lll}
\text{Region I} & \psi = Ce^{\beta x} + De^{-\beta x} & \\
\text{Region II} & \psi = Ae^{i\alpha x} + Be^{-i\alpha x} & (2.51) \\
\text{Region III} & \psi = C'e^{\beta x} + D'e^{-\beta x} &
\end{array}$$

To keep ψ finite we may at once set C' and D equal to zero. While the direct application of the methods used above would give the correct results, a transformation suggested by the classical picture

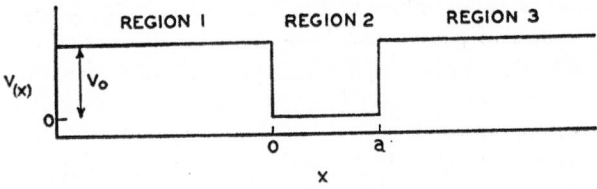

Fig. 2.4. A potential box.

simplifies the procedure. Classically, a particle trapped between these barriers would bounce back and forth between them. It would therefore be equally likely to be moving toward $+x$ as toward $-x$. Now the functions

$$\cos \alpha x = \frac{1}{2}\left(e^{i\alpha x} + e^{-i\alpha x}\right)$$

$$\sin \alpha x = \frac{1}{2i}\left(e^{i\alpha x} - e^{-i\alpha x}\right)$$

express just this idea. Thus it is preferable to use the equally general mathematical expression

$$\text{Region II} \qquad \psi = A'\cos \alpha x + B'\sin \alpha x \qquad (2.51')$$

Then, making ψ and ψ' continuous at 0 and a, one finds at $x = 0$,

$$C = A'; \qquad \beta C = \alpha B'$$

giving

$$C = A' = (\alpha/\beta)B' \qquad (2.52)$$

and at $x = a$,

$$D'e^{-\beta a} = A'\cos \alpha a + B'\sin \alpha a = B'\left(\frac{\alpha}{\beta}\cos \alpha a + \sin \alpha a\right) \qquad (2.53)$$

$$-\beta D'e^{-\beta a} = -\alpha A'\sin \alpha a + \alpha B'\cos \alpha a = -\alpha B'\left(\frac{\alpha}{\beta}\sin \alpha a - \cos \alpha a\right)$$

However, from the last two equations above, we may obtain two expressions for $D'e^{-\beta a}$ which must be equal.

$$B'\left(\frac{\alpha}{\beta}\cos \alpha a + \sin \alpha a\right) = \frac{\alpha}{\beta}B'\left(\frac{\alpha}{\beta}\sin \alpha a - \cos \alpha a\right)$$

$$2\frac{\alpha}{\beta}\cos \alpha a = \left(\frac{\alpha^2}{\beta^2} - 1\right)\sin \alpha a$$

$$\cot \alpha a = \frac{1}{2}\left(\frac{\alpha}{\beta} - \frac{\beta}{\alpha}\right) \qquad (2.54)$$

This transcendental equation is satisfied by a series of values of α. Substitution of these values in Eqs. (2.51) to (2.53) shows that the negative values of α give identical wave functions to those of the positive values and hence are not different solutions; also, the solution $\alpha = 0$ gives a wave function everywhere zero and should therefore be discarded as not physically significant.

The energy is given by Eq. (2.22), which rearranges to

$$E = \alpha^2 h^2 / 8\pi^2 m \qquad (2.22')$$

Consequently only certain particular energy values are permitted, since only certain values of α satisfy the above equations. A few of these are given diagrammatically in Fig. 2.5. This represents another example of discrete, stationary energy states.

The mathematical expressions are simplified if the potential wall height V_0 approaches infinity. Then $\beta \to \infty$ and $\alpha/\beta \to 0$, and solutions are obtained for

$$\alpha a = n\pi \qquad (2.55)$$

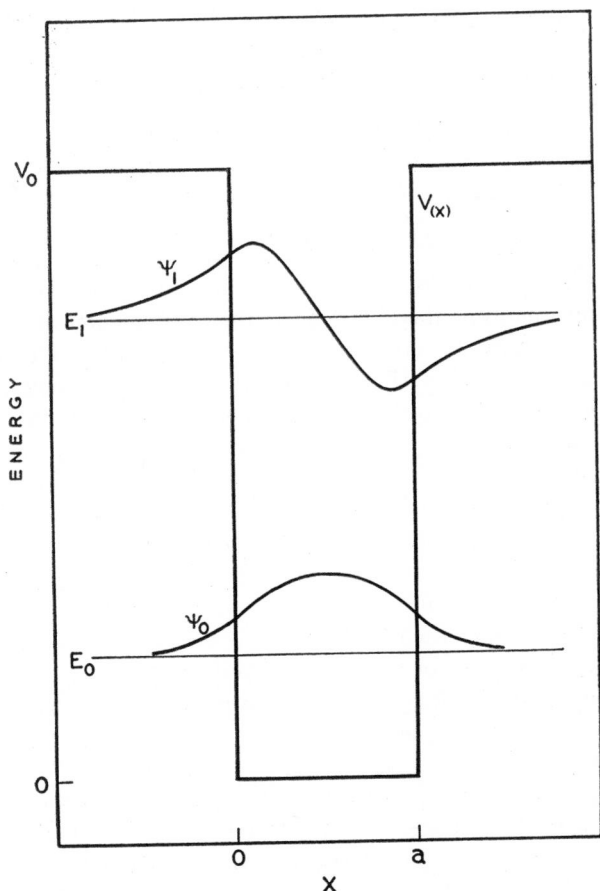

Fig. 2.5.   Energy levels and wave functions for a particle in a box.

where n is a positive integer. As explained above, negative integers give the same wave functions, hence are not additional solutions; zero gives a wave function of zero, hence is not a significant solution.

Thus the expression for the energy levels is

$$E = n^2h^2/8ma^2; \qquad n = 1, 2, 3, \ldots \qquad (2.56)$$

The wave functions are

$$\psi = B' \sin (n\pi x/a), \qquad 0 \leqslant x \leqslant a \qquad (2.57)$$
$$\psi = 0 \qquad\qquad\qquad \text{elsewhere}$$

Since $|\psi|^2\, dx$ represents the probability of finding the particle in the region dx, it is convenient to assign B' so that the total probability is unity. This procedure is called *normalization*.

$$1 = \int_{-\infty}^{+\infty} |\psi|^2\, dx = (B')^2 \int_0^a \sin^2 \frac{n\pi x}{a}\, dx$$
$$1 = (B')^2(a/2); \qquad B' = \sqrt{2/a}$$
$$\psi = \sqrt{2/a} \sin (n\pi x/a) \qquad (2.58)$$

From these calculations we notice additional fundamental characteristics of quantum theory. One is the phenomenon of *zero point energy*. The lowest energy is not zero but $h^2/8ma^2$. This may be interpreted in terms of the *uncertainty principle* as follows. Since the particle is known to be within the box, the uncertainty in x is a, which is a finite quantity. Consequently, there must be an uncertainty in momentum which means that the momentum cannot be a definite zero. Thus the particle must have kinetic energy. This result is quite general wherever a particle is confined to a definite region in space without regard to the exact character of the potential barrier which confines it.

Another general characteristic concerns the zeros of the wave function; i.e., the number of times ψ crosses its zero axis. If we ignore the beginning and ending at zero, the lowest energy level has no zeros, the next level has one zero, the next two, and so on, as shown in Fig. 2.6.

This is a general property of differential equations of the Schrödinger type with $V \to \infty$ at $x \pm \infty$ according to Sturm-Liouville theory.[1] There is one and only one solution with a given number of zeros.

[1] See, for example, Ince, E. L., *Ordinary Differential Equations*, London: Longmans, Green & Co., Ltd., 1927, Chap. 10.

Consequently, even though a detailed solution is not possible in a given case for an arbitrary shape of potential barrier, it is still possible to conclude that a series of energy levels will exist whose corresponding wave functions have zero, one, two, three, etc. zeros besides the beginning and ending at zero. Furthermore, since the functions with more zeros must show greater curvature, the corresponding momentum and kinetic energy must be greater.

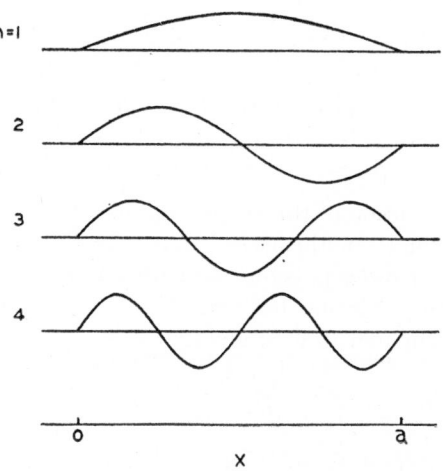

Fig. 2.6.   Wave functions for a particle in an infinite walled box.

2i. Harmonic oscillator. The problem of a particle vibration under a Hooke's law restoring force is basic in both classical and quantum theory.   Let us review the classical problem very briefly.

$$F_x = -kx; \qquad V = \frac{1}{2} kx^2$$

$$m\ddot{x} = -kx; \qquad x = A \cos 2\pi\nu(t - t_0)$$

$$\nu = \frac{1}{2\pi} \sqrt{k/m}; \qquad T = \frac{1}{2} m\dot{x}^2$$

$$E = T + V = \frac{1}{2} A^2 \left[k \cos^2 2\pi\nu(t - t_0) + m \left(\frac{k}{m} \right) \sin^2 2\pi\nu(t - t_0) \right]$$

$$= \frac{1}{2} kA^2 \qquad\qquad (2.59)$$

The potential and kinetic energies (V and T) oscillate, but the total energy is constant. The frequency of the motion ν is independent of the amplitude.

Turning now to quantum theory, one first writes the Schrödinger equation for the problem:

$$H\psi = \frac{-h^2}{8\pi^2 m} \frac{d^2\psi}{dx^2} + \frac{1}{2} kx^2\psi = E\psi \qquad (2.60)$$

This may be rearranged into the form

$$\frac{d^2\psi}{dx^2} + (\lambda - \alpha^2 x^2)\psi = 0 \qquad (2.61)$$

with $\lambda = 8\pi^2 mE/h^2$ and $\alpha^2 = 4\pi^2 mk/h^2$, or in terms of the classical frequency ν,

$$\alpha = 4\pi^2 m\nu/h \qquad (2.62)$$

The general solution of this differential equation is not expressible in terms of ordinary mathematical functions, but may be given by infinite series. However, before obtaining these series, let us consider the limiting solution for large x. Now the term λ may be neglected as compared to $\alpha^2 x^2$, giving

$$\frac{d^2\psi}{dx^2} = \alpha^2 x^2 \psi \qquad (2.63)$$

which has the asymptotic solutions $e^{\alpha x^2/2}$ and $e^{-\alpha x^2/2}$. This statement may be verified by differentiation.

$$\frac{d}{dx}\left(e^{\pm \alpha x^2/2}\right) = \pm \alpha x e^{\pm \alpha x^2/2}$$

$$\frac{d^2}{dx^2}\left(e^{\pm \alpha x^2/2}\right) = (\alpha^2 x^2 \pm \alpha)e^{\pm \alpha x^2/2}$$

The second term, α, is negligible as compared with $\alpha^2 x^2$ when x is large.

This suggests that a solution may be obtained by writing

$$\psi = e^{-\alpha x^2/2} \sum_{j=0}^{\infty} a_j x^j \qquad (2.64)$$

where the alternate form with positive exponent has been discarded because it would lead to an infinite value of ψ as $x \to \infty$. Substituting this expression in (2.61) we obtain

$$\frac{d\psi}{dx} = e^{-\alpha x^2/2} \sum_{j=0}^{\infty} [(j+1)a_{j+1} - \alpha a_{j-1}]x^j$$

$$\frac{d^2\psi}{dx^2} = e^{-\alpha x^2/2} \sum_{j=0}^{\infty} [(j+2)(j+1)a_{j+2} - \alpha(2j+1)a_j + \alpha^2 a_{j-2}]x^j$$

$$(\lambda - \alpha^2 x^2)\psi = e^{-\alpha x^2/2} \sum_{j=0}^{\infty} [\lambda a_j - \alpha^2 a_{j-2}]x^j$$

Adding according to the equation gives

$$0 = e^{-\alpha x^2/2} \sum_{j=0}^{\infty} [(j+2)(j+1)a_{j+2} + (\lambda - 2\alpha j - \alpha)a_j]x^j$$

However, this equation can hold for all values of x only if the coefficient of each power of x is separately equal to zero. Thus

$$a_{j+2} = \frac{2\alpha j + \alpha - \lambda}{(j+2)(j+1)} a_j \tag{2.65}$$

which determines a_2 in terms of a_0, a_4 in terms of a_2 etc., where a_0 was an arbitrary constant. Also a_1 is arbitrary, while a_3, a_5, etc., are determined. With two arbitrary constants, we have a general solution and have only to investigate its acceptability as a quantum mechanical wave function. It is evidently continuous and single valued and is finite for finite x. However, in general, the series fails to converge to a finite value as $x \to \infty$. To show this, let us consider how this series compares with $e^{\alpha x^2}$ for the terms with high powers of x. Let us write

$$e^{\alpha x^2} = 1 + \alpha x^2 + \frac{(\alpha x^2)^2}{2} + \ldots + \frac{\alpha^l x^{2l}}{l!} + \frac{\alpha^{l+1} x^{2l+2}}{(l+1)!} + \ldots$$

Thus the ratio of the coefficients of the terms in x^{2l+2} and x^{2l} is α/l, or if we write $l = j/2$, the ratio is $2\alpha/j$, which can be seen to be just the limit of the ratio of a_{j+2}/a_j as j becomes large. Consequently, this series defined by Eqs. (2.64) and (2.65) behaves as $e^{-\alpha x^2/2} \cdot e^{+\alpha x^2}$ or as $e^{+\alpha x^2/2}$ when $x \to \infty$, which means that it approaches infinity and is not a physically acceptable solution.

The only escape from this situation arises if the series terminates, because then the negative exponential factor $e^{-\alpha x^2}$ will cause the wave function to approach zero for large values of x. From Eq. (2.65) we see that the series will terminate if $(\lambda - 2\alpha n - \alpha)$ is zero where n is an integer. The final term will be a_n. Also if n is even,

a_1 must be set at zero to avoid an infinite series of odd powers of x, and vice versa, if n is odd, a_0 must be zero. Thus we obtain as the condition for an acceptable wave function

$$\lambda = \alpha(2n + 1)$$
$$E = h\nu(n + \tfrac{1}{2}) \tag{2.66}$$

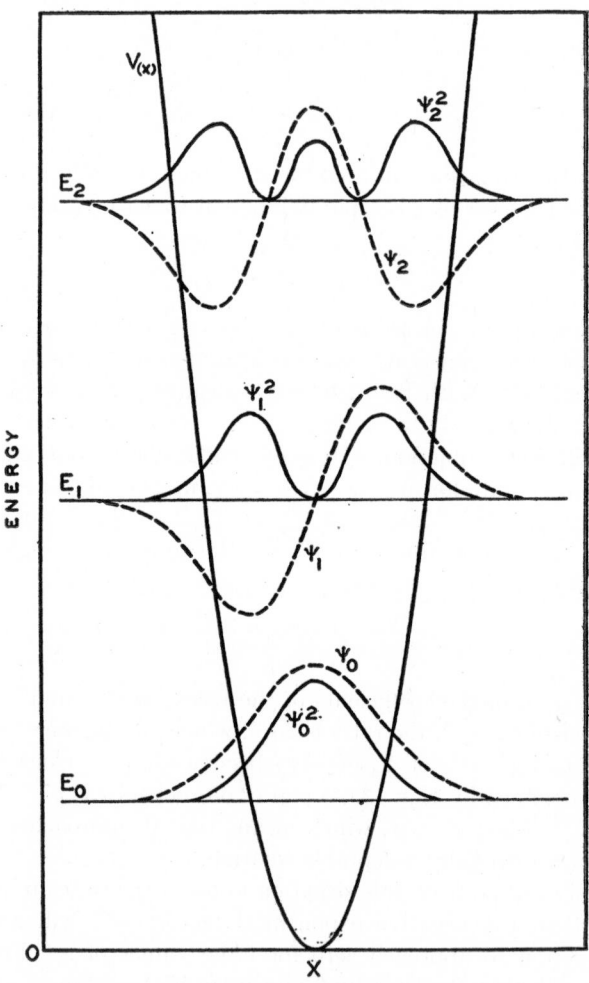

Fig. 2.7.   The harmonic oscillator, showing the potential curve, the energy levels, the wave functions, and probability distributions.

which gives again a set of discrete energy states.   Zero and all positive integers are acceptable values of n.

The first few wave functions are readily calculated and normalized.

$$\psi_0 = \left(\frac{\alpha}{\pi}\right)^{1/4} e^{-\alpha x^2/2}$$

$$\psi_1 = \left(\frac{4\alpha^3}{\pi}\right)^{1/4} x e^{-\alpha x^2/2}$$

$$\psi_2 = \left(\frac{\alpha}{4\pi}\right)^{1/4} (1 - 2\alpha x^2) e^{-\alpha x^2/2} \tag{2.67}$$

$$\psi_3 = \left(\frac{9\alpha^3}{\pi}\right)^{1/4} \left(x - \frac{2\alpha}{3} x^3\right) e^{-\alpha x^2/2}$$

Figure 2.7 shows a few of these wave functions, together with the corresponding probability functions $|\psi|^2$. We note here again the existence of zero point energy and the same general characteristics of the wave functions as for the particle in the box.

There are numerous physical systems which are approximately harmonic oscillators.   The vibration of a diatomic molecule is one example, and this will be discussed in the next chapter.   Other examples will appear later in the book.

2j. Bound and free particles.   In the examples considered so far it may be noted that a continuous range of energy levels is found for a particle which has enough energy to escape to infinity but that discrete energy levels are found when the particle is bound to a finite region of space.   This result is generally valid, as will be demonstrated in this section.   Let us take an arbitrary potential curve of the qualitative form shown in Fig. 2.8, i.e., approaching constant energy as x approaches infinity.   At large positive x the general solution to the Schrödinger equation is given by Eq. (2.31)

$$\psi = Ce^{\beta x} + De^{-\beta x} \tag{2.31}$$

with $\beta = (2\pi/h)\sqrt{2m(V - E)}$

Since V is greater than E, β is real, and the only acceptable solution is $C = 0$, $\psi = De^{-\beta x}$.

This solution at large x may be extended inward by some numerical integration of the wave equation.   Writing the Schrödinger equation in the form

$$\frac{d^2\psi}{dx^2} = \frac{8\pi^2 m}{h^2} (V - E)\psi \tag{2.68}$$

one sees that the curvature of the wave function will reverse at the point $V = E$ as indicated by the vertical dotted lines in Fig. 2.8. This is the *turning point* of the classical oscillation where the velocity is zero.

A solution at large negative x is also easily found to be $\psi = C'e^{\beta'x}$ and it can likewise be extended inward. Although one may adjust the ratio of D to C' as indicated by the dotted curve on the right, this allows one only to make the value of ψ continuous at the joining point. In general, the slopes of the right and left curves will not be the same.

Suppose an initial attempt, using the energy value E_1, yields the

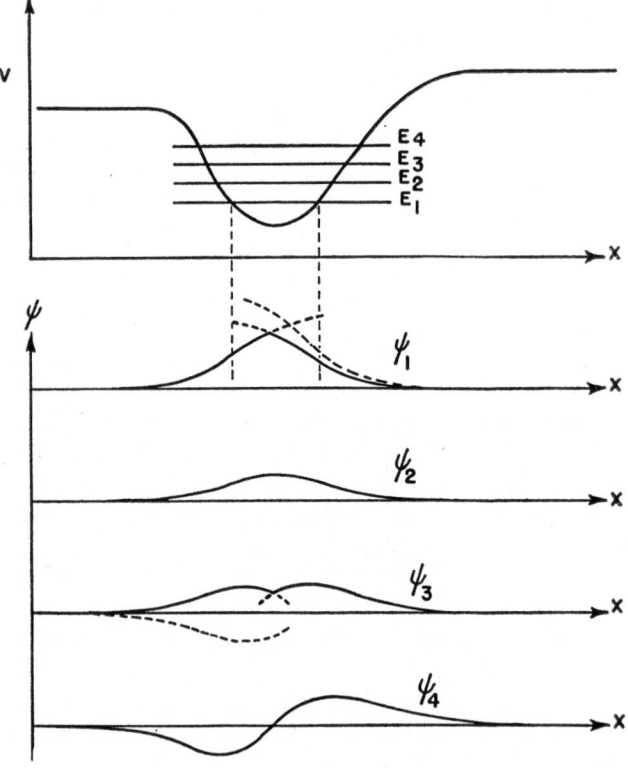

Fig. 2.8. Quantization of linear motion for an arbitrary shape of potential well.

result indicated. Now by increasing the energy value, the turning points (where $V = E$) will move outward. This will increase the region where the curvature of ψ is toward the axis. At some point E_2, a continuous wave function is obtained. This value E_2 is sometimes called an *eigenvalue* or characteristic value and the corresponding function an *eigenfunction* or characteristic function.

Further increase in the energy value yields unsatisfactory results such as ψ_3 for E_3 until E_4 is reached. Then one again obtains a continuous ψ_4 with one zero or crossing of the axis. Thus one obtains a progression of discrete E values so long as E remains below V at infinity and the particle is bound.

When E exceeds V at infinity, the limiting solution for ψ becomes of the type

$$\psi = A \sin \alpha x + B \cos \alpha x$$

With two arbitrary constants, it can always be joined (both as to value and slope) to a solution arising from the opposite side. Thus, if E exceeds the value of V at $-\infty$ even though it does not exceed the value of V at $+\infty$, nevertheless a continuous range of energy values is permitted. Of course, if E exceeds V at both limits, a continuous series of solutions is obtained; in fact, now one has two solutions for each energy value.

To recapitulate, if the particle is bound on both left and right, a discrete set of energy levels is obtained. If the particle is free on the left but bound on the right, any energy is permitted but the only motion is that of a particle coming up from the left, colliding with the barrier, and bouncing back off to the left. If the particle is free on both the left or right it may move across in either direction with any energy.

Before closing this chapter, let us mention again that there is an equivalent formulation of quantum mechanics in terms of matrix algebra. For most purposes of this book, wave mechanics is more convenient, besides using the more familiar mathematical methods. Occasionally, matrix mechanics yields the solution more easily. The elements of matrix mechanics, together with the solution of the harmonic oscillator problem are given in Appendix 15. However, a full account of matrix mechanics and its relationship to wave mechanics is beyond the scope of this book.

GENERAL REFERENCES

Discussions of the fundamental postulates of quantum mechanics and treatments of one-dimensional problems are given in practically all books on that subject. Among those listed below the book by Rojansky has a particularly extensive treatment of one-dimensional examples. The books by Dirac and Tolman give the most general formulations of the theory, but have a correspondingly abstract and mathematical character.

Bohm, D., *Quantum Theory*, New York: Prentice-Hall, Inc., 1951.

Dirac, P. A. M., *The Principles of Quantum Mechanics*, New York: Oxford University Press, 1935.

Dushman, S., *The Elements of Quantum Mechanics*, New York: John Wiley & Sons, Inc., 1938.

Pauling, L. and Wilson, E. B., Jr., *Introduction to Quantum Mechanics*, New York: McGraw-Hill Book Company, Inc., 1935.

Persico, E., *Fundamentals of Quantum Mechanics*, New York: Prentice-Hall, Inc., 1950.

Rojansky, V., *Introductory Quantum Mechanics*, New York: Prentice-Hall, Inc., 1938.

Schiff, L. I., *Quantum Mechanics*, New York: McGraw-Hill Book Company, Inc., 1949.

Tolman, R. C., *The Principles of Statistical Mechanics*, New York: Oxford University Press, 1938.

PROBLEMS

2.1 For a stream of particles represented by Eq. (2.21), calculate both the average momentum $\bar{p}$ and the average squared momentum $\overline{p^2}$. Show that the results correspond to a situation where all particles have the same absolute momentum but the fraction $A^2/(A^2 + B^2)$ have positive momentum and the fraction $B^2/(A^2 + B^2)$ have negative momentum.

2.2 Evaluate C in eq. (2.34) and show for that example: incident particles = transmitted particles + reflected particles. Note that the number of particles is given by the product of their velocity and the probability of finding them in a unit distance.

2.3 Calculate the probability of each of the following particles passing through a potential barrier 20 kcal./mole higher than the energy of the particles and 0.7×10^{-8} cm. thick: (a) electron, (b) proton, (c) deuteron, (d) carbon nucleus. If the particle collides with the barrier 10^{13} times per second, what will be the half life before penetration for each particle?

2.4 Calculate $\overline{x^2}$ and $\overline{p_x^2}$ for the harmonic oscillator in the zero and first states. From these obtain the average kinetic and potential energies and compare with the classical values.

2.5 Obtain and normalize the harmonic oscillator wave function with $n = 4$.

Plot $|\psi|^2$ as a function of x and show also the amplitude of classical oscillation for the same total energy.

2.6 For the lowest energy level of the particle in the infinite potential walled box, calculate the average value of p_x and of p_x^2. Discuss these results together with the uncertainty in p_x calculated from the Heisenberg uncertainty principle.

2.7 Discuss the problem of a particle under the potential: $V = +\infty$ for $x < 0$; $V = 0$ for $0 < x < a$; and $V = +V_0$ for $x > a$. Obtain the lowest energy level value and the corresponding wave function for the case with $2\pi a\sqrt{2mV_0} = 6h$.

Chapter 3

THE HYDROGEN-LIKE ATOM AND THE
DIATOMIC MOLECULE

In Chapter 2 a number of one-dimensional problems were considered which illustrated both the methods and qualitative phenomena of quantum theory. We now wish to treat probably the most important practical case, namely, two particles with a central force acting between them. If the force varies inversely as the square of the distance between particles, we have a hydrogen-like atom (H, He⁺, Li⁺⁺, etc.). Also we shall consider the two nuclei in a diatomic molecule as an example of this type.

3a. Separation of variables. Let the two particles have masses m_1 and m_2, and their Cartesian coordinates be x_1, y_1, z_1 and x_2, y_2, z_2. Then define

$$M = m_1 + m_2, \qquad \mu = \frac{m_1 m_2}{m_1 + m_2} \qquad (3.1)$$

where M is thus the total mass and μ is called the reduced mass. Also define

$$\begin{aligned}
X &= (1/M)(m_1 x_1 + m_2 x_2) \\
Y &= (1/M)(m_1 y_1 + m_2 y_2) \\
Z &= (1/M)(m_1 z_1 + m_2 z_2) \\
x &= x_1 - x_2 \\
y &= y_1 - y_2 \\
z &= z_1 - z_2
\end{aligned} \qquad (3.2)$$

where X, Y, Z are thus the coordinates of the center of mass.

According to our postulates in Chapter 2 the Schrödinger equation for this system is

$$\frac{-h^2}{8\pi^2 m_1}\left(\frac{\partial^2 \psi_T}{\partial x_1^2} + \frac{\partial^2 \psi_T}{\partial y_1^2} + \frac{\partial^2 \psi_T}{\partial z_1^2}\right) - \frac{h^2}{8\pi^2 m_2}\left(\frac{\partial^2 \psi_T}{\partial x_2^2} + \frac{\partial^2 \psi_T}{\partial y_2^2} + \frac{\partial^2 \psi_T}{\partial z_2^2}\right)$$
$$+ [V(x,y,z) - E_T]\psi_T = 0 \qquad (3.3)$$

where E_T is the total energy and ψ_T is the total wave function (time independent). Let us factor ψ_T into a function for the translation of the center of gravity $\psi_t(X,Y,Z)$ and a function of the internal coordinates $\psi(x,y,z)$:

$$\psi_T = \psi_t(X,Y,Z) \cdot \psi(x,y,z)$$
$$E_T = E_t + E \qquad (3.4)$$

Substituting Eqs. (3.4) into (3.3) and using the various definitions in (3.1) and (3.2), one eventually obtains

$$\frac{-h^2}{8\pi^2 M}\left(\frac{\partial^2 \psi_t}{\partial X^2} + \frac{\partial^2 \psi_t}{\partial Y^2} + \frac{\partial^2 \psi_t}{\partial Z^2}\right) - E_t \psi_t = 0 \qquad (3.5)$$

$$\frac{-h^2}{8\pi^2 \mu}\left(\frac{\partial^2 \psi}{\partial x^2} + \frac{\partial^2 \psi}{\partial y^2} + \frac{\partial^2 \psi}{\partial z^2}\right) + [V(x,y,z) - E]\psi = 0 \qquad (3.6)$$

Now Eq. (3.5) applies to the translation of the center of gravity of the system. It will yield the solutions of a free particle discussed in Chapter 2. We shall not be concerned further with it. Equation (3.6) concerns the internal motion and contains the potential energy. If the force is central, i.e., acts along the line connecting the particles, then by transforming to spherical polar coordinates we may express the potential energy as a function of a single variable, the distance r between the particles.

We may remark at this point that the equations of this chapter also apply to a single particle in a three-dimensional potential field. In that case Eq. (3.6) applies with the single change of m, the mass of the single particle, for μ the reduced mass.

There is a general theory of transformations among orthogonal coordinate systems.[1] Those not familiar with this theory may verify our transformed Eq. (3.7) by the somewhat lengthy process of partial differentiation, making use of the transformation Eq. (3.8).

$$\frac{-h^2}{8\pi^2 \mu r^2}\left[\frac{\partial}{\partial r}\left(r^2 \frac{\partial \psi}{\partial r}\right) + \frac{1}{\sin\theta}\frac{\partial}{\partial\theta}\left(\sin\theta \frac{\partial \psi}{\partial\theta}\right) + \frac{1}{\sin^2\theta}\frac{\partial^2 \psi}{\partial\phi^2}\right]$$
$$+ [V(r) - E]\psi = 0 \qquad (3.7)$$

[1] Margenau, H. and Murphy, G. M., *The Mathematics of Physics and Chemistry*, New York: D. Van Nostrand Company, Inc., 1943, Chap. 5.

$$x = r \sin \theta \cos \phi$$
$$y = r \sin \theta \sin \phi \tag{3.8}$$
$$z = r \cos \theta$$

The next step is to separate variables if possible. We write

$$\psi(r,\theta,\phi) = R(r) \cdot \Theta(\theta) \cdot \Phi(\phi) \tag{3.9}$$

On substitution of (3.9) in (3.7) and division by $R \cdot \Theta \cdot \Phi$ one obtains

$$\frac{-h^2}{8\pi^2 \mu r^2} \left[\frac{1}{R} \frac{d}{dr} \left(r^2 \frac{dR}{dr} \right) + \frac{1}{\Theta \sin \theta} \frac{d}{d\theta} \left(\sin \theta \frac{d\Theta}{d\theta} \right) + \frac{1}{\Phi \sin^2 \theta} \frac{d^2 \Phi}{d\phi^2} \right]$$
$$+ V(r) - E = 0 \tag{3.10}$$

On multiplication by $(-8\pi^2 \mu r^2 \sin^2 \theta / h^2)$ one obtains

$$\frac{\sin^2 \theta}{R} \frac{d}{dr} \left(r^2 \frac{dR}{dr} \right) + \frac{\sin \theta}{\Theta} \frac{d}{d\theta} \left(\sin \theta \frac{d\Theta}{d\theta} \right) + \frac{1}{\Phi} \frac{d^2 \Phi}{d\phi^2}$$
$$+ \frac{8\pi^2 \mu r^2 \sin^2 \theta}{h^2} [E - V(r)] = 0 \tag{3.11}$$

where now the third term is a function only of ϕ, while all other terms are functions of only θ and r. However, the sum of all terms can be zero for all values of ϕ only if this third term is constant; consequently we may write (calling the constant $-m^2$)

$$\frac{d^2 \Phi}{d\phi^2} = -m^2 \Phi \tag{3.12}$$

3b. Solution of the ϕ equation. Equation (3.12) has the general solution

$$\Phi = A e^{im\phi} + B e^{-im\phi} \tag{3.13}$$

or the alternate mathematical expression

$$\Phi = A' \cos m\phi + B' \sin m\phi \tag{3.13'}$$

It can be easily seen that this is a complete solution containing the required two arbitrary constants. As was pointed out in Section 2a, these functions are single valued only if m is an integer. There are two solutions for all integral values of m except zero, where only one solution (a constant) exists. Alternatively one may take the imaginary exponential form $e^{im\phi}$, and say that m (later called m_l) can have both positive and negative integral values. This latter form is most convenient in treating angular momentum and magnetic moment phenomena, as will be seen in the following chapters.

3c. Solution of the θ equation. Now returning to Section 3a, substituting Eq. (3.12) into (3.11) and dividing by $\sin^2 \theta$, one obtains

$$\frac{1}{R}\frac{d}{dr}\left(r^2 \frac{dR}{dr}\right) + \frac{1}{\Theta \sin \theta}\frac{d}{d\theta}\left(\sin \theta \frac{d\Theta}{d\theta}\right) - \frac{m^2}{\sin^2 \theta} + \frac{8\pi^2 \mu r^2}{h^2}[E - V(r)] = 0 \tag{3.14}$$

where the second and third terms are the only ones depending on θ. Similarly, setting these θ terms equal to a constant, $-\beta$, one obtains

$$\frac{1}{\sin \theta}\frac{d}{d\theta}\left(\sin \theta \frac{d\Theta}{d\theta}\right) - \frac{m^2}{\sin^2 \theta}\Theta + \beta\Theta = 0 \tag{3.15}$$

Equation (3.15) may be solved by standard methods of differential equations, and had indeed been solved before its appearance in quantum theory. By arguments generally similar to those used for the harmonic oscillator equation it is found that a solution may be expected of the type[2]

$$\Theta = (\sin \theta)^{|m|} \sum_{j=0}^{\infty} a_j \cos^j \theta \tag{3.16}$$

Substituting in Eq. (3.15), one obtains

$$\beta\Theta = \beta (\sin \theta)^{|m|} \sum a_j \cos^j \theta$$

$$\frac{-m^2\Theta}{\sin^2 \theta} = -m^2 (\sin \theta)^{|m|-2} \sum a_j \cos^j \theta$$

$$\frac{1}{\sin \theta}\frac{d}{d\theta}\left(\sin \theta \frac{d\Theta}{d\theta}\right) = m^2 (\sin \theta)^{|m|-2} \sum a_j \cos^j \theta$$

$$-m^2 (\sin \theta)^{|m|}\sum a_j \cos^j \theta - |m| (\sin \theta)^{|m|} \sum (j + 1)a_j \cos^j \theta$$

$$-(|m| + 2)(\sin \theta)^{|m|} \sum ja_j \cos^j \theta + (\sin \theta)^{|m|} \sum j(j - 1)a_j \cos^{j-2} \theta$$

$$- (\sin \theta)^{|m|} \sum j(j - 1)a_j \cos^j \theta$$

Now collecting all terms to give the coefficient of $(\sin \theta)^{|m|} \cos^j \theta$, one finds

$$a_j[\beta - m^2 - |m|(j + 1) - (|m| + 2)j - j(j - 1)]$$
$$+ a_{j+2}(j + 2)(j + 1) = 0 \tag{3.17}$$

---

[2] It is not expected that these arguments will be obvious to most readers, rather it is felt that they are not important enough to consider in detail here. This equation is transformed by the substitution $x = \cos \theta$ into the associated Legendre equation which is treated in most books on differential equations.

where this must equal zero if it is a solution for all values of θ. This gives

$$a_{j+2} = a_j \frac{(j + |m| + 1)(j + |m|) - \beta}{(j + 2)(j + 1)} \tag{3.17'}$$

We may note at once that for j very large we will have the approximate equation $a_{j+2} = a_j$; hence the series will not converge for $\cos \theta = 1$. Thus the series must terminate as with the harmonic oscillator. If we write l for the terminal value of $(j + |m|)$, we obtain

$$\beta = l(l + 1) \tag{3.18}$$

with l having the possible values: $|m|$, $|m| + 1$, $|m| + 2$, etc.

As in the harmonic oscillator case, only the odd (or even) series of powers can be terminated by the value of β, the other is eliminated completely by setting a_0 (or a_1) to zero.

TABLE 3.1

ANGULAR FACTORS FOR TWO-PARTICLE WAVE FUNCTIONS

$l = 0,\ m = 0$: $\Theta\Phi = \left(\dfrac{1}{4\pi}\right)^{1/2}$

$l = 1,\ m = 0$: $\Theta\Phi = \left(\dfrac{3}{4\pi}\right)^{1/2} \cos \theta$

$l = 1,\ m = \pm 1$: $\Theta\Phi = \left(\dfrac{3}{8\pi}\right)^{1/2} \sin \theta e^{\pm i\phi}$

or $\left(\dfrac{3}{4\pi}\right)^{1/2} \sin \theta \cos \phi$

and $\left(\dfrac{3}{4\pi}\right)^{1/2} \sin \theta \sin \phi$

$l = 2,\ m = 0$: $\Theta\Phi = \left(\dfrac{5}{16\pi}\right)^{1/2} (3 \cos^2 \theta - 1)$

$l = 2,\ m = \pm 1$: $\Theta\Phi = \left(\dfrac{15}{8\pi}\right)^{1/2} \sin \theta \cos \theta e^{\pm i\phi}$

or $\left(\dfrac{15}{4\pi}\right)^{1/2} \sin \theta \cos \theta \cos \phi$

and $\left(\dfrac{15}{4\pi}\right)^{1/2} \sin \theta \cos \theta \sin \phi$

$l = 2,\ m = \pm 2$: $\Theta\Phi = \left(\dfrac{15}{32\pi}\right)^{1/2} \sin^2 \theta e^{\pm 2i\phi}$

or $\left(\dfrac{15}{16\pi}\right)^{1/2} \sin^2 \theta \cos 2\phi$

and $\left(\dfrac{15}{16\pi}\right)^{1/2} \sin^2 \theta \sin 2\phi$

Finally returning to Eq. (3.14) and remembering that the second and third terms were equal to $-\beta$, one obtains

$$\frac{d}{dr}\left(r^2\frac{dR}{dr}\right) - l(l+1)R + \frac{8\pi^2\mu r^2}{h^2}[E - V(r)]R = 0 \quad (3.19)$$

We can proceed further only after making some assumption as to $V(r)$, but first let us summarize the angular wave functions $\Theta\Phi$ for the first few values of m and l. These functions are sometimes called spherical harmonics and are of importance in other than quantum theory problems. They have been normalized by the relationship

$$1 = \int_0^\pi \int_0^{2\pi} \Theta^*\Phi^*\Theta\Phi \sin\theta \, d\phi \, d\theta \quad (3.20)$$

and are given in Table 3.1. These angular wave functions apply to any problem of this type with spherical symmetry of potential energy.

3d. Hydrogen-like atom. For an atom with charge $+Ze$ on the nucleus and a single electron of charge $-e$ the potential energy is

$$V(r) = -Ze^2/r \quad (3.21)$$

If we substitute (3.21) into (3.19) and introduce also the new symbols

$$\alpha^2 = -\frac{8\pi^2\mu E}{h^2} \quad \text{and} \quad \lambda = \frac{4\pi^2\mu Ze^2}{h^2\alpha} \quad (3.22a)$$

and the new variable

$$\rho = 2\alpha r \quad (3.22b)$$

we obtain

$$\frac{d}{d\rho}\left(\rho^2\frac{dR}{d\rho}\right) + \left[-\frac{\rho^2}{4} - l(l+1) + \lambda\rho\right]R = 0 \quad (3.23)$$

Investigating the behavior of this equation both for ρ near zero and for ρ very large, leads one to write

$$R = e^{-\rho/2}\rho^l \sum_{k=0}^\infty b_k\rho^k \quad (3.24)$$

Substituting, one obtains

$$-\frac{\rho^2}{4}R = e^{-\rho/2}\rho^l\left(-\frac{1}{4}\right)\sum b_k\rho^{k+2}$$

$$-l(l+1)R = e^{-\rho/2}\rho^l[-l(l+1)]\sum b_k\rho^k$$

$$+\lambda\rho R = e^{-\rho/2}\rho^l(+\lambda)\sum b_k\rho^{k+1}$$

$$\frac{d}{d\rho}\left(\rho^2\frac{dR}{d\rho}\right) = e^{-\rho/2}\rho^l\left[\frac{1}{4}\sum b_k\rho^{k+2} - \sum(k+l+1)b_k\rho^{k+1}\right.$$

$$\left. + \sum(k+l)(k+l+1)b_k\rho^k\right]$$

and collecting the coefficient of $e^{-\rho/2}\rho^{k+l+1}$ gives

$$b_k(\lambda - k - l - 1) + b_{k+1}[-l(l+1) + (k+l+1)(k+l+2)] = 0$$

$$\text{(3.25)}$$

$$b_{k+1} = b_k \frac{k+l+1-\lambda}{(k+1)(k+2l+2)} \qquad (3.25')$$

Since in this series only b_0 is arbitrary, one may ask about the second arbitrary constant. Another series exists but involves negative powers of ρ and is unacceptable because it will not remain finite at the origin.

Again it is found that unless the series terminates, ψ cannot remain finite as $\rho \to \infty$. This requires λ to be an integer, which we may designate n. We also note that in terms of the terminal value of k our new quantum number n is $k + l + 1$. Now we may return to our definitions of λ and α so as to solve for the energy levels.

$$\lambda = n = 4\pi^2\mu Z e^2 / h^2 \alpha$$

$$E = -\frac{h^2\alpha^2}{8\pi^2\mu} = -\frac{2\pi^2\mu Z^2 e^4}{h^2 n^2} \qquad (3.26)$$

$$n = 1, 2, 3, \text{ etc.}$$

This result for the energy levels of the hydrogen atom is the famous one first obtained by Bohr from his early form of quantum theory. Except for extremely small corrections which arise from the electron magnetic moment and from relativistic corrections (indeed the magnetic moment itself comes out of Dirac's relativistic equations), this formula (3.26) accounts fully for the atomic spectrum of hydrogen.

It should be noted that when n is greater than one, there are several ways of combining $k + l + 1$ to give a single total, and hence that there are several wave functions giving the same energy. In other words, if n is greater than one the state is degenerate. In particular

$$m = 0, \pm 1, \pm 2, \ldots, \pm l$$

$$l = 0, 1, 2, \ldots, n - 1 \qquad (3.27)$$

so that for $n = 2$ we can have $l = 0$, $m = 0$; $l = 1$, $m = 0$, and $l = 1$, $m = \pm 1$, giving four wave functions or quantum states in all. For $n = 3$ we find nine states, for $n = 4$ we find sixteen, etc.

In writing out several of the radial wave functions, let us introduce a new unit of distance, sometimes called the radius of the first Bohr orbit in hydrogen and given the symbol a_0.

$$a_0 = \frac{h^2}{4\pi^2\mu e^2} = 0.529 \times 10^{-8} \text{ cm.} \qquad (3.28)$$

Strictly μ depends on the mass of the nucleus, hence the second equality is only approximate. Then writing $\sigma = Zr/a_0 = n\rho/2$ one obtains Table 3.2.

TABLE 3.2

RADIAL FACTORS FOR HYDROGEN-LIKE WAVE FUNCTIONS

$n = 1, l = 0$: $R_{1s} = 2\left(\dfrac{Z}{a_0}\right)^{3/2} e^{-\sigma}$

$n = 2, l = 0$: $R_{2s} = \left(\dfrac{Z}{2a_0}\right)^{3/2}(2 - \sigma)e^{-\sigma/2}$

$n = 2, l = 1$: $R_{2p} = 3^{-1/2}\left(\dfrac{Z}{2a_0}\right)^{3/2}\sigma e^{-\sigma/2}$

$n = 3, l = 0$: $R_{3s} = \dfrac{2}{27}\left(\dfrac{Z}{3a_0}\right)^{3/2}(27 - 18\sigma + 2\sigma^2)e^{-\sigma/3}$

$n = 3, l = 1$: $R_{3p} = \dfrac{1}{81\sqrt{3}}\left(\dfrac{2Z}{a_0}\right)^{3/2}(6 - \sigma)\sigma e^{-\sigma/3}$

$n = 3, l = 2$: $R_{3d} = \dfrac{1}{81\sqrt{15}}\left(\dfrac{2Z}{a_0}\right)^{3/2}\sigma^2 e^{-\sigma/3}$

These are all normalized on the basis

$$1 = \int_0^\infty R^2 r^2 \, dr = \left(\frac{a_0}{Z}\right)^3 \int_0^\infty R^2\sigma^2 \, d\sigma$$

so that the complete wave function is

$$\psi(r,\theta,\phi) = R\Theta\Phi \qquad (3.29)$$

as defined above.

In these terms the energy may be rewritten as

$$E = -\frac{Z^2 e^2}{2a_0 n^2} \qquad (3.30)$$

The spectroscopists commonly report data in the reciprocal of the wave length, i.e., in cm.$^{-1}$, which is equivalent to E/hc. In their terms the hydrogen-like energy levels are

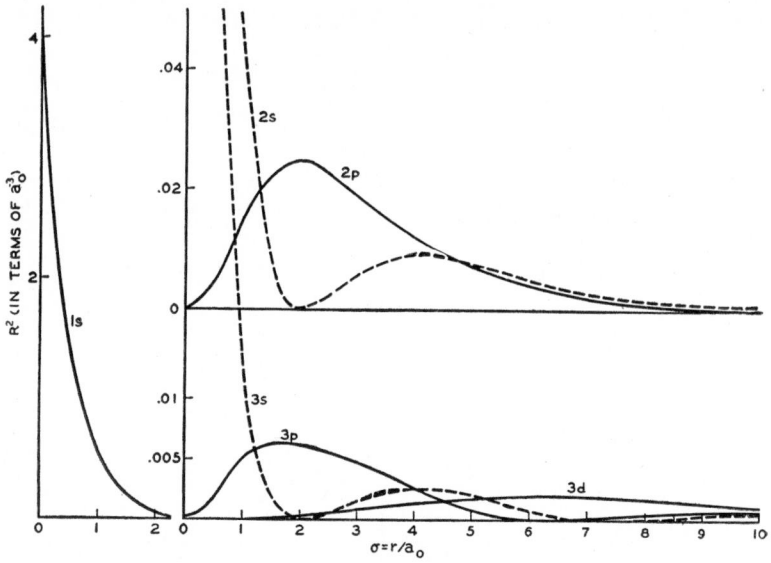

Fig. 3.1.   The electron density R^2 for various states of the hydrogen atom. Note that the radius scale is the same throughout but that the density scale is changed for the different functions.

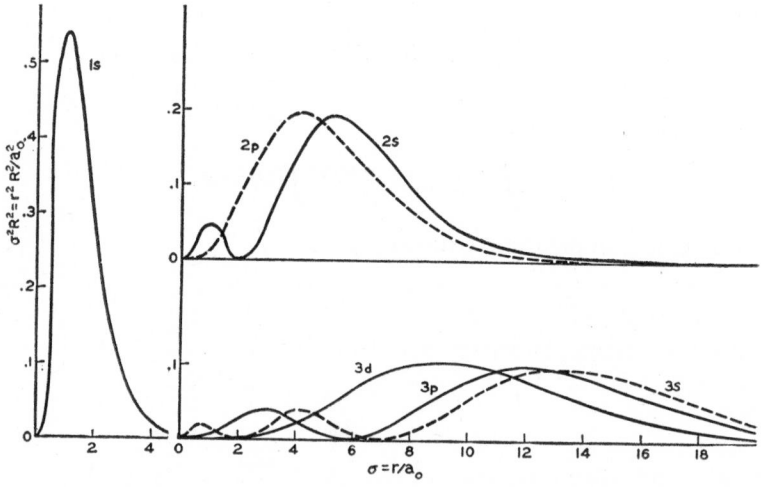

Fig. 3.2.   The radial distribution function for various states of the hydrogen atom.   Note that the scale is the same for all curves.

$$\frac{E}{hc} = -\frac{Z^2R}{n^2}, \qquad R = \frac{2\pi^2\mu e^4}{h^3c} \qquad (3.30a)$$

where the constant R is called the Rydberg constant.   Strictly, the Rydberg constant varies with the reduced mass μ as does a_0.   Thus there are given R_H for normal hydrogen, R_D for deuterium, R_∞ for a nucleus of infinite mass, etc.

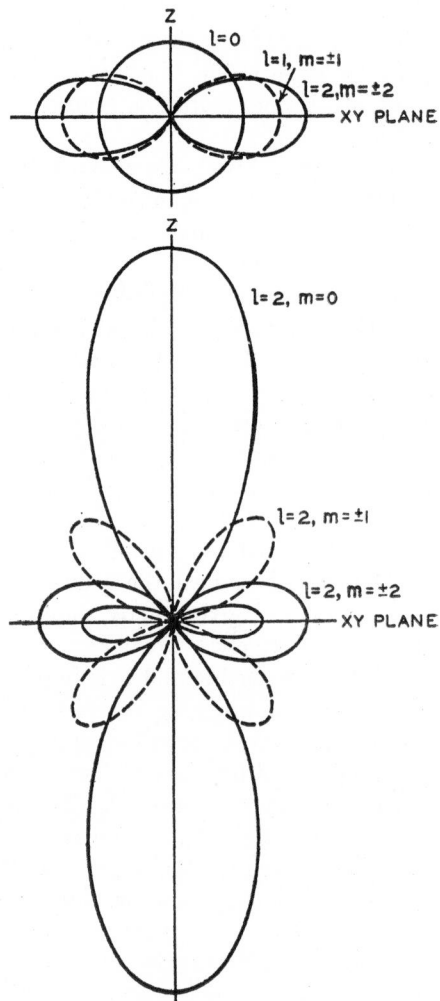

These wave functions and energy levels for hydrogen-like atoms are of great importance. Most simple discussions of complex atoms and of directional valence, to mention only two subjects, are based on these results. It is desirable to gain a mental picture of the qualitative character of the wave functions as shown in Figs. 3.1 to 3.3.   Figure 3.1 shows R^2 and hence gives the relative probability of finding the electron in unit volume (except for angular variation when l is not zero). The radial distribution functions, r^2R^2, which give the relative probability of finding the electron in a spherical shell of radius r, are shown in Fig. 3.2.   Figure 3.3 shows angular distribution characteristics.

The s functions with zero l are all spherically symmetrical.   There is no variation with angle. The 1s

Fig. 3.3.   Angular properties of the electron density of hydrogen in several states.

function gives just an exponential drop of electron probability density from a maximum value at the nucleus. However, the other s functions all have nodes in the radial function. At these values of the radius the wave function itself changes sign. The probability function is always positive, as shown in Figs. 3.1 and 3.2, but is reduced to a zero value at each node. Although the maximum electron density is at the origin for any s function, the volume of spherical shells of large radius is so much greater that the electron spends most of its time in the outermost zone, i.e., outside the outermost spherical node.

The increased probable distance from the nucleus for the functions of larger principal quantum number is shown clearly in Fig. 3.2. There are much smaller differences between the probable radii for functions of the same n but different l.

The functions with l other than zero are harder to visualize. One must superimpose radial and angular probabilities by taking their product. The $2p$ radial function is quite simple. It is zero at the origin, increases to a maximum, and then decreases again exponentially. There are three different $2p$ angular functions. Although Table 3.1 indicates that there is some freedom of selection, we may choose the real trigonometric formulation. The first function, $\cos \theta$, has a node in the xy plane. With zero probability in the nodal plane, and small probability near it, one can see that the probable region for the electron is near the z axis. The other functions, $\sin \theta \sin \phi$ and $\sin \theta \cos \phi$, give exactly the same distributions near the y and x axes, respectively.

In interpreting Fig. 3.3 it is important to remember that the distance from the origin to the curve gives the relative probability of finding the electron at any distance in that direction. The relative probability as a function of distance is an independent quantity and was given in Figs. 3.1 and 3.2. The angular properties do not depend on the principal quantum number. It is the radial function that changes between the $2p$, $3p$, etc., states.

It is not possible to present all the d functions in equivalent form. The $l = 2, m = 0$ function gives primarily a very concentrated distribution along the z axis but also a secondary region of probability in the xy plane. The $l = 2, m = \pm 2$ functions are highly concentrated in the xy plane. If one takes the $\cos 2\phi$ and $\sin 2\phi$ formulations, one has the probability concentrated near the x and y axes for the

cos 2ϕ function. That wave function has nodes at 45° to the axes. The sin 2ϕ function has nodes in the xz and yz planes. Its square, $\sin^4 \theta \sin^2 2\phi$, yields the principal probability near the xy plane but near the diagonals at 45° to the x and y axes. The other two d wave functions, in the form $\sin \theta \cos \theta \cos \phi$ and $\sin \theta \cos \theta \sin \phi$, both have nodes in the xy plane. The first has a node also in the yz plane and the second in the xz plane. Thus their regions of principal probability are above and below the xy plane around a maximum at 45° to the xy plane. The first function is also concentrated near the xz plane. The last four d functions are equivalent except for their orientation. They have in each case two mutually perpendicular nodal planes, and their distribution is concentrated near the plane perpendicular to both of the nodal planes.

Since we shall be concerned frequently with completed shells of electrons, the net probability for such a shell is of interest. A useful theorem (Unsöld, 1927) states that the sum of all the probability distribution functions for a given l is a constant, thus

$$\sum_{m=-l}^{+l} \Theta_{l,m}^*(\theta)\Phi_m^*(\phi)\Theta_{l,m}(\theta)\Phi_m(\phi) = \text{constant} \qquad (3.31)$$

This means that any closed shell atom or ion has perfect spherical symmetry.

3e. Diatomic molecule. A diatomic molecule will have, in addition to the two nuclei, several electrons. However, the electrons are so light compared with the nuclei that their motion is relatively very rapid and completes many cycles before the nuclei move appreciably. Consequently the total energy of the electronic system may be taken as a potential energy for the nuclear motion which we shall discuss in this section. A mathematical discussion of this point was given by Born and Oppenheimer,[3] in which they expanded the various quantities in series of increasing powers of the ratio of electronic to nuclear mass. They found the above conclusion to be true in the first approximation, and showed also what form the higher approximations would take. These higher approximations are not needed, however, in ordinary cases.

We are not at present prepared to handle the problem of the motion of several electrons, so we shall have to accept the curves for that

---

[3] Born, M. and Oppenheimer, J. R., *Ann. Physik*, **84**, 457 (1927).

energy which were obtained elsewhere.   Qualitatively they have the
form shown in Fig. 3.4 (solid curve).

Large values of r correspond to separated atoms.   With decreasing
r the energy decreases, corresponding to the formation of a molecule,
then increases again at very short distances.   While a function proposed by Morse,

$$V(r) = D[1 - e^{-a(r-r_0)}]^2 \qquad (3.32)$$

fits the observed curves well over the full range, we shall use a more
approximate form which fits near the energy minimum.

$$V(r) = \frac{k}{2}(r - r_0)^2 \qquad (3.33)$$

This is a harmonic or Hooke's law potential and corresponds to the
dotted parabola in Fig. 3.4.   This approximate form may be justified
mathematically by expanding the true potential as a Taylor's series
in $(r - r_0)$, obtaining

$$V(r - r_0) = V(r_0) + \left(\frac{dV}{dr}\right)_{r_0}(r - r_0) + \frac{1}{2}\left(\frac{d^2V}{dr^2}\right)_{r_0}(r - r_0)^2 + \dots$$

The first term on the right becomes zero if one takes the zero of
energy at the minimum of the curve, while the second term is zero
because the slope is zero at the potential minimum at r_0.   If one

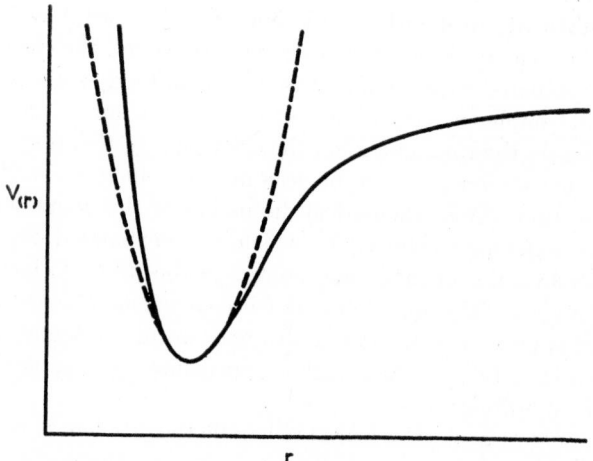

Fig. 3.4.   The potential energy as a function of r, the internuclear distance, in a
diatomic molecule.

neglects terms involving higher than the second power of $(r - r_0)$ one obtains Eq. (3.33).

Proceeding then to obtain the energy levels, one notes that the problem is exactly the same as that treated above in this chapter through Eq. (3.20), and the wave functions for ϕ and θ are still applicable. Equation (3.19) now becomes

$$\frac{d}{dr}\left(r^2 \frac{dR}{dr}\right) - l(l + 1)R + \frac{8\pi^2 \mu r^2}{h^2}\left[E - \frac{k}{2}(r - r_0)^2\right]R = 0 \qquad (3.34)$$

First let us substitute

$$R(r) = S(r)/r$$

obtaining

$$\frac{d^2S}{dr^2} - \frac{l(l + 1)}{r^2}S + \frac{8\pi^2 \mu}{h^2}\left[E - \frac{k}{2}(r - r_0)^2\right]S = 0 \qquad (3.35)$$

Now since we are interested in a small region of r near r_0, let us write $q = r - r_0$, obtaining

$$\frac{d^2S}{dq^2} - \frac{l(l + 1)}{(r_0 + q)^2}S + \frac{8\pi^2 \mu}{h^2}\left(E - \frac{k}{2}q^2\right)S = 0 \qquad (3.36)$$

But q is to be small compared with r_0; hence the second term is nearly constant and will be considered constant as an approximation. Note also that the moment of inertia of the molecule in its equilibrium configuration is

$$I_e = \mu r_0^2 = \left(\frac{m_2 r_0}{m_1 + m_2}\right)^2 m_1 + \left(\frac{m_1 r_0}{m_1 + m_2}\right)^2 m_2 \qquad (3.37)$$

where at the right the terms in parentheses are the distances of particles one and two from the center of mass. Then

$$\frac{d^2S}{dq^2} + \frac{8\pi^2 \mu}{h^2}\left[\left(E - \frac{h^2 l(l + 1)}{8\pi^2 I_e}\right) - \frac{k}{2}q^2\right]S = 0 \qquad (3.38)$$

But Eq. (3.38) is essentially the equation for the harmonic oscillator discussed in Chapter 2. Strictly the boundary conditions are now that $S = 0$ at $-r_0$ and $+\infty$, while before $\psi = 0$ at $-\infty$ and $+\infty$. However, ψ approaches zero so rapidly outside the region of classical oscillation that this difference is trivial.

Then we obtain for the energy levels

$$E = \frac{h^2 J(J + 1)}{8\pi^2 I_e} + h\nu\left(n + \frac{1}{2}\right) \qquad (3.39)$$

where we have replaced the quantum number l by J to conform with the usual symbols of molecular spectroscopy. The first term is clearly to be identified with the rotation of the molecule, and the second with the vibration of the molecule. Regardless of n there is a $2J + 1$ degeneracy of any Jth state. The complete wave functions are

$$\psi = \Theta(\theta)\Phi(\phi)\psi_{HO}(r - r_0)r^{-1} \tag{3.40}$$

where ψ_{HO} is the harmonic oscillator wave function given in Section 2i.

It is possible to remove the approximations we have made by more complex mathematical methods; however, the final energy is expressed in a series of which (3.39) represents the leading terms. A typical expression is

$$\frac{E}{hc} = \omega_e\left(n + \frac{1}{2}\right) - \omega_e x\left(n + \frac{1}{2}\right)^2 + B_e J(J + 1) - DJ^2(J + 1)^2$$
$$-\alpha\left(n + \frac{1}{2}\right)J(J + 1) \tag{3.41}$$

where

$$\omega_e = \nu/c, \qquad B_e = h/8\pi^2 I_e c, \qquad D = 4B_e^3/\omega_e^2$$

and x and α depend on the exact shape of the potential energy curve away from the minimum. The term in x can be attributed to deviation of the potential energy from the harmonic force law, hence is called the anharmonicity; the term in D arises from the stretching of the molecule from its own centrifugal force, while the term in α comes from the difference between the average moment of inertia of the molecule in an excited vibrational state and that of the molecule at rest.[4]

As an example of the relative magnitude of these quantities we give here the values for HCl^{35}: $\omega_e = 2988.95$, $\omega_e x = 51.65$, $B_e = 10.5909$, $\alpha = 0.3019$, $D = 0.0004$, all cm.$^{-1}$ From these one can judge the accuracy of the more approximate formula, Eq. (3.38), which is sometimes referred to as the rigid-rotator, harmonic-oscillator approximation. For many complex molecules there are data only for that approximation.

---

[4] For further discussion, see Herzberg, G., *Molecular Spectra and Molecular Structure, I Diatomic Molecules*, 2d ed., New York: D. Van Nostrand Company, Inc., 1950, Chap. III-2.

GENERAL REFERENCES

Herzberg, G., *Molecular Spectra and Molecular Structure, I: Diatomic Molecules,* 2d ed., New York: D. Van Nostrand Company, Inc., 1950. This is the standard work on diatomic molecules.

Pauling, L. and Wilson, E. B., Jr., *Introduction to Quantum Mechanics,* New York: McGraw-Hill Book Company, Inc., 1935. Chapter 5 comprises a most thorough treatment of the hydrogen-like atom. Chapters 5 and 10 combined give a comparable treatment of the diatomic molecule.

All the general references at the end of Chapter 2 are appropriate for this chapter also.

PROBLEMS

3.1 Obtain $\bar{r}$ for the first few values of n, all with $l = 0$, and propose a general formula in terms of n, a_0, and Z which appears to hold.[5]

3.2 Verify Unsöld's theorem, Eq. (3.31), for $l = 2$.

3.3 Calculate the fractional change in r for HCl in the lowest vibrational state between the most probable value, r_e, and a value of one-tenth of that probability.

[5] If interested in proving this formula, study Section 20 of Pauling, L. and Wilson, E. B., Jr., *Introduction to Quantum Mechanics.* New York: McGraw-Hill Book Company, Inc., 1935.

Chapter 4

PROPERTIES OF WAVE FUNCTIONS; APPROXIMATE METHODS

In the present chapter we will establish certain mathematical properties of solutions of the Schrödinger equation for stationary states which are useful for further work, in particular for certain methods of approximation.

We have already mentioned the conditions of single valuedness, finiteness, and continuity which were imposed as postulate 2 in Section 2d. Also we saw that where the particle (or particles) are confined by potential barriers that approach high values at infinity in all directions, the wave function approaches zero at infinity. Then the wave function can be normalized so that

$$\int \psi^* \psi \, dv = 1 \qquad (4.1)$$

where dv is an element of volume in the coordinates appropriate to the problem and the integration is over all space.

4a. Orthogonality. Next we wish to show that the wave functions are orthogonal, i.e., if ψ_m and ψ_n are two different solutions of the Schrödinger equation, then

$$\int \psi_m^* \psi_n \, dv = 0 \qquad (4.2)$$

The Schrödinger equation may be written for a general case (of a stationary state)

$$\sum \frac{-h^2}{8\pi^2 m_i} \frac{\partial^2 \psi_n}{\partial q_i^2} + V\psi_n = E_n \psi_n \qquad (4.3a)$$

where q_i is a Cartesian coordinate (x, y, or z) of the particle of mass m_i. Similarly one may write

$$\sum \frac{-h^2}{8\pi^2 m_i} \frac{\partial^2 \psi_m^*}{\partial q_i^2} + V\psi_m^* = E_m \psi_m^* \qquad (4.3b)$$

60

Now multiply (4.3a) by ψ_m^*, and (4.3b) by ψ_n, and then subtract, obtaining

$$\sum -\frac{h^2}{8\pi^2 m_i}\left(\psi_m^*\frac{\partial^2\psi_n}{\partial q_i^2} - \psi_n\frac{\partial^2\psi_m^*}{\partial q_i^2}\right) = (E_n - E_m)\psi_m^*\psi_n \qquad (4.4)$$

where the term in V has dropped out identically. We next note that

$$\frac{\partial}{\partial q_i}\left(\psi_m^*\frac{\partial\psi_n}{\partial q_i} - \psi_n\frac{\partial\psi_m^*}{\partial q_i}\right) = \psi_m^*\frac{\partial^2\psi_n}{\partial q_i^2} - \psi_n\frac{\partial^2\psi_m^*}{\partial q_i^2} \qquad (4.5)$$

Hence when (4.4) is integrated over all space we obtain from a typical term in the left sum upon integration over q_i:

$$\int_{-\infty}^{+\infty}\cdots\int_{-\infty}^{+\infty}\left(\psi_m^*\frac{\partial^2\psi_n}{\partial q_i^2} - \psi_n\frac{\partial^2\psi_m^*}{\partial q_i^2}\right)dq_i\,dq_j$$

$$= \int_{-\infty}^{+\infty}\cdots\int_{-\infty}^{+\infty}\left[\psi_m^*\frac{\partial\psi_n}{\partial q_i} - \psi_n\frac{\partial\psi_m^*}{\partial q_i}\right]_{-\infty}^{+\infty}dq_j\cdots \qquad (4.6)$$

However, ψ_m^* and ψ_n are both zero at $+\infty$ and $-\infty$; hence the term is zero and since all terms are essentially similar the entire sum is zero. Thus we have

$$0 = (E_n - E_m)\int\cdots\int\psi_m^*\psi_n\,dv \qquad (4.7)$$

which proves the orthogonality of ψ_m^* and ψ_n provided E_n and E_m are different. If the energies are the same, we are dealing with the members of a degenerate set. As we saw with the Φ functions for the two particle rotation, there are alternate forms of the wave functions when a degenerate set is involved. However, they can always be orthogonalized. If ψ_a and ψ_b are arbitrarily selected as the two normalized functions, we may take as the orthogonal functions

$$\psi_1 = \psi_a$$
$$\psi_2 = (1 - |\alpha|^2)^{-1/2}(\psi_b - \alpha\psi_a)$$
$$(1 - |\alpha|^2)^{1/2}\int\psi_1^*\psi_2\,dv = \int\psi_a^*\psi_b\,dv - \alpha\int\psi_a^*\psi_a\,dv = 0 \qquad (4.8)$$
$$\alpha = \int\psi_a^*\psi_b\,dv$$
$$\int\psi_2^*\psi_2\,dv = (1 - |\alpha|^2)^{-1}(1 + |\alpha|^2 - \alpha\int\psi_b^*\psi_a\,dv - \alpha^*\int\psi_a^*\psi_b\,dv) = 1$$

Thus we can always arrange the wave functions for the degenerate states so that all wave functions are orthogonal and normalized. In further work we shall assume that this has been done and that the wave functions are arranged in a single series with the one corresponding to lowest energy first, etc.

4b. Series expansion. In a manner similar to the Fourier series, it is possible to express arbitrary functions as a series of normalized, orthogonal functions, provided the latter cover the same coordinate space and constitute a sufficiently complete set. The first condition is obvious; questions of completeness and convergence of the series can be investigated, if necessary, but will be assumed here. If ϕ is the arbitrary function, we write

$$\phi = a_0\psi_0 + a_1\psi_1 + a_2\psi_2 + \ldots + a_n\psi_n + \ldots \quad (4.9)$$

where the ψ's are the set of orthogonal functions. Then multiplying by ψ_n^* and integrating, one has

$$\int \psi_n^* \phi \, dv = a_n \quad (4.10)$$

since all other terms on the right were zero. In this manner all coefficients might be evaluated.

4c. Symmetry properties. Another type of wave function property arises when the problem contains elements of symmetry. A full treatment of this topic would involve a study of the mathematics of symmetry groups. However, without this, we can still develop certain worth-while results.

Let us first consider a one-particle, one-dimensional case where the potential energy is symmetrical about $x = 0$, i.e., $V(x) = V(-x)$. Let us denote by the symbol R, the operation of replacing x by $-x$. Then $RV(x) = V(-x) = V(x)$ and $RH = H$ since

$$\partial^2/\partial x^2 = \partial^2/\partial(-x)^2.$$

Consequently, operating on the Schrödinger equation itself,

$$R(H\psi) = RH(R\psi) = H(R\psi) = E \cdot R\psi \quad (4.11)$$

since R naturally has no effect on the number E. Then we can conclude that $\psi(-x)$ must be a solution with the same energy as ψ. If this is not from a degenerate set, then

$$\psi(-x) = \pm\psi(x) \quad (4.12)$$

This result follows because a nondegenerate ψ may be, and for simplicity is, taken as a real function. This may be easily seen. Since all the variables in ψ are real, a complex ψ may be expressed as

$$\psi = f + ig$$

where f and g are real functions. However, both f and g must be solutions of the Schrödinger equation for the same energy; hence if the state is nondegenerate, g must be merely a constant times f, and f normalized may be taken as a real function for ψ.

If the positive sign applies in Eq. (4.12), the wave function is said to be *symmetric* to the operation R; if the negative sign applies it is *antisymmetric*.

We will now state that the above result is quite general. Nondegenerate wave functions are either symmetric or antisymmetric to all symmetry operations. If they are symmetric to all symmetry operations of the problem, they are called *totally symmetric*.

For degenerate sets of wave functions one can only say that

$$R\psi_k = \sum a_i\psi_i \qquad (4.13)$$

where R is a symmetry operation and the sum is over the wave functions of the degenerate set of which ψ_k is a member.

In a diatomic molecule, if the two nuclei are identical, the interchange of these nuclei is a symmetry operation. This may be accomplished by the changes $\theta \to \pi - \theta$ and $\phi \to \pi + \phi$. Substitution in the angular wave functions gives the result that, regardless of m and of the associated degeneracy, the function is symmetric if J is even, and antisymmetric if J is odd (J replaced the l of the hydrogen atom expressions in Table 3.1).

4d. Angular momentum. A quantity of great importance and one which helps to give physical significance to our mathematical functions is the angular momentum. The following equations give first the classical definition, and then the quantum mechanical operator in Cartesian coordinates.

$$M_x = yp_z - zp_y = \frac{h}{2\pi i}\left(y\frac{\partial}{\partial z} - z\frac{\partial}{\partial y}\right)$$
$$M_y = zp_x - xp_z = \frac{h}{2\pi i}\left(z\frac{\partial}{\partial x} - x\frac{\partial}{\partial z}\right) \qquad (4.14)$$
$$M_z = xp_y - yp_x = \frac{h}{2\pi i}\left(x\frac{\partial}{\partial y} - y\frac{\partial}{\partial x}\right)$$

These may be transformed to polar coordinates, yielding

$$M_x = \frac{h}{2\pi i}\left(-\sin\phi\frac{\partial}{\partial\theta} - \cot\theta\cos\phi\frac{\partial}{\partial\phi}\right)$$
$$M_y = \frac{h}{2\pi i}\left(\cos\phi\frac{\partial}{\partial\theta} - \cot\theta\sin\phi\frac{\partial}{\partial\phi}\right) \qquad (4.15)$$
$$M_z = \frac{h}{2\pi i}\cdot\frac{\partial}{\partial\phi}$$

While these transformations are rather cumbersome, the reverse transformations back to Cartesian coordinates are easily verified. We shall also be interested in the square of the total angular momentum.

$$M^2 = M_x^2 + M_y^2 + M_z^2 \qquad (4.16)$$

To obtain this we apply the operator to itself.

$$M_x^2 = M_x M_x = \frac{-h^2}{4\pi^2}\left(\sin^2\phi\,\frac{\partial^2}{\partial\theta^2} - \frac{\sin\phi\cos\phi}{\sin^2\theta}\,\frac{\partial}{\partial\phi} + \cot\theta\cos^2\phi\,\frac{\partial}{\partial\theta}\right.$$
$$\left. + 2\cot\theta\sin\phi\cos\phi\,\frac{\partial^2}{\partial\theta\,\partial\phi} + \cot^2\theta\cos^2\phi\,\frac{\partial^2}{\partial\phi^2}\right) - \cot^2\theta\sin\phi\cos\phi\,\frac{\partial}{\partial\phi}$$

Similarly computing the other terms and adding, one obtains

$$M^2 = \frac{-h^2}{4\pi^2}\left(\frac{\partial^2}{\partial\theta^2} + \cot\theta\,\frac{\partial}{\partial\theta} + \frac{1}{\sin^2\theta}\,\frac{\partial^2}{\partial\phi^2}\right) \qquad (4.17)$$

Let us now investigate the angular momentum of the states of the hydrogen atom and the diatomic molecule.

All s states have zero angular momentum. This is easily seen since for any s state $\psi = f(r)$ and all derivatives with respect to angles vanish.

For p states $M^2 = 2h^2/4\pi^2$. Also $M_z = \pm h/2\pi$ or zero if one selects the imaginary exponential expressions in Φ. This may be said to correspond to the values ± 1, 0 for the quantum number m (or m_l). If, however, we select the $\sin\phi$ and $\cos\phi$ wave functions, we obtain

$$M_z \sin\phi = \frac{h}{2\pi i}\,\frac{\partial}{\partial\phi}\sin\phi = \frac{h}{2\pi i}\cos\phi$$

which indicates a distribution of values of M_z. Furthermore, for neither type of wave function do M_x and M_y give the unchanged wave function; consequently a distribution of values of these momenta is expected.

In general $M^2 = l(l+1)h^2/4\pi^2$, and using the imaginary exponential functions for ϕ, $M_z = mh/2\pi$. Of course for the diatomic molecule, J replaces l.

While one cannot make perfect classical analogies to quantum states, it seems helpful to picture classical motions corresponding to these angular momenta. For an s state the electron must oscillate linearly back and forth, passing the nucleus each time. Classically we would worry about the collision with the nucleus, but in quantum theory we may assume that it penetrates or in some other manner gets past the nucleus. Likewise, although the classical oscillation would repeat itself indefinitely in the same direction, we must assume in quantum theory that the direction of oscillation gradually shifts to give an average spherical distribution.

For p and other states we replace the linear oscillation by elliptical orbits of the proper angular momentum. Also in this case the angular momentum about the z axis remains constant.

4e. Magnetic fields, Zeeman effect. If there is a magnetic field present, these angular momenta of charged particles become energy effects. For convenience let us take the z axis as that of the field. Then the magnetic dipole moment along that axis for a hydrogen atom where the charge e is associated with the electron mass m is

$$\mu_z = M_z(e/2mc) \qquad (4.18)$$

where c is the velocity of light. If we define the quantity $\mu_0 = (eh/4\pi mc)$, called the "Bohr magneton," then combining the value for M_z given above with Eq. (4.18) we obtain

$$\mu_z = m_l\mu_0 \qquad (4.19)$$

where m_l is the quantum number called m previously.

Then if the field strength is $\mathfrak{IC}$, the interaction energy is

$$E_m = \mathfrak{IC}\mu = m_l\mathfrak{IC}\mu_0 \qquad (4.20)$$

Thus a magnetic field removes the degeneracy of states of different m_l. Actually, the situation is further complicated by the presence of electron spin and magnetic moment which we will discuss later.

APPROXIMATE METHODS

In classical mechanics only two-body systems are soluble in closed form; approximate methods must be used for three or more particles. Essentially the same situation exists in wave mechanics. There are two approximate methods which are of particular importance. The perturbation method is applicable if the system of interest differs only slightly from a system where exact solutions are known. The variation method gives an upper limit to the true energy which in favorable cases may be made to approach the true energy. Since the mathematical form of the final working equations is essentially the same for both methods, they will be described together.

4f. Variation method theorem. The variation method is based on a theorem which we shall now prove, namely, that the integral

$$W = \int \phi^* H \phi \, dv \geqq E_0; \qquad (\int \phi^* \phi \, dv = 1) \qquad (4.21)$$

where ϕ is any normalized function which satisfies the general conditions (continuous, single valued, etc.) for a wave function for the problem at hand, H is the true Hamiltonian operator for the problem, E_0 is the energy of the lowest quantum state, and the integration is over the entire space appropriate to the problem.

To prove this, let us proceed as follows.

$$\int \phi^*(H - E_0)\phi \, dv = \int \phi^* H \phi \, dv - E_0 \int \phi^* \phi \, dv = \int \phi^* H \phi \, dv - E_0 \qquad (4.22)$$

Hence we must prove that the first integral in (4.22) is greater than or equal to zero. To do this let us expand ϕ in a series of the normalized, orthogonal functions which are solutions of the Schrödinger equation $H\psi = E\psi$. To be sure we do not have these ψ's, but their properties were established earlier in this chapter. Then

$$\phi = \sum_{k=1}^{\infty} a_k \psi_k \qquad (4.23)$$

and since the ψ's are eigenfunctions of H,

$$H\phi = \sum a_k H\psi_k = \sum a_k E_k \psi_k \qquad (4.24)$$

Substituting into (4.22) we obtain

$$\int \phi^*(H - E_0)\phi \, dv = \int \sum a_j^* \psi_j^* \sum a_k (E_k - E_0) \psi_k \, dv$$
$$= \sum \sum a_j^* a_k (E_k - E_0) \int \psi_j^* \psi_k \, dv \qquad (4.25)$$

Because of the orthogonality and normalization of the ψ's this simplifies to

$$\int \phi^*(H - E_0)\phi \, dv = \sum a_k^* a_k (E_k - E_0) \qquad (4.26)$$

Since $a_k^* a_k$ is necessarily positive, and $(E_k - E_0)$ is either zero or positive, the sum must be positive or zero. This was the point to be proved.

Without further thought this result would not appear very useful. However, by introducing a number of parameters into ϕ, and then minimizing the resulting integral W with respect to these parameters, the value of W may be made to approach E_0. If enough parameters covering all essential characteristics of ϕ are included, this approach may be made as close as desired.

4g. Linear variation functions. A type of variation function ϕ, which is particularly useful is a series

$$\phi = c_1 f_1 + c_2 f_2 + c_3 f_3 + \ldots + c_n f_n \tag{4.27}$$

where each function f satisfies the general conditions for a wave function. For simplicity we shall assume that all quantities in (4.27) are real. In this case we will not assume that ϕ is normalized, but rather write

$$W = \frac{\int \phi H \phi \, dv}{\int \phi \phi \, dv} = \frac{\sum\limits_{j=1}^{n} \sum\limits_{k=1}^{n} c_j c_k H_{jk}}{\sum\limits_{j=1}^{n} \sum\limits_{k=1}^{n} c_j c_k \Delta_{jk}} \tag{4.28}$$

where

$$H_{jk} = \int f_j H f_k \, dv; \qquad \Delta_{jk} = \int f_j f_k \, dv \tag{4.29}$$

Equation (4.28) may be rearranged to

$$W \sum \sum c_j c_k \Delta_{jk} = \sum \sum c_j c_k H_{jk} \tag{4.30}$$

which may then be differentiated with respect to c_i in order to locate the minimum in W.

$$\frac{\partial W}{\partial c_i} \sum_{j=1}^{n} \sum_{k=1}^{n} c_j c_k \Delta_{jk} + W \sum_{k=1}^{n} 2 c_k \Delta_{ik} = \sum_{k=1}^{n} c_k (H_{ik} + H_{ki}) \tag{4.31}$$

One may readily prove that $H_{ik} = H_{ki}$.[1] The condition that $\partial W / \partial c_i$ be zero then becomes

$$\sum_{k=1}^{n} c_k (H_{ik} - \Delta_{ik} W) = 0 \qquad i = 1, 2, \ldots, n \tag{4.32}$$

This is a set of n simultaneous, homogeneous linear equations. If they are to have a solution other than the trivial one of all c's equal to zero, the determinant of the coefficients of the c's must vanish.

[1] See Problem 4.3.

$$\begin{vmatrix} H_{11} - \Delta_{11}W & H_{12} - \Delta_{12}W \ldots H_{1n} - \Delta_{1n}W \\ H_{21} - \Delta_{21}W & H_{22} - \Delta_{22}W \ldots H_{2n} - \Delta_{2n}W \\ & & \\ \cdot & \cdot & \cdot \\ \cdot & \cdot & \cdot \\ \cdot & & \cdot \\ \cdot & \cdot & \cdot \\ \cdot & \cdot & \cdot \\ H_{n1} - \Delta_{n1}W & H_{n2} - \Delta_{n2}W \ldots H_{nn} - \Delta_{nn}W \end{vmatrix} = 0 \qquad (4.33)$$

This determinantal equation, commonly called the secular equation, may be solved for W by numerical methods. The lowest of the n roots is, of course, selected as an approximation to E_0. It has been shown by MacDonald[2] that the next lowest root is $\geqslant E_1$, the next $\geqslant E_2$, and so on.

It is interesting that we have obtained the result of primary interest, the minimum value of W, without actually evaluating the c's. The c's can be obtained, if desired, by substituting the value of W into (4.32). If the problem has elements of symmetry, they should be considered, and only those f's included which have the symmetry properties expected for the wave function of the lowest energy.

4h. Perturbation method.[3] If the problem to be solved differs from a problem already solved by the addition of a small term in the Hamiltonian, one might expect the wave functions of the new problem to be closely related to those of the other. While the perturbation method is really a series development of the new problem in terms of the old, many of the results are immediately evident from the variation method. If $\psi_0^0, \psi_1^0, \psi_2^0, \ldots$ are the wave functions available from the "unperturbed" problem, the first approximation to the lowest energy level of the "perturbed" problem is clearly

$$W_0 = \int \psi_0^0 H \psi_0^0 \, dv \geqslant E_0 \qquad (4.34)$$

since ψ_0^0 will be an acceptable function for the variation integral.

For other levels the first-order perturbation theory result

$$W_n = \int \psi_n^0 H \psi_n^0 \, dv \cong E_n \qquad (4.35)$$

---

[2] MacDonald, J. K. L., *Phys. Rev.*, **43**, 830 (1933).

[3] For a full but simple account of perturbation theory, see Chapter 6 of Pauling, L. and Wilson, E. B., Jr., *Introduction to Quantum Mechanics*, New York: McGraw-Hill Book Company, Inc., 1935.

does not fall under within the variation method theorem. Consequently its validity is based entirely on the smallness of the additional term in the Hamiltonian of the perturbed case. If the nth energy level is degenerate, one must use all of the set of degenerate wave functions in a manner entirely analogous to the linear variation function, obtaining the results from a corresponding secular equation. This is necessary because the perturbation may break the degeneracy of these functions. If so, the wave functions will no longer be arbitrary linear combinations, and all of the set must be fed into the calculation in order that the proper combinations may be obtained.

Higher approximations may be derived from the perturbation theory expansions. Perturbation theory through the second order is outlined in Appendix 20. The second-order theory is particularly valuable where the first-order perturbation energy is zero, as it is for the effect of an electric field on an atom. An electric field shifts the electron cloud of an atom so as to induce a dipole moment or to polarize the atom, but it has only a second-order effect on the energy. In addition to the full treatment in Appendix 20 we give a simple variation method treatment for the hydrogen atom in the next section.

4i. Polarizability of the normal hydrogen atom. As an example of simple variation (or perturbation) method calculations, let us calculate the energy of a normal hydrogen atom in an electric field, F, along the z axis. We assume the field to be small enough that the shift in energy is small compared with the energy of the hydrogen atom itself. The Hamiltonian function for this system is

$$H = H_0 + eFz = H_0 + eFr \cos \theta \qquad (4.36)$$

where H_0 is the Hamiltonian for the hydrogen atom without the field. We have made the approximation of infinite nuclear mass, as compared to the electron, so that the coordinates are simply those of the electron relative to either the center of mass or the nucleus.

The first order perturbation calculation simply uses the $1s$ wave function of hydrogen. The result is

$$W = \int \psi_{1s} H_0 \psi_{1s}\, dv + eF \int \psi_{1s}^2 r \cos \theta\, dv = -\frac{e^2}{2a_0}$$

which is just the normal energy of hydrogen, since the second or perturbation integral is zero. This can be easily seen because the factor $\cos \theta$ makes equal positive and negative contributions over the range 0 to π for θ.

Thus we must go either to second-order perturbation theory or to an appropriate variation function to obtain a significant result. Let us take a simple two-term linear variation function

$$\phi = c_1 f_1 + c_2 f_2 \tag{4.37}$$

with

$$f_1 = \psi_{1s} = (\pi a_0^3)^{-1/2} e^{-r/a_0}$$

$$f_2 = \left(\frac{z}{a_0}\right) \psi_{1s} = (\pi a_0^3)^{-1/2} e^{-r/a_0} \left(\frac{r}{a_0}\right) \cos \theta$$

This f_2 has been selected as the simplest function which will shift the electron density in the z direction when combined with f_1.

The necessary integrals for these functions are readily evaluated to be

$$H_{11} = -\frac{e^2}{2a_0}, \qquad \Delta_{11} = 1$$

$$H_{12} = eFa_0, \qquad \Delta_{12} = 0$$

$$H_{22} = 0, \qquad \Delta_{22} = 1$$

and the secular equation is

$$\begin{vmatrix} -\dfrac{e^2}{2a_0} - W & eFa_0 \\ eFa_0 & -W \end{vmatrix} = 0$$

The lower energy solution is simplified by the use of the binomial series, after which powers of F higher than F^2 are neglected. The result is then found to be

$$W = -\frac{e^2}{2a_0} - 2a_0^3 F^2 \tag{4.38}$$

where the second term shows that the energy does decrease with the second power of the electric field.

An electric field is said to polarize a system by inducing a dipole moment according to the equation

$$\mathbf{\mu} = \alpha \mathbf{E} \tag{4.39}$$

where $\mathbf{\mu}$ and $\mathbf{E}$ are the vector dipole moment and the vector field, respectively, and α is called the *polarizability*. The polarizability is a tensor in the general case, but for spherically symmetrical systems, such as the hydrogen atom, α simplifies to a scalar, a simple numerical constant. In our simple case with the polarizability a constant and a uniform field of magnitude F, the electrostatic energy is $-\frac{1}{2}\alpha F^2$. Consequently our result above gives the following value for the polarizability of the normal hydrogen atom:

$$\alpha = 4a_0^3 = 0.59 \times 10^{-24} \text{ cm.}^3$$

It has been possible by several methods[4] to show that the exact value for the polarizability of the normal hydrogen atom is $(\frac{9}{2})a_0^3$ or 0.670×10^{-24} cm.[3] Thus our simple solution is in error by $\frac{1}{9}$, or 11%.

GENERAL REFERENCES

Eyring, H., Walter, J., and Kimball, G. E., *Quantum Chemistry*, New York: John Wiley & Sons, Inc., 1944. This text gives particular attention both to angular momentum problems and to the symmetry properties of wave functions.

Pauling, L. and Wilson, E. B., Jr., *Introduction to Quantum Mechanics*, New York: McGraw-Hill Book Company, Inc., 1935. Chapters 6 and 7 contain excellent treatments of approximate methods in quantum mechanics.

Rojansky, V., *Introductory Quantum Mechanics*, New York: Prentice-Hall, Inc., 1938. Chapter 5 treats methods of approximation.

Schiff, L. I., *Quantum Mechanics*, New York: McGraw-Hill Book Company, Inc., 1949. Chapters 7 and 8 discuss approximate methods with additional topics appropriate to time-dependent and collision problems.

PROBLEMS

4.1 Verify the symmetry properties of the rotational wave functions of the diatomic molecule.

4.2 Investigate the symmetry properties of the harmonic oscillator wave functions.

4.3 Prove the statement that $H_{ik} = H_{ki}$ by expanding f_i and f_k as a series in the true wave functions of the problem.

4.4 Apply the variation method to the particle in the box in one dimension. For simplicity let $V = 0$ from $-1 \leqslant x \leqslant +1$ and $V = +\infty$ elsewhere. Take first $f_1 = 1 - x^2$, then use also $f_2 = 1 - x^4$, $f_3 = 1 - x^6$, etc., as necessary to obtain agreement with the true energy to within 0.01%. The use of a calculating machine is desirable for the second part.

4.5 Investigate the problem of the lowest energy level of the particle in a spherical box of unit radius, selecting your own variation function. Start from Eq. (3.19) of Chapter 3, and, of course, take $l = 0$ for the lowest level. Then compare with the exact solution, which can be obtained from Appendix 22.

4.6 Starting with the sin ϕ and cos ϕ wave functions for the $2p$ states of a hydrogen atom, investigate the effect of a small magnetic field along the z axis

----

[4] Pauling, L. and Wilson, E. B., Jr., *Introduction to Quantum Mechanics*, New York: McGraw-Hill Book Company, Inc., 1935.

on the energy levels. As noted above, be sure to use both the sine and cosine functions and obtain the corresponding secular equation.

4.7 Calculate the polarizability of the normal hydrogen atom by the same method as Section 4i, but use the hydrogen wave functions ψ_{1s} and ψ_{2p} with $m = 0$ (the one with angular factor $\cos \theta$).

4.8 Evaluate c_1 and c_2 in Eq. (4.37) for the energy level given in Eq. (4.38). Calculate the actual dipole moment from this wave function and verify the agreement with Eq. (4.39). The dipole moment in this case is just $-\overline{ez}$, and the average must, of course, be that of postulate 4, Section 2d.

Chapter 5

MANY-ELECTRON ATOMS

5a. Electron spin and the Pauli exclusion principle: mathematical formulation. Let us now return to the problem introduced in Sections 1h and 1i of the electronic energy of an atom. Both the Pauli exclusion principle and the concept of electron spin and magnetic moment were introduced at that time. The former may be said to be derived from the known periodic table of the elements, and the latter from fine structure of spectral lines or the Stern-Gerlach experiment. We shall hope to tie these concepts together.

An electron is postulated to have a component angular momentum of $h/4\pi$ or $-h/4\pi$ on the z axis, which has been arbitrarily selected as the axis where angular momentum is exactly quantized. On other axes one would find a distribution of values of angular momentum. However, as in the hydrogen atom, the sum of the squares of all components of angular momentum is definite, in this case $3h^2/16\pi^2$. The only very satisfactory theory of electron spin is that of Dirac, who obtained these results (already known experimentally) from an attempt to make the wave equation consistent with relativity theory. His equation also gave the magnetic moment of the spinning electron whose z component is $\pm eh/4\pi mc$. This result is anomalous in that for orbital motion the ratio of magnetic moment to angular momentum is always $e/2mc$, whereas here the ratio is twice as large. The effect of this anomalous ratio is very important in the effect of a magnetic field on atomic spectra, but is not within the scope of our present discussion. For our work it will suffice to graft electron spin onto an ordinary wave function by multiplying it by the symbol α if the z axis spin is $+h/4\pi$, and by β if the spin is $-h/4\pi$. Since angular momentum usually comes in units of $h/2\pi$, we say the spin quantum number m_s may be $\pm\frac{1}{2}$.

73

Now the interchange of two identical particles is certainly a symmetry operation. In the preceding chapter we concluded that on a nondegenerate wave function such a symmetry operation must either leave the wave function unchanged or change its sign. If it leaves it unchanged, the wave function is said to be *symmetric;* if the sign is changed it is said to be *antisymmetric.*

There is another reason for believing that wave functions must be either symmetric or antisymmetric to the exchange of identical particles. To see this, let us assume a nonsymmetric wave function for a system containing two identical particles. Assume that the two particles do not interact with one another and are confined in a box. Also let u_k and u_l be two different wave functions for one particle in the box which we will assume to be real functions. Then the function

$$\psi_1 = u_k(q_1)u_l(q_2)$$

with q_1 and q_2 the coordinates of the first and second particles, respectively, would satisfy the Schrödinger equation for the problem. However, the probability of finding the particles in given locations is

$$\psi_1^2 = u_k^2(q_1)u_l^2(q_2)$$

Since u_k and u_l are different functions, this implies a different probability distribution for particle one from that of particle two. But such a conclusion is impossible of verification experimentally. Any experiment could show only where a particle was at a given moment —not which one of two identical particles it was.

This difficulty is avoided in symmetrical or antisymmetrical wave functions. Actually ψ_1 above is one of a degenerate pair of solutions of the Schrödinger equation. The other function is obtained by exchanging the particles to yield

$$\psi_2 = u_k(q_2)u_l(q_1)$$

Now, as for any degenerate pair of wave functions, any linear combination of these two is also a solution of the Schrödinger equation. Consider the sum combination

$$\psi_s = (\psi_1 + \psi_2)/\sqrt{2} = [u_k(q_1)u_l(q_2) + u_k(q_2)u_l(q_1)]/\sqrt{2}$$

This function is clearly unchanged by the exchange of particles, i.e., the change of q_1 to q_2 and q_2 to q_1. It is a symmetric function. Since the coordinates q_1 and q_2 enter this function in an entirely equivalent manner, it is clear that the probability distribution ψ_s^2 implies exactly the same distribution for particle one as for particle two.

The antisymmetric function

$$\psi_A = (\psi_1 - \psi_2)/\sqrt{2} = [u_k(q_1)u_l(q_2) - u_k(q_2)u_l(q_1)]/\sqrt{2}$$

merely changes sign on the exchange of the two particles. Thus the probability function, ψ_A^2, is unchanged by particle exchange and again implies the same distribution for each particle. These symmetric and antisymmetric functions are consistent with the experimental impossibility of distinguishing between the two identical particles.

We shall now show that the Pauli exclusion principle is obtained if we postulate that *only those wave functions are physically significant which are antisymmetric to the exchange of any pair of electrons.* This is assumed to apply even to states in a degenerate set.

The property of changing sign upon the interchange of any two rows or columns makes determinants convenient for the expression of antisymmetric wave functions. Let us use the symbols $1s\alpha(1)$, $2p\beta(2)$, etc. to represent electron 1 in a hydrogen-like $1s$ wave function with $m_s = +\frac{1}{2}$, electron 2 in a $2p$ wave function with $m_s = -\frac{1}{2}$, etc. The term *orbital* is frequently used for such a one-electron wave function. If the repulsion of the electrons were negligible, the lowest state of He would be

$$\psi = \begin{vmatrix} 1s\alpha(1) & 1s\beta(1) \\ 1s\alpha(2) & 1s\beta(2) \end{vmatrix}$$
$$= 1s\alpha(1)\ 1s\beta(2) - 1s\alpha(2)\ 1s\beta(1) \qquad (5.1)$$

which is clearly antisymmetric to the interchange of electrons 1 and 2. Even with electronic repulsion, the complete wave function must be qualitatively similar to this.

For a Li atom in its lowest state one writes

$$\psi = \begin{vmatrix} 1s\alpha(1) & 1s\beta(1) & 2s\alpha(1) \\ 1s\alpha(2) & 1s\beta(2) & 2s\alpha(2) \\ 1s\alpha(3) & 1s\beta(3) & 2s\alpha(3) \end{vmatrix} \qquad (5.2)$$

or the similar function where the spin associated with the $2s$ orbital is changed to β. If one attempted to put all three electrons into $1s$ orbitals one would obtain

$$\psi = \begin{vmatrix} 1s\alpha(1) & 1s\beta(1) & 1s\beta(1) \\ 1s\alpha(2) & 1s\beta(2) & 1s\beta(2) \\ 1s\alpha(3) & 1s\beta(3) & 1s\beta(3) \end{vmatrix} = 0 \qquad (5.3)$$

but this function is identically zero because two columns of the determinant are now identical. Thus one can see generally that if any two electrons are in identical orbitals, including spin, two columns of the determinant will be identical and the complete wave function identically zero. This is just the exclusion principle.

5b. Energy of the normal helium atom. As was mentioned earlier, approximate methods must be used for the solution of the two-electron problem. A first approximation is obtained by taking Eq. (5.1) either as a variation method trial function or regarding the electronic repulsion as a perturbation. The actual equations are identical from either point of view. While we shall not go through this calculation completely, it is instructive to rearrange (5.1) into the form

$$\begin{aligned} \psi &= 1s(1)1s(2)[\alpha(1)\beta(2) - \alpha(2)\beta(1)] \\ &= \frac{8}{\pi a_0^3} e^{-2(r_1+r_2)/a_0}[\alpha(1)\beta(2) - \alpha(2)\beta(1)] \end{aligned} \qquad (5.4)$$

The last factor (relating to the spin) is very important in making the wave function antisymmetric to exchange of electrons, but it affects the numerical calculation of the energy only in the interaction of the two electron magnetic moments. This magnetic moment interaction energy is very small as compared with the electrostatic potential and the kinetic energy terms. Hence we may drop the spin factor for the remainder of our calculation.

If one proceeds to carry out the energy calculation with the function (5.4) one obtains $W = -11e^2/4a_0 = -74.80$ electron volts as an approximation for the helium atom. The energy zero is based on all particles separated to infinity. Appendix 1 gives the mathematical details for this calculation. The experimental value is -78.98 e.v., a difference of 4.18 e.v. or about 5%. The approximation may be improved by various adjustments or modifications in the trial or variation function. For example, if one regards the effective atomic number Z in ψ to be a variable, instead of 2 as in Eq. (5.4), one reduces the error to 1.5 e.v. or 2%. Hylleraas[1] investigated more complex

---

[1] Hylleraas, E. A., Z. Physik, **65**, 209 (1930).

functions. The most important item to be added is the explicit distance between the two electrons, r_{12}. Since the potential energy depends on this distance very markedly, it is to be expected that the wave function should also vary with it. The simplest function including this variable is

$$\psi = Ae^{-Z(r_1+r_2)/a_0}(1 + cr_{12}) \tag{5.5}$$

where Z and c are varied to minimize the energy. This function gives an energy too large by only 0.34 e.v. or 0.4%. Addition of further terms in the parentheses such as $c'(r_1 + r_2)$, $c''(r_1 - r_2)^2$ and $c'''r_{12}^2$ further reduce the calculated energy until agreement within 0.002 e.v. is obtained. These calculations follow the method indicated for linear variation functions but naturally become very laborious when a large number of terms are included.

This quantitative agreement between the calculated and observed energies of helium was a major achievement of the Schrödinger form of quantum mechanics, since earlier theories had not succeeded in obtaining even semiquantitative agreement at this point.

Equally successful calculations have been made of the energies of other two electron atoms such as excited states of helium and Li^+, Be^{++}, B^{+++}, etc. Additional details are given in Appendix 1.

While two-electron calculations have been very successful, the labor of three-electron calculations is so great that only rough approximations have been actually carried out. Hence, although close agreement has not been obtained, there is no reason to doubt the validity of quantum theory if it were properly applied. An application of qualitative and semiquantitative quantum theory has led to a good understanding of the observed spectra of complex atoms. In the remainder of this chapter, we shall touch on the salient features from this point of view.

5c. Excited states of the helium atom: the $1s2s$ state. Let us consider an excited state of He, primarily to illustrate in the simplest terms phenomena common to most complex atoms. A low excited state will be that with one electron in the $1s$ state and the other in the $2s$ state. While we could set up all possible determinants of the type of Eq. (5.1) and take the appropriate linear combinations, it is simpler to consider the orbital and spin factors separately.

For the spin of two electrons one can write four possible wave functions.

$$\alpha(1)\alpha(2) \qquad \beta(1)\beta(2) \qquad \alpha(1)\beta(2) \qquad \beta(1)\alpha(2)$$

The first two are symmetric but the last two are neither symmetric nor antisymmetric. Instead one changes to the other on exchange of electrons. Consequently one takes the sum and difference combinations of the last two, giving altogether

$$\text{symmetric} \quad \begin{cases} \alpha(1)\alpha(2) \\ [\alpha(1)\beta(2) + \beta(1)\alpha(2)]2^{-1/2} \\ \beta(1)\beta(2) \end{cases} \tag{5.6}$$

$$\text{antisymmetric} \quad [\alpha(1)\beta(2) - \beta(1)\alpha(2)]2^{-1/2}$$

where the factor $2^{-1/2}$ was introduced for normalization.

Of the symmetric spin functions one may say that the first corresponds to an angular momentum on the z axis of $h/2\pi$, the second to zero, and the third to $-h/2\pi$. Thus one may picture the spins of the two electrons to have been coupled parallel to one another and then oriented so as to give the component $h/2\pi$, 0 or $-h/2\pi$ on the z axis. However, for the antisymmetric function the net spin is zero, which one may picture as arising from the antiparallel arrangement of the individual spins.

For the orbital functions one has $1s(1)2s(2)$ and $2s(1)1s(2)$ which, when combined for symmetry, become

$$\text{symmetric} \quad [1s(1)2s(2) + 2s(1)1s(2)]2^{-1/2} \tag{5.7}$$
$$\text{antisymmetric} \quad [1s(1)2s(2) - 2s(1)1s(2)]2^{-1/2}$$

Antisymmetric complete wave functions may be constructed by making either factor symmetric provided the other is antisymmetric. This gives

$$\text{triplet} \quad [1s(1)2s(2) - 2s(1)1s(2)] \begin{cases} \alpha(1)\alpha(2)2^{-1/2} \\ [\alpha(1)\beta(2) + \beta(1)\alpha(2)]2^{-1} \\ \beta(1)\beta(2)2^{-1/2} \end{cases} \tag{5.8}$$

$$\text{singlet} \quad [1s(1)2s(2) + 2s(1)1s(2)] \cdot [\alpha(1)\beta(2) - \beta(1)\alpha(2)]2^{-1}$$

where the first three wave functions are grouped together and labeled a *triplet* because they have the same energy in the absence of a magnetic field. The *singlet* constitutes a single state.

As before the spin factors can be ignored and the approximate energy computed from the orbital factor. Writing S,T for the singlet and triplet which correspond to the $+$ and $-$ signs, respectively, one has

$$\psi_{S,T} = [1s(1)2s(2) \pm 2s(1)1s(2)]2^{-1/2}$$

$$W_{S,T} = \int \psi_{S,T} H \psi_{S,T} \, dv = H_c \pm H_x$$

$$H_c = \int 1s(1)2s(2)H1s(1)2s(2) \, dv$$

$$= \frac{-5e^2}{2a_0} + e^2 \int \frac{1s^2(1)2s^2(2)}{r_{12}} \, dv \qquad (5.9)$$

$$H_x = \int 1s(1)2s(2)H1s(2)2s(1) \, dv$$

$$= e^2 \int \frac{1s(1)2s(1)1s(2)2s(2)}{r_{12}} \, dv$$

where terms equal by symmetry have been combined and the effective atomic number taken as 2 throughout. H_c is sometimes called the coulomb integral, and would represent the entire energy if the wave function were just $1s(1)2s(2)$. However, the identity of the electrons and the requirement of antisymmetry of the entire wave function leads to the term H_x, called the exchange integral. The reduction of H_x to the single term involving r_{12} arises from the orthogonality of the $1s$ and $2s$ functions. Where such orthogonality exists it may be shown generally (see Appendix 2) that the exchange integral will be positive, and consequently the triplet state will lie lower than the corresponding singlet.

While the remaining integrals in (5.9) may be evaluated without too much difficulty, the results are not very close to the experimental values. One can improve the agreement by using an effective atomic number of one instead of two in the $2s$ function, corresponding to complete shielding by the $1s$ electron of second charge on the nucleus. However, with the different Z the $2s$ orbital is no longer orthogonal to the $1s$ orbital, which complicates things considerably. Thus, while it is interesting to know that Hylleraas has obtained good agreement with the observed excited states of helium, his methods are sufficiently complex that detailed consideration is hardly practical at this point.

The important results of this study are the spin wave functions in Eq. (5.6), the resulting singlet and triplet states, and the conclusion that generally the triplet will lie at lower energy provided the orbital functions are orthogonal. Let us now consider complex atoms generally.

5d. Complex atoms: one-electron orbitals. Even though the quantitative calculations of quantum theory have proven to be too laborious, interesting qualitative results are obtained concerning complex atoms. While the energy is the property of greatest interest, size and other properties will be mentioned. A complex atom is described in terms of the corresponding hydrogen-like one-electron wave functions or orbitals which are occupied. The discussion will be divided into two parts. The first concerns the energy and other properties of these one-electron orbitals in a complex atom. The second deals with smaller energy differences which arise between states based on the same set of one-electron orbitals.

The energy of the hydrogen-like atom was given in terms of charge Ze on the nucleus and a principal quantum number n. However, it is an accidental property of the inverse first power potential that the energy is independent of l and m. For example, the rotation-vibration energy of the diatomic molecule depends on two quantum numbers. Since the effect of inner shells of electrons is essentially to change the potential energy function for an outer electron, it is to be expected that the energy of the outer electron will now depend on l. The potential energy is very large negatively inside of inner shells; hence outer orbitals which give considerable probability of the electron being in this region have lower energy than those which do not. The former are called *penetrating* orbitals. Classically an oscillation "through" the nucleus and all inner shells would have no angular momentum and hence corresponds to an s orbital. While the analogy is not too good, the conclusion that s orbitals are most penetrating is correct and can be verified from the probabilities calculated from ψ^2. Then, in order, p, d, and f orbitals are less penetrating and have higher energy for the same principal quantum number in a complex atom.

In any particular atom, and for orbitals with the same principal quantum number, the successive energy differences are about the same between s and p orbitals as between p and d orbitals, etc. Thus in potassium the $4p$ orbital is 1.6 volts above the $4s$; the $4d$ orbital is 1.8 volts above the $4p$. In this case the $4f$ orbital is only a little above the $4d$, but the $4d$ energy is already fairly well up toward the ionization energy.

Similarly in calcium the $4s$ to $4p$ and $4p$ to $4d$ energy differences are each about 2 volts. In sodium the $3s$ to $3p$ difference is 2.1 volts, while the $3p$ to $3d$ difference is 1.5 volts.

These energy differences with successive values of the quantum number l increase steadily as the valence shell is filled in. With two valence electrons, when an s shell is filled, the value is 3 to 4 volts. By the eighth group it has increased severalfold. In argon the $3p - 3d$ difference is 14 volts. The trend across any given row is roughly linear. Thus in phosphorus the $3s - 3p$ difference is 7 volts and the $3p - 3d$ difference is 9 volts.

We see that by the time the s and p subshells are filled, the $p - d$ energy difference has become as large or larger than the energy difference to the next higher principal quantum number s orbital. Consequently, the rare gas is obtained on completion of the s,p shell of eight. The d electrons fill in along with the s and p of one higher n value, giving the transition elements and the rows of 18. Similarly the $4f$ electrons, in the rare earths, are of comparable energy to the $5d$ and $6s$ electrons.

As we have indicated, these energy differences among orbitals of the same n value are to be attributed to the different degrees to which the orbitals penetrate the shells of electrons. The effect increases as there are more electron shells to be penetrated. We see that the valence shell itself makes the largest contribution. Nevertheless, the ten $3d$ electrons filled in between calcium and zinc increase the $4s - 4p$ difference from 2 volts to 4 volts. Also the valence shell $s - p$ energy difference is actually higher in mercury than in zinc, whereas it decreases from calcium to barium. In the case of mercury there is the shell of fourteen $4f$ electrons to be partially penetrated, in addition to the usual s, p, and d shells.

For certain calculations one may assign an effective nuclear charge Z^*e so that the orbital has the observed energy. The difference $(Z - Z^*)$ is commonly called the screening constant, S. These screening constants form a self-consistent system from which values may be estimated for the rarer atoms or for other properties. Slater[2] and Pauling and Sherman[3] have given systems of screening constants.

It may be shown that size depends more on the principal quantum number and less on the effective charge, Z^*, than does the energy. We write for the energy

$$E = -R(Z^*)^2/n^2 \qquad (5.10)$$

where R is a constant, and for the wave function

$$\psi = r^{n-1}e^{-Z^*r/na_0} + \ldots \qquad (5.11)$$

[2] Slater, J. C., *Phys. Rev.*, **36**, 57 (1930).
[3] Pauling, L. and Sherman, J., *Z. Krist*, **81**, 1 (1932).

There may be additional terms in ψ with r to a smaller power but these are negligible (in a first approximation) near the outside of the atom.   A rough measure of the size of the atom is the radius of the outermost maximum in ψ.   This may be approximated by

$$\frac{d\psi}{dr} = e^{-Z^*r/na_0}\left[(n-1)r^{n-2} - \frac{Z^*}{na_0}r^{n-1}\right] = 0$$

$$\frac{r}{a_0} = \frac{n(n-1)}{Z^*} \simeq \frac{n^2}{Z^*} \tag{5.12}$$

Thus while E depends on the square of both Z^* and n, r depends essentially on n^2 but Z^* to the first power.   Hence, if in the rare earths $4f$ electrons have the same energy as $5d$ and $6s$, the $4f$ orbitals will be considerably smaller.   Consequently the $4f$ electrons may be said to be well inside rare earth atoms and ions, a conclusion confirmed by their extreme similarity of chemical properties.

In addition to the screening constant system of one-electron orbitals

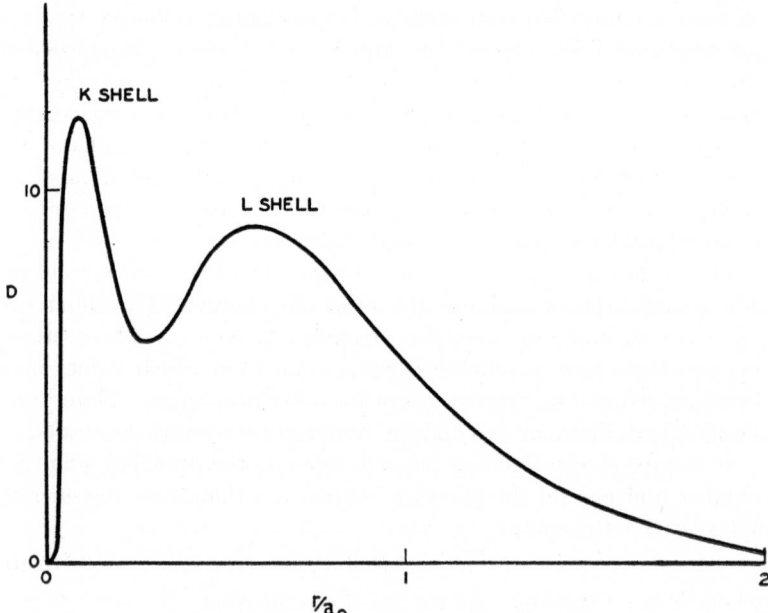

Fig. 5.1.   The radial distribution function for a sodium atom.

there is the *self-consistent-field* method of Hartree.[4] In this method
the wave equation is solved by numerical methods for a one-electron
orbital. The potential energy is taken to be that of the nucleus and
the other electrons in their statistical positions as determined by their
one-electron wave functions. In practice, it is a method of successive
approximations. Certain initial orbitals (possibly screening constant
orbitals) are assumed for the potential energy; then the wave equation
is integrated for each type of electron ($1s$, $2s$, etc.) present to give
an improved set of orbitals. The process is repeated until the improved orbitals are the same to the desired accuracy as those assumed
in that stage.

The electron distribution of Na^+ by Hartree's calculations is shown
in Fig. 5.1. The shell structure shows very clearly.

5e. Complex atoms: electron interactions. Let us now turn
to the second topic concerning complex atoms, the consideration of
differences between possible states comprising the same one-electron
orbitals. These states are described in terms of new symbols to be
presented below. The discussion will follow partly the model of
coupling angular momentum vectors in a quantized fashion. This
is simpler than the direct application of the Schrödinger equation,
although confirmed by the latter.

First, couple the individual spin angular momentum vectors in a
parallel or antiparallel fashion to give a total spin vector of absolute
magnitude S. The number of spin wave functions of each type is
$2S + 1$, and this number is used to name the corresponding states.
Thus two electrons were found above to give $S = 0$ or 1, yielding
singlet and triplet states. Three electrons give doublet and quartet
states, while four electrons give singlet, triplet, and quintet states
with S values 0, 1, and 2, respectively.

Second, couple the orbital angular momentum l vectors in a parallel, antiparallel, or intermediate but quantized manner to give the
total orbital vector of absolute magnitude L. Intermediate coupling
is allowed to give values of L less than that for parallel coupling by
an integer. Thus one p and one d electron couple their l vectors
parallel to give $L = 3$ or antiparallel to give $L = 1$. The intermediate value $L = 2$ is also possible.

[4] Hartree, D. R., *Proc. Cambridge Phil. Soc.*, **24**, 89, 111, 426 (1928); *Proc. Roy. Soc.*,
A141, 282; **A143**, 506 (1933).

The array of individual quantum states of given S and L is said to constitute a *term* and is represented by a term symbol. The value of L is indicated by a capital letter as follows:

$$L \quad 0 \quad 1 \quad 2 \quad 3 \quad 4 \quad 5$$
$$\text{Symbol} \quad S \quad P \quad D \quad F \quad G \quad H \quad \ldots$$

The value of S is indicated by writing the number $2S + 1$ as a preceding superscript. Thus the $1s$, $2s$ configuration in He led to ^1S and ^3S states.

Third, if both S and L differ from zero, they may be coupled to one another differently to give a series of values of the total angular momentum J.

$$J = L + S, \quad L + S - 1, \quad \ldots, \quad |L - S| + 1, \quad |L - S|$$

Of course if $L = 0$, $J = S$, and if $S = 0$, $J = L$. The value of J is indicated as a subscript.

The energy difference between states of different J is usually very much less than between states of different L or S. Consequently one obtains in the energy level diagram a multiplet comprising the states of the same L and S but different J. If, as is frequently the case $L > S$, then the number of states is $2S + 1$. Actually each of these states has a $2J + 1$ fold degeneracy which can be broken by a magnetic field. Then the component of total angular momentum in the field direction may be J, $J - 1$, $\ldots$, $1 - J$, $-J$.

Indeed the Hamiltonian operator as we have employed it in preceding sections would give no energy difference at all for states differing only in J. We were previously considering states involving only s orbitals which have no angular momentum or magnetic moment. However, when orbitals with magnetic moment are occupied, there is an interaction between the spin magnetic moment and the orbital magnetic moment. This interaction requires further terms in the Hamiltonian operator and leads to the energy effects we are now considering.

Fourth, although a term with given S and L always has all possible component levels with different J, there are further limitations on the terms arising from a given electron configuration. These arise from the Pauli exclusion principle and the identity of the electrons.

Let us take the normal carbon atom as an example. There are two electrons in $1s$ orbitals, one with $m_s = +\frac{1}{2}$ and one with $m_s = -\frac{1}{2}$;

hence for that, as for any, closed shell $L = S = 0$. Similarly there are two electrons in a closed $2s$ shell. Then there remain two electrons to put into $2p$ orbitals. Since there are three such orbitals, many combinations are possible. The following procedure will indicate the possible states. We make a table of the possible values of the component of L, which we will call M_L, by summing algebraically the values of m_l.

$$m_1 = 1 \qquad\qquad 0 \qquad\qquad -1$$

The two sides of the diagonal differ only in numbering of the electrons, hence are not really different. When $S = 0$ so that all combinations of m_l are allowed because the two electrons have different m_s, the series of values of M_L may be as follows:

$$2 \quad 1 \quad 0 \quad -1 \quad -2$$
$$0$$

which may be regarded as the possible components of a term with $L = 2$ and another with $L = 0$. Consequently one expects $^1D_2$ and $^1S_0$ terms. When $S = 1$ the diagonal is eliminated because it places both electrons in the same orbital with the same m_s. The remainder may be easily recognized as the components of a term with $L = 1$; hence one expects a $^3P_2$, $^3P_1$, $^3P_0$ multiplet.

The following rules were first deduced empirically (Hund, 1927) concerning the lowest state among a set based on the same single electron orbitals. They are listed in order of decreasing importance, so far as energy is concerned.

1. States with higher S (i.e., higher multiplicity) lie lower.

2. States with higher L lie lower.

3. When a shell of electrons is less than half full, states with lower J are lower. When the shell is more than half full, the reverse applies.

Although it is covered by Rule 1 above, it is worth-while to note that a state placing two electrons in the same orbital will be higher in energy than one placing them in different orbitals of the same de-

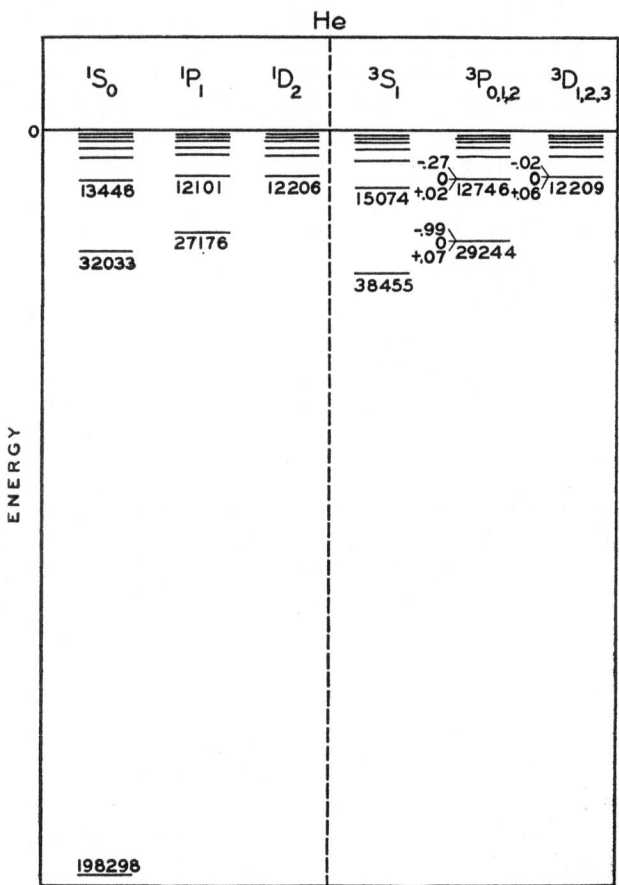

Fig. 5.2a. The energy levels of helium. The numbers give the energies below ionization in cm⁻¹. The energy differences between triplet levels are also shown.

generate set. The cause is clearly the repulsion between electrons, which is less if they are farther apart, as they would be in different orbitals. This makes a half-filled shell one of some special stability. The states are ^4S for a p shell, ^6S for a d shell, and ^8S for an f shell.

Even when half-filled shells are not involved it is found that the energy terms leading to Rule 1 are electron repulsions as is seen in Eq. (5.9).

The energy differences covered in Rule 2 are also due to electron

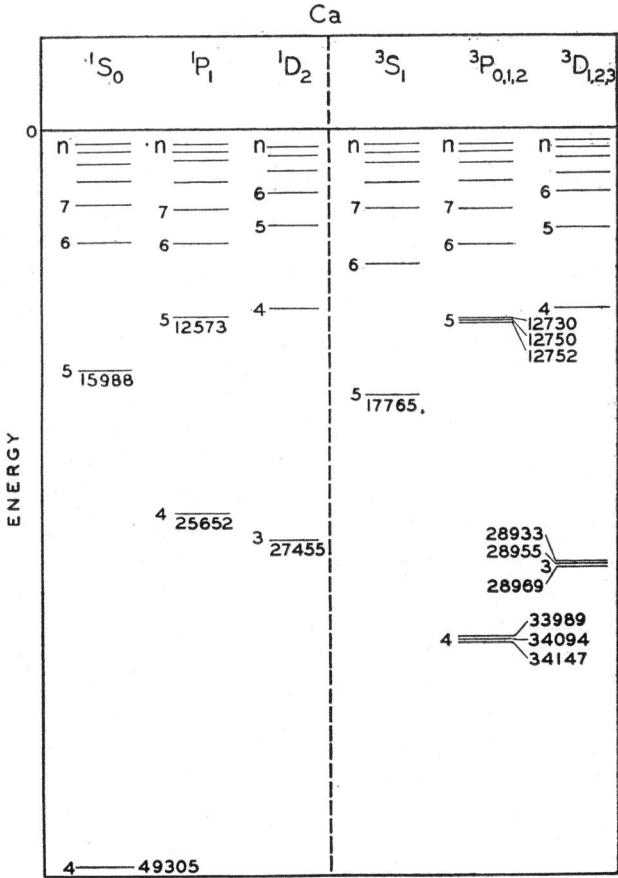

Fig. 5.2b.   The energy levels of calcium.   The numbers give the energies below ionization in cm^{-1}.   The energy differences between triplet levels are also shown.

repulsions but it is not so easy to explain them in simple terms.   The energies considered in Rule 3 are the spin-orbit interactions of a magnetic character as mentioned above.   We shall not attempt to explain Rule 3 except to say that detailed analysis[5] shows the absence of an electron from a completed shell to be equivalent to the presence of an electron except for sign of charge.

[5] Condon, E. U. and Shortley, G. H., *The Theory of Atomic Spectra*, London: Cambridge University Press, 1935.

Figure 5.2 illustrates these rules with diagrams of the experimental energy levels of He and Ca. Note the increased multiplet separations for the heavier element. Also for Ca there are p orbitals of the same principal quantum number as that of the ground state s orbital, whereas for He there are not. Consequently, the lowest P and D states of Ca have no counterpart in the He spectrum.

The sequence of vector coupling which we have described above is commonly called LS *coupling* or sometimes *Russell-Saunders* coupling. It assumes that the electrostatic energy terms are more important than the terms arising from the interaction of electron spin with orbital angular momenta. This is the case for all the lighter elements. However, we noticed in Fig. 5.2 the increased multiplet separations in Ca as compared to He. This indicates an increased spin-orbit interaction in the heavier element. In elements considerably heavier than Ca, the spin-orbit interaction energy becomes comparable with the electrostatic energy terms, and the LS coupling system breaks down. In the opposite extreme, where the spin-orbit terms predominate, the jj *coupling* system holds. In that case the spin and orbital angular momenta are first coupled to give a j vector for each electron, and then the resulting j vectors are coupled for the entire atom. For very heavy atoms, the excited states frequently approach jj coupling closely, but the normal states are at most intermediate cases between jj and LS coupling. Apparently jj coupling holds within nuclei.

The cause of this increased spin-orbit interaction energy is not understandable on a nonrelativistic basis. The interaction operator[6] is

$$\frac{1}{2m^2c^2} \cdot \frac{1}{r} \cdot \frac{dV}{dr} \, (\boldsymbol{L}_k \cdot \boldsymbol{S}_k)$$

for an electron in a spherically symmetrical potential. The appearance of the velocity of light, c, in the coefficient indicates that this is a relativistic phenomenon. Only the large potential gradients near the center of large atoms make this term important.

GENERAL REFERENCES

Condon, E. U. and Shortley, G. H., *The Theory of Atomic Spectra*, London: Cambridge University Press, 1935. This is the extensive treatise on the theory of many electron atoms and of their spectra.

[6] See Schiff, L. I., *Quantum Mechanics*, New York: McGraw-Hill Book Company, Inc., 1949, pp. 276, 321.

Herzberg, G., *Atomic Spectra and Atomic Structure*, New York: Prentice-Hall, Inc., 1937; reprinted Dover Publications, 1944. This is an excellent general presentation of atomic structure.

Born, M., *Atomic Physics*, 5th ed., London and Glasgow: Blackie and Son Ltd., 1951. Chapter 6 contains some excellent sections on atomic structure and on electron spin.

Eyring, H., Walter, J., and Kimball, G. E., *Quantum Chemistry*, New York: John Wiley & Sons, Inc., 1944. Chapter 9 gives a relatively thorough account of the quantum theory of many-electron atoms, although less extensive than that of Condon and Shortley.

Houston, W. V., *Principles of Quantum Mechanics*, New York: McGraw-Hill Book Company, Inc., 1951. Chapter 10 contains a most complete treatment of a two-electron atom. This illustrates most of the effects of many-electron atoms with minimum complexity.

Mott, N. F. and Sneddon, I. N., *Wave Mechanics and Its Applications*, New York: Oxford University Press, 1948. Chapter 6 gives an account of various approximate methods for many-electron atoms.

PROBLEMS

5.1 Plot the ionization potential of the elements from Li to Ne and account for the breaks in the curve.

5.2 The $5p$ electrons essentially determine the size of the rare earth ions. How do you account for their decrease in size with increase in atomic number? Discuss other chemical properties related to this contraction, for example, the similarity of properties of Hf^{+4} to Zr^{+4} and the stability of the $6s$ shell ions Tl^+, Pb^{++}, etc.

5.3 The separation of the singlet and triplet states for a series such as He with one electron each in $1s$ and ns orbitals ($n = 2, 3, . . .$) decreases rapidly as n increases. Explain in terms of the argument in Appendix 2.

5.4 Point out examples where half-filled d or f shells are associated with surprising stability of chemical species.

Chapter 6

TIME DEPENDENT PHENOMENA, SPECTRA

Certain properties such as chemical equilibria and thermodynamic properties are determined by a knowledge of the energies of all stationary quantum states. Other properties such as the rates of certain reactions and the absorption and emission of light are related to the rate of change from one stationary quantum state to another. This rate of change will be the topic of this chapter.

6a. Preliminary discussion of radiation theory. Before beginning the more formal treatment let us talk a bit about the emission of electromagnetic waves or photons. According to classical electromagnetic theory it is the acceleration of the motion of a charge that leads to radiation. If our system has no net charge, we consider the dipole moment μ, and say that radiation arises when $d^2\mu/dt^2$ is not zero.

Now the x component of dipole moment for a given configuration is

$$\mu_x = \sum e_k x_k \tag{6.1}$$

where the sum covers all the particles of the atom or molecule and e_k is the charge on that particle. The quantum mechanical value for the nth quantum state is

$$(\mu_x)_{nn} = \int \Psi_n^* \mu_x \Psi_n \, dv \tag{6.2}$$

The time-dependent factors of Ψ^* and Ψ cancel one another, so one may say that the dipole moment is constant and that its second time derivative is zero. This helps one to understand the stationary state concept, since the zero value of $d^2\mu/dt^2$ indicates no radiation.

In passing one may mention that for atoms $(\mu_x)_{nn}$ is not only constant but also zero. Molecules in general have a time average dipole moment, but in many particular cases involving symmetry it is again zero.

90

Let us now calculate a dipole moment associated with the change from state m to state n.

$$(\mu_x)_{nm}(t) = \int \Psi_n^* \mu_x \Psi_m \, dv = (\mu_x)_{nm} e^{-2\pi i (E_m - E_n)t/h} \quad (6.3)$$

with

$$(\mu_x)_{nm} = \int \psi_n^* \mu_x \psi_m \, dv \quad (6.4)$$

We have chosen to use the plain symbol, $(\mu_x)_{nm}$, as the amplitude of the oscillating dipole for reasons which will be apparent later. Now if $(\mu_x)_{nm}$ is not zero, $(\mu_x)_{nm}(t)$ not only has a value but its second derivative also has a value which indicates the emission of radiation. Furthermore the frequency of oscillation is

$$\nu_{nm} = \frac{E_m - E_n}{h} \quad (6.5)$$

which is just the equation first proposed somewhat arbitrarily by Bohr (1913).

This argument, which is by no means rigorous, nevertheless has given correctly the essentials of radiation theory. These are first the nonzero value of $(\mu_x)_{nm}$ or $(\mu_y)_{nm}$ or $(\mu_z)_{nm}$, and second the Bohr radiation equation. We shall now develop these same results and some others by a method following more nearly our basic postulates.

6b. Time-dependent perturbations. Let us assume that we have the stationary state energies and wave functions for a certain system when isolated, and that we now wish to investigate its behavior when influenced by an oscillating electric field or other small time-dependent perturbation $H'(t)$. Here H' may also depend on the coordinates and momenta (replaced by derivates of coordinates). Following then the theory developed principally by Dirac (1926–1927), we write the time-dependent Schrödinger Eq. (2.25) in the form

$$H^\circ \Psi + H'(t)\Psi = \frac{-h}{2\pi i} \frac{\partial \Psi}{\partial t} \quad (6.6)$$

where H° is the Hamiltonian operator for the isolated system. The time-dependent wave function is assumed in the form

$$\Psi = \sum a_k(t)\Psi_k^\circ \quad (6.7)$$

where Ψ_k° is the time-dependent wave function for the wave equation without $H'(t)$, and the $a(t)$ functions are to have such character as to make Ψ a solution of Eq. (6.6). Substituting, we find

$$\sum a_k(t)H^\circ \Psi_k^\circ + \sum a_k(t)H'(t)\Psi_k^\circ$$

$$= \frac{-h}{2\pi i}\sum \frac{da_k(t)}{dt}\,\Psi_k^\circ + \sum a_k(t)\left(\frac{-h}{2\pi i}\right)\frac{\partial \Psi_k^\circ}{\partial t} \qquad (6.8)$$

The first and last terms cancel, leaving

$$\sum a_k(t)H'(t)\Psi_k^\circ = \frac{-h}{2\pi i}\sum \frac{da_k(t)}{dt}\,\Psi_k^\circ \qquad (6.8')$$

Then multiply by $\Psi_n^{\circ *}$ and integrate over the appropriate space. All terms but one on the right drop out because of orthogonality, yielding

$$\frac{da_n(t)}{dt} = \frac{-2\pi i}{h}\sum a_k(t)\int \Psi_n^{\circ *}H'(t)\Psi_k^\circ\,dv \qquad (6.9)$$

This is as far as the general theory will be carried. We shall now assume that at zero time we know from some experiment that the system is in the mth quantum state. In other words $a_m(0) = 1$ and all other $a(0)$'s are zero. Then write

$$H'_{nm} = \int \psi_n^* H'(t)\psi_m\,dv \qquad (6.10)$$

where ψ is the time-independent wave function. For a short time after zero we may neglect all terms in the sum in (6.9) except a_m, which is one, obtaining

$$\frac{da_n(t)}{dt} = -H'_{nm}\frac{2\pi i}{h}\,e^{2\pi i(E_n - E_m)t/h} \qquad (6.11)$$

which gives in $a_n^* a_n$ an expression for the probability that the system has changed to the nth quantum state because of the perturbation H'.

This interpretation of $a_n^* a_n$ as the probability that the system is in the n's quantum state was not explicitly among the postulates in Section 2d. However, it can be readily verified to be consistent with postulate 4 and Eq. (2.26). Thus if we observe the energy we will find the various values $E_0, E_1, \ldots, E_n, \ldots$ with different frequency, so that the average is

$$\overline{E} = \frac{\int \Psi^* E\Psi\,dv}{\int \Psi^*\Psi\,dv} = \frac{\sum a_n^* a_n E_n}{\sum a_n^* a_n} \qquad (6.12)$$

Thus the probability of measurement leading to E_n is $a_n^* a_n$ as postulated above.

6c. Absorption and induced emission of radiation. The complete analysis of the interaction of a photon with an atom or molecule is very complex. However, the wave length of infrared, visible, or near ultraviolet light is long compared with distances in atoms or molecules. Consequently as a first approximation we may take an electric field oscillating in time but constant in space to be the effect of the photon on the atom or molecule. For reasons which will be more apparent as we proceed, this is called a calculation for electric dipole radiation.

If this first approximation leads to a calculated zero interaction, then higher terms, called magnetic dipole and electric quadrupole radiation, may be investigated. However, the intensity of spectral lines of these later types is many orders of magnitude weaker than for electric dipole radiation.

Let us take for the electric field in the x direction of radiation of frequency ν

$$F_x(\nu,t) = 2F_x^\circ(\nu) \cos 2\pi\nu t = F_x^\circ(\nu)(e^{2\pi i\nu t} + e^{-2\pi i\nu t}) \qquad (6.13)$$

where $F_x^\circ(\nu)$ is a function only of ν and not of t, and the imaginary exponential form is introduced for convenience later. Then the time-dependent perturbation energy for the single frequency ν is

$$H'(t) = F_x(\nu,t) \sum e_k x_k = F_x(\nu,t)\mu_x \qquad (6.14)$$

where μ_x is the instantaneous dipole moment as defined in Eq. (6.1). Then we recall the integral which we defined above as $(\mu_x)_{nm}$

$$(\mu_x)_{nm} = \int \psi_n^* \mu_x \psi_m \, dv \qquad (6.4)$$

We see that H'_{nm} can be expressed in terms of $(\mu_x)_{nm}$ as follows.

$$H'_{nm} = F_x(\nu,t)(\mu_x)_{nm} \qquad (6.15)$$

Returning to Eq. (6.11) we now have

$$\frac{da_n(t)}{dt} = -(\mu_x)_{nm}F_x^\circ(\nu)\left(\frac{2\pi i}{h}\right)\left[e^{2\pi i\left(\frac{E_n}{h} - \frac{E_m}{h} + \nu\right)t} + e^{2\pi i\left(\frac{E_n}{h} - \frac{E_m}{h} - \nu\right)t}\right]$$

which integrates to

$$a_n(t) = (\mu_x)_{nm}F_x^\circ(\nu)\left[\frac{1 - e^{2\pi i\left(\frac{E_n}{h} - \frac{E_m}{h} + \nu\right)t}}{E_n - E_m + h\nu} + \frac{1 - e^{2\pi i\left(\frac{E_n}{h} - \frac{E_m}{h} - \nu\right)t}}{E_n - E_m - h\nu}\right]$$

$$(6.16)$$

where the constant of integration was set at zero to be consistent with our postulate that at zero time $a_m = 1$ and $a_n = 0$.

The important feature of Eq. (6.16) is the nature of the denominators in the brackets. If $E_n > E_m$, corresponding to light absorption, the second denominator is zero for

$$\nu_{nm} = \frac{E_n - E_m}{h} \qquad (6.5')$$

which is just the Bohr frequency relationship. Similarly if $E_n < E_m$, corresponding to light emission, the first denominator can be zero, leading to our earlier Eq. (6.5). Since the other factors in Eq. (6.16) are of limited or constant magnitude it is at once apparent that the transition probability will be large only when the Bohr relationship (6.5) holds.

Let us now carry on the calculation, but with the additional concept that we have not a single frequency of light but a more or less continuous range of frequencies. The transition probability is related to $a_n^* a_n$, which we shall sum (by integration) over the range of frequencies. Remembering then that Eq. (6.16) was for the single frequency ν, and that only one term on the right will be important, we have

$$a_n^*(t) a_n(t) = 4(\mu_x)_{nm}^2 \int [F_x^\circ(\nu)]^2 \frac{\sin^2 \pi t \left(\frac{E_n}{h} - \frac{E_m}{h} - \nu \right)}{(E_n - E_m - h\nu)^2} \, d\nu \qquad (6.17)$$

where the second term in (6.16) was taken corresponding to absorption. The rearrangement of the imaginary exponential to the sine function may be readily verified by expansion. Now the integrand will be large over only a small region where the denominator is small, hence $F_x^\circ(\nu)$ may be taken as a constant, $F_x^\circ(\nu_{nm})$, and the integration limits made $-\infty$ and $+\infty$. Then using the relationship

$$\int_{-\infty}^{+\infty} \frac{\sin^2 x}{x^2} \, dx = \pi$$

one finds

$$a_n^*(t) a_n(t) = \frac{4\pi^2}{h^2} (\mu_x)_{nm}^2 F_x^{\circ 2}(\nu_{nm}) t \qquad (6.18)$$

with $(\mu_x)_{nm}$ the important determining factor as in our preliminary discussion, since the others will be essentially the same in one case as another.

Finally let us transform this result to the Einstein coefficient of absorption, namely, the probability that the molecule (or atom) will absorb a quantum in unit time with unit radiation density. In mathematical form the probability of absorption is

$$B_{nm}\rho(\nu_{nm})$$

where B_{nm} is the Einstein coefficient, and the radiation energy per cubic centimeter of frequency between ν and $\nu + d\nu$ is $\rho(\nu)\, d\nu$.

Now if we assume the radiation to be isotropic,

$$\rho(\nu) = \frac{1}{4\pi} \left[\overline{F_x^2}(\nu) + \overline{F_y^2}(\nu) + \overline{F_z^2}(\nu) \right]$$

$$= \frac{3}{4\pi} \overline{F_z^2}(\nu) = \frac{6}{4\pi} F_x^{\circ 2}(\nu) \qquad (6.19)$$

where the bar indicates a time average and we have used the average value $\frac{1}{2}$ for $\cos^2$, together with Eq. (6.13) in the last equality. We then have

$$B_{nm} = \frac{8\pi^3}{3h^2} \left[(\mu_x)_{nm}^2 + (\mu_y)_{nm}^2 + (\mu_z)_{nm}^2 \right] \qquad (6.20)$$

since we must include also the dipole integrals in the y and z directions. In case any μ is complex, the square of the absolute magnitude is used in (6.20).

Calculation using the other term in Eq. (6.16) shows the Einstein coefficient of induced emission to be the same, i.e., $B_{nm} = B_{mn}$.

6d. Spontaneous emission of radiation. A molecule in an excited state has a certain probability of emitting a photon in the absence of other radiation. Indeed this was the concept in our preliminary discussion. However a rigorous calculation (Dirac) of the coefficient of this spontaneous emission is relatively complex and will not be given here. It involves the "quantization" of the radiation field and a full consideration of the electrodynamic interaction of the field and the various other particles present.

We shall, however, in Section 7k calculate this coefficient of spontaneous emission by the statistical method of Einstein (1916) with the result

$$A_{mn} = \frac{8\pi h \nu_{nm}^3}{c^3} B_{mn}$$

$$= \frac{64\pi^4 \nu_{nm}^3}{3hc^3} \left[(\mu_x)_{nm}^2 + (\mu_y)_{nm}^2 + (\mu_z)_{nm}^2 \right] \qquad (6.21)$$

where c is the velocity of light and B_{mn} is the coefficient of induced emission, which is in turn equal to the absorption coefficient B_{nm} given in Eq. (6.20).

6e. Selection rules for the hydrogen atom. We have now in Eq. (6.20) and the related discussion the basic formula for the probability of a transition or the intensity of a spectral line. It is found that the transition probability is zero in many particular cases, i.e., the transition is *forbidden*. Indeed for most purposes the information of greatest interest is which transitions are forbidden and which are not. This comprises the *selection rules*. Furthermore, as mentioned earlier, our present theory is only a first approximation. Consequently many so-called "forbidden" transitions do occur but usually with a probability several orders of magnitude lower than "permitted" transitions. To illustrate the derivation of selection rules in a simple case let us consider possible changes in the quantum number m_l. For the case of essentially a single particle, Eq. (6.4) may be simplified to

$$(\mu_x)_{nm} = e \int \psi_n^* x \psi_m \, dv \qquad (6.4')$$

with corresponding equations for μ_y and μ_z. Also x, y, and z may be written as $r \sin \theta \cos \phi$, $r \sin \theta \sin \phi$, and $r \cos \theta$, respectively. Now the integral in (6.4') may be split up into three separate integrals with the variables r, θ, and ϕ. For selection rules with respect to m_l we need consider only the ϕ integral, which we will call f. For μ_z we have

$$f_z = \int_0^{2\pi} e^{i(m' - m'')\phi} \, d\phi \qquad (6.22)$$

where we have substituted single and double primes for n and m to avoid confusion. We see that f_z is zero unless $m' = m''$.

For the calculation of f_x, let us first write

$$\cos \phi = \tfrac{1}{2}(e^{i\phi} + e^{-i\phi})$$

then

$$f_x = \tfrac{1}{2}\int_0^{2\pi} e^{i(m' - m'' + 1)\phi} \, d\phi + \tfrac{1}{2}\int_0^{2\pi} e^{i(m' - m'' - 1)\phi} \, d\phi \qquad (6.23)$$

The first term will be zero unless $m' = m'' - 1$, and the second will be zero unless $m' = m'' + 1$. The results for f_y are essentially the same as for f_x; hence the selection rules for m_l are $\Delta m_l = \pm 1$ or 0.

Similar but somewhat more involved calculations with the integrals in θ give for the quantum number l the selection rule $\Delta l = \pm 1$. From consideration of the integrals in r no selection rule arises, hence all values of Δn are allowed.

Since the energies of states of a given n but different l and m are almost the same, the effect of these selection rules on the hydrogen spectrum is not very marked. For complex atoms, however, the effects of selection rules are of major importance.

6f. Selection rules for complex atoms. In dealing with complex atoms we shall wish to make use of symmetry. An atom naturally has a center of symmetry at its nucleus, i.e., if all electronic coordinates are transformed from x, y, z to $-x$, $-y$, $-z$, the atom is unchanged. The wave function will be either even or odd (symmetric or antisymmetric) to this transformation. Consequently the integrand in Eq. (6.4) will be odd if ψ_n and ψ_m have the same symmetry, because their product is then even and μ is odd. However, if the integrand is odd, it will contribute equal positive and negative quantities to the integral, giving a zero result. Thus we obtain the Laporte selection rule that dipole radiation *transitions can take place only from even to odd or from odd to even states* and not between two even or two odd states.

It is easy to decide whether a state is even or odd. By actual test we find that s orbitals are even, p orbitals are odd, d are even, f are odd, etc. In other words if l is even, the orbital is even, and if l is odd the orbital is odd (corresponding to the result for the diatomic molecule in Section 4c). Then we need only sum the l values for all electrons to see whether the total wave function is even or odd, since the product of two odd orbitals is even and the sum of the two odd l values is also even.

A second general but approximate selection rule is that *only one electron changes its orbital*. Two electron changes are of a lower order of probability.

A third general rule is $\Delta S = 0$, i.e., no transitions with change in net spin or multiplicity. This may be explained on the basis that the integration in (6.4) strictly covers also the spin factors. Where the spin factors are different, and consequently orthogonal, this gives a zero result, since the quantity μ does not involve the spin variables. This selection rule is again not absolutely strict. Triplet-singlet transitions do occur with relatively low intensity as compared to singlet-singlet and triplet-triplet in a number of cases. It seems that with high atomic number, the spin and orbital angular momenta become more interrelated and the spin selection rule less strict, until in mercury the relatively strong line at $\lambda = 2537$ A comes from a $^3P_1 \rightarrow {}^1S_0$ transition.

Finally we shall add two rules which have been verified both empirically and theoretically without attempting adequate explanation at this point. They are

$$\Delta L = \pm 1 \qquad \Delta J = \pm 1 \text{ or } 0$$

with the special limitation that $J = 0$ states do not undergo transition to other $J = 0$ states. The effect of these selection rules is illustrated in Fig. 6.1, where the permitted transitions between several lower levels of Ca are indicated. In addition certain "forbidden" transitions are observed weakly. These are shown by dotted lines.

For further discussion of atomic spectra one of the several excellent

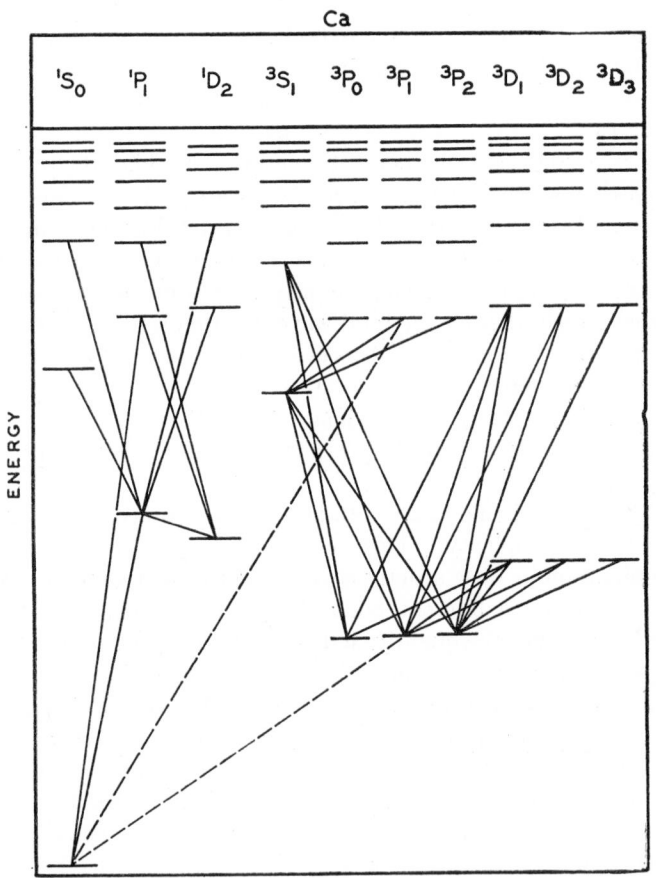

Fig. 6.1. Transitions between states in calcium (see Fig. 5.2b). Solid lines indicate permitted transitions; broken lines, "forbidden" transitions observed but weak.

treatises on that subject should be consulted. The spectra of molecules will be considered in a later chapter.

GENERAL REFERENCES

The books included as general references for Chapter 5 can be recommended for their treatments of the selection rules for the emission and absorption of radiation. In addition the following books include the more advanced approach through the quantization of wave fields.

Dirac, P. A. M., *The Principles of Quantum Mechanics*, New York: Oxford University Press, 1935.

Schiff, L. I., *Quantum Mechanics*, New York: McGraw-Hill Book Company, Inc., 1949.

PROBLEMS

6.1 Verify the selection rules for l and n by considering transitions from the $1s$ state to the $2s$, $2p$, $3p$, and $3d$ states (for hydrogen).

6.2 From the results of this chapter and the preceding one, predict a few of the lower excited states for aluminum, and with the selection rules pick out the permitted transitions among them.

Chapter 7

KINETIC THEORY AND STATISTICS

We have considered now most of the fundamental ideas of quantum theory in terms of simple examples of the behavior of single atoms. However, the chemist is usually interested in and usually performs experiments on samples composed of a vast number of molecules. The branch of science which relates the macroscopic properties of a substance to the properties of the individual molecules is sometimes called *statistical mechanics*. The term *kinetic theory* is usually applied to some of the simpler sections of statistical mechanics, particularly those connected with perfect gases.

7a. Statistical distribution laws. Before proceeding with statistical mechanics let us illustrate the mathematical methods to be used with a simple example whose correct solution is self-evident. Suppose that we have a large flat box divided into compartments or cells of size a_1, a_2, . . . , a_z, see Fig. 7.1. Now we wish to find the most probable distribution of particles, say marbles, among the compartments. A distribution is defined by stating the number of particles in each cell, n_1, n_2, n_3, . . . , n_z. The total number of particles is fixed; therefore

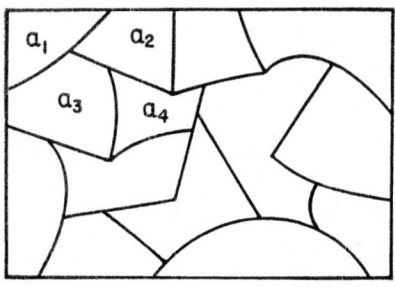

Fig. 7.1. An arbitrary division into cells.

$$n_1 + n_2 + n_3 + . . . + n_z = n$$

Experimentally one might determine this distribution by throwing the marbles at the box in a fashion such that neither the center nor any edge was favored.   The number of marbles in each compartment is recorded and the throw repeated again and again.   Eventually it would be found that one distribution occurred more frequently than any other, this being then the most probable distribution.

Mathematically, the probability of a given distribution W is given by the product of two factors, the first being the a priori probability of a particle falling into the given cell.   The probability, g_i, of any one particle falling in a certain cell is given by the ratio of the size of that cell to the size of the box, $g_i = a_i/a$, where $a = a_1 + a_2 + a_3 + \ldots + a_z$.   The sum of the probabilities for all cells is of course unity.   The probability of n_i particles falling in the ith cell is $g_i^{n_i}$; therefore the a priori probability of a distribution is

$$g_1^{n_1} g_2^{n_2} g_3^{n_3} \ldots g_z^{n_z}$$

The second factor is the number of ways the particles may be rearranged and still leave the distribution the same, i.e., the total number of particles in each cell left as before.   The number of ways n particles can be permuted among themselves is $n!$ Of these, however, $n_1!$ represent meaningless exchanges of particles already in the first cell.   Therefore the number of ways particles in different cells may be exchanged leaving the total number in each cell fixed is

$$\frac{n!}{n_1! n_2! n_3! \ldots n_z!}$$

The final probability is then

$$W = \frac{n!}{n_1! n_2! \ldots n_z!} g_1^{n_1} g_2^{n_2} \ldots g_z^{n_z} \qquad (7.1)$$

We may use the polynomial theorem to verify this calculation by noting that the sum of probabilities for all distributions must be unity.[1]

$$\sum W = \sum \frac{n!}{n_1! n_2! \ldots n_z!} g_1^{n_1} g_2^{n_2} \ldots g_z^{n_z}$$

$$= (g_1 + g_2 + \ldots + g_z)^n = 1^n = 1 \qquad (7.2)$$

Next, we must select the distribution which has the largest value of W.   Actually we shall be interested in systems containing such

[1] If the reader is not familiar with the polynomial theorem, he can quickly convince himself of its probable validity by expanding simple examples such as

$$(a + b + c)^2 = \frac{2!}{2!}a^2 + \frac{2!}{2!}b^2 + \frac{2!}{2!}c^2 + \frac{2!}{1!1!}ab + \frac{2!}{1!1!}ac + \frac{2!}{1!1!}bc$$

enormous numbers of particles ($\sim 10^{23}$) that the numbers in each cell, n_i, will also be very large. Thus, although in principle the n_i's must be integers, actually we may treat them as continuously variable and use the methods of the calculus to find the maximum value of W. For reasons which will be apparent later it is preferable to work with ln W. Obviously a maximum in ln W corresponds to a maximum in W. If ln W were to be at a maximum with respect to the independent variation of each n_1 separately, all its partial derivatives, ∂ ln $W/\partial n_i$, would have to be zero. Actually the n_i's must satisfy an auxiliary condition, $n_1 + n_2 + \ldots + n_z = n$, corresponding to a fixed total number of particles. Such a condition may be formulated as $f(n_1 \ldots n_z) =$ constant, where in this case

$$f = \sum_{i=1}^{z} n_i$$

Lagrange's method of undetermined multipliers is employed in solving problems of this type. We consider the function ln $W - \alpha f$, where α is an undetermined multiplier not dependent on the n_i's. Since both α and f are to be constant with respect to changes in the n_i's, it is apparent that the maximum in this function gives the maximum in ln W consistent with the given α and f. Now the z equations

$$\frac{\partial (\ln W - \alpha f)}{\partial n_i} = \frac{\partial \ln W}{\partial n_i} - \alpha \frac{\partial f}{\partial n_i} = 0 \qquad (7.3)$$

together with the equation $f =$ constant, give a set of $z + 1$ equations in $z + 1$ unknowns $(n_i, \ldots, n_z, \alpha)$ whose solution must represent an extremum in ln W. Whether this is a maximum, minimum, or saddle point may be investigated if necessary.

In order to proceed conveniently we must also introduce Stirling's approximation for large factorials.[2]

$$\ln x! \cong x \ln x - x \qquad x \gg 1$$

---

[2] The approximate form of Stirling's formula may be most conveniently derived as follows.

$$\ln x! \cong \int_1^x \ln y \, dy = \left[y \ln y - y \right]_1^x = x \ln x - x + 1$$

Evidently if x is large, the one may be neglected. The more exact form derived by advanced methods is

$$\ln x! \cong x \ln x - x + \tfrac{1}{2} \ln (2\pi x)$$

but the refinements will not be needed here.

Then we obtain for $\ln W$:

$$\ln W = \ln n! - \ln n_1! - \ln n_2! - \ldots$$
$$- \ln n_z! + n_1 \ln g_1 + \ldots + n_z \ln g_z$$
$$= \ln n! + n_1 \ln \frac{g_1}{n_1} + n_1 + n_2 \ln \frac{g_2}{n_2} + n_2 + \ldots + n_z \ln \frac{g_z}{n_z} + n_z$$
$$(7.4)$$

Next we take the partial derivative with respect to each n_i. In taking these derivatives we regard $\ln n!$ as a constant.

$$\frac{\partial (\ln W - \alpha f)}{\partial n_i} = \ln \frac{g_i}{n_i} - \alpha = 0$$

$$\ln \frac{g_i}{n_i} = \alpha$$

$$n_i = g_i e^{-\alpha} \qquad (7.5)$$

$$n_1 + n_2 + \ldots + n_z = n = e^{-\alpha}(g_1 + g_2 + \ldots + g_z) = e^{-\alpha} = n$$

$$n_i/n = g_i \qquad (7.6)$$

Thus we have finally obtained the result that the most probable number of particles in each cell is proportional to the size of the cell, a result which is obviously correct. We shall now proceed to use these methods in problems where the result is not obvious.

7b. The Boltzman distribution law. Let us next consider a set of n identical subsystems which do not interact with one another and which we shall call molecules, although they need not be molecules in the ordinary sense. Let these molecules be capable of existence in a series of states of energy $\epsilon_0, \epsilon_1, \epsilon_2, \ldots, \epsilon_z$, where ϵ_0 is the lowest. The a priori probabilities of these states are $g_0, g_1, \ldots, g_z$. Actually these states may or may not be discrete quantum states of the type mentioned in earlier sections. If they are quantum states, g_i is the integral number of states in that energy range, otherwise the g's are merely relative a priori probabilities. We assume that there is no limit to the number of molecules that can be in a given state. Evidently a distribution is defined by the numbers of molecules in each state, $n_0, n_1, \ldots, n_z$. Since the number of molecules is constant, the distribution is subject to the condition $f(n_0, \ldots, n_z) = n_0 + n_1 + \ldots + n_z = n = $ constant as above. The total energy E of the entire system, which we shall regard as fixed, is given by the equation

$$E = n_0\epsilon_0 + n_1\epsilon_1 + \ldots + n_z\epsilon_z = \text{const.}$$

This then represents a second condition on the distribution, whose probability W is the same as Eq. (7.1) above.

To find the most probable distribution we then take the following derivatives.

$$\frac{\partial \, (\ln W - \alpha f - \beta E)}{\partial n_i} = \ln \frac{g_i}{n_i} - \alpha - \beta \epsilon_i = 0 \qquad (7.7)$$

$$\ln \frac{g_i}{n_i} = \alpha + \beta \epsilon_i \qquad (7.8)$$

$$n_i = g_i e^{-\alpha - \beta \epsilon_i} = g_i e^{-\alpha} e^{-\beta \epsilon_i} \qquad (7.9)$$

Since $e^{-\alpha}$ is a constant, one may write

$$\frac{n_i}{n_j} = \frac{g_i}{g_j} e^{-\beta(\epsilon_i - \epsilon_j)} \qquad (7.10)$$

$$E = \text{const.} \ (g_0 \epsilon_0 e^{-\beta \epsilon_0} + g_1 \epsilon_1 e^{-\beta \epsilon_1} + \ldots) = E(\beta) \qquad (7.11)$$

We see that for a given number and kind of molecules the energy depends only on β, which is thus a sort of temperature. We shall presently calculate the pressure of a perfect gas and thus relate β to the ordinary form of temperature. In order to avoid rewriting all equations derived in the meantime, we shall anticipate the result and write from now on:

$$\beta = \frac{1}{kT} \qquad (7.12)$$

$$\frac{n_i}{n_j} = \frac{g_i}{g_j} e^{-(\epsilon_i - \epsilon_j)/kT} \qquad (7.13)$$

where k is a constant known as the Boltzmann constant, whose value is approximately 1.3803×10^{-16} erg per degree, and T is the ordinary absolute temperature in degrees Kelvin. The expression for n_i/n_j is the Boltzmann distribution law, and the exponential factor by itself is commonly known as the Boltzmann factor.

Before accepting the above equations as a valid description of a physical system we must consider two somewhat related possible difficulties. First, is there any appreciable probability of finding the system with other than the most probable distribution? Second, noting the exponential form of the distribution law, we cannot now maintain that all values of n_i will be large compared with unity if the sequence of energy states continues to indefinitely high energies. We must conclude that any small n_i's will be doubtful as individual values. However, if only a negligible fraction of the total number of molecules is involved, it can be seen that the analysis is still valid for the rest of the distribution.

The probable magnitude of fluctuations from the most probable distribution has been calculated and is presented in certain treatises on statistical mechanics. Roughly, the probable deviation in a given n_i is $\sqrt{n_i}$ (see Problem 7.2). If a system contains 10^{23} molecules, even an energy level populated with one part in 10^{15} of the molecules would have $n_i = 10^8$, and n_i would consequently be accurate to 0.01%. Thus, for most physically significant systems the numbers are so large that the most probable distribution is, for practical purposes, indistinguishable from all other distributions of appreciable probability. Nevertheless, one should remember that in the strict sense of exact numbers of molecules, n_i, in the various states, there are many distributions of substantially equal probability. Also, it may be necessary to group together quantum states of nearly equal energy in order to avoid small values of the n's in the lower energy range.

7c. Phase space. It proves convenient in considering the behavior of molecules to consider an imaginary space whose axes are (for a monatomic molecule) x, y, z, the ordinary space coordinates, and p_x, p_y, p_z, the momenta of the molecule in these directions. A point in this space then defines a molecule exactly, and the distribution in this space of the points corresponding to all the molecules defines the state of the system exactly. Furthermore, if this state is known at one time, it is in principle defined at all later times if one assumes the laws of classical mechanics. Indeed, an interesting theorem due to Liouville (proven in most treatises of classical statistical mechanics) states that the density of points (representing molecules) in phase space near a given point remains constant as that point moves with time.

We may remark at this stage that the idea of a point in phase space is inconsistent with the uncertainty principle, since the latter states that the uncertainty in a coordinate times that in the corresponding momentum must be at least approximately h. Thus the closest one can define a point in this phase space is to place it within a cell of volume h^3 (or for n coordinates and n momenta, h^n).

As one might suppose from the uncertainty principle conclusions just mentioned, *a single quantum state corresponds to a volume h^n in*

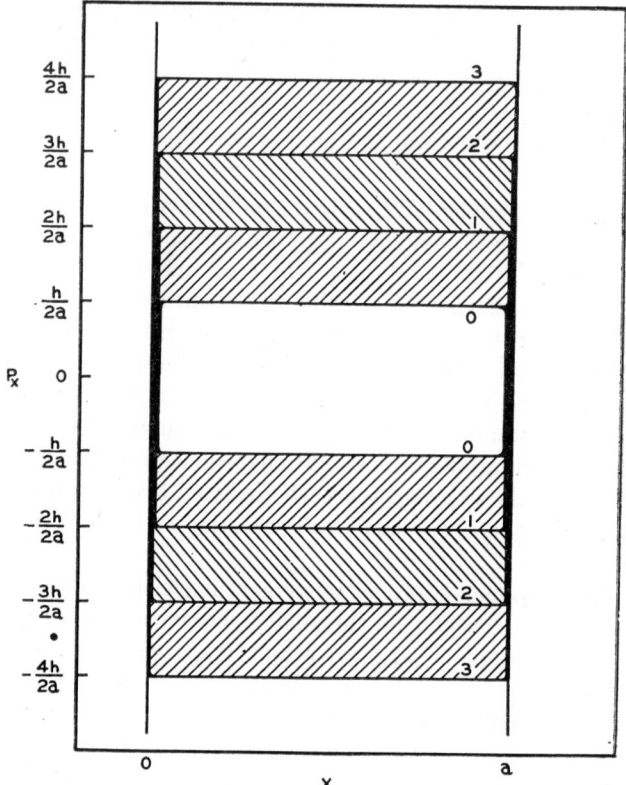

Fig. 7.2.   Paths in phase space for a particle in a box.

phase space. A general proof of this statement is not readily given but it is easy to verify its truth for numerous examples. Let us consider the particle in an infinite walled box and the harmonic oscillator. In each case we can find the path in phase space for a classical motion with the same energy as the quantum state. We then calculate the area in phase space between the paths for successive states and find it to be h.

Figure 7.2 shows the paths for the particle in the box following the notation of Section 2h. Note that the area between successive paths is in two sections, each a rectangle of length a and width $h/2a$. The total area between paths is thus h. Figure 7.3 shows the correspond-

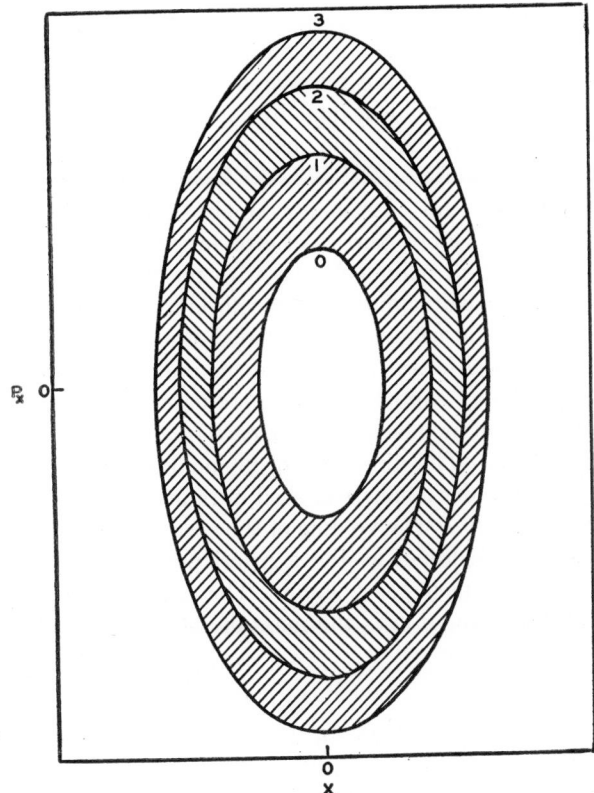

Fig. 7.3. Paths in phase space for a harmonic oscillator.

ing curves for the harmonic oscillator which was considered in Section 2i. Here a path is an ellipse with semiaxes $[(n + \frac{1}{2})h/\pi\sqrt{km}]^{1/2}$ and $[(n + \frac{1}{2})h\sqrt{km}/\pi]^{1/2}$. The total area inside the nth path is therefore $(n + \frac{1}{2})h$, and the area between successive paths is again just h.

Thus we may use phase space as a means of estimating the number of quantum states in a given energy range provided that number is large enough so that the exact shape of the cells is not important. We postulate that the *a priori probabilities of all single quantum states are equal.* Thus we may also take the volume in phase space as a relative measure of a priori probability. This last statement was an assumption in classical statistical mechanics, but is now seen to follow from the axiomatic postulate of equal probability of quantum states. Also it is now possible to put relative probabilities from phase space on an absolute basis. This is done by considering a volume in phase space of h^n, corresponding to one quantum state, as the absolute unit of probability.

7d. The perfect gas. Let us now apply the phase space concept to a perfect gas. The properties of a perfect gas may be calculated on the assumption of point particles with no forces acting between them except at negligible moments of collision. Classical mechanics is adequate for this calculation provided the temperature is high enough. Since positions in ordinary space are of no significance for the present, we may suppress these coordinates in phase space and consider the cells in momentum space, each occupying all the volume in ordinary space. The directions of momentum are certainly random. Let us consider a spherical shell of radius p and thickness dp. Its volume is $4\pi p^2 dp$. The volume of the corresponding phase space cell, which may be taken as the a priori probability, is $4\pi V p^2 dp$, where V is the ordinary gas volume. The energy corresponding to this cell is $p^2/2m$ where m is the mass of the particle. The distribution law is therefore

$$dn = (\text{const.})(4\pi V p^2 dp)e^{-p^2/2mkT}$$

where dn is written instead of n_i to correspond with the differential notation used with the momentum. One evaluates the constant by integration.[3]

$$n = (\text{const.})4\pi V \int_0^\infty e^{-p^2/2mkT} p^2\, dp = (\text{const.}) V (2\pi mkT)^{3/2}$$

$$dn = \frac{n}{(2\pi mkT)^{3/2}} e^{-p^2/2mkT} 4\pi p^2\, dp \tag{7.14}$$

or in terms of energy,

$$\epsilon = p^2/2m, \qquad\qquad d\epsilon = (p\,dp)/m$$

$$dn = \frac{2n}{\pi^{1/2}(kT)^{3/2}} e^{-\epsilon/kT} \epsilon^{1/2}\, d\epsilon \tag{7.15}$$

Another form of interest is obtained by considering the components of momentum p_x, p_y, p_z, and observing that the volume element is now just $dp_x\, dp_y\, dp_z$.

[3] $\int_0^\infty x^2 e^{-ax^2}\, dx = \frac14 \sqrt{\pi/a^3}$

$$dn = \frac{n}{(2\pi mkT)^{3/2}} e^{-(p_x{}^2 + p_y{}^2 + p_z{}^2)/2mkT} dp_x\, dp_y\, dp_z \qquad (7.16)$$

In terms of the total velocity U, the distribution law is

$$dn = \frac{nm^{3/2}}{(2\pi kT)^{3/2}} e^{-mU^2/2kT} 4\pi U^2\, dU \qquad (7.17)$$

This law of distribution of molecular velocities in a perfect gas was first suggested by Maxwell (1859) and proven by analysis of collisional processes by Boltzmann (1896). It is commonly known as the Maxwell-Boltzmann distribution law.

7e. The pressure of a perfect gas. Identification of temperature scales. To calculate the pressure exerted by such a gas we follow the usual procedure of considering the momentum change of collisions with the wall. Let us consider a cylinder extending perpendicularly from an area of 1 cm.^{2} on the wall. For convenience let the x axis be parallel with this cylinder. A molecule within this cylinder and moving toward the wall with velocity v_x will strike within 1 second if it is not further than v_x from the wall. Actually some molecules moving obliquely will move outside this cylinder, but they will be replaced, on the average, by others moving in from outside. The total number of molecules striking in unit time with velocity v_x and momentum p_x will be those in a volume v_x, thus

$$(v_x/V)\, dn = (p_x/mV)\, dn$$

where V is the total volume and dn is the total number of molecules with the required component velocity and momentum.

The change in momentum on collision is $2p_x$, and the pressure is the total change in momentum per unit time and area.

$$P = \frac{2}{mV} \int p_x^2\, dn$$

Substituting dn from above we have

$$P = \left(\frac{n}{V}\right)\left(\frac{2}{m}\right)\frac{1}{(2\pi mkT)^{3/2}} \int_{-\infty}^{+\infty}\int_{-\infty}^{+\infty}\int_{0}^{+\infty} p_x^2 e^{-(p_x{}^2 + p_y{}^2 + p_z{}^2)/2mkT}$$
$$dp_x\, dp_y\, dp_z \qquad (7.18)$$

The integration over p_x is only from zero to infinity because particles with negative velocities will not strike the area considered. To perform the integrations one expands the exponential

$$P = \left(\frac{n}{V}\right) \frac{1}{(2\pi mkT)^{3/2}} \left(\frac{2}{m}\right) \left(\int_{-\infty}^{+\infty} e^{-p_y^2/2mkT} dp_y\right)^2 \left(\int_0^\infty e^{-p_x^2/2mkT} p_x^2\, dp_x\right)$$

$$= \left(\frac{n}{V}\right) kT$$

or for one mole

$$P = N_0 kT/V = RT/V \tag{7.19}$$

This result is really an evaluation of the temperature parameter β introduced in earlier sections. Had the distribution laws been left in terms of β, it would now be found that the pressure was $N/\beta V$, which would, of course, lead to the relation between β and T which was assumed above.

Let us also calculate the energy content of a perfect monatomic gas. Since there is no potential energy, we need consider only the kinetic energy, which is to be summed for all molecules.

$$E = \int_0^\infty \epsilon\, dn = \frac{2n}{\pi^{1/2}(kT)^{3/2}} \int_0^\infty e^{-\epsilon/kT} \epsilon^{3/2}\, d\epsilon$$

Integrating by parts we obtain

$$E = \frac{2n}{\pi^{1/2}(kT)^{3/2}} \left[\left(-kT\epsilon^{3/2} e^{-\epsilon/kT}\right)_0^\infty + \frac{3}{2} kT \int_0^\infty \epsilon^{1/2} e^{-\epsilon/kT} d\epsilon\right] \tag{7.20}$$

The first term within the brackets is zero, and the second term may be identified as merely $\int dn$ except of the factor $\frac{3}{2}kT$. Thus the energy is just $\frac{3}{2}nkT$, and the heat capacity (at constant volume) is $\frac{3}{2}nk$. For one mole of gas the energy becomes $\frac{3}{2}RT$, and the heat capacity $\frac{3}{2}R$.

7f. Indistinguishable particles. Before proceeding further, it is necessary to consider the significance of strictly indistinguishable particles. Ordinarily, if two pennies are simultaneously flipped, one regards the probability of one head and one tail to be double that of two heads or two tails because either penny A or penny B may be head in the first case. Penny A and penny B are not strictly indistinguishable even though their "flipping characteristics" are identical. It is a question, however, whether atoms of helium which cannot conceivably be distinguished from one another (except by methods which change their properties, e.g., ionization) should be treated by such methods. In fact it is found that agreement with experiment and consistency with quantum mechanical principles can be had only if one ignores any additional probability arising from the exchange of indistinguishable particles.

The Pauli exclusion principle states that two electrons can never occupy the same quantum state (have all quantum numbers the same) if the spin is considered. If one ignores spin in defining the quantum states, the limit is two electrons per state. Such an exclusion principle applies also to protons and some other particles, but not to helium atoms. The rule which now appears to be general, and has been shown to arise from attempts to make quantum mechanics consistent with relativity, is that particles with half integral spin are subject to an exclusion principle while those of zero or integral spin are not.

These rules related to indistinguishable particles can be derived from the symmetry properties of wave functions. In Section 5a we saw how the Pauli exclusion principle can be derived from a postulate that wave functions must be antisymmetric to the exchange of any two electrons. It was also indicated there that the only other possibility consistent with general principles is for the wave function to be symmetric to the exchange of two identical particles. Let us examine the symmetric case for two particles and two quantum states. There are three possible symmetric wave functions, as follows.

$$\psi_A(1)\psi_A(2)$$
$$[\psi_A(1)\psi_B(2) + \psi_B(1)\psi_A(2)]2^{-1/2}$$
$$\psi_B(1)\psi_B(2)$$

It is to be noted in particular that there is but a single wave function for the distribution with one particle in each state.

7g. Fermi-Dirac and Bose-Einstein distribution laws. Let us now make the type of calculation which led to the Boltzmann distribution law, but with assumptions consistent with the preceding section. For the Bose-Einstein statistics we assume indistinguishable particles in states of energy, $\epsilon_0, \epsilon_1, \ldots, \epsilon_z$, subject to the conditions of constant number of particles and constant total energy. There is no limit on the number of particles in a given state. These assumptions correspond to wave functions which are symmetric to the exchange of any two particles. The g's may now be regarded as the numbers of quantum states having the given energies; it being assumed that all single quantum states have equal a priori probability. It is necessary to calculate the number of ways of placing n_i indistinguishable particles in g_i quantum states. If for the moment we imagine the particles to be distinguishable, we may consider an array of $n_i + g_i - 1$ objects to be arranged along a line. Of these, $g_i - 1$ are considered as partitions which separate off g_i compartments into which the n_i particles are placed. There are $(n_i + g_i - 1)!$ possible permutations, but the permutations of the particles among themselves or the partitions among themselves are not significant. Thus the total number of arrangements of this group of particles is $(n_i + g_i - 1)!/n_i!(g_i - 1)!$ Considering all the groups of energy states, we find the total number of arrangements (or probability) for a given distribution to be

$$W = \prod_i \frac{(n_i + g_i - 1)!}{n_i!(g_i - 1)!} \qquad (7.21)$$

Proceeding as above, we use Stirling's approximation and ignore 1 as compared with $(g_i + n_i)$.

$$\ln W = \sum_i \left[(n_i + g_i) \ln (n_i + g_i) - n_i \ln n_i - \ln (g_i - 1)! - g_i \right]$$

$$(7.22)$$

$$\frac{\partial(\ln W - \alpha f - \beta E)}{\partial n_i} = \ln \frac{n_i + g_i}{n_i} - \alpha - \beta \epsilon_i = 0$$

$$1 + \frac{g_i}{n_i} = e^{\alpha + \beta \epsilon_i}$$

$$n_i = \frac{g_i}{e^{\alpha + \beta \epsilon_i} - 1} = \frac{g_i}{e^{\alpha + \epsilon_i/kT} - 1} \qquad (7.23)$$

where α is to be evaluated so that

$$\sum_i n_i = n$$

the total number of particles.

The Fermi-Dirac statistics assumes, in addition to the indistinguishability of the particles, that only one particle per state is allowed. This corresponds, of course, to wave functions which are antisymmetric to the exchange of any pair of particles. Then with g_i states and n_i particles there will be n_i filled cells and $g_i - n_i$ vacant cells. There are $g_i!$ arrangements of the cells, but the permutations of the filled or empty cells among themselves are insignificant. Therefore the desired number of arrangements is $g_i!/n_i!(g_i - n_i)!$ For the entire distribution we find

$$W = \prod_i \frac{g_i!}{n_i!(g_i - n_i)!} \tag{7.24}$$

$$\ln W = \sum_i g_i \ln g_i - n_i \ln n_i - (g_i - n_i) \ln (g_i - n_i) \tag{7.25}$$

$$\frac{\partial(\ln W - \alpha f - \beta E)}{\partial n_i} = \ln \frac{g_i - n_i}{n_i} - \alpha - \beta\epsilon_i = 0$$

$$\frac{g_i}{n_i} - 1 = e^{\alpha + \beta\epsilon_i}$$

$$n_i = \frac{g_i}{e^{\alpha + \beta\epsilon_i} + 1} = \frac{g_i}{e^{\alpha + \epsilon_i/kT} + 1} \tag{7.26}$$

where α is to be evaluated as before.

The Fermi and Bose distribution laws may thus be written

$$n_i = \frac{g_i}{e^{\alpha + \epsilon_i/kT} \pm 1}$$

where the sign is $+$ for the Fermi and $-$ for the Bose laws, respectively. Further calculations with these exact laws are very difficult. There are, however, several important propositions applying to limiting cases which are given in Problems 7.3 and 7.4.

7h. Entropy. The statistical analogue of the second law of thermodynamics is the axiomatic statement that systems change in the direction of increasing probability subject, of course, to conservation of energy. The function known as entropy defined by this law must then be closely related to the statistical probability W, defined above. Classically, one can consider only changes in entropy and relative values of W. The form found to be correct is

$$S_2 - S_1 = k \ln (W_2/W_1) \tag{7.27}$$

Here k is a numerical constant which will be found to be the same Boltzmann constant that has already been used. In quantum statistics the probability W becomes the very definite number of arrangements of particles among the quantum states. One can then define an absolute entropy as

$$S = k \ln W \tag{7.28}$$

Actually, it proves convenient to ignore the entropy contributions of nuclear spin, and this is done in practical thermodynamical calculations. Also one ignores entropies of mixing of isotopes unless isotope separation is being considered.

The absolute entropy of a perfect gas without nuclear spin may be calculated as follows.

$$\ln W = \sum_i \left[(n_i + g_i) \ln (n_i + g_i) - n_i \ln n_i - g_i \ln g_i \right] \qquad (7.29)$$

This is the expression for the Bose statistics with an additional use of Stirling's approximation. We use the high-temperature form of the distribution law, which becomes the Boltzmann law, and arises because e^α is large compared with unity.

$$n_i = g_i e^{-\alpha} e^{-\epsilon/kT} \qquad (7.30)$$

Under these conditions, n_i is necessarily much smaller than g_i because $e^{-\alpha}$ is very small. Then

$$\ln (n_i + g_i) = \ln g_i + \ln \left(1 + \frac{n_i}{g_i} \right) \cong \ln g_i + \frac{n_i}{g_i}$$

$$\ln W = \sum_i \left(n_i \ln g_i + g_i \ln g_i + n_i - n_i \ln n_i - g_i \ln g_i \right)$$

$$= \sum_i n_i \left(1 + \ln \frac{g_i}{n_i} \right) = \sum_i n_i \left(1 + \alpha + \frac{\epsilon_i}{kT} \right) \qquad (7.31)$$

This result is valid for any perfect gas. We now limit the discussion to a monatomic gas, and taking the energy value obtained above in Eq. (7.20), we obtain

$$\ln W = (1 + \alpha) \sum n_i + \frac{1}{kT} \sum \epsilon_i n_i = (1 + \alpha)n + \frac{1}{kT} \frac{3}{2} nkT$$

$$= n \left(\alpha + \frac{5}{2} \right) \qquad (7.32)$$

We have then for one mole of gas,

$$S = k \ln W = R \left(\alpha + \frac{5}{2} \right) \qquad (7.33)$$

It remains to evaluate α. This is accomplished by obtaining g_i, which is the number of cells of volume h^3 in phase space. Differential notation is convenient with each incremental volume occupying the entire volume V of ordinary space and a spherical shell in momentum space.

$$dg = \frac{4\pi V}{h^3} p^2 \, dp$$

$$dn = \frac{4\pi V}{h^3} e^{-\alpha} e^{-p^2/2mkT} p^2 \, dp$$

$$n = \frac{4\pi V}{h^3} e^{-\alpha} \int_0^\infty e^{-p^2/2mkT} p^2 \, dp = e^{-\alpha} V \left(\frac{2\pi mkT}{h^2}\right)^{3/2}$$

$$\alpha = \ln \frac{V}{n} + \frac{3}{2} \ln \frac{2\pi mkT}{h^2} \tag{7.34}$$

Returning now to the entropy for one mole, we find

$$\begin{aligned}
S &= R\left[\frac{5}{2} + \ln \frac{V}{N_0} + \frac{3}{2} \ln \frac{2\pi mkT}{h^2}\right] \\
&= R\left[\ln V + \frac{3}{2} \ln T + \frac{3}{2} \ln M\right] + R\left[\frac{5}{2} + \ln \left(2^{3/2}\pi^{3/2}k^{3/2}/h^3 N_0^{5/2}\right)\right] \\
&= R\left[\ln V + \frac{3}{2} \ln T + \frac{3}{2} \ln M\right] - 11.052 \quad \text{cal. per degree} \tag{7.35}
\end{aligned}$$

in which M is the ordinary molecular weight and V is in cubic centimeters.

We may now verify our assumption that e^α is large compared with unity. For hydrogen at its boiling point, $20°K$, e^α is 140, while at $300°K$ and 1 atmosphere pressure, e^α is 120,000. For argon at $300°K$, e^α is 10^7.

We may note that the expression for the entropy contains the term $R \ln V$, which is in agreement with the results of thermodynamics. Since any thermodynamic process can be related to perfect gas processes, it is now proven that the statistical expression of entropy is correct.

7i. Third law of thermodynamics. The third law of thermodynamics states that the entropy of perfect crystalline substances approaches zero as the temperature approaches zero. In terms of statistics we see that this means that W must approach one or at least a small number which can be expressed as follows.

$$\begin{aligned}
W &= (1 + \delta)^{N_0} \cong 1 + N_0\delta + \ldots, \\
S &= k \ln W = R \ln (1 + \delta) \cong R\delta \tag{7.36}
\end{aligned}$$

Thus the requirement is really that δ be small compared with unity. This means that there must be a reasonably limited group of lowest energy quantum states into which all molecules fall at the absolute zero. Even if a crystal has $W > 1$ at $0°K$, it may be considered perfect with respect to the third law if W is limited in the manner indicated above. We are not yet prepared to discuss the quantum states of a crystal, but may remark that when the third law is interpreted statistically, it is a very useful and valuable basis of thermodynamic data.

7j. Photon gas—blackbody radiation. We may now turn to the topic that led Planck first to introduce the quantum theory. It is the question of the relative intensity, as a function of wave length, for light in equilibrium with matter at a definite temperature. We may consider it as merely the distribution law for the energies of photons in a photon gas. Experimentally, photons follow the Bose-Einstein statistics. We use the distribution law given above with the omission of α since the number of photons need not be conserved.

$$dn = \frac{dg}{e^{\epsilon/kT} - 1} \tag{7.37}$$

To obtain dg we divide phase space into cells of volume h^3 and assign each cell a weight 2, because there are two states of polarization for otherwise identical photons. Remembering the relativistic expression for particles moving with the velocity of light,

$$p = E/c = h\nu/c \tag{1.6'}$$

we find

$$dg = \frac{8\pi V p^2 \, dp}{h^3} = \frac{8\pi V \nu^2 \, d\nu}{c^3} \tag{7.38}$$

To find the energy density of photons we divide by V and multiply by the energy of the photon $h\nu$. Combining the equations one obtains

$$\rho(\nu) = \frac{8\pi h\nu^3}{c^3} \cdot \frac{1}{e^{h\nu/kT} - 1} \tag{7.39}$$

the Planck distribution law, which has been experimentally verified.

We may reverse the historical order and derive the classical "Rayleigh-Jeans" radiation law by taking the limit of Eq. (7.39) as $h \to 0$. Expanding the exponential and noting that the -1 cancels the first term, one obtains

$$\rho(\nu) = \frac{8\pi\nu^2}{c^3} kT \tag{7.40}$$

This law is, of course, a good approximation so long as $h\nu \ll kT$, but fails otherwise. In particular if one attempts to sum the total energy by integrating with respect to ν, one finds an infinite result. This arises from the high-frequency end of the spectrum and was known as the "ultraviolet catastrophe."

7k. Absorption and emission coefficients. We are now prepared to give the Einstein theory of absorption, spontaneous and induced emission referred to in 6d. Let us suppose we have some molecules of a character to follow the Boltzmann statistics which are passing between the mth and nth single quantum states by absorption and emission of radiation. The number of photons absorbed and of molecules changed from the mth to the nth state is

$$n_m B_{nm}\rho(\nu_{nm})$$

while the number of photons emitted and of molecules changed from the nth to the mth state is

$$n_n[B_{mn}\rho(\nu_{nm}) + A_{mn}]$$

where we have included the spontaneous emission coefficient A_{mn} in addition to the induced emission coefficient B_{mn}. Now at equilibrium the two quantities above must be equal, giving for the ratio of the numbers of molecules in the two states

$$\frac{n_n}{n_m} = \frac{B_{nm}\rho(\nu_{nm})}{B_{mn}\rho(\nu_{nm}) + A_{mn}} \tag{7.41}$$

but this ratio must have the value given by the Boltzmann relationship (7.13)

$$\frac{n_n}{n_m} = e^{-(\epsilon_n - \epsilon_m)/kT} = e^{-h\nu_{nm}/kT} \tag{7.42}$$

since $g_n = g_m = 1$. Combining these results, one obtains after some rearrangement

$$B_{nm}\rho(\nu_{nm})e^{h\nu_{nm}/kT} = B_{mn}\rho(\nu_{nm}) + A_{mn}$$

which leads to the following equation for the radiation energy density.

$$\rho(\nu_{nm}) = \frac{A_{mn}}{B_{nm}e^{h\nu_{nm}/kT} - B_{mn}} \tag{7.43}$$

However, this result (7.43) must be equivalent to the result from Bose-Einstein statistics, Eq. (7.39). For this to be so, $B_{mn} = B_{nm}$, which we found to be true in Section 6c, and

$$A_{mn} = \frac{8\pi h\nu_{nm}^3}{c^3} B_{mn} \tag{7.44}$$

which is the result we have been seeking.

71. Degenerate Fermi and Bose gases. The deviation of Fermi
or Bose gases from the perfect gas law at low temperatures is known
as gas degeneration. (This is a different use of the word *degenerate*
from that indicating several quantum states of the same energy.)
In the Bose case, all molecules fall into the lowest quantum state.
The peculiar properties of liquid helium near 1°K are almost certainly
related to Bose degeneracy; however, a treatment of this case is complicated by the necessity of considering the intermolecular forces,
which are by no means negligible. This one very interesting example,
and that of photons discussed above, constitute the known important
cases of Bose degeneracy.

The properties of a degenerate Fermi gas are of great importance,
since almost all chemical effects arise from the electron clouds about
atomic nuclei, and these electron clouds are, to a first approximation,
degenerate Fermi gases. However, since electrostatic forces are very
important in an electron cloud, this analysis which neglects these
forces is necessarily only a crude approximation.

The state of complete degeneracy is obtained when all quantum
states up to a given energy are completely occupied and all of higher
energy are vacant. Remembering that two electrons may occupy a
quantum state if spin is ignored, we find from the phase space the
number of quantum states to be

$$dg = \frac{8\pi V}{h^3} p^2 \, dp = \frac{8\sqrt{2}m^{3/2}\pi V}{h^3} \epsilon^{1/2} \, d\epsilon \tag{7.45}$$

which upon integration gives

$$g = n = \frac{2^{7/2}m^{3/2}\pi V}{h^3} \epsilon_m^{3/2} \frac{2}{3}$$

and

$$\epsilon_m = \frac{h^2}{8m}\left(\frac{3n}{\pi V}\right)^{2/3} \tag{7.46}$$

where ϵ_m is the highest energy state that is filled. The zero point
energy content of this gas is as follows.

$$E_0 = \int \epsilon \, dg = \frac{8\sqrt{2}m^{3/2}\pi V}{h^3} \int_0^{\epsilon_m} \epsilon^{3/2} \, d\epsilon$$

$$= \frac{2^{7/2}m^{3/2}\pi V}{h^3} \frac{2}{5} \epsilon_m^{5/2}$$

$$= \frac{h^2(3n)^{5/3}}{40m(\pi V)^{2/3}} = \frac{3}{5} n\epsilon_m \tag{7.47}$$

This interesting result shows that the energy increases with the concentration (n/V) of the gas, and varies inversely with the mass of the particle. Although the electrostatic forces of electrons (and nuclei) are by no means completely negligible, for most qualitative purposes this energy is the important term. Thus even at the absolute zero an electronic system resists crowding into an indefinitely small space.

One may compute the zero point pressure corresponding to this energy by noting that the entropy is zero, so that the energy is the work content A, and by using the thermodynamic equation

$$P_0 = -\frac{dA_0}{dV}$$

$$= \frac{h^2}{20m}\left(\frac{3}{\pi}\right)^{2/3}\left(\frac{n}{V}\right)^{5/3} \tag{7.48}$$

Inserting values for physical constants, one finds for electron gas of molal volume V in cubic centimeters,

$$E_0 = 360V^{-2/3} \quad \text{kcal.} \tag{7.47'}$$

$$P_0 = 1.0 \times 10^7 V^{-5/3} \quad \text{atm.} \tag{7.48'}$$

Since V is of the order of magnitude 10 for most metals, these energies and pressures are enormous. This pressure is counterbalanced by the electrical attraction of the electrons for the nuclei.

At temperatures above the absolute zero, the degeneracy is not complete. However, as one can see from Fig. 7.4, at low temperatures the distribution is still essentially like the case of complete degeneracy. Formulas may be derived for the region of almost com-

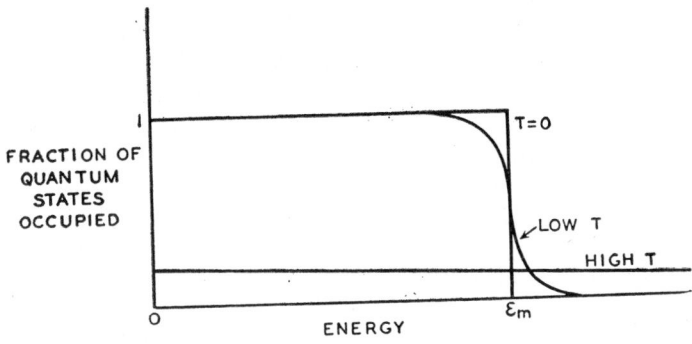

Fig. 7.4.   The distribution of occupied quantum states for a Fermi gas.

plete degeneracy.[4] We reproduce a few without burdening the present section with their lengthy proofs. Let

$$X = \frac{kT}{\epsilon_m} = \frac{3RT}{5E_0} = \frac{TV^{2/3}}{302,000} \qquad (V \text{ in cc./mole})$$

$$E = E_0(1 + 4.11X^2 + \ldots)$$

$$C_v = R\frac{\pi^2}{2}X + \ldots \tag{7.49}$$

$$S = R\frac{\pi^2}{2}X + \ldots$$

This result for the heat capacity of an almost degenerate Fermi gas cleared up a most puzzling situation. The phenomenon of electric conductivity indicated that many electrons in a metal must be free to move throughout the lattice, yet the observed specific heat conformed to the estimates based on the assumption that only nuclei or entire atoms were free to absorb thermal energy. When appropriate values are substituted into Eq. (7.49), one finds that the electronic contributions to the specific heat are very small. Thus for silver at 300°K, X is 0.0047, if we take one free electron per atom. Then the electronic heat capacity is only $0.023R$ as compared with about $3R$ for the atomic vibrations.

Among the interesting and important results of the Fermi statistics as applied to electron gas are the following. First, atoms have a size; they have a natural volume and resist compression to a smaller volume. Second, the electrons in a metal may be free to move from place to place and thus conduct electricity, yet they do not contribute appreciably to the heat capacity. Third, any change which increases the volume available to the electrons, leaving other things equal, will lower the energy. The phenomena usually called *chemical bonds* and *resonance* may be considered in this light. Thus in forming H_2 from 2H, additional low-potential energy volume is made available to each electron. Likewise in benzene as compared with a hypothetical hexatriene there are six places for the double bonding electrons instead of three. These ideas will be considered in greater detail in later sections.

7m. Quantum states and thermodynamic states. The classi-

[4] See Tolman, R. C., *The Principles of Statistical Mechanics*, New York: Oxford University Press, 1938, p. 391. Also Mayer, J. E. and Mayer, M. G., *Statistical Mechanics*, New York: John Wiley & Sons, Inc., 1940, p. 378.

cal term *thermodynamic state* refers to groups of quantum states which are easily distinguished experimentally, e.g., the solid state as compared to the liquid or gas, or to the substance in the form NO_2 as compared to N_2O_4, or to HI as compared to $H_2 + I_2$, etc. Within any thermodynamic state there are many quantum states, even for one molecule. In a strict sense statistical mechanics would consider all the quantum states for the system of interest, and therefore calculate only the properties of the system at complete equilibrium. Actually, it is usually possible to classify essentially all the quantum states as belonging to one thermodynamic state or another, and thus to calculate the properties of the system in any thermodynamic state. A few quantum states will be of ambiguous nature but they are so few that they are of no consequence.

As an example, at low temperatures and pressures the thermal energy quantum states of N_2O_4 will fall into two groups. One group consists of those with the two nitrogen atoms close together, and therefore corresponds to N_2O_4. The other group involves long distances between the nitrogen atoms, and is clearly $2NO_2$. Large numbers of other states involve isolated atoms such as $NO_2 + NO + O$ but are of such high energy that they would not be occupied at moderate temperatures anyway. There will be states which represent $2NO_2$ at ambiguously intermediate distances but they will be few in number. Thus separate statistical calculations for NO_2 and for N_2O_4 are possible. At high temperatures and pressures, however, the maximum distance between molecules is much smaller, and consequently the relative number of states corresponding to ambiguous distances is large. Under these conditions one could not separate experimentally the ordinary gas imperfection of NO_2 from the formation of N_2O_4, and the theoretical treatment breaks down correspondingly.

These ideas should be kept in mind when, in later sections, we calculate the properties of a substance in a given thermodynamic state by a summation over the quantum states (or the regions in phase space) corresponding to that thermodynamic state.

7n. The partition function. Statistical formulas for thermodynamic functions. In this section we shall develop general formulas for calculating the important thermodynamic quantities from the appropriate properties of individual molecules. If we except the cases already discussed as degenerate Fermi or Bose gases, most chemical systems are such that only a very small fraction of the available quantum states are occupied. At zero energy this fraction is $e^{-\alpha}$, which was found to be small even for hydrogen at its boiling point. Consequently exclusion rules are unimportant, and the Boltzmann distribution law applies. However, we retain the concept of the indistinguishability of identical particles.

Let us refer back to Section 7h. Through Eq. (7.31) the treatment is quite general and is only thereafter limited to a perfect monatomic gas. We may then write

$$n_i = g_i e^{-\alpha} e^{-\epsilon_i/kT}$$

$$S = k \ln W = k \sum_i n_i \left(1 + \alpha + \frac{\epsilon_i}{kT}\right)$$

$$= k(1 + \alpha) \sum_i n_i + \frac{1}{T} \sum_i n_i \epsilon_i \qquad (7.31')$$

If we now use capital letters to refer to molal quantities and remember that $N_0 k = R$, we have

$$S = R(1 + \alpha) + E/T$$

Let us define the *partition function* (for a molecule) as

$$Q = \sum_i g_i e^{-\epsilon_i/kT} \qquad (7.50)$$

where we assume the lowest energy level to have $\epsilon = 0$, as we shall throughout these sections.

Then we have

$$Q = e^{\alpha} \sum n_i = N_0 e^{\alpha}$$

$$\alpha = \ln \frac{Q}{N_0}$$

$$S = R \left[1 + \ln \frac{Q}{N_0}\right] + E/T$$

However, from thermodynamics $S = (E/T) - (A/T)$; consequently

$$-\frac{A}{T} = R \left[1 + \ln \frac{Q}{N_0}\right] \qquad (7.51)$$

$$P = -\frac{\partial A}{\partial V} = RT \frac{\partial \ln Q}{\partial V} \qquad (7.52)$$

$$\frac{E}{T} = T \frac{\partial(-A/T)}{\partial T} = RT \frac{\partial \ln Q}{\partial T} \qquad (7.53)$$

$$S = \frac{E}{T} - \frac{A}{T} = R\left[1 + \ln\left(\frac{Q}{N_0}\right) + T\frac{d\ln Q}{dT}\right] \qquad (7.54)$$

$$C_v = \frac{\partial E}{\partial T} = R\left[2T\frac{d\ln Q}{dT} + T^2\frac{d^2\ln Q}{dT^2}\right] \qquad (7.55)$$

The corresponding results for F and H are obtained by adding (PV) to A and E, while C_p is the temperature derivative of H. Thus we have all important thermodynamic properties related to the statistical partition function.

7o. Formulas for calculations of thermodynamic properties for perfect gases. By making the assumptions appropriate to a perfect gas we can make further simplifications and at the same time verify our earlier calculation of its entropy. We now consider, however, that the gas may be composed of complex molecules with many internal motions and corresponding energies.

The energy of each quantum state for an entire polyatomic molecule can be accurately separated into an energy of translation and an internal energy. Furthermore, for each translational energy there will be just the same series of internal energy levels. Thus all the energy levels of the molecule are given by

$$\epsilon_k = \epsilon_t + \epsilon_i \qquad (7.56)$$

Where t refers to translation and i to the internal energy. Then

$$Q = \sum_t \sum_i g_t e^{-\epsilon_t/kT} g_i e^{-\epsilon_i/kT}$$

$$= \left(\sum_t g_t e^{-\epsilon_t/kT}\right)\left(\sum_i g_i e^{-\epsilon_i/kT}\right)$$

$$= Q_t Q_i \qquad (7.57)$$

If the energy levels in either factor of the partition function are closely spaced as compared with kT, one may replace the sum by an integral and may further use the phase space to set up the integral

$$Q = \frac{1}{\sigma h^m} \int \cdots \int e^{-\epsilon(q,p)/kT} dq_1 \ldots dq_m \, dp_1 \ldots dp_m \qquad (7.58)$$

where the q's and p's are the coordinates and momenta appropriate to the problem, $\epsilon(q,p)$ is the energy expressed in these terms, and the integration is over that region of phase space corresponding to the thermodynamic state. The division by h^m accounts for the volume of phase space corresponding to one quantum state. If certain particles are indistinguishable, only one of the several regions in phase space which differ by mere exchange of indistinguishable particles should be included. It is sometimes convenient to integrate over all such regions and then divide by a symmetry number σ, which is the number of indistinguishable regions included.

Let us now evaluate Q_t, which for a monatomic gas is the entire Q. The integration over the coordinates leads merely to the volume V. Using polar coordinates for momentum space we obtain

$$Q_t = \frac{V}{h^3} 4\pi \int_0^\infty e^{-p^2/2mkT} p^2 \, dp = V \left(\frac{2\pi mkT}{h^2} \right)^{3/2}$$

From the above result and Eqs. (7.54) and (7.57), we find the entropy to be

$$S = R \left[1 + \ln \left(\frac{V}{N_0} \right) + \frac{3}{2} \ln \left(\frac{2\pi mkT}{h^2} \right) + \frac{3}{2} + \ln Q_i + T \frac{d \ln Q_i}{dT} \right]$$
$$(7.59)$$

which checks exactly Eq. (7.35) if Q_i is set equal to unity.

For practical working equations it is desirable to express the results in terms of P in atmospheres and M in atomic weight units. Then one obtains

$$\frac{H_0^\circ - F_T^\circ}{T} = R \left[\ln V + \frac{3}{2} \ln \frac{2\pi mkT}{h^2} - \ln N_0 + \ln Q_i \right]$$

$$= R \left[-\ln P + \frac{3}{2} \ln M + \frac{5}{2} \ln T + \ln Q_i + \ln \frac{2^{3/2} \pi^{3/2} R^{5/2}}{h^3 N_0^4} \right]$$

$$= R \left[-\ln P + \frac{3}{2} \ln M + \frac{5}{2} \ln T + \ln Q_i \right]$$
$$- 7.282 \quad \text{cal./deg.} \quad (7.60)$$

$$H_T^\circ - H_0^\circ = T^2 \frac{\partial (H_0^\circ - F_T^\circ)/T}{\partial T} = R \left[\frac{5}{2} T + T^2 \frac{\partial \ln Q_i}{\partial T} \right]$$

$$= R \left[\frac{5}{2} T + \frac{T^2}{Q_i} \frac{\partial Q_i}{\partial T} \right]$$
$$(7.61)$$

$$S_T^\circ = \frac{H_T^\circ - H_0^\circ}{T} + \frac{H_0^\circ - F_T^\circ}{T}$$

$$= R \left[-\ln P + \frac{3}{2} \ln M + \frac{5}{2} \ln T + \ln Q_i + \frac{T}{Q_i} \frac{\partial Q_i}{\partial T} + \frac{5}{2} \right]$$
$$- 7.282 \quad \text{cal./deg.}$$

$$C_p^\circ = \frac{\partial(H_T^\circ - H_0^\circ)}{\partial T} = R\left[\frac{5}{2} + \frac{2T}{Q_i}\frac{\partial Q_i}{\partial T} + \frac{T^2}{Q_i}\frac{\partial^2 Q_i}{\partial T^2} - \frac{T^2}{Q_i^2}\left(\frac{\partial Q_i}{\partial T}\right)^2\right]$$

$$(7.62)$$

where P is 1 atmosphere in the usual standard state.

In practice it is often more convenient to replace the derivatives of Q by sums related to the partition function and defined as follows.[5]

$$Q_i' = \sum_i g_i\left(\frac{\epsilon_i}{kT}\right)e^{-\epsilon_i/kT} = T\frac{\partial Q_i}{\partial T} \tag{7.63}$$

$$Q_i'' = \sum_i g_i\left(\frac{\epsilon_i}{kT}\right)^2 e^{-\epsilon_i/kT} = T^2\frac{\partial^2 Q_i}{\partial T^2} + 2T\frac{\partial Q_i}{\partial T} \tag{7.64}$$

In these terms the thermodynamic quantities take the form

$$H_T^\circ - H_0^\circ = RT\left[\frac{5}{2} + \frac{Q_i'}{Q_i}\right] \tag{7.65}$$

$$S^\circ = R\left[-\ln P + \frac{3}{2}\ln M + \frac{5}{2}\ln T + \ln Q_i + \frac{Q_i'}{Q_i} + \frac{5}{2}\right]$$
$$- 7.282 \quad \text{cal./deg.} \tag{7.66}$$

$$C_p^\circ = R\left[\frac{5}{2} + \frac{Q_i''}{Q_i} - \left(\frac{Q_i'}{Q_i}\right)^2\right] \tag{7.67}$$

We may note that the equation above has given the correct heat capacity at constant pressure for a monatomic gas, $\frac{5}{2}R$, since the latter terms are zero in that case.

This completes the fundamental statistical equations needed for the calculation of the thermodynamic properties of perfect gases. The actual calculations for polyatomic molecules must await further knowledge of the internal energy levels. If these energy levels are known from experiments alone, one need only evaluate Q_i, Q_i', and Q_i'', and substitute in the desired equations. However, usually some further quantum theory of the energy level pattern is needed in interpreting the experimental spectroscopic data. This theory will be given in Chapter 9, and these calculations will then be carried to completion.

---

[5] The second equality in Eq. (7.64) is most easily verified by differentiating with respect to T the quantity

$$T^2\frac{\partial Q}{\partial T} = \sum_i g_i\left(\frac{\epsilon_i}{k}\right)e^{-\epsilon_i/kT}$$

GENERAL REFERENCES

Fowler, R. and Guggenheim, E. A., *Statistical Thermodynamics*, London: Cambridge University Press, 1939. The most extensive treatise on the statistical treatment of thermodynamic problems.

Gurney, R. W., *Introduction to Statistical Mechanics*, New York: McGraw-Hill Book Company, Inc., 1949. This is an elementary introduction to statistical mechanics.

Mayer, J. E. and Mayer, M. G., *Statistical Mechanics*, New York: John Wiley & Sons, Inc., 1940. An excellent general presentation of statistical mechanics.

Rushbrooke, G. S., *Introduction to Statistical Mechanics*, New York: Oxford University Press, 1949. An excellent book which is written at a somewhat more advanced level than Gurney's.

PROBLEMS

7.1 Investigate the distribution law for a system composed of two different kinds of particles having energies ϵ_0', ϵ_1', . . . and ϵ_0'', ϵ_1'', ... Note that the total energy of the system containing both kinds of particles is the quantity to be held constant. Show that this leads to Boltzmann distribution laws with the same temperature applying to both sets of particles.

7.2 Consider the simple case of the distribution of n molecules between two states of equal energy and equal a priori probability. Show that the most probable distribution has $n/2$ molecules in each state and that a distribution with x more molecules in one state and x less in the other has a probability reduced by the factor

$$e^{-2x^2/n}$$

What is the probable error in the value $n/2$ for the number of molecules in each state?

7.3 Prove that the Fermi and Bose distribution laws both reduce to the Boltzmann distribution at sufficiently high temperatures, if there are many more states available than there are molecules in the system.

7.4 Show what distributions the Bose and Fermi laws give as the temperature approaches the absolute zero. Hint: define a quantity ϵ_m such that $\alpha = -\epsilon_m/kT$. Are the distributions what would be expected from the basic assumptions?

7.5 Show that the results of Section 7h could have been obtained from the Fermi statistics instead of the Bose statistics.

7.6 Estimate the contribution of the electrons to the heat capacity of sodium at 300°K. Assume one free electron per atom. How does this compare with the total heat capacity?

7.7 Calculate the work of compression of 1 cc. of potassium to a volume of 0.8 cc. from the value 2×10^{-6} cm.²/kg for the compressibility. How does this compare with the increase in zero point energy given by the equations for a free electron gas assuming one free electron per atom? Discuss these results in terms of possible changes in the electrical energy of the system.

7.8 Generalize the results of Section 2h to give the energy levels in an infinite walled cubical box. Use these energy levels to calculate the partition function for translation Q_t, and compare with the result given above.

Chapter 8

CHEMICAL BONDS AND VALENCE

8a. Introductory survey of bond types. Primary chemical bonds show an essentially continuous variation of characteristics; however, it proves convenient to discuss them in terms of three extreme types as follows:

1. Ionic bonds
2. Covalent or shared electron pair bonds
3. Metallic bonds

Ionic bonds are essentially the classical electrostatic attraction of unlike charges. Consequently their principal characteristics are readily understood without quantum theory, and only a brief review will be included here. The covalent bond has long been represented by a dash connecting the symbols of the two atoms bonded, but its detailed nature can be understood only in terms of quantum theory. The nature of metallic bonding is also a quantum mechanical problem, but one which has been less completely elucidated, and which is more appropriately discussed in detail in Chapter 11 along with other properties of crystalline solids.

The valence of an atom is a measure of its capacity to form primary bonds, i.e., the number of electrons which can be accepted, shared, or given. After the valences of the atoms are completely satisfied by primary bonds there remain residual attractions between the molecules which are occasionally dignified by the term bond but are more commonly called van der Waal's forces. Again most actual cases are intermediate but we may recognize the following extreme types:

1. Hydrogen bonds
2. Dipole forces (other than hydrogen bonds)
3. London forces (dispersion forces)

Dipole forces are described by classical electrostatics. Hydrogen

127

bonds differ primarily in the exposed location of the positive charge of the dipole, which gives much stronger bonding. However, the residual attraction which even argon atoms show for one another was inexplicable until quantum theory was well developed. Although the term dispersion forces is sometimes used for this phenomenon, the author prefers *London forces*, after F. London, who was principally responsible for their explanation in 1930.

Finally, we must not ignore the repulsive force which counterbalances whatever attractive force may be operating in a given case. We have already mentioned this effect in connection with degenerate Fermi-Dirac gases. We saw there that degenerate electron gases, such as constitute the outer part of atoms and molecules, will strongly resist compression to smaller size because of the consequent increase in zero point kinetic energy. Indeed this repulsive force arises so suddenly when atoms or ions are brought together that to a first approximation they may be regarded as incompressible. Furthermore it makes possible the assignment of approximate radii to atoms and ions, from which bond lengths may be computed.

In this chapter we shall emphasize the essentially quantum mechanical bonds and forces, making only occasional reference to the other types which we assume are already understood on the basis of classical theory.

8b. The covalent bond in H_2 according to Heitler and London. The hydrogen molecule is the simplest example of a shared electron pair bond; indeed it is the only example where quantitative quantum theoretical calculation has proven feasible. There are two principal contributions to the quantum theory of H_2: the relatively simple calculation of Heitler and London,[1] and the complex one giving quantitative agreement with experiment made by James and Coolidge.[2] These, together with the proposal of Lewis in 1916 that the covalent bond consisted of a shared pair of electrons, comprise the most notable recent contributions to the theory of the covalent bond.

Let us consider two hydrogen atoms initially far apart and gradually brought closer together. Remembering the discussion of Section 3e, we may regard the nuclei as fixed for our calculation of the electronic energy, because the nuclei are so much heavier than the electrons. A possible wave function for this system is

---

[1] Heitler, W. and London, F., *Z. Physik*, **44**, 455 (1927).
[2] James, H. M. and Coolidge, A. S., *J. Chem. Phys.*, **1**, 825 (1933).

$$\psi = 1s_A(1)1s_B(2)$$

where $1s_A(1)$ represents electron 1 in a $1s$ orbital about nucleus A, and $1s_B(2)$ represents electron 2 in a similar orbital about nucleus B. However, as in the case of atoms, the orbital wave function must be either symmetric or antisymmetric to the exchange of electrons. If we take the sum and the difference combinations of the two possible terms involving one electron in a $1s$ orbital on each nucleus we have

symmetric: $[1s_A(1)1s_B(2) + 1s_A(2)1s_B(1)]2^{-1/2}$ (8.1a)

antisymmetric: $[1s_A(1)1s_B(2) - 1s_A(2)1s_B(1)]2^{-1/2}$ (8.1b)

These factors correspond to those of Eq. (5.7) in our treatment of an excited helium atom. One can easily verify their symmetry to exchange of electrons.

The spin factors are identical to those of Eq. (5.6). We then obtain the following as the only possible wave functions based on a $1s$ orbital for each nucleus which are in accord with the Pauli exclusion principle.

singlet,

$$\psi_S = [1s_A(1)1s_B(2) + 1s_A(2)1s_B(1)] \quad [\alpha(1)\beta(2) - \alpha(2)\beta(1)]2^{-1}$$

(8.2)

triplet,

$$\psi_T = [1s_A(1)1s_B(2) - 1s_A(2)1s_B(1)] \begin{cases} \alpha(1)\alpha(2)2^{-1/2} \\ [\alpha(1)\beta(2) + \alpha(2)\beta(1)]2^{-1} \\ \beta(1)\beta(2)2^{-1/2} \end{cases}$$

where the spin factors are included, but the normalization will be correct only if $1s_A$ and $1s_B$ are orthogonal. As in the case of complex atoms, we may ignore the spin factors for the energy calculation.

The Hamiltonian operator for the system is

$$H = -\frac{h^2}{8\pi^2 m}(\nabla_1^2 + \nabla_2^2) - \frac{e^2}{r_{A1}} - \frac{e^2}{r_{B1}} - \frac{e^2}{r_{A2}} - \frac{e^2}{r_{B2}} + \frac{e^2}{r_{12}} + \frac{e^2}{r_{AB}} \quad (8.3)$$

where ∇^2 is the Laplace operator,

$$\nabla^2 = \frac{\partial^2}{\partial x^2} + \frac{\partial^2}{\partial y^2} + \frac{\partial^2}{\partial z^2}$$

the subscripts referring to electrons 1 and 2, and the various r's are the distances between the indicated particles as shown in Fig. 8.1. The term e^2/r_{AB} is not strictly an electronic term, but it must be included in the total potential energy for the motion of the nuclei.

Now one cannot assert that the wave functions in Eq. (8.2) are true solutions of the Schrödinger equation except when the distance r_{AB} is infinite. However, these functions may be used in the variation method, and may be expected to give energies close to the correct ones when the interatomic distance is large.

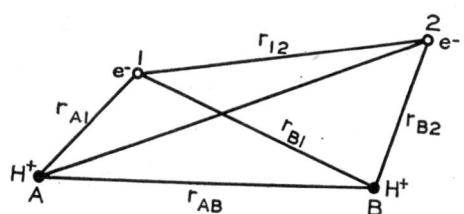

Fig. 8.1.   Coordinates for the hydrogen molecule.

Since these wave functions are essentially similar to those for an excited state in helium, Eq. (5.8), we may express the results for the energy in somewhat similar form:

$$W_{S,T} = \frac{\int \psi_{S,T} H \psi_{S,T} \, dv}{\int \psi_{S,T}^2 \, dv} = \frac{H_c \pm H_x}{1 \pm \Delta}$$

$$H_c = \int 1s_A(1)1s_B(2) H 1s_A(1)1s_B(2) \, dv = 2E_H + H_c'$$

$$H_c' = \int 1s_A^2(1)1s_B^2(2) \left[-\frac{e^2}{r_{B1}} - \frac{e^2}{r_{A2}} + \frac{e^2}{r_{12}} + \frac{e^2}{r_{AB}} \right] dv \qquad (8.4)$$

$$H_x = \int 1s_A(1)1s_B(2) H 1s_A(2)1s_B(1) \, dv = 2\Delta E_H + H_x'$$

$$H_x' = \int 1s_A(1)1s_B(1)1s_A(2)1s_B(2) \left[-\frac{e^2}{r_{A1}} - \frac{e^2}{r_{B2}} + \frac{e^2}{r_{12}} + \frac{e^2}{r_{AB}} \right] dv$$

$$\Delta = \int 1s_A(1)1s_B(1)1s_A(2)1s_B(2) \, dv$$

In these calculations certain terms in H operating on ψ gave just the energy of a hydrogen atom in the $1s$ state, E_H, times the wave function. This permitted the reduction of H_c and H_x into terms in E_H plus H_c', or H_x'. The integral Δ is just the nonorthogonality quantity.

Introducing the various expressions into that for the energy we obtain

$$W_{S,T} = \frac{2E_H + H_c' \pm 2\Delta E_H \pm H_x'}{1 \pm \Delta} = 2E_H + \frac{H_c' \pm H_x'}{1 \pm \Delta} \qquad (8.5)$$

in which the first term is just the energy of the two hydrogen atoms and the second must consequently be the change in energy because of interaction between the hydrogen atoms.

Let us illustrate the evaluation of these integrals by considering the simplest, Δ. First it may be broken up into two identical factors involving only one electron each.

$$\Delta = \left[\int 1s_A(1)1s_B(1)\, dv_1 \right]^2$$

$$= \left[\frac{1}{\pi a_0^3} \int e^{-(r_{A1}+r_{B1})/a_0}\, dv_1 \right]^2 \qquad (8.6)$$

This integration is most readily made by transforming to confocal elliptical coordinates, which will be discussed in the next section, yielding

$$\Delta = e^{-2D}(1 + D + \frac{1}{3} D^2)^2 \qquad (8.7)$$

where

$$D = \frac{r_{AB}}{a_0} \qquad (8.8)$$

Similar evaluation yields for H_c' the formula

$$H_c' = \frac{e^2}{a_0} e^{-2D} \left(\frac{1}{D} + \frac{5}{8} - \frac{3}{4} D - \frac{1}{6} D^2 \right) \qquad (8.9)$$

The evaluation of H_x' is much more difficult, and was carried out only approximately by Heitler and London. Later Sugiura[3] obtained an exact formula which, however, involves the special function known as the integral logarithm. Appendix 3 gives the expression for H_x', together with some other details on the evaluation of these integrals. For our purpose, however, it is more important to note Fig. 8.2, which shows these results graphically.

We note in Fig. 8.2 that H_x' is negative and more important than H_c', so that the energy of the triplet state increases as the atoms come together, while the energy of the singlet state decreases. This means that the triplet state is repulsive at all distances, while the singlet state gives attraction and the formation of a bond. Although there is no reason to expect accurate results from this simple wave function at the bond distance, we may note that the energy at the minimum is 3.16 e.v. lower than at infinity. This bond energy may be compared with true value, obtained from the spectrum of H_2, 4.75 e.v. These are values to the bottom of the potential curve and do not include the zero point vibrational energy of the nuclei. The cal-

[3] Sugiura, Y., Z. Physik, **45**, 484 (1927).

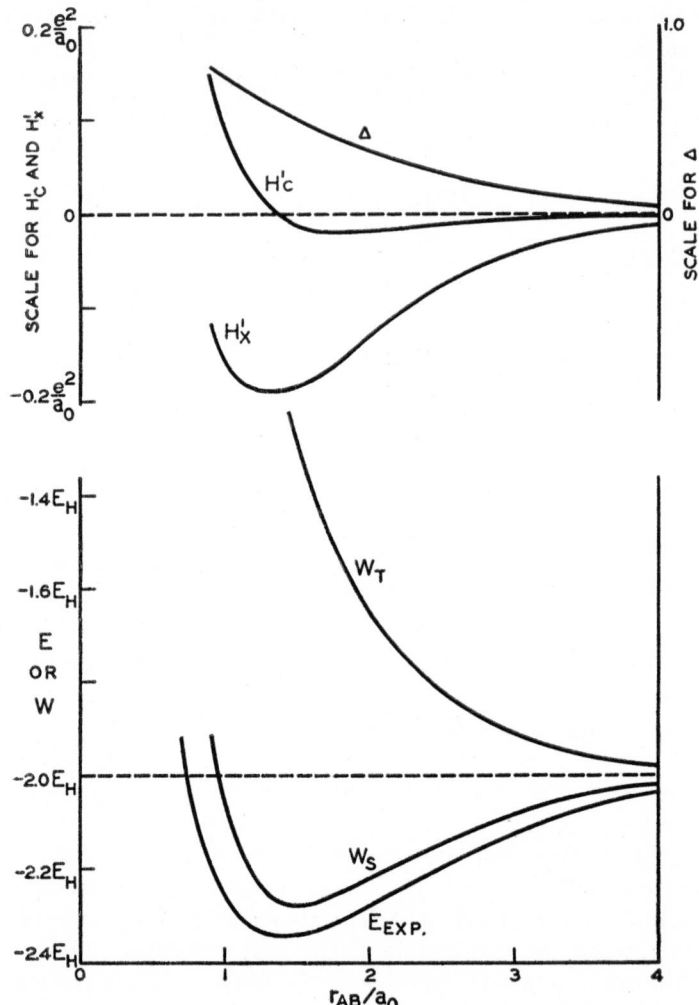

Fig. 8.2. Calculated and experimental energies for H_2 (below) and the values of certain integrals (above).

culated bond distance is 0.80 A as compared with the experimental value from spectra of 0.740 A. By introducing a variable effective atomic number Z in the Heitler and London wave function, Wang[4] obtained the improved values 0.76 A and 3.78 e.v. with $Z = 1.166$.

[4] Wang, S. C., *Phys. Rev.*, **31**, 579 (1928).

We shall return to quantitative comparisons later. However, the real importance of the Heitler and London treatment lies in qualitative ideas one may obtain concerning the electron pair bond. As was pointed out in Section 5c, the term H_x and consequently H'_x are associated with the exchange of the two electrons. The requirement of symmetry or antisymmetry of the orbital function to the electron exchange made necessary this exchange term. The effect of the exchange term is to increase the electron density between the two nuclei for the singlet state and to decrease this density for the triplet state. To see this let us write out the probability function ψ^2,

$$2\psi^2_{S,T} = 1s^2_A(1)1s^2_B(2) + 1s^2_A(2)1s^2_B(1)$$
$$\pm 2[1s_A(1)1s_B(1)1s_A(2)1s_B(2)] \qquad (8.10)$$

We note that the exchange term (in brackets) is large only in the region between the two nuclei where both $1s_A$ and $1s_B$ have a considerable value. At other points either $1s_A$ or $1s_B$ is so small that this last term is essentially zero.

While quantum theory does not allow us to speak of definite portions of an orbit as one might classically, nevertheless somewhat similar ideas can be derived from Eq. (8.10) for the probability function. The first term indicates a probability of finding electron 1 near nucleus A and electron 2 near nucleus B. The second term indicates an equal probability of finding electron 1 near B and electron 2 near A. Since these functions ($1s_A$ and $1s_B$) overlap in the region between nuclei, these terms already imply a moderate probability of finding one or the other or even both electrons in that region. The final term concerns the probability of finding both electrons between the nuclei. It increases that probability for the singlet state and reduces it to practically zero for the triplet state.

In the case of the excited helium atom the exchange term merely increased the repulsion between electrons and consequently made the triplet state the one of lower energy. However, in the case of H_2 this region between nuclei where the orbitals overlap is one of low potential energy because it is the positive field of both nuclei. Thus although the potential energy of electron repulsion is increased in the singlet state, the total potential energy is actually lowered because the additional attraction to the nuclei is more important. This effect of the wave function symmetry on the electron density (probability) between the two nuclei is further illustrated by Fig. 8.3.

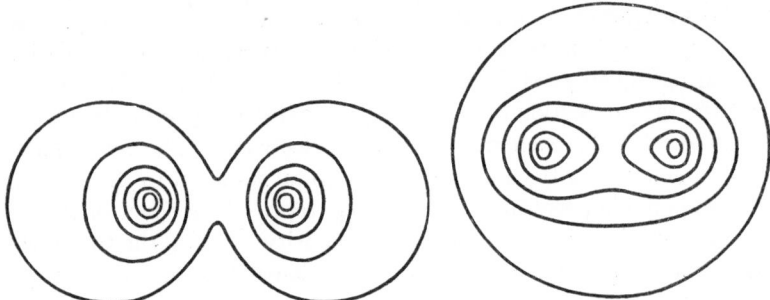

Fig. 8.3. Contours of electron probability for H_2 according to Heitler and London.

The primary conclusion of this section is that if two atoms have a single stable orbital each, the two electrons forming a bond must have spins antiparallel (paired) because that gives an increased electron probability in the region between the two nuclei. Certainly the electrons must spend extra time in that region if they are to bond the two nuclei together with the electrical attraction of opposite charges.

8c. The hydrogen molecule ion. Although the hydrogen molecule ion H_2^+ is of little importance experimentally, it plays a considerable role in the quantum theory of diatomic molecules. This is because the one-electron orbitals of H_2^+ play a part in the theory of other diatomic molecules similar to the part hydrogen atom orbitals play in the theory of complex atoms.

Before actually obtaining the orbitals of H_2^+ we must select and discuss an appropriate coordinate system. If we look at Eq. (8.6) we note in the exponent the quantity $(r_{A1} + r_{B1})/a_0$. An ellipse is the curve of constant value of this quantity, since it holds the sum of the distances of a point from the two foci constant. Taking this as a hint, we set up the following coordinate system, sometimes called confocal elliptic coordinates.

$$\xi = (r_A + r_B)/r_{AB}$$
$$\eta = (r_A - r_B)/r_{AB}$$
(8.11)

In addition, the angle of rotation about the A-B axis is designated by ϕ, which gives it a significance entirely analogous to ϕ in spherical polar coordinates. The following additional relationships are given without proof. The foci are located $\pm r_{AB}/2$ from the origin on the z axis.

$$x = \tfrac{1}{2}r_{AB}(\xi^2 - 1)^{1/2}(1 - \eta^2)^{1/2} \cos \phi$$
$$y = \tfrac{1}{2}r_{AB}(\xi^2 - 1)^{1/2}(1 - \eta^2)^{1/2} \sin \phi \qquad (8.12)$$
$$z = \tfrac{1}{2}r_{AB}\xi\eta$$
$$dv = \tfrac{1}{8}r_{AB}^3(\xi^2 - \eta^2)\, d\xi\, d\eta\, d\phi \qquad (8.13)$$

$$\nabla^2 = \frac{4}{r_{AB}^2(\xi^2 - \eta^2)} \left\{ \frac{\partial}{\partial\xi}\left[(\xi^2 - 1)\frac{\partial}{\partial\xi}\right] + \frac{\partial}{\partial\eta}\left[(1 - \eta^2)\frac{\partial}{\partial\eta}\right] \right\}$$
$$+ \frac{4}{r_{AB}^2(\xi^2 - 1)(1 - \eta^2)} \frac{\partial^2}{\partial\phi^2} \qquad (8.14)$$

The range of ξ is from 1 to ∞, that of η is from -1 to $+1$, while that of ϕ is 0 to 2π. The surfaces of constant ξ are ellipsoids of revolution, the surfaces of constant η are hyperboloids of revolution which have the same foci as the ellipsoids, while the surfaces of constant ϕ are planes which intersect at the A-B axis. This is an orthogonal system since the surfaces always intersect perpendicular to one another.

The Hamiltonian operator for a system of two stationary nuclei of charge $+Ze$, and one electron takes the form

$$H = \frac{-h^2}{8\pi^2 m}\nabla^2 - \frac{4Ze^2\xi}{r_{AB}(\xi^2 - \eta^2)} + \frac{Z^2e^2}{r_{AB}} \qquad (8.15)$$

where the second term is the potential energy of the electron, $-Z(e^2/r_A + e^2/r_B)$, and the final term is potential energy of the two nuclei which, of course, does not involve the electronic coordinates.

It was first pointed out by Burrau (1927) that the Schrödinger equation for H_2^+ was separable in this coordinate system, and he proceeded to offer a solution. Other, more precise solutions have been given by Hylleraas[5] and by Jaffe.[6] We shall not discuss the mathematical detail of any of these solutions because they are relatively complex, and a far simpler variation function calculation gives almost as great accuracy. Furthermore, the exact orbitals are also much more complex than the variation function.

James[7] applied the variation method to the simple function (not normalized)

$$\psi = e^{-b\xi}(1 + c\eta^2) \qquad (8.16)$$

[5] Hylleraas, E. A., Z. Physik, **71**, 739 (1931).
[6] Jaffe, G., Z. Physik, **87**, 535 (1934).
[7] James, H. M., J. Chem. Phys., **3**, 9 (1935).

and adjusted b and c to minimize the energy. For H_2^+ he found $b = 1.35$, $c = 0.448$ for the energy minimum at $r_{AB} = 2.0(a_0) = 1.06$ A. The total energy (compared with all particles at infinity) is -16.381 e.v., while the exact value is -16.386 e.v., given by the Hylleraas and Jaffe calculations. If we base our energy zero on a proton and a normal hydrogen atom (energy -13.595 e.v.) these values become -2.786 and -2.791 e.v., respectively, for the bond energy of H_2^+.

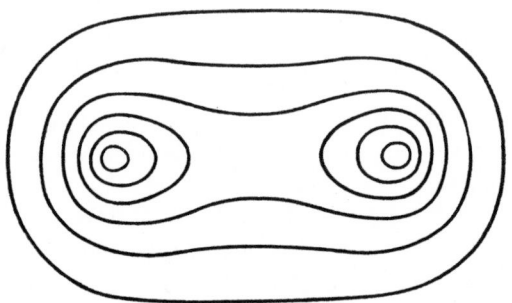

Fig. 8.4. Contours of electron probability for H_2^+.

Figure 8.4 shows the electron probability distribution corresponding to Eq. (8.16). It should be noticed that the nuclei are actually further apart in H_2^+ than in H_2. Presumably this is caused by the net positive charge on the entire system. Also this large internuclear distance allows the electron to be roughly between the nuclei most of the time.

8d. The electronic energy of H_2 according to James and Coolidge.[8] Instead of approaching the normal state of H_2 by bringing together two hydrogen atoms, we might regard the protons as fixed at the correct distance and feed in successively the two electrons. We would then take as a first approximation an H_2^+ orbital for each electron.

$$\psi = \psi_{H_2^+}(1)\psi_{H_2^+}(2) \tag{8.17}$$

From the experience with the helium atom one would expect then to add further terms, particularly terms in r_{12}, the actual distance between electrons.

---

[8] Certain other treatments of H_2 are listed in Appendix 4.

Let us recall the essential principles of the variation method. The exact Hamiltonian function must be used. Any function which conforms to the general conditions for an acceptable wave function may be taken as a trial wave function, and its success is judged by the energy value that it yields. Since this energy value is an upper limit to the true energy, one seeks the function yielding the lowest energy and adjusts any parameters in the function to minimize the energy.

Since the very simple function (8.16) was so successful for the system H_2^+ it is reasonable to start with that form of function for H_2. This was done by James and Coolidge, who report results for 1-, 5-, 11-, and 13-term functions. Let us examine the 5-term function since it includes a term of each general type and gives the correct bond energy within 5%, or the total electronic energy within 1%.

$$\psi = e^{-0.75(\xi_1 + \xi_2)} \left[0.7123 + 0.1281(\eta_1^2 + \eta_2^2) - 0.0971(\xi_1 + \xi_2) \right.$$
$$\left. - 0.0891\eta_1\eta_2 + 0.1268 \frac{r_{12}}{r_{AB}} \right] \qquad (8.18)$$

These constants are for the bond distance $r_{AB} = 1.4a_0$. It may be noted that this function is symmetric to electron exchange. The first two terms follow naturally from Eq. (8.16). The third modifies the exponential dependence on $(\xi_1 + \xi_2)$ slightly. The last two terms tend to favor positions with the electrons farther apart rather than closer together. The fourth term favors positions with one electron near each nucleus rather than both near one nucleus, while the fifth term specifically favors distance between the electrons.

It is not easy to compare the James and Coolidge wave function with that of Heitler and London. The J. and C. function is more compressed, and in this respect is similar to the Wang modification of the H. and L. function with $Z = 1.166$. The probability of finding both electrons nearer one nucleus than the other is increased slightly, corresponding to a little $H^+ H^-$ character, symmetrical of course. The features explicitly keeping the two electrons apart have already been emphasized. However, there remain also detailed, quantitative differences which are also important but have no simple significance.

Although the above function already represented a major advance over all other calculations for H_2 and could easily be regarded as indicating quantitative agreement, James and Coolidge added further terms up to a total of thirteen. Furthermore, with the 11-term function they investigated variation of the distance, r_{AB}, and found the entire potential curve near the minimum to be in close agreement with not only the observed bond distance but also the experimental frequency of nuclear vibration.

For the dissociation energy the 5-term function gave 4.528 e.v., the 13-term function, 4.721, and James and Coolidge estimate that still further terms would probably increase this to 4.75 ± 0.02. To compare this with experiment we should first take account of the vibrational energy of the lowest state ($\frac{1}{2}h\nu_e$). Also, because the protons are not infinitely heavier than the electrons, a slight correction is

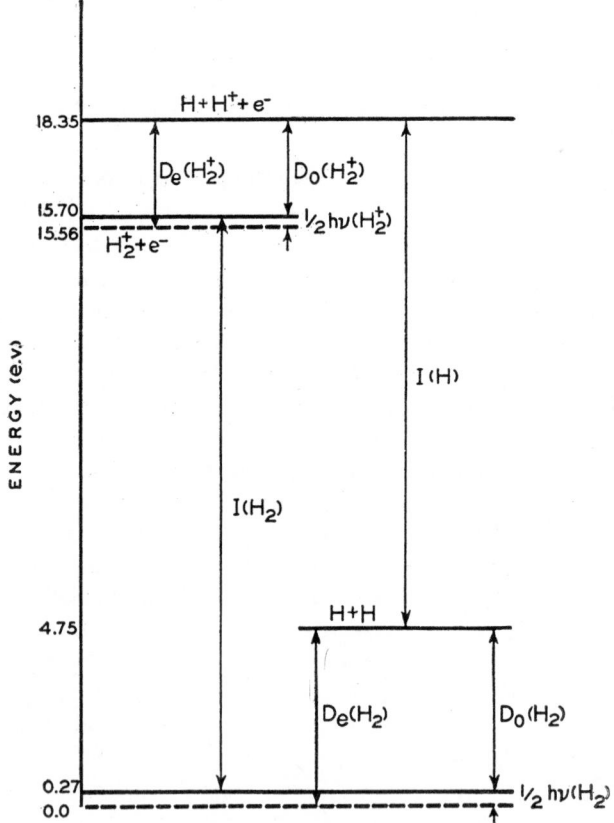

Fig. 8.5. Energy relationships for H_2, $H_2{}^+$, etc.

needed analogous to the use of a reduced mass. These reduce the calculated energy of dissociation from the lowest real quantum state to $D_0 = 4.48 \pm 0.02$ e.v. By an extrapolation of the observed vibrational energy levels of H_2, the experimental value 4.476 ± 0.001 e.v. was obtained.[9]

Further checks are involved in the entire consistency of the energy diagram of Fig. 8.5. The masterly but laborious calculations of James and Coolidge have thus established the adequacy of the Schrödinger quantum theory for electron pair bond in H_2, and presumably, if the corresponding calculations could be carried out, for the bonding in other molecules. However, for the present we will have to be content with qualitative and semiquantitative considerations of more complex molecules.

8e. The virial theorem and the nature of the electron pair bond. Let us now complete our discussion of the normal electron pair bond by considering in this section the changes in potential and kinetic energy when the bond is formed, and in the next section, the transition from ionic to covalent bonding.

While we could compute the average potential and kinetic energies from the James and Coolidge wave functions, it is easier to make use of the *virial theorem*. This theorem states

$$2\overline{T} = - \sum_i \overline{x_i F_{x_i}} \tag{8.19}$$

where T is the total kinetic energy, x_i is the x coordinate of the ith particle, F_{x_i} is the x component of force on that particle, and the sum covers the x, y, and z coordinates of all particles. The bars indicate time averages in classical mechanics. It is shown in Appendix 5 that this theorem also holds in quantum theory if the usual quantum mechanical averages are taken.

If the forces in a given set of particles are the electrostatic interactions of charges, the right side of (8.19) can be shown to be merely the negative of the potential energy V. To do this let us first note that $V = \sum V_{mn}$, the sum of the interactions of pairs of particles with $V_{mn} = e_m e_n / r_{mn}$. Let us now calculate $\sum x_i (-\partial V_{mn}/\partial x_i)$, since the force is the negative derivative of the potential energy. Then

$$r_{mn} = [(x_m - x_n)^2 + (y_m - y_n)^2 + (z_m - z_n)^2]^{1/2}$$

[9] See Herzberg, G., *Molecular Spectra and Molecular Structure, I. Spectra of Diatomic Molecules*, New York: D. Van Nostrand Company, Inc., 1950.

and $\quad \dfrac{\partial r_{mn}}{\partial x_m} = \dfrac{(x_m - x_n)}{r_{mn}}, \qquad \dfrac{\partial r_{mn}}{\partial x_n} = -\dfrac{(x_m - x_n)}{r_{mn}}, \quad$ etc.

Next, since $(\partial V / \partial x_m) = (\partial V / \partial r_{mn}) \cdot (\partial r_{mn} / \partial x_m)$, etc.,

$$\sum x_i \frac{\partial V_{mn}}{\partial x_i} = -\frac{e_m e_n}{r_{mn}^2}\left[x_m \frac{(x_m - x_n)}{r_{mn}} - x_n \frac{(x_m - x_n)}{r_{mn}} + \dots \right]$$

$$= -\frac{e_m e_n}{r_{mn}^3}\left[(x_m - x_n)^2 + (y_m - y_n)^2 + (z_m - z_n)^2 \right]$$

$$= -\frac{e_m e_n}{r_{mn}} = -V_{mn} \qquad (8.20)$$

However, extending the sum to all pairs, one has

$$\sum x_i \left(-\frac{\partial V}{\partial x_i} \right) = \sum V_{mn} = V \qquad (8.21)$$

where V is the total potential energy. Hence returning to Eq. (8.19), we have

$$\overline{2T} = -\overline{V} \qquad (8.22)$$

for the system of charged particles. Since $E = T + V$ we can also write

$$E = -\overline{T} = \tfrac{1}{2}\overline{V} \qquad (8.23)$$

The hydrogen molecule and the pair of separated hydrogen atoms are both systems of charged particles; hence Eq. (8.23) applies. We can then say that the larger negative total energy of the H_2 molecule comes from a larger negative potential energy in spite of an increase of kinetic energy. Thus in the bond the electrons must spend more time in regions of low potential energy, particularly between the nuclei.

A further application of the virial theorem can be made to a diatomic molecule with the nuclei held by some other force in a position other than the equilibrium position. Assuming the molecule to be along the x axis and that this external force on nucleus A is F^*, the force on nucleus B must be $-F^*$. These forces are along the x axis, of course. Then

$$\overline{2T} = -\sum_i \overline{x_i F_{x_i}} - x_A F^* + x_B F^*$$

$$= -\overline{V'} + (x_B - x_A)F^*$$

where the sum over the various internal electrostatic forces yields the electrostatic potential V' as before. However, this external force

F^* must be balanced by an equal and opposite internal force related in the usual way to the derivative of the potential energy for nuclear motion, which we shall call $E(r)$. Consequently

$$\overline{2T} = -\overline{V}' - r \frac{dE(r)}{dr} \qquad (8.24)$$

This potential energy for nuclear motion is just the total internal energy, both kinetic and potential, as we have shown before. Thus we can use this relationship $E = T + V'$ further to obtain

$$\overline{T} = -E - r \frac{dE}{dr}$$

$$\overline{V}' = 2E + r \frac{dE}{dr} \qquad (8.25)$$

Since we can obtain E as a function of r from the series of vibrational energy levels we can obtain $\overline{T}$ and $\overline{V}'$ also as a function of r. Figure 8.6 shows these functions for H_2. In each case the difference between the molecule and separated atoms is shown.

Of particular interest in Fig. 8.6 is the situation at interatomic distances about three times that of the potential minimum. Here the value of $\overline{V}' - \overline{V}$ (atoms) is actually positive, so that the decrease in E from that of separated atoms is due to the decrease in kinetic energy. This is easily understandable from the properties of the degenerate electron gas. At this interatomic distance the region between atoms is of low enough potential energy to be occupied by the electrons but not low enough to lower the average potential energy. However, the extra volume accessible to the electrons lowers their kinetic energy. As the nuclei move closer together the potential energy of this region between nuclei drops lower but its volume decreases. Consequently, near the normal bond distance the potential energy curve is dropping with decreasing distance, while the kinetic energy curve is increasing.

Back in Section 71 we discussed the formation of chemical bonds in terms of increased volume available to the electron gas which was considered as a degenerate Fermi gas. From the results of this section we must interpret the conclusion that the bond arises from a decrease in kinetic energy as applicable at somewhat greater than the true bond distance. At an appropriate distance one can see in Fig. 8.6 that the average potential energy remains unchanged in

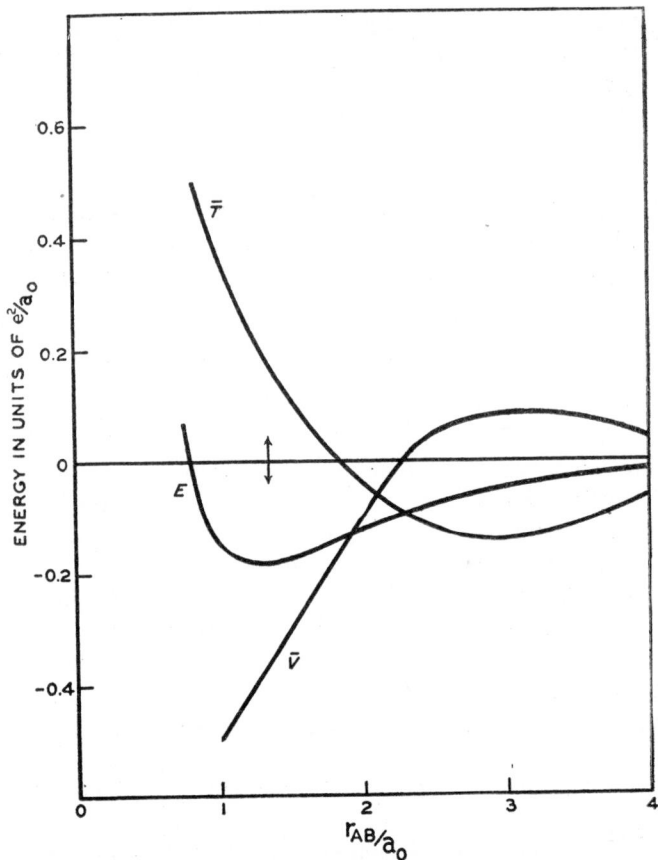

Fig. 8.6. Average kinetic and potential energies for H_2. In each case the difference between the value for the molecule and that for the separated atoms is given.

forming the bond, but the kinetic energy decreases. At the actual bond distance, however, the change in potential energy is the major effect.

The virial theorem has been applied to various wave functions for hydrogen by Hirshfelder and Kincaid.[10] They showed that the Heitler and London wave function gives completely erroneous values of $\overline{T}$ and $\overline{V}$, while the Wang function, which differs only in the ad-

[10] Hirschfelder, J. O. and Kincaid, J. F., *Phys. Rev.*, **52**, 658 (1937). See also Coulson, C. A. and Bell, R. P., *Trans. Faraday Soc.* **41**, 141 (1945).

justment of Z, gives quite reasonable values.   This indicates that a
variation function must contain a scale parameter such as Z to
adjust the over-all size if it is to apportion properly the potential
and kinetic energies.

8f. The transition from ionic to covalent bonding. When an
electron pair bond connects two identical atoms, it is called purely
covalent with no ionic character.[11]   However, if one of the atoms
has a greater attraction for electrons (electronegativity) than the
other, we may expect an increased probability of finding both electrons near the first nucleus.   Let us consider this problem, taking
the hydrogen halides and alkali halides as examples.

Let the symbol ψ_B represent a complete wave function for the molecule AX which contains a factor for the covalent bond analogous to
Eqs. (8.1a) or (8.18).   Then the symbol ψ_I will represent another
complete wave function containing, however, a factor placing in an
orbital of atom X the two electrons which formed the bond in ψ_B.
We assume at this point that each function involves the same factor
for electron spin.   This is the usual case, but exceptions arise and
are considered in Section 8r.   Now these two functions are by no
means orthogonal, since both will involve considerable probabilities
of finding electrons near the X nucleus and in the region between
nuclei.   However, the variation method does not require orthogonality of the components of a linear variation function.   Hence we
may assume

$$\psi = c_B\psi_B + c_I\psi_I \tag{8.26}$$

and adjust the constants c_B and c_I to give the minimum energy and
therefore the best approximation to the true wave function for the
normal state of the molecule AX.

This type of calculation is commonly called a *resonance* calculation.
The author does not believe the analogy to the classical mechanical
phenomenon of resonance is close enough in the present case to be
helpful.   Consequently the explanation of that relationship will be
postponed until an appropriate example is considered, and the term
resonance will be regarded as arbitrary at this point.

---

[11] Some authors consider the bond in H_2 to have a contribution from $H:^-\ \ H^+$ and
$H^+\ \ :H^-$, and therefore to have a small but symmetrical ionic character.   While it is
true that the James and Coolidge wave function does indicate a moderate probability
of finding both electrons near one nucleus, it seems preferable to regard this as part of
the normal covalent itself.

No attempt will be made actually to carry out this calculation numerically. However, we shall show that the character of the lowest energy state will vary continuously from ionic to covalent as the energy difference between the two structures varies. To do this we must consider the relative magnitude of c_B and c_I.

Remembering Section 4g and particularly Eq. (4.32), one can write

$$c_B(H_{BB} - W) + c_I(H_{BI} - \Delta_{BI}W) = 0 \qquad (8.27a)$$

$$c_B(H_{BI} - \Delta_{BI}W) + c_I(H_{II} - W) = 0 \qquad (8.27b)$$

Where we have assumed ψ_B and ψ_I to be normalized ($\Delta_{BB} = \Delta_{II} = 1$) and the meaning of the other quantities can be readily seen from Eq. (4.29). Either of these equations can be used to determine the ratio of c_B to c_I when the values of the other quantities are specified. In particular the value of W is obtained from the secular equation

$$\begin{vmatrix} H_{BB} - W & H_{BI} - \Delta_{BI}W \\ H_{BI} - \Delta_{BI}W & H_{II} - W \end{vmatrix} = 0 \qquad (8.28)$$

It is hardly feasible to calculate H_{BB}, the energy of the purely covalent bond, quantitatively in a complex case; however, it can be estimated from the energies of purely covalent single bonds in related elements.

For the energy of the purely ionic bond H_{II}, one can make a rough calculation. Basing our energy zero on the separated atoms A + X, the following steps may be considered .

$$\begin{aligned} A &= A^+ + e^- & \Delta E &= I_A \\ X + e^- &= X^- & \Delta E &= -E_X \\ \underline{A^+ + X^- = (A^+X^-)} & & \underline{\Delta E = -e^2/r_{AX}} \\ A + X &= (A^+X^-) & \Delta E &= H_{II} = I_A - E_X - e^2/r_{AX} \end{aligned} \qquad (8.29)$$

where I_A is the *ionization potential* of A, E_X the *electron affinity* of X, and the term e^2/r_{AX} is merely the classical electrostatic energy. One should also include in the third step a repulsive term which will set in at short distances, but it suffices to consider it qualitatively.

It has already been pointed out that Δ_{BI} will not be zero since the functions are not orthogonal. Likewise H_{BI} will not be zero. The exact values of these quantities are not needed.

Now from the character of variation method one knows that the lower root for W in Eq. (8.28) is equal or less than the lower of H_{BB} or H_{II}. Thus if $H_{BB} < H_{II}$ and $(H_{BI} - \Delta_{BI}W)$ is zero, $W = H_{BB}$. Furthermore, one can show from Eq. (8.28) that W will ordinarily be lower than H_{BB} because $(H_{BI} - \Delta_{BI}W)$ will not ordinarily be zero.

Rearranging Eq. (8.27) to give the ratio of c_B to c_I yields

$$\frac{c_B}{c_I} = -\frac{H_{BI} - \Delta_{BI}W}{H_{BB} - W} = -\frac{H_{II} - W}{H_{BI} - \Delta_{BI}W} \qquad (8.30)$$

From this we can easily see that if $H_{BB} < H_{II}$ so that $(H_{BB} - W)$ is small and $(H_{II} - W)$ is large, then $|c_B| > |c_I|$ as would be expected. From the symmetry of the equations one can easily see that if $H_{II} < H_{BB}$, then $|c_I| > |c_B|$ for the lower energy state. Let us now consider the remaining possibility, $H_{BB} = H_{II}$.

$$(H_{BB} - W) = (H_{II} - W) = \pm(H_{BI} - \Delta_{BI}W)$$

the sign being selected to make $W < H_{BB}$. Returning to Eq. (8.30), one finds $|c_B| = |c_I|$, so that the actual state of the molecule is half ionic, half covalent. Thus if H_{BB} could be gradually increased from less than H_{II} to greater than H_{II}, the bond would gradually change from principally covalent in nature to principally ionic. One must remember that the basic assumptions of this section included one that the spin factor was the same for ψ_B and ψ_I (since otherwise Δ_{BI} and H_{BI} would be zero). So long as this condition is met, the conclusion of a continuous transition from ionic to covalent bond character is general.

Figure 8.7 shows estimated or calculated curves of H_{BB}, H_{II}, and W for several simple molecules. Among these examples, only in CsF is the ionic state stable at large distances. However, in NaCl the bond is essentially ionic at the equilibrium distance. In HF the bond is about an equal mixture of ionic and covalent character, while for HCl it is mostly covalent, and for HI almost completely covalent.

A scale of electronegativity has been set up, principally by Pauling,[12] which gives a very useful although rough measure of the ionic character of bonds. Pauling assumes that the energy of the purely covalent single bond between two unlike atoms may be taken as the arithmetic mean of the single bond energies for the two elements. Then he takes the decrease in the actual energy below the covalent

[12] Pauling, L., *The Nature of the Chemical Bond*, Ithaca: Cornell University Press, 1939, Sections 11, 12.

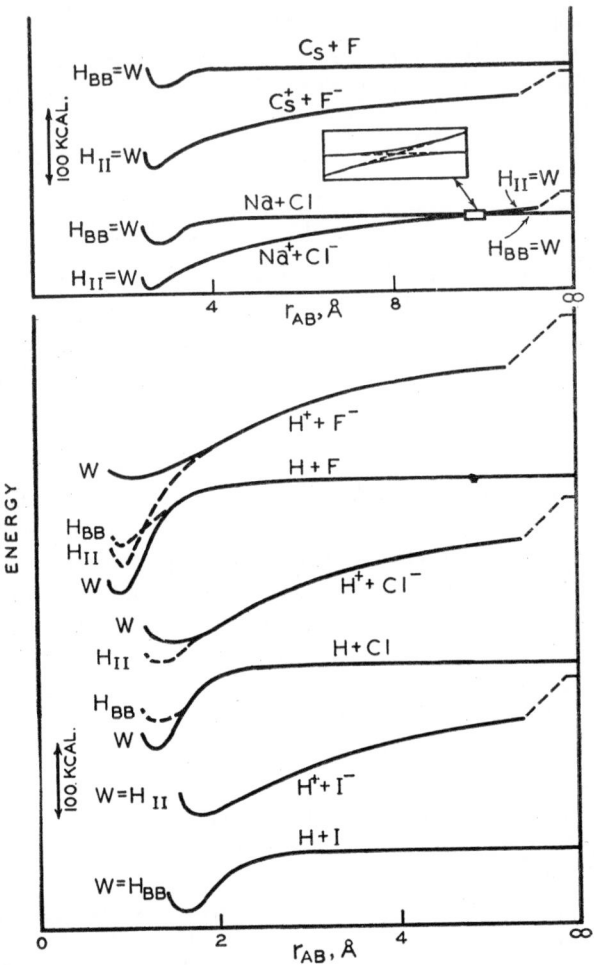

Fig. 8.7. Ionic and covalent bond character for several diatomic molecules.

energy as a measure of the difference in electronegativity of the atoms, thus

$$H_{BB} - W = (x_A - x_B)^2 \qquad (8.31)$$

where the unit of energy is the electron volt, and x_A and x_B are the electronegativities of the atoms forming the bond $A—B$. Pauling's success in fitting the experimental heat of formation of many compounds with a few x values is the chief evidence in favor of this formulation. However, it is also important to note that approximately the same electronegativity values for monovalent atoms are given by a formula of the type suggested by Mulliken.

$$x = (I + E)/130 \qquad (8.32)$$

where I and E are the ionization potential and electron affinity, and the unit is again the volt. Equation (8.32) offers an absolute scale of electronegativity, while (8.31) gives only relative values. Table 8.1 lists the electronegativity values for several elements as given by Pauling, together with the values given by Eq. (8.32) for the monovalent elements.

TABLE 8.1
ELECTRONEGATIVITY VALUES

	x Eq. (8.31)	x Eq. (8.32)		x Eq. (8.31)		x Eq. (8.31)
H	2.1	2.52	Be	1.5	Ge	1.7
Li	1.0	0.95	Mg	1.2	Sn	1.7
Na	0.9	0.91	Ca	1.0	N	3.0
K	0.8	0.77	Sr	1.0	P	2.1
Rb	0.8	0.74	Ba	0.9	As	2.0
Cs	0.7	0.69	B	2.0	Sb	1.8
F	4.0	4.06	Al	1.5	O	3.5
Cl	3.0	3.01	Sc	1.3	S	2.5
Br	2.8	2.76	Y	1.3	Se	2.4
I	2.5	2.46	C	2.5	Te	2.1
			Si	1.8		
			Ti	1.6		
			Zr	1.6		

For the transition elements, x is between 1.5 and 2.0.

Pauling then proceeds to set up a relationship between fractional ionic character and electronegativity difference based on the dipole moments of the hydrogen halides. He gets 22% ionic character for $|x_A - x_B| = 1$, and 63% for $|x_A - x_B| = 2$. This scheme works fairly well in most cases, but cannot be considered entirely reliable. For example the atoms H, C, and I have approximately equal electronegativities. The dipole moment of HI is very small (0.4×10^{-18}) as expected. However, the dipole moment of CH_3I (1.6×10^{-18}) is quite large; indeed it is larger than that of HCl, where the electronegativity difference is much greater.

Other proposals for measuring ionic or covalent character have been

made, including one by Hildebrand and the writer[13] that the change
in color (or absorption spectrum) from that of the component ions
is an indication of covalent bonding.   These are even more qualitative, however, than the scale described above.   Thus, although the
picture of a continuous change from covalent to ionic bonding is well
established, there are yet at best only semiquantitative scales of ionic
character.   Nor is this situation surprising when one realizes the
difficulty of defining in really fundamental terms a measurement of
ionic vs. covalent bond character.

8g. Molecular orbitals for diatomic molecules.   In considering
the normal electronic state of molecules more complex than hydrogen,
one is restricted mostly to crude approximations of qualitative rather
than quantitative significance.   Nevertheless, these are valuable for
increased understanding of valence and bonding, and of spectra
and magnetic properties.

Two general methods or starting approximations are commonly
employed.   One will be called the *bond orbital* method and is due
principally to Pauling and Slater.   The orbital for the two electrons
of a single bond is made up of a Heitler and London type of function
of atomic orbitals.   Other electrons are placed in atomic orbitals
for their respective atoms.   This method is sometimes called the
Heitler-London-Slater-Pauling or H.L.S.P. method.

The second method will be called the *molecular orbital* method and
has been investigated by Hund, Mulliken, and Huckel among others.
It follows the point of view already mentioned in Sections 8c and 8d,
where electrons are placed in one-electron orbitals appropriate to the
whole set of nuclei in their proper configuration.   For symmetrical
diatomic molecules the orbitals of H_2^+ are appropriate.   The molecular orbital method in its crudest form considers merely the energies
of the one-electron orbitals occupied, corresponding to the one-
electron orbitals for complex atoms discussed in Section 5d.   However, the electron interactions (Section 5e for complex atoms) are
always present and must be considered in cases where not all electrons
are paired.

Either method represents a permissible starting approximation,
and the addition of appropriate further terms in the wave function
would lead to the same final result in each case.   However, these
terms are virtually never added, so that the results of the two approxi-

[13] Pitzer, K. S. and Hildebrand, J. H., *J. Am. Chem. Soc.*, **63**, 2472 (1941).

mations must be carried along separately.   The bond orbital method is more closely akin to the chemist's well-established ideas of covalent bonds, but the information derived from atomic spectra is more easily carried over to the molecular orbital method.[14]   A number of illustrations of each method will be given.

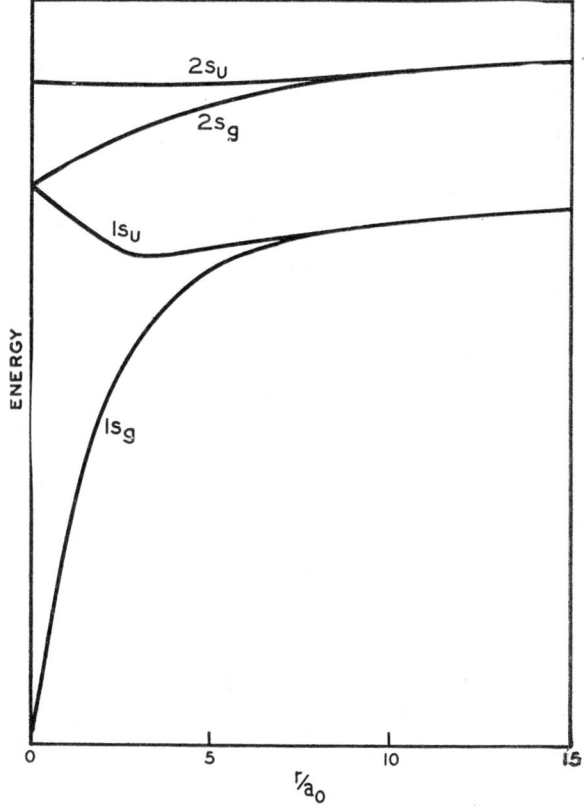

Fig. 8.8.   The electronic energy of H_2^+ for the states based on $1s$ and $2s$ orbitals for separated atoms.

[14] A very recent series of papers by J. Lennard-Jones and his collaborators (J. A. Pople and G. G. Hall) in *Proc. Roy. Soc.* (London), **A198**, 1, 14 (1949); **A202**, 155, 166, 323 (1950); etc., gives a theory of transformations between molecular orbitals and *equivalent orbitals* for symmetrical molecules. These equivalent orbitals have the property of being identical except for orientation in space, and in appropriate cases are therefore bond orbitals.

In order to discuss symmetrical diatomic molecules by the molecular orbital method, the energy levels for excited states of H_2^+ are needed. These have been calculated by Teller[15] and others. The states based on $1s$ and $2s$ orbitals for separated atoms are shown in Fig. 8.8. The nuclear repulsion energy is not included, in order to

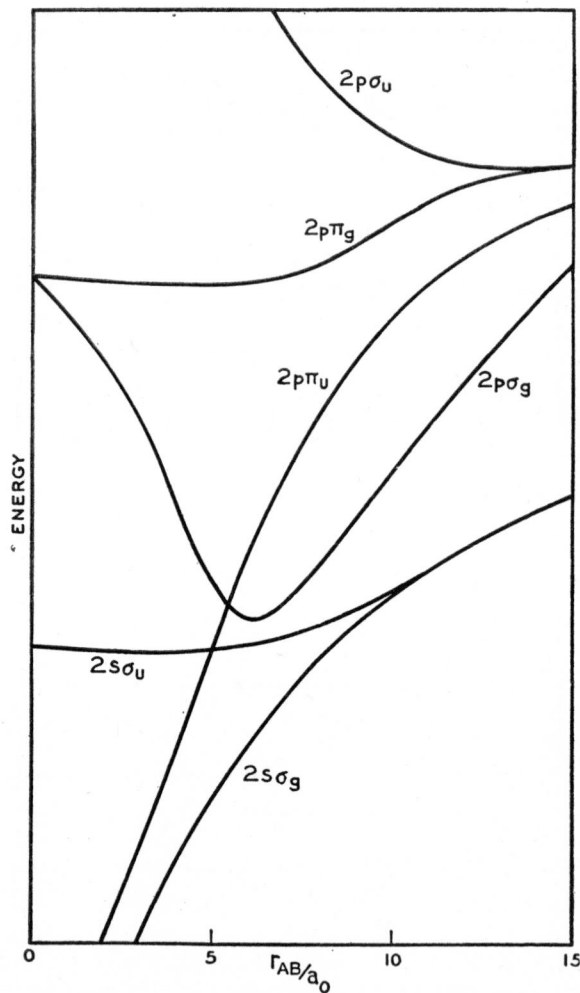

Fig. 8.9. The electronic energy of H_2^+ for states based on $2s$ and $2p$ orbitals. The energy of $2s$ states is lowered to correspond approximately to the $2s - 2p$ energy difference in atoms from Li to F.

[15] Teller, E., Z. Physik, **61**, 458 (1930).

allow the curves to extend to zero distance where the molecular orbitals become atomic orbitals for the "combined atom."

It is interesting to note the characteristics which the H_2^+ orbitals retain even as the internuclear distance d varies from zero to infinity.

1. The coordinate ϕ retains its meaning if d is taken along the polar axis of the atom. Consequently the factor in ψ is $e^{im_l\phi}$ throughout, so that m_l retains its meaning. Orbitals with $m_l = 0$ are labeled σ, those with $m_l = \pm 1$ are labeled π, etc., using the Greek equivalents of s, p, d, etc. All except σ states are doubly degenerate.

2. The symmetry to inversion through the center midway between nuclei is maintained. For intermediate distances the orbitals are labeled g (gerade) if symmetric and u (ungerade) if antisymmetric to inversion. In the combined atom the orbitals are g if l is even and u if l is odd.

For a discussion of the symmetrical diatomic molecules from Li_2 to F_2, the molecular orbitals based on $2s$ and $2p$ orbitals for separated atoms are of principal interest. Since shielding and penetration will give $2s$ orbitals a lower energy than $2p$ orbitals in such molecules, they have been so indicated in Fig. 8.9. The states based on $2s$ orbitals were also shown in Fig. 8.8.

At large internuclear distances the molecular orbitals may be expressed as sum and difference combinations of atomic orbitals. This provides a convenient system of labeling. Thus

$$2s\sigma_g = (2s_A + 2s_B)/\sqrt{2}$$
$$2s\sigma_u = (2s_A - 2s_B)/\sqrt{2}$$

The Pauli exclusion principle applies here as well as in atoms. Thus the low-energy orbitals are filled with two electrons each (four if degenerate), starting with the lowest energy and continuing until all electrons are included. This filling in of orbitals is illustrated in Table 8.2, where the orbitals are listed in the approximate order of increasing energy. It may be noted that at a certain distance, r_{AB}, the orbitals $2p\sigma_g$ and $2p\pi_u$ have the same energy, and that in C_2 each orbital is partially filled. The curves for $2s\sigma_u$ and $2p\pi_u$ also cross.

The state or term symbols are related to those for atoms. The Greek letters Σ, Π, Δ, ... represent values of $0, 1, 2, \ldots$ for Σm_l. The over-all symmetry to inversion is indicated by u or g, and the net electron spin by the superscript $(2S + 1)$. The $+$ or $-$ refers to symmetry to a plane through the nuclei and applies only to Σ states.

TABLE 8.2

Mole-cule	Electrons in Molecular Orbitals						States (lowest first)	No. of Bonds
	$2s\sigma_g$ bonding	$2s\sigma_u$ anti-bonding	$2p\sigma_g$ bonding	$2p\pi_u$ bonding	$2p\pi_g$ anti-bonding	$2p\sigma_u$ anti-bonding		
Li_2	2						$^1\Sigma_g{}^+$	1
$Be_2{}^*$	2	2					$^1\Sigma_g{}^+$	0
B_2	2	2	0	2			$^3\Sigma_g{}^-, {}^1\Delta_g, {}^1\Sigma_g{}^+$	1
C_2	2	2	1	3			$^3\Pi_u, {}^1\Pi_u$	2
N_2	2	2	2	4			$^1\Sigma_g{}^+$	3
O_2	2	2	2	4	2		$^3\Sigma_g{}^-, {}^1\Delta_g, {}^1\Sigma_g{}^+$	2
F_2	2	2	2	4	4		$^1\Sigma_g{}^+$	1
$Ne_2{}^*$	2	2	2	4	4	2	$^1\Sigma_g{}^+$	0

* These structures indicate no primary bonding; only the weak London forces would operate. The actual state of Be_2 is not known.

Probably the most interesting result of Table 8.2 is that for O_2. Three states arise because the degenerate π_g orbitals are only half filled. With spins antiparallel the two electrons can have $m_l = 1$ and -1, yielding the $^1\Sigma$ state, or the m_l can be $+1$ for both or -1 for both, yielding the two components of the $^1\Delta$ state. If the electron spins are parallel, the m_l values must be $+1$ and -1, giving the $^3\Sigma$ state. If Hund's rules apply to molecules, the $^3\Sigma$ should be the lowest energy or normal state, as is experimentally observed. Thus one is led quite definitely to the result that oxygen should be paramagnetic because of the unpaired electron spins.

The molecular orbitals can be classified as *bonding* if their energy decreases markedly when the separated atoms are brought to a typical bond distance. In agreement with ideas expressed above, it is found that these orbitals give increased electron probability between the nuclei. The orbitals $2s\sigma_g$, $2p\sigma_g$, $2p\pi_u$ are regarded as bonding.

The term *antibonding* is used to describe the other orbitals which give decreased electron density between nuclei and consequently no marked decrease in electronic energy. Addition of the nuclear repulsive energy makes antibonding orbitals actually repulsive at reasonable distances, while bonding orbitals are attractive at larger than the equilibrium distances. The excess in the number of pairs of electrons in bonding orbitals over the number of pairs in antibonding orbitals may be taken as the number of bonds present, as given in the last column of Table 8.2.

In addition to the bonding and the antibonding orbitals there are frequently orbitals of one atom which are essentially unaffected by the other atom, such as inner shell orbitals. These are usually called *nonbonding*.

8h. Molecular orbitals for polyatomic molecules. In treating more complex molecules by the molecular orbital method, not only has it been necessary to use cruder orbitals, but also the basic approximation of the method becomes less satisfactory. Consequently we shall expect only qualitative results or suggestions for the form of empirical equations in most cases. Nevertheless these results are of great value. Let us consider first the limitations of the method and then proceed to the more positive results.

In a complex atom containing say 30 electrons, the influence of the nuclear attraction clearly predominates over that of the detailed repulsion of any pair of electrons. Thus if the electronic repulsion is considered in some statistical manner, the resulting atomic orbitals are a reasonable approximation. However, a polyatomic molecule with 30 or more electrons can easily have no nucleus with a charge greater than 6, and many nuclei with only a single positive charge. In this case the effect on the electronic motion of the position of the nuclei is only somewhat more important than that of the positions of the other electrons. Thus the validity of the basic approximation of the molecular orbital method, the use of one-electron orbitals, becomes more doubtful as the positive charge is distributed among more particles.

In its crudest form, molecular orbitals are taken to be linear combinations of atomic orbitals. Thus for hydrogen one takes a molecular orbital

$$\psi_{M.O.} = (1s_A + 1s_B)/\sqrt{2} \tag{8.33}$$

which is normalized if one neglects the nonorthogonality of the two $1s$ functions. Then each of the two electrons is placed in this orbital, necessarily with antiparallel spin.

The electronic energy associated with this one electron molecular orbital is

$$W = (H_c + H_x)/(1 + \Delta) \tag{8.34}$$

where the molecular orbital coulomb integral is

$$H_c = \int 1s_A H 1s_A \, dv = E_H + H_c' \qquad (8.35)$$

$$H_c' = - \int (1s_A)^2 \frac{e^2}{r_B} \, dv$$

the exchange integral is

$$H_x = \int 1s_A H 1s_B \, dv = \Delta E_H + H_x' \qquad (8.36)$$

$$H_x' = - \int (1s_A)(1s_B) \frac{e^2}{r_A} \, dv$$

and the nonorthogonality integral is

$$\Delta = \int (1s_A)(1s_B) \, dv \qquad (8.37)$$

In many of the crude calculations the stated assumptions are that H_c is just E_H, that Δ is neglected in comparison to one, and that H_x is evaluated empirically (and usually called β). This gives $W = E_H + \beta$. However these assumptions are entirely unjustified. For example Δ can easily exceed 0.5 and cannot possibly be neglected when $(1 + \Delta)$ divides the leading term, E_H. The situation is actually not quite so bad, as was pointed out by Mulliken and Rieke.[16] Their method differs somewhat from that given here, but is similar in net result. By introducing Eqs. (8.35) and (8.36) into (8.34), one finds

$$W = E_H + \frac{H_c' + H_x'}{1 + \Delta} \qquad (8.34)$$

Then by making the less strenuous assumptions that $H_c'/(1 + \Delta)$ approximately compensates the nuclear repulsion (omitted in these equations) and that Δ is small compared with one for the relatively small term, $H_x'/(1 + \Delta)$, one has the same final result $W = E_H + \beta$. Now one interprets β as H_x'. Neglecting interactions between electrons, there are two electrons each at energy $E_H + \beta$ in H_2, giving a bond energy of 2β. We shall write W_b for the change in orbital energy because of bonding, in this case $(W - E_H)$ or β.

With these preliminaries completed, let us consider six hydrogen nuclei arranged in a regular hexagon at the usual bond distance. (The calculation will be used again in discussing benzene). With the six electrons added, this would be an H_6 molecule, and its energy will be compared to $3H_2$. The molecular orbitals will be taken as linear combinations of the six $1s$ atomic orbitals. While one could

[16] Mulliken, R. S. and Rieke, C. A., *J. Am. Chem. Soc.*, **63**, 1770 (1941).

take all six functions as components of a linear variation function and obtain a sixth order secular equation, it is easier to make use of the symmetry of the hexagon and obtain directly the following molecular orbitals (see Appendix 6). Writing A, B, C, D, E, F for the six normalized atomic orbitals, one has

$$\psi_1 = (A + B + C + D + E + F)/\sqrt{6} \qquad W_b = +2\beta$$
$$\psi_2 = (2A + B - C - 2D - E + F)/\sqrt{12} \qquad W_b = +\beta$$
$$\psi_3 = (B + C - E - F)/2 \qquad W_b = +\beta$$
$$\psi_4 = (2A - B - C + 2D - E - F)/\sqrt{12} \qquad W_b = -\beta \qquad (8.38)$$
$$\psi_5 = (B - C + E - F)/2 \qquad W_b = -\beta$$
$$\psi_6 = (A - B + C - D + E - F)/\sqrt{6} \qquad W_b = -2\beta$$

The orthogonality of these six molecular orbitals is readily verified, and it is seen that they would be normalized if the atomic orbitals were orthogonal. The energies given at the right involve the same approximations mentioned above.

Since there are six electrons, the three lowest energy orbitals will be occupied. With β negative these will be the first three. Then neglecting all further interactions, one finds the total bond energy in H_6 to be $2(2\beta) + 4(\beta) = 8\beta$, while that of $3H_2$ is 6β. Thus H_6 is calculated to be more stable than $3H_2$ by the bond energy of H_2, which is over 100 kcal. This incorrect result can easily be attributed to the various approximations involved, and is presented only to illustrate the dangers of such crude calculations. More refined calculations have been made in a few cases but have not as yet proven too fruitful.

Let us now consider the qualitative conclusions which can be drawn from molecular orbital theory. We have seen in several examples that half the molecular orbitals formed from a given set of atomic orbitals are bonding, since they give lower energies as the atoms come together. The other half are antibonding. It is also possible that certain atomic orbitals fail to interact at all, but they can be excluded from the discussion. Since a given molecular orbital can hold but two electrons, the maximum number of electrons that can be accommodated in the bonding molecular orbitals is equal to the number of atomic orbitals used in making up the molecular orbitals. This leads to our first general rule.

1. *The number of bonding electrons cannot exceed the number of atomic orbitals involved in the bonding.*

In the simplest case, that of normal electron pair bonding, the atoms have one electron in each of the orbitals which lead to bonds. In donor-acceptor or generalized base-acid bonding the donor atom has both electrons, and the acceptor has merely a vacant low-energy orbital. These cases will be equally well explained on the bond orbital theory to be given below. However it is important to note that the number of electrons may be less than the number of atomic orbitals, in which case the higher energy or less strongly bonding orbitals are left vacant. This situation arises with metals and with electron-deficient molecules such as diborane. Thus metallic and electron-deficient bindings, which appear fundamentally different in some theories, are closely related to ordinary covalent bonding in terms of molecular orbitals.

2. *The spins of all electrons involved in bonding will be paired unless (a) there is an odd number of electrons, or (b) two or more molecular orbitals are either approximately or exactly degenerate and are only partially filled.*

Ordinarily, as the molecular orbitals are filled with the pairs of electrons, one finds a considerable energy difference between the highest occupied and the lowest vacant orbital. In this case the lowest state has all bonding electrons paired, and the substance is diamagnetic (unless there is paramagnetism outside of the bonding system). Occasionally two or more molecular orbitals of the highest energy to be occupied are exactly degenerate, as in O_2, or approximately degenerate, as in C_2. Then the lowest state will have some spins unpaired. Thus the pairing of spins appears not as a fundamental property of the covalent bond, but merely a situation that usually arises.

3. *Bonding will occur at directions where the atomic orbitals have large values.*

Since the bonding arises from the exchange integral (8.36), it is evident that no bonding can occur in directions in which one of the orbitals has a zero value. While other things may influence the exact bond directions, it is clear that they will tend toward the directions of maximum value of the component atomic orbitals. Atomic s orbitals have no directional character, but p, d, etc. orbitals all give directional effects. These will be discussed in detail in later sections, along with the corresponding results by the bond orbital method. Indeed we shall be frequently applying the molecular orbital method to various problems in succeeding sections.

8i. Bond orbitals and hybridization of atomic orbitals. As we have already mentioned, in the simplest form of the bond orbital method (H.L.S.P. method) the complete wave function contains a Heitler and London type of factor for each bond in the molecule. These factors will be called individual bond orbitals, and each involves two electrons with spins paired.

In its basic structure the bond orbital method avoids certain weaknesses of molecular orbitals. For example, in molecular orbitals each electron has a certain probability of being near a given nucleus, irrespective of where the other electrons are. This allows excessive local accumulations of electrons. However, bond orbitals keep the electrons distributed one to a component atomic orbital at all times. The truth lies somewhere in between but is probably closer to the bond orbital expression.

Let us now consider first the H_4 and then the H_6 problem in bond orbitals. The results again will be useful in discussing benzene later. The complete wave function is set up to be antisymmetric to the exchange of any pair of electrons in full accord with the Pauli exclusion principle. This gives a rather complicated sum of terms, each of the type

$$A\alpha(1)B\beta(2)C\alpha(3)D\beta(4)$$

where A, B, C, and D again refer to the atomic orbitals and the α and β refer to the spin of the electron on that atom. The 1, 2, 3, 4 designate the electrons. If a bond is assumed between A and B, there must also be a term

$$B\alpha(1)A\beta(2)C\alpha(3)D\beta(4)$$

The details of these wave functions are given in Appendix 7. However, the essential features may be described in a few simple rules as follows.

The atomic orbitals are designated as points on a ring, which need have no relation to the location of the atoms in space. Lines are drawn between the pairs of orbitals bonded. So long as none of these lines cross, each pattern represents a different wave function. Figure

8.10 illustrates these patterns. The energy corresponding to a given bond pattern, say I, is

$$W_I = \frac{H_{I,I}}{\Delta_{I,I}} = \frac{H_c + \sum H_x \text{ bonded} - \frac{1}{2}\sum H_x \text{ nonbonded}}{1 + \sum \Delta \text{ bonded} - \frac{1}{2}\sum \Delta \text{ nonbonded}} \qquad (8.39)$$

where the integrals H_c, H_x, and Δ are entirely analogous to those in Eq. (8.4). For example the coulomb integral is

$$H_c = \int A(1)B(2)C(3)D(4)HA(1)B(2)C(3)D(4)\ dv$$

An exchange integral between orbitals A and B would be

$$H_x(AB) = \int B(1)A(2)C(3)D(4)HA(1)B(2)C(3)D(4)\ dv$$

There are also integrals involving more than one exchange, such as

$$\int B(1)A(2)D(3)C(4)HA(1)B(2)C(3)D(4)\ dv$$

but these are supposed to be relatively smaller, and are neglected in

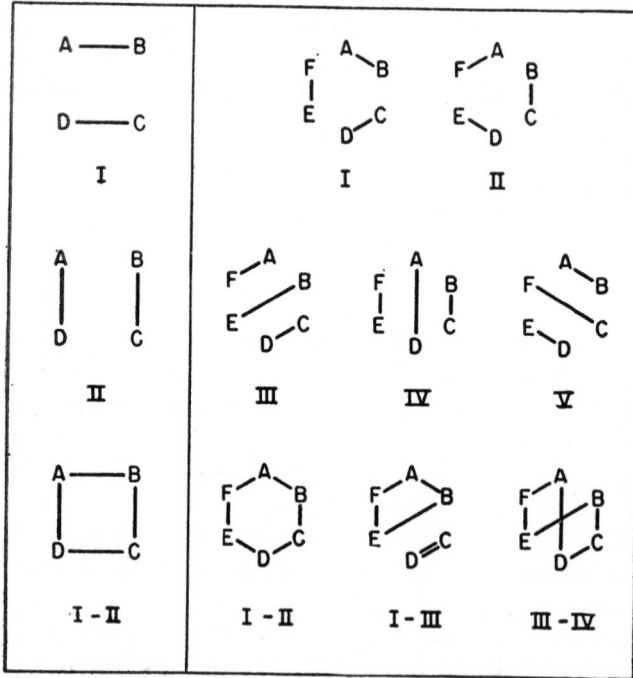

Fig. 8.10. Bond diagrams for four and six orbitals and some of their superposition patterns.

both $H_{I,I}$ and $\Delta_{I,I}$. In many calculations all the sums of Δ's are dropped. This appears to be an extremely poor approximation, but in an exactly similar manner to the corresponding step for molecular orbitals, one may show that the real approximation is not so bad. The necessary transformations are given in Eqs. (8.4) and (8.5), which show that the energy of the separated atoms can be removed as a separate term not containing Δ. Equation (8.39) then becomes

$$W_b = (W_I - E_{\text{atoms}}) = \frac{H_c' + \sum H_x' \text{ bonded} - \frac{1}{2} \sum H_x' \text{ nonbonded}}{1 + \sum \Delta \text{ bonded} - \frac{1}{2} \sum \Delta \text{ nonbonded}}$$

$$(8.40)$$

where $(W_I - E_{\text{atoms}})$ is the desired total bond energy, and the H_c' and H_x' are essentially similar to the corresponding expressions for hydrogen in Eq. (8.4). For an initial approximation, H_c' and all Δ's are dropped in Eq. (8.40), as are exchange integrals between non-adjacent atoms. Then if α represents the exchange integral between adjacent atoms, one has for H_2 the result $W_b = \alpha$, in agreement with Section 8b. With H_4 one finds for bond diagram I the result

$$W_b = 2\alpha - \tfrac{1}{2}(2\alpha) = \alpha \qquad (8.41)$$

Bond diagram II leads to the same result. Since the wave functions corresponding to both diagrams are acceptable, a better result will be obtained if both are used as a linear variation function. The resulting secular equation is

$$\begin{vmatrix} H_{I,I} - \Delta_{I,I}W & H_{I,II} - \Delta_{I,II}W \\ H_{I,II} - \Delta_{I,II}W & H_{II,II} - \Delta_{II,II}W \end{vmatrix} = 0 \qquad (8.42)$$

To proceed, $H_{I,II}$ and $\Delta_{I,II}$ must be evaluated. $H_{I,II}$ is the sum of coulomb and exchange integrals with the following coefficients. Let the number of electrons be $2n$ and let i be the number of completely separate islands in the superposition pattern of the two bond diagrams. Thus in the H_4 problem $n = 2$ and $i = 1$ for the I-II superposition pattern. In H_6, $n = 3$ throughout and $i = 1$ for I-II and III-IV, but $i = 2$ for I-III. The coefficient of the coulomb integral is $(\tfrac{1}{2})^{n-i}$. If the two orbitals are adjacent or are separated by an odd number of bonds but are in the same island, the coefficient of their exchange integral is also $(\tfrac{1}{2})^{n-i}$. If the orbitals are in the same island but separated by an even number of bonds, the coefficient is $-(\tfrac{1}{2})^{n-i-1}$, and if the orbitals are in different islands the coefficient of their exchange integral is $-(\frac{1}{2})^{n-i+1}$. Again multiple exchange integrals are neglected. Following these rules one finds

$$H_{I,II} = \tfrac{1}{2}H_c + \tfrac{1}{2}[(AB) + (BC) + (CD) + (DA)] - (AC) - (BD)$$

where the exchange integrals are indicated by the pairs of letters in parentheses. The quantity $\Delta_{I,II}$ is obtained from $H_{I,II}$ by replacing H_c by unity, and the exchange integrals by the corresponding non-orthogonality integrals, i.e., by removing the operator H from each integral.

Again it proves to be possible to remove the quantity $(\Delta_{I,II} E_{atoms})$ from $H_{I,II}$, leaving the primed quantities H_c' and H_x'. If as before we also neglect H_c', all Δ's and exchange integrals, H_x', between non-adjacent atoms, and let α represent adjacent exchange integrals, we have

$$H_{I,II} - \Delta_{I,II}W = 2\alpha - \tfrac{1}{2}(W - E_{atoms}) = 2\alpha - \tfrac{1}{2}W_b \quad (8.43)$$

One can easily verify that Eqs. (8.39), (8.40), and (8.41) follow these more general rules and may be rearranged into

$$H_{I,I} - \Delta_{I,I}W = \alpha - W_b$$

Then the secular equation becomes

$$\begin{vmatrix} \alpha - W_b & 2\alpha - \tfrac{1}{2}W_b \\ 2\alpha - \tfrac{1}{2}W_b & \alpha - W_b \end{vmatrix} = 0 \quad (8.42')$$

which has the solutions $W_b = 2\alpha, -2\alpha$.

Since the total bond energy in $2H_2$ is also 2α, this makes the energy of H_4 and $2H_2$ the same, and with a much lower entropy for H_4 predicts correctly its nonexistence.

The calculation for H_6 is entirely similar and is given in Appendix 7. If only structures I and II are used, one obtains for the bond energy 2.4α and 0. If all five structures are taken, the lowest energy is $W_b = (\sqrt{13} - 1)\alpha = 2.61\alpha$ (with α negative). Since this is smaller than the energy of $3H_2$, 3α, the nonexistence of H_6 is predicted correctly.

When atoms larger than hydrogen are considered, one immediately finds that the usual atomic orbitals are not necessarily appropriate. To be sure Li_2 can be represented as closed $1s$ shells for each Li, and a bond involving the two $2s$ orbitals. Likewise in HF one may consider the $1s$, $2s$, and two $2p$ orbitals of fluorine filled with electron pairs, and the bond made up from the remaining $2p$ orbital of fluorine and the $1s$ orbital of hydrogen. There is also considerable ionic character, as was mentioned above. However, if one takes the corresponding point of view for CH_4, one has the $2s$ and three $2p$ orbitals of carbon, which are not at all equivalent, whereas we feel sure that all four bonds in CH_4 are exactly the same. The accepted solution of this dilemma was first proposed by Pauling.[17] He assumed that one might take linear combinations of the s and p orbitals so as to get four equivalent *hybrid* orbitals which would form the bonds. He further showed that the directions of maximum value of these orbitals were indeed toward the points of a regular tetrahedron. Let us represent the p functions as p_x, p_y, and p_z when their angular factors are $\sin \theta \cos \phi$, $\sin \theta \sin \phi$, and $\cos \theta$ respectively. Then the four sp^3 hybrid orbitals may be written as

$$\psi_1 = \tfrac{1}{2}(s + p_x + p_y + p_z)$$
$$\psi_2 = \tfrac{1}{2}(s - p_x - p_y + p_z)$$
$$\psi_3 = \tfrac{1}{2}(s + p_x - p_y - p_z)$$
$$\psi_4 = \tfrac{1}{2}(s - p_x + p_y - p_z)$$

(8.44)

for which the orthogonality and normalization can be readily verified. It may be shown that the directions of maximum intensity are $\theta = 54° 44'$, $\phi = 45°$ and $225°$ for one and two, and $\theta = 125° 16'$, $\phi = 135°$ and $315°$ for three and four, respectively. Thus the angle between any two bonds is $109° 28'$.

The objection has been raised that in a heavier atom such as carbon the $2s$ and $2p$ orbitals are not degenerate and that linear combinations are not permissible for the atom itself. However, in the highly perturbed field of the four hydrogen nuclei it may be reasonable to disregard the $s - p$ energy difference. In any event one may use the hybrid orbitals in a variation method calculation since they are single valued, continuous, and finite.

Thus in the bond orbital method, methane is regarded as having an unshared pair of electrons in the $1s$ orbital of carbon and four pairs in four bond orbitals, each made up of one sp^3 hybrid orbital from carbon and the corresponding $1s$ orbital from hydrogen.

So long as only single bonds are involved, more complex hydrocarbons can be described in an entirely equivalent fashion. Strictly,

[17] Pauling, L., *Proc. Nat. Acad.*, **14**, 359 (1928).

the hybridization may become unsymmetrical, since the bonds will be partly to other carbons and partly to hydrogens. However, as yet there is no evidence for serious departure from tetrahedral angles unless strains are present, as in cyclopropane.

The normal state of the carbon atom is a ^3P state based on two $2s$ and two $2p$ electrons ($1s^2\,2s^2\,2p^2$), but the state required for four bonds is $1s^2\,2s\,2p^3$, ^5S, since all four valence electrons must be alone in atomic orbitals. After many years of searching, this ^5S state has finally been located spectroscopically by Shenstone.[18] It is 4.16 e.v. or 96.4 kcal./mole above the normal ^3P state. This is roughly the energy of one C—H bond. Since two additional bonds are made possible by the promotion of the $2s$ electron to a $2p$ orbital, it is readily seen that carbon should be tetravalent rather than bivalent.

At this point it is appropriate to introduce the concept of *bond strength* or more explicitly the *bonding strength of atomic orbitals*, either hybrid or nonhybrid. The bond energy may be considered to arise from the overlap of the two orbitals involved in the bond. Consequently an orbital which is concentrated in a given direction will overlap more and give a stronger bond. Pauling takes the spherically symmetrical s orbital as a standard of strength 1.0. From Table 3.1 one can see that the maximum angular intensity of a p orbital is $\sqrt{3}$ or 1.732 times that for the s orbital. A p orbital is then said to have a bond strength of 1.732. The strength of an sp^3 tetrahedral orbital is readily computed. Substituting the angles for maximum value, one obtains

$$\sin(54°\,44') = \sqrt{\tfrac{2}{3}}, \qquad \cos(54°\,44') = \sqrt{\tfrac{1}{3}}$$
$$\sin 45° = \cos 45° = \sqrt{\tfrac{1}{2}}$$
$$\frac{1}{2}\,p_x = \frac{1}{2}\left(\frac{1}{4\pi}\right)^{1/2}\sqrt{3}\cdot\sqrt{\frac{2}{3}}\cdot\sqrt{\frac{1}{2}} = \frac{1}{2}\left(\frac{1}{4\pi}\right)^{1/2}$$
$$\psi_1 = \left(\frac{1}{4\pi}\right)^{1/2}\left(\frac{1}{2}+\frac{1}{2}+\frac{1}{2}+\frac{1}{2}\right) = \left(\frac{1}{4\pi}\right)^{1/2}(2) \qquad (8.45)$$

Since the factor $(1/4\pi)^{1/2}$ is the standard value of an s orbital, the bond strength of the tetrahedral orbital is 2.0. This is appreciably higher than that for a p orbital, and is readily shown to be the maximum possible for a hybrid of s and p orbitals (see Problem 8.7). Table 8.3 lists a number of sets of hybrid orbitals, together with the

[18] Shenstone, A. G., *Phys. Rev.*, **72**, 411 (1947).

corresponding geometry and bond strength.   The orbitals of each set in Table 8.3 are all equivalent although there are other situations where nonequivalent orbitals arise.   It is seen that the greater angular concentration of d orbitals yields higher bond strengths for hybrids involving d orbitals than for sp hybrids.   However, in most practical cases the d orbitals are of one lower principal quantum number than the s and p orbitals, and hence are of smaller radius.   The decreased radius reduces the overlap and partially compensates for the increased angular concentration.   Bond strength as here defined is a useful qualitative concept but it has never been shown to have exact quantitative significance in relation to dissociation energies or other measurable quantities.

TABLE 8.3

SETS OF HYBRID ORBITALS FOR BONDING

Geometry	Bond angle	Orbitals	Bond strength
(Nondirectional)	. .	s	1.0
Pyramidal	90°	p^3	1.732
Tetrahedral	109° 28′	sp^3	2.0
Triangular (plane)	120°	sp^2	1.991
Linear	180°	sp	1.932
Square	90°	dsp^2	2.694
Octahedral	90°	d^2sp^3	2.923

Although many other hybrids might be listed, there is frequently the additional complication of unequal proportions of the component orbitals, which makes a complete list of this type impractical.   The molecule H_2O is a good illustration.   If the $s - p$ energy difference were the predominant factor, the oxygen atom would have its $2s$ orbital filled with an unshared pair, because a bond puts only one electron on oxygen instead of two.   This leaves two $2p$ orbitals for the bonds and one for the other unshared pair, and gives a bond angle of 90°, or slightly larger because of electrostatic repulsion of the positive hydrogen atoms.   However if the bond strength were the predominant factor, sp^3 orbitals would be used—two for bonds and two for the unshared pairs.   This would give an angle of 109.5° or a little more.   The observed value is 105° for H_2O, and 92° for the comparable H_2S.

Since the polarity is small for H_2S, the angle for it clearly indicates p^2 bonding and that the $s - p$ energy difference is the more important factor. While one may conclude that the polarity or ionic character of the O—H bonds is primarily responsible for the larger bond angle in H_2O, it seems probable that the bonding orbitals take on some s component also. Thus one has presumably a compromise with the maxima of the bonding orbitals at an angle less than the 105°, at which the protons lie, but greater than the 90° of pure p^2 bonding. Finally, the bond strength factor seems to be less important than the energy separation of the atomic orbitals.

Where the nucleus of the atom of interest has a nuclear quadrupole moment, it has been found that the coupling of this moment with the field of the electrons yields information about the orbitals involved in bond formation. Unfortunately none of the abundant isotopes of carbon or oxygen has a quadrupole moment, but considerable data of interest is accumulating on nitrogen, chlorine, and some other atoms. A description of the essential principles is given in Appendix 21.

With this initial survey of the bond orbital method, let us summarize the qualitative conclusions.

1. *The number of bonding electrons equals the number of atomic orbitals involved and is twice the number of bonds.*

2. *The spins of all bonding electrons are paired.*

3. *Bonding will occur at directions where the atomic orbitals have large values.*

Conclusion three follows because a hybrid orbital with high concentration in a given direction can be formed only from atomic orbitals that have large values in that direction. This conclusion is in complete agreement with that from molecular orbitals.

Conclusions one and two, however, are significantly more restricted than the corresponding conclusions from molecular orbitals. Consequently we may regard bond orbitals as a more specialized description of the commonest type of covalent bonding. In this respect it follows closely the simple chemical concept of a definite electron pair shared between two atoms. The two dots or the dash connecting the atom symbols in a structural formula may be said to represent a bond orbital for the two electrons. A complete structural formula then represents a complete wave function.

In cases such as H_4, where the location of the bonds is indefinite, two or more structural formulas and corresponding wave functions are needed. While this situation is readily handled, the bond orbital method becomes relatively less satisfactory in cases of degeneracy such as O_2 and C_2, or where the number of atomic orbitals exceeds the number of electrons.

8j. Multiple bonds. In our discussion of diatomic molecules by molecular orbitals, examples of multiple bonds appeared. In this section further characteristics will be considered and the bond orbital approach will be included. Let us first take ethylene for an example of a double bond.

It is well established that all six atoms in ethylene lie in one plane, which will be taken as the xy plane, with the C—C axis as the x axis. Now the xy plane is certainly an element of symmetry, so that the molecular orbitals must be either symmetric or antisymmetric to reflection through the plane (change from z to $-z$). The s and the p_x and p_y orbitals as defined for Eq. (8.44) are symmetrical to the plane, while the p_z orbitals are antisymmetric. Thus there are $1s$ orbitals for the four hydrogens, two $2s$, two $2p_x$, and two $2p_y$ orbitals of carbon, or ten in all which are symmetric to the xy plane and appropriate for the bonding electrons. These ten atomic orbitals yield five bonding molecular orbitals, which hold ten of the twelve valence electrons and form the four C—H bonds and one C—C bond. The two $2p_z$ orbitals combine to give one additional bonding orbital, which is antisymmetric to the xy plane and is sometimes called a π *orbital*. The corresponding term is σ orbital for one symmetrical to the plane. Thus the last two electrons occupy this π orbital and form the second or π bond. Since there are two electrons in the π orbital, the antisymmetric factor appears twice, and the complete wave function is symmetric to the plane of the nuclei.

In the bond orbital method one may take four sp^3 hybrid orbitals for each carbon atom. Using two for C—H bonds in the xy plane, there remain two which point at an angle, one above and one below the plane of the atoms. These may serve to form the double bond. The orbital from one carbon pointing above the plane is combined with the corresponding orbital from the other carbon atom to form one bond, and the orbitals below the plane similarly form the other bond. Thus the complete wave function for the molecule is symmetric in the xy plane, as it should be. This formulation is important in showing that π bonds and orbitals are mere language rather than fact. However, even in bond orbital representations, the use of σ and π bonds is usually more convenient. In that case one may take

sp^2 hybrid orbitals to form the two C—H bonds and the single C—C bond. Then one combines the p_z orbitals into a π bond orbital.

Strictly the two descriptions given above are equivalent only if the hybrid orbitals for the C—H bonds are exactly the same. If two of the equivalent sp^3 orbitals are used, a 109.5° H—C—H angle is expected, while if sp^2 orbitals are used, the angle should be 120°. The observed angle is almost exactly 120° for ethylene, so that the $\frac{1}{3}s$, $\frac{2}{3}p$ hybrids are indicated for the C—H bonds. However, we may retain the first type of bond orbital description of the double bond by using $\frac{1}{6}s$ and $\frac{5}{6}p$ hybrid orbitals for the C—C bonds above and below the plane of the atoms (instead of the sp^3 hybrids).

The overlapping region of increased electron density for the π bond is not directly between the carbon atoms, since that is in the xy plane where the p_z orbitals have zero value. Rather there are two regions, one above and one below the plane, where the π bonding electron density arises. Since the orbitals are really directed perpendicular to the bond rather than along it, the overlap is less than for a σ or single bond. Also the potential energy in these regions away from the C—C axis is not so low as on the axis. Hence we may expect the additional bonding energy for the π bond ordinarily to be less than that for the σ bond. This is almost always true, but O_2 and N_2 are exceptions.

One compensating effect tending to increase double bond strength is the reduction in repulsion of nonbonding electrons, which permits the bond distance to decrease and the σ bond to grow stronger. To see this one notes in Eq. (8.39) the coefficient of $-\frac{1}{2}$ for nonbonded exchange integrals. Thus in C_2H_6 or N_2H_4 three orbitals on each carbon or nitrogen will have nonbonding interaction with the corresponding orbitals at the other end of the single C—C or N—N bond. With exchange integrals in molecules negative, this interaction is repulsive. In C_2H_4 there are only two orbitals on each carbon having this nonbonding interaction. Thus decreasing the repulsion allows even the attractive effect of the σ bond to lower the energy and shorten the distance. In the case of N_2H_4 and N_2 the number of nonbonding and therefore repulsive interactions across the N—N bond decreases from nine (three orbitals on each nitrogen atom) to one. Also careful consideration of the differences between sp^3 bonding in the carbon compounds and something approaching p^3 bonding with an unshared pair in the s orbital for nitrogen indicates that these repulsive effects will be larger for singly bonded nitrogen. Thus one can understand to a certain extent the peculiar stability of N_2.

The situation in O_2 is rather similar to N_2, although the peculiarity of the $^3\sum$ state contributes also to the stability of the doubly bonded O_2.

Returning to the picture of the overlap regions of the p_z orbitals, one can easily see why ethylene is planar. If the z axis of one carbon were perpendicular to that of the other, the two p_z orbitals would be exactly orthogonal and no bonding would arise. Conversely, the maximum overlap of the p_z orbitals occurs when the z axes are parallel and the molecule is planar.

In the triple bond in acetylene or N_2, both the p_y and p_z orbitals are employed in π bonding. In acetylene the C—H and σ C—C bonds may be based on sp hybrids which have 180° bond angles. Thus acetylene has the linear H—C≡C—H structure.

Another interesting property of multiple bonding is its almost complete localization to the first row of eight in the periodic table (Li to Ne). This implies effectively the elements O, N, C, B, and possibly Be, since univalent elements could not normally form multiple bonds. There are very few examples of multiple bonding in the stable form of substances involving heavier atoms. Comparisons of physical properties between CO_2 and SiO_2, nitrogen and phosphorus, or oxygen and sulfur illustrate the marked effect of multiple bonding.

While some suggestions have been made as to the possible cause of this striking difference between the multiple bonds with $2s$-$2p$ orbitals and those with larger principal quantum number,[19] the correct explanation is far from clear at present. The ratio of the triple bond length to single bond length is 0.74 in nitrogen but is 0.86 in phosphorus. Comparison of the double to single bond lengths in oxygen and sulfur shows a similar effect. This clearly indicates that the change from repulsive to attractive interaction of the π orbitals has less effect on the bond distance in the heavier atoms. However, it is not clear whether this is because the overlap of the $3p(\pi)$ orbitals is much smaller, or whether some other effect holds the bond distance more constant in the larger atoms.

8k. Rotation about single bonds. It has long been established

[19] See, for example, Mulliken, R. S., *J. Am. Chem. Soc.*, **72**, 4493 (1950); Pitzer, K. S., *J. Am. Chem. Soc.*, **70**, 2140 (1948).

that while a double bond resists the rotation of the group of atoms at one end with respect to the group at the other, a single bond allows such rotation at least to the extent that isomers cannot be isolated. More recently it has been possible to find the changes in potential energy with rotation about single bonds. For example Kemp and the writer[20] found that a potential barrier of about 3000 cal. per mole restricts rotation in C_2H_6. The method of determination will be given in Chapter 9, but the result is interesting in connection with the last topic discussed concerning multiple bonds.

A σ bond itself is axially symmetrical and therefore is unaffected by rotation of attached groups. The influence of the protons in ethane on the axial symmetry of the C—C bond may be estimated by perturbation or variation methods and is found to be negligible. However, we have assumed that the σ bond is pulling the two CH_3 groups together against the repulsive forces between the C—H bonding electrons. Now if the C—H bonds were quantitatively represented by the sp^3 orbitals, the carbon atoms would be axially symmetrical, and again the only restriction to rotation would be a small interaction between the more distant hydrogen atoms. Our experience with quantitative calculations for H_2 suggests rather that the sp^3 orbitals will be only a rough approximation. Then it is reasonable to assume that the C—H bonding electrons are concentrated more along the C—H bond axes, and that the repulsive effect can be minimized by staggering the C—H bonds of one CH_3 group with respect to those of the other CH_3 group. It is found that this staggered configuration is the stable one.

Undoubtedly electrostatic effects contribute to these potential barriers when the bonds are highly polar. It has been suggested that the quadrupole moments of bonds with small dipole moment are large enough to yield barriers such as are observed in the paraffin hydrocarbons. However, this seems doubtful at present.[21]

81. Bond energies. Various formulas have been proposed for the heat of formation of relatively nonpolar compounds, which are equivalent to the assumption that the energy of a given bond between two atoms is constant regardless of the other bonds to those atoms. Naturally exceptions appear for various reasons, but where no steric

[20] Kemp, J. D. and Pitzer, K. S., *J. Chem. Phys.*, **4**, 749 (1936); see also Pitzer, K. S., *Faraday Soc.* Discussion, **10**, 66 (1951).

[21] Lassettre, E. N. and Dean, L. B., Jr., *J. Chem. Phys.*, **17**, 317 (1949); Oosterhoff, L. J., *Faraday Soc.* Discussion, **10**, 79 (1951).

or other serious complications are present, such formulas usually fit the observed values within a few kcal. per mole.

If one examines the bond orbital formulas, the condition for bond energy additivity is found to be the omission of exchange integrals between nonadjacent atoms, and invariance in the orbital hybridization. Since exchange integrals fall off fairly rapidly with increasing distance, this is a reasonable first approximation. Also there is considerable evidence from bond angles that the hybridization does not vary much. It is also assumed that a single bond formula represents the molecule satisfactorily. The corresponding requirements in the molecular orbital method are not so simple and will not be discussed.

In Table 8.4 are listed values for the energies of a number of common bonds. The energy to dissociate the molecule completely into atoms (in their normal states) is given by the sum of the bond energies for all the bonds in the molecule. The energy of formation of a compound is the difference between the sum of bond energies for the compound and the sum for the component elements in their standard states.

The values in Table 8.4 come from a number of authors, of whom the most important is Gaydon,[22] who has recently published a very fine compilation of dissociation energies. Furthermore his recommended value of 170.4 kcal. for the heat of sublimation of graphitic carbon (to normal ^3P atoms) has been confirmed by new thermodynamic measurements of Brewer, Gilles, and Jenkins.[23] The heat of vaporization values of Kelley,[24] together with some revision of these values by Brewer,[25] have been employed. These new data supplement the older values of Bichowsky and Rossini[26] upon which Pauling[27] based most of his bond energies.

In some cases the single bond energies for elements must be taken from solids, where there may be additional weak bonding of a van

[22] Gaydon, A. G., *Dissociation Energies and Spectra of Diatomic Molecules*, London: Chapman & Hall, Ltd., 1947.

[23] Brewer, L., Gilles, P., and Jenkins, F. A., *J. Chem. Phys.*, **16**, 797 (1948).

[24] Kelley, K. K., *U. S. Bureau of Mines Bulletin 383* (1935).

[25] Brewer, L., *The Thermodynamic and Physical Properties of the Elements*, Vol. IV-19B, National Nuclear Energy Series, New York: McGraw-Hill Book Company, Inc., 1950, p. 13.

[26] Bichowsky, F. R. and Rossini, F. D., *Thermochemistry of Chemical Substances*, New York: Reinhold Publishing Corp., 1936.

[27] Pauling, L., *The Nature of the Chemical Bond*, Ithaca: Cornell University Press, 1939.

TABLE 8.4

BOND ENERGIES

(Units: kcal./mole at 0°K)

Elements		Hydrides		Chlorides	
H—H	103.2	H—H	103.2	H—Cl	102.1
Li—Li	26	Li—H	58	Li—Cl	118.5
C—C	80.5(85)	C—H	98.2	C—Cl	78
N—N	37	N—H	92.2	N—Cl	46(?)
O—O	34	O—H	109.4	O—Cl	49
F—F	38	F—H	135	F—Cl	59.0
Na—Na	17.8	Na—H	47	Na—Cl	97.7
Si—Si	(45)	Si—H	76(?)	Si—Cl	87
P—P	(52)	P—H	77	P—Cl	77
S—S	63(?)	S—H	87(?)	S—Cl	65(?)
Cl—Cl	57.1	Cl—H	102.1	Cl—Cl	57.1
K—K	11.8	K—H	42.9	K—Cl	101.4
Cu—Cu	. .	Cu—H	62	Cu—Cl	83
Ge—Ge	(42)	Ge—H	. .	Ge—Cl	. .
As—As	(39)	As—H	56	As—Cl	69
Se—Se	(50)	Se—H	67	Se—Cl	59
Br—Br	45.4(53)	Br—H	86.7	Br—Cl	52.1
Rb—Rb	11.1	Rb—H	39	Rb—Cl	101.0
Ag—Ag	. .	Ag—H	53	Ag—Cl	71
Sn—Sn	(35)	Sn—H	. .	Sn—Cl	76
Sb—Sb	(42)	Sb—H	. .	Sb—Cl	75
Te—Te	(49)	Te—H	59	Te—Cl	. .
I—I	35.6(51)	I—H	70.6	I—Cl	49.6
Cs—Cs	10.4	Cs—H	41	Cs—Cl	103

Multiple Bonds

	Single	Double	Triple
C—C	80.5	145	198
N—N	37	. .	225.1
O—O	34	117.2	. .
P—P	(52)	. .	116.0
S—S	63(?)	101(?)	. .
As—As	(39)	. .	90.8
Se—Se	(50)	65	. .
Sb—Sb	(42)	. .	69
Te—Te	(49)	53	. .
C—N	66	. .	189
C—O	79	173	. .
P—N	. .	. .	138(?)
S—O	. .	120(?)	. .
Te—O	. .	62.8	. .

der Waals or semimetallic nature. Such values are enclosed in parentheses.

The first value 80.5 given for the C—C bond is an average of several hydrocarbons.[28] It would be 77.7 for ethane (with C—H bond energy from CH_4) but approaches 81.0 for higher and branched paraffins. The value from diamond, 85 kcal., is given in parenthesis. The values for N—N and O—O come from hydrazine and hydrogen peroxide on the basis of the values for N—H and O—H from ammonia and steam, respectively. The details for phosphorus will be typical of many other cases. The value for P≡P is from Gaydon.[22] Since the P—P bonds in P_4 are considerably strained, red phosphorus was taken as a basis. Brewer[25] gives 42 kcal. for the heat of vaporization to P_2. The heat of dissociation of two-gram atoms of red phosphorus to atoms is therefore $42 + 116 = 158$ kcal. Since this involves three bonds per two atoms, the value for P—P is 53 kcal.

Since the heats of formation of the simpler hydrocarbons are known with great accuracy, they are a good test of the constancy of bond energies. Table 8.5 compares the experimental heat of formation with that calculated from Table 8.4. It should be noted that the calculated values for the pentane isomers are necessarily the same, so that the differences between the experimental values are definite deviations from bond energy additivity.

TABLE 8.5

A TEST OF BOND ENERGIES IN HYDROCARBONS

(ΔH of formation from diamond of the ideal gas at 0°K in kcal./mole)

		Calc. table 8.5	Experiment[28]
Ethane	C_2H_6	−20.1	−17.67
Propane	C_3H_8	−23.8	−21.21
n-Pentane	⎫		⎧ −30.15
Isopentane	⎬ C_5H_{12}	−31.2	⎨ −31.54
Neopentane	⎭		⎩ −34.18
n-Octane	⎫ C_8H_{18}	−42.3	⎧ −42.94
2,2,3,3-Tetramethyl butane	⎭		⎩ −45.70

The values in Table 8.4 are for 0°K. For strict comparisons of electronic binding energy one should remove the zero point vibrational energy of the nuclei. However, the necessary vibration fre-

[28] Prosen, E. J., Pitzer, K. S., and Rossini, F. D., *J. Research, Natl. Bur. Standards* **34**, 403 (1945).

quency data are not generally available. In a few cases where the data are available the constancy of the bond energies is only somewhat improved by this correction. Thus other interactions are certainly involved in the differences shown in Table 8.5.

8m. Directional properties of covalent bonds. Reference has been made previously to the condition that a strong bond can be formed only in a direction where the component atomic orbital has a large value. Similarly a π bond requires orbitals on each atom which are antisymmetric to a plane through the two atomic nuclei. Kimball[29] has applied the methods of group theory to obtain a completely general table of the orbitals that form σ and π bonds in given directions. Unfortunately group theory tells only whether the bond strength is zero or not. The writer has selected in Table 8.6 a considerable number of the more likely examples of Kimball, and has

TABLE 8.6

DIRECTIONAL PROPERTIES OF COVALENT BONDS

C. N.	Arrangement	Orbitals for σ bonds	Orbitals for π bonds
2	Linear	$p(s,d)$	p^2d^2
	Angular	p^2	$d^2(p,d)(s,d)$
	Angular	$d(s,d)$	$dp(p^2,d^2)$
3	Trigonal plane	$s(p^2,d^2)$	$d^2p[p^2,d^2]$
	Unsymmetrical plane	dsp	$d^3p(p,d)$
	Trigonal pyramid	$(p,d)(p^2,d^2)$	$d^2[p,d][p^2,d^2]$
4	Tetrahedral	$s(p^3,d^3)$	$d^2[p^3,d^3]$
	Tetragonal plane	dsp^2	d^3p
5	Trigonal bipyramid	$dsp(p^2,d^2)$	$d^2[p^2,d^2]$
	Tetragonal pyramid	$d^2(s,p)(p^2,d^2)$	$d[s,p][p^2d^2]$
	Pentagonal plane	d^3p^2	pd^2
6	Octahedron	d^2sp^3	d^3
	Trigonal antiprism	d^3p^3	sd
	Trigonal prism	$d^4p(s,d)$	$p^2[s,d]$
7	ZrF_7^{-3}*	$d^3sp(p^2,d^2)$	$[p^2,d^2]$
	TaF_7^{-2}†	d^3sp^3	d^2
8	Dodecahedral	d^4sp^3	d
	Tetragonal antiprism‡	$d^4p^3(s,d)$	$[s,d]$
		d^5sp^2	p

* A distorted octahedron with one face centered.
† A distorted trigonal prism with one square face centered.
‡ A distorted trigonal prism with two square faces centered.

[29] Kimball, G. E., *J. Chem. Phys.*, **8**, 188 (1940).

attempted, furthermore, to examine them and to eliminate cases where the bonds would be weak. In particular, one can see from Fig. 3.3 that the d orbital $l = 2$, $m_l = 0$ has a large value along the z axis and a small but nonzero value in the xy plane. Consequently this orbital was assumed to form good bonds only along the z axis.

In Table 8.6 the first column contains the coordination number, and the second the geometry. The atomic orbitals of the central atom that can form strong σ bonds are listed next, and those that can form π bonds in the last column. Where the two orbitals are placed in parentheses, either may be used or a linear combination of both. In the last column the square brackets mean that this is the same set of orbitals that appeared in the σ bond column. For example, in a compound MX_5 with trigonal bipyramid configuration, the σ bonds can be formed from either dsp^3 or d^3sp orbitals. If π bonds are also present they may involve either d^4 or d^2p^2, respectively, depending on which orbitals were used for the σ bonds. One must remember that in many cases either ionic or repulsive steric forces may predominate over the directed valence forces, so that apparent exceptions to these results may arise.

8n. The benzene problem, mesomerism. There are certain molecules, including benzene, for which a single arrangement of co-valent bonds is not satisfactory. These molecules were a puzzle to early valence theory and are understandable only in terms of quantum theory. In the case of benzene one has a planar molecule with a σ bonding system of six C—C bonds and six C—H bonds. This accounts for 24 of the 30 valence electrons, and for the $2s$, $2p_x$, and $2p_y$ orbitals of the carbon atoms. There remain six electrons and the six $2p_z$ orbitals. The problem is reduced to that of the hypothetical molecule H_6, which was discussed in Sections 8h and 8i, except that the approximate geometry is already fixed by the system of σ bonds. Thus the question of the relative stability of three isolated H_2 molecules compared with H_6 does not arise here. One must assume either a regular or a nearly regular hexagonal arrangement.

If one follows the molecular orbital method, there is nothing very unusual about benzene. The six $2p_z$ orbitals are combined into three bonding molecular orbitals (and three antibonding orbitals). The six electrons occupy the three bonding orbitals, which might be said to contribute a half bond to each C—C linkage.

However, following bond orbital methods one may write wave

functions corresponding to either Kekulé structure (I and II of Fig. 8.10). Since each wave function gives the same energy, neither represents a satisfactory basic approximation. One must assume a linear combination, $a\psi_I + b\psi_{II}$, and let the variation method adjust a and b to give the lowest energy. Thus it is found that structures I and II contribute equally to ψ and that the energy is lower than that of either I or II.

The detailed analysis here is very similar to that of the electron pair bond itself. Thus if $\psi = a(\psi_I + \psi_{II})$, the physically significant probability function is

$$\psi^2 = a^2(\psi_I^2 + \psi_{II}^2 + 2\psi_I\psi_{II}) \tag{8.46}$$

with a merely the normalizing factor. Now the last term $\psi_I\psi_{II}$ is by no means negligible. Indeed it is responsible for the decrease in energy below that corresponding to ψ_I or ψ_{II} alone. Thus it should be remembered that benzene is not properly described as a mere time average of the two Kekulé forms. It has a distinct electronic structure that is not describable by simple bond diagrams at all.

In many respects it would seem best to simply discard the usual bond diagrams for molecules such as this, and to develop some other language. However, chemists have used such diagrams long enough that there is a strong tendency to save them in some way. The concept of *resonance*, which will be discussed in the next section, was extended for this purpose, largely by Pauling.[30] A somewhat similar system was developed on purely chemical bases by Ingold and Robinson[31] who propose the term *mesomerism*. (The latter was foreshadowed in part by the work of Arndt and co-workers.[32])

All these theories are similar in recognizing that a molecule may have an electronic structure intermediate between simple bond formulas.

We shall see that resonance is a method of quantum mechanical analysis which applies even more appropriately to some other problems. Consequently it seems desirable to use the term *mesomerism* in connection with electronic bonding systems not representable by

[30] Pauling, L., *The Nature of the Chemical Bond*, Ithaca: Cornell University Press, 1939; also a series of papers appearing in *J. Am. Chem. Soc.* and *J. Chem. Phys.*, 1931-1933.

[31] Ingold, C. K., *Nature*, **141**, 314 (1938); Ingold, C. K. and Ingold, E. H., *J. Chem. Soc.*, (**1926**), p. 1310; Robinson, R. *et al.*, *J. Chem. Soc.*, (**1926**), p. 401.

[32] Arndt, F., Scholz, E., and Nachtwey, P., *Ber.* **57**, 1903 (1924).

one bond structure. However, it should be realized that the term *resonance* is also commonly used in this sense.

The term *mesomerism* applies to the electronic structure. The mesomeric molecule has a single arrangement of the nuclei which may be intermediate between that expected for any one bond structure. However, the difference in nuclear configuration between the various bond structures must not be very great or mesomerism will not arise.

80. Resonance. The term *resonance* has long been used to denote phenomena which arise when two systems have very closely the same natural frequency. It normally implies systems almost completely isolated from each other, so that little interaction is expected unless resonance occurs. For example, suppose two pendulums are suspended from the same slightly flexible rod, as indicated in Fig. 8.11. If the two have different natural frequencies, each will behave as if the other were not there. However, if the two pendulums have exactly the same frequency, when one is excited the energy is gradually transferred to the other and then back again, etc.

The direction of energy transfer depends on the phase difference between the two oscillators. With appreciably different frequencies,

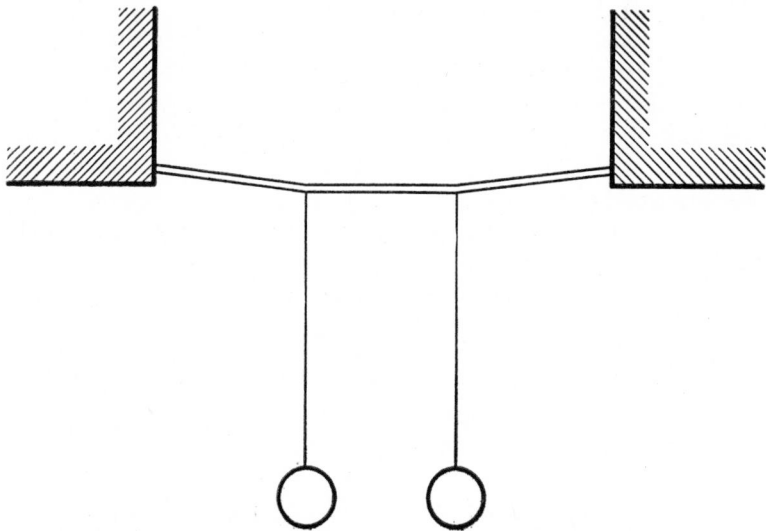

Fig. 8.11.   A pair of pendulums subject to resonance.

this phase difference is continually changing so that energy is first transferred one way and then the other. For real resonance to occur the phase difference must remain constant until essentially all the energy is transferred.

Heisenberg[33] was the first to point out the presence of a resonance-like phenomenon in quantum theory. To illustrate it in simplest terms, let us consider a one-dimensional problem of a particle and two potential boxes or wells separated by a moderate barrier, as illustrated in Fig. 8.12.

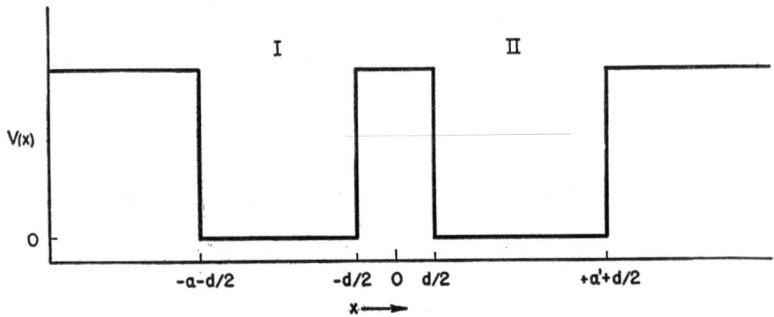

Fig. 8.12.   Potential energy curve for a particle in two boxes.

Now particularly if $a = a'$ it is easy enough to solve this problem exactly. However, let us approach it by obtaining the solutions for the particle in one box, neglecting the other box. These wave functions will then be introduced as components in a linear variation function. We shall regard a as variable and note the behavior as a becomes equal to a'.

The solution for a particle in one box is given in Section 2h. The variation method equations have been given several times. Letting ψ_I and ψ_{II} be the two normalized wave functions and as usual,

$$H_{I,I} = \int \psi_I H \psi_I \, dv$$
$$H_{II,II} = \int \psi_{II} H \psi_{II} \, dv$$
$$H_{I,II} = \int \psi_I H \psi_{II} \, dv$$
$$\Delta = \int \psi_I \psi_{II} \, dv \qquad (8.47)$$

$$\begin{vmatrix} H_{I,I} - W & H_{I,II} - \Delta W \\ H_{II,I} - \Delta W & H_{II,II} - W \end{vmatrix} = 0$$

[33] Heisenberg, W., Z. Physik, 38, 411 (1926).

Since the mathematical methods involved in this problem are familiar, we merely indicate in Fig. 8.13 the results in graphical form with the true energy levels shown as solid lines and the one-box "component" levels dotted.   One notes that the lowest true energy level is always lower than either of the one-box component levels. However, more important is the feature that this lowering is much greater when the two component levels are of equal energy.   This is

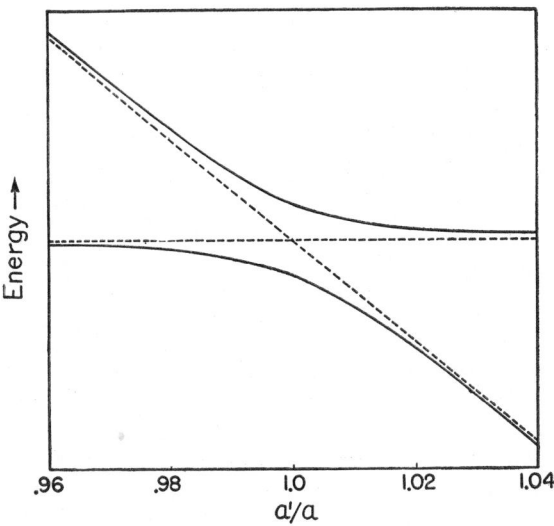

Fig. 8.13.   The energy levels of the two-box system shown in Fig. 8.12.   Solid lines are the true energy levels, broken lines are single box energies.   The numerical values of a'/a shown are valid only for a particular set of values of other parameters.

the analogy to classical resonance, where the interaction is important only when the component frequencies are the same.

A good example of resonance is that first recognized by Fermi[34] where excited vibrational quantum states in polyatomic molecules interact unexpectedly when their energies are accidentally close together.   This will be discussed further in a later chapter.

The term resonance has come to have additional, related meanings in quantum theory.   It is used in cases such as benzene, where the

[34] Fermi, E., *Z. Physik*, **71**, 250 (1931).

interaction is not very small. Thus the π bonding energy of a single Kekulé structure is 1.5α (Section 8i), while the energy of the lowest resulting state after considering mesomerism is 2.6α. The interaction energy of 1.1α is thus almost as large as the bonding energy of the component state. This is much as if two pendulums were fastened together by a strong spring rather than having a weak interaction through their supporting rod.

Now if the interaction is large, even component structures of higher energy may have an effect on the lowest resulting state. This also was illustrated in the H_6 or benzene case where the Dewar structures (III, IV, and V in Fig. 8.10) have distinctly higher energy than the Kekulé structures. However, their inclusion lowers the resulting lowest state from 2.4α to 2.61α.

By now the situation has lost most of its resemblance to classical resonance. In this extended sense, resonance is a method of quantum mechanical calculation in which the linear variation function is employed. The only further characteristic is that the component functions should have some meaning by themselves, as in the case of the Kekulé structures of benzene or the particle in one box functions for the two-box problem.

It should always be remembered that the use of the resonance method is optional and may yield only a crude approximation. There will be other methods of expressing or approximating the true wave functions and energy levels. The justification of the resonance method for mesomeric molecules should be its success in correlating experimentally determined quantities and predicting others. The quantum mechanical understanding of mesomeric molecules such as benzene can be had either with or without the resonance method.

This extensive discussion is not intended to either favor or oppose the resonance viewpoint in electronic binding. Rather its purpose is to show the proper relationship of resonance to quantum mechanical theory and to the chemists' language of electron pair bonds.

8p. Resonance energies, conditions for mesomerism. It was seen in the preceding section that the energy of the lowest resulting state in a resonance problem is never higher than, and is usually appreciably lower than, that of the lowest component state. This energy difference is known as the *resonance energy*. The resonance energy may be calculated from bond energies and thermal data. It may also be calculated to a certain approximation from quantum theory.

As an example let us calculate the resonance energy of benzene. From calorimetric data, the heat of formation of benzene gas[35] from graphite and hydrogen is $\Delta H = 24.00$ kcal./mole at $0°$K. The total bond energy for a Kekulé structure is 1266, while the energy of dissociation of 6C and $3H_2$ to atoms is 1332.0 kcal./mole. Thus the expected heat of formation of Kekulé benzene is $\Delta H = 66$, giving a resonance energy of 66 less 24 or 42 kcal./mole.

There is an ambiguity in the definition of resonance energy, and its consideration will bring out an important factor in mesomerism. The true nuclear configuration of a mesomeric molecule is seldom identical with that expected for the lowest bond structure. It is customary to compare the energies with each in its equilibrium con-

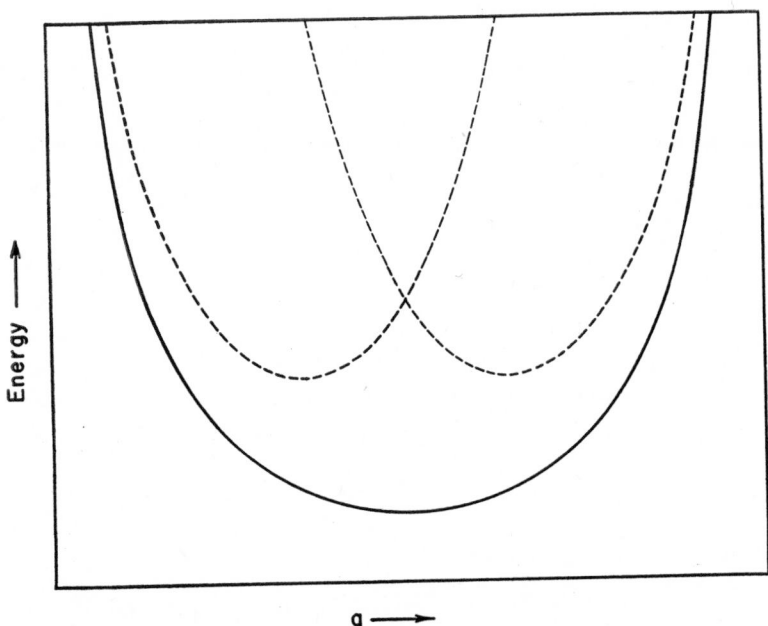

Fig. 8.14.   Energy diagram for a mesomeric molecule—see text.

[35] Rossini, F. D. et al., Selected Values of Properties of Hydrocarbons, Natl. Bur. Standards Circular C461, Washington: Government Printing Office, 1947.

figuration. However, for some purposes one probably should use the energies for the same configuration of nuclei. If the difference in nuclear configuration of the component electronic structures is too great, the true mesomeric molecule may not have a single equilibrium configuration. This is illustrated in Figs. 8.14 and 8.15.

The dotted lines indicate the expected energy of each component bond structure, while the solid line shows the true energy of the mesomeric molecule. The horizontal coordinate q measures the difference in nuclear position between those corresponding to the component structures. In actual cases more than one such coordinate[36]

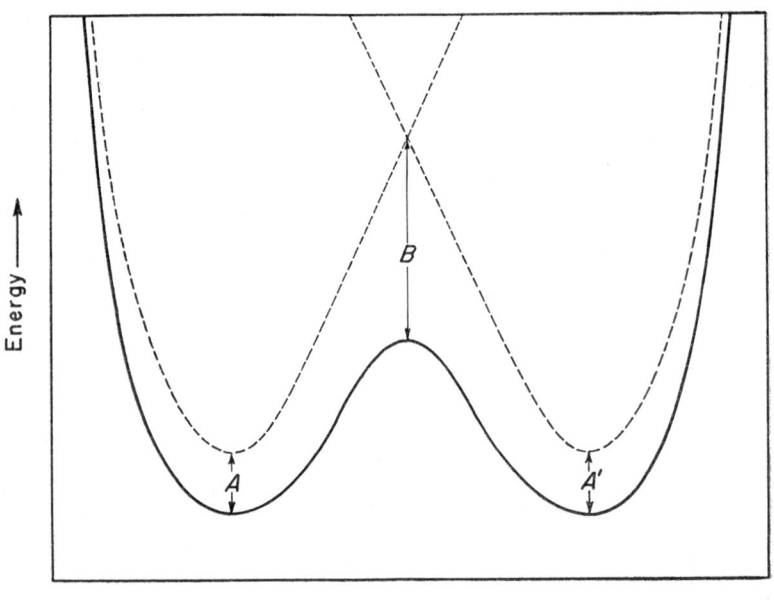

Fig. 8.15.   Energy diagram showing tautomeric forms.

[36] For benzene we might take the difference between successive C—C bond lengths as our first coordinate. Normal single C—C bonds are 1.54 A while double bonds are about 1.34 A. Thus the minima corresponding to the Kekulé structures are at −0.20 and +0.20 A. Benzene actually has all C—C bond lengths equal and 1.39 A. Thus this coordinate is zero for the true potential minimum. However, another coordinate would be the average bond length, and we see that it changes from 1.44 A for a Kekulé structure to 1.39 A at the true minimum. The effect of these coordinates on the energy of benzene has been given by Hornig, D. F., *J. Am. Chem. Soc.*, **72**, 5772 (1950).

would usually be needed. Figure 8.14 shows the case where the resonance lowers the energy of an intermediate configuration to give a single potential minimum (as in benzene). However, where the difference in configuration of component structures is great, as in Fig. 8.15, there are two potential minima and consequently two tautomeric (or isomeric) forms of the substance. Each tautomer may have a resonance energy A and A', while the potential barrier between the tautomers may be lowered by an even greater resonance energy B.

The magnitude of the resonance energy is, of course, primarily determined by the interaction integral $H_{I,II}$, Eq. (8.47). It is not easy to predict its value except that under certain conditions it will be very small.

1. If there are different numbers of unpaired electrons, the spin factors will be different in ψ_I and ψ_{II}. Then to the first approximation $H_{I,II}$ is zero. Due to spin-orbit interactions, higher approximations may give a small value to $H_{I,II}$ but not large enough to give appreciable resonance energy.

2. Unless ψ_I and ψ_{II} have appreciable values for the same configuration of all particles, including electrons, $H_{I,II}$ will be small. Since the amplitudes of electronic motion are usually of the magnitude of a bond length (1-2 A), the interaction is large if electrons are moved no further than adjacent bonds or atoms.

Thus if conditions (1) and (2) above are satisfied, mesomerism will arise, but will be important only if the energies and nuclear configurations of the component structures are very similar.

Empirical resonance energies have been calculated by Pauling and Sherman[37] for a number of mesomeric molecules. Relatively extensive tables are given elsewhere[38] from which a few representative values are given in Table 8.7. In order to have a sense of proportion with respect to these values, it should be remembered that Table 8.5 showed nonmesomeric molecules to be as much as 4 kcal. more stable than calculated from bond energies. Thus unless the indicated resonance energy exceeds 5 kcal. one can hardly be sure that the mesomerism is significant.

In addition the molecule carbon monoxide should be mentioned. On the molecular orbital basis its electronic structure is entirely

[37] Pauling, L. and Sherman, J., *J. Chem. Phys.*, **1**, 606 (1933).
[38] Pauling, L., *The Nature of the Chemical Bond*, Ithaca: Cornell University Press, 1939. Also, Branch, G. E. K. and Calvin, M., *The Theory of Organic Chemistry*, New York: Prentice-Hall, Inc., 1941.

TABLE 8.7

EMPIRICAL RESONANCE ENERGIES

(From Pauling,[38] unless labeled "revised." The first structure given
is the reference point for the resonance energy)

Substance	Structures	Resonance energy
Benzene		42 (revised)
Naphthalene		75
Anthracene	plus 3 others of equal energy	105
Phenanthrene	plus 4 others of equal energy	115
1,3-Butadiene		1 (revised)
Styrene	and 2 others similar to the last	48 (revised)
Pyridine		43
Pyrrole	and 3 others similar to the last	31
Acids		28
Urea		37
Carbon dioxide	$O{=}C{=}O$, $\overset{+}{O}{\equiv}C{-}\bar{O}$, $\bar{O}{-}C{\equiv}\overset{+}{O}$	33

analogous to that of nitrogen. The same molecular orbitals are occupied, although the electron density naturally is shifted toward the oxygen nucleus because of its greater charge. Indeed the similarity of physical properties, dissociation energies, etc. between carbon monoxide and nitrogen make this approach a very satisfactory one. On the bond orbital basis one may write the structures

$$:C: :O: \qquad A$$
$$^-:C: : :O:^+ \qquad B$$
$$^+:C:\ddot{O}:^- \qquad C$$

no one of which is at all satisfactory by itself. Thus both A and C show an incomplete valence shell for carbon, suggesting high reactivity and instability in extreme disagreement with the actual properties of carbon monoxide. Similarly both B and C indicate large (but opposite) dipole moment. The actual dipole moment is very small, in fact barely measurable. Only by assuming mesomerism involving all these structures, and with a great energy stabilization from any of them, can the properties of carbon monoxide be explained on the bond orbital basis.

This situation for carbon monoxide again emphasizes that it is not the mesomeric molecule itself that is peculiar, but rather the inadequacy of bond symbolism and language that makes the molecule appear peculiar. In many cases molecular orbital methods can treat mesomeric molecules in exactly the same way as other molecules. Indeed, when one attempts to calculate resonance energies by the molecular orbital method, one finds it necessary to make an arbitrary decision as to the energy of a component state, while the energy of the true molecule arises from a straightforward calculation.

Calculations of resonance energies have been carried out following both the molecular orbital and bond orbital methods for the π electron systems in certain mesomeric molecules. Taking benzene as an example, the problem of the 6π electrons is formally identical with the calculations for H_6 in Sections 8h and 8i. The bond orbital method introduced Kekulé structures into the calculation; consequently one has very explicitly the value $W_b = 1.5\alpha$ for the energy of a Kekulé structure. The more complete resonance calculation, considering the 3 Dewar structures (III to V in Fig. 8.10) as well as the two Kekulé structures, yielded $W_b = 2.61\alpha$. The difference of 1.11α is then the resonance energy.   By following exactly the same methods, analogous results can be obtained for naphthalene, anthracene, and phenanthrene.   In each case the result is in terms of the exchange integral for adjacent π orbitals, α.   Thus a single value of α should fit all this series of molecules.   This comparison is given in Table 8.10.

In the molecular orbital method some assumption must be made concerning the energy of the reference structure from which the empirical resonance energies are calculated.   It is customary to simply count the bonds in the π electron system and assign the value 2β obtained for an isolated bond to each bond in the larger system.   Thus for benzene, the reference value is 6β; and with a calculated energy of 8β, the resonance energy of 2β is obtained.   The results for larger molecules are given in Table 8.8 also.

Table 8.8
Calculated Resonance Energies

Substance	Empirical R.E.	Bond orbital R.E.	α	Molecular orbital R.E.	β
Benzene	42	1.11α	38	2.00β	21
Naphthalene	75	2.04α	37	3.68β	20
Anthracene	105	3.09α	34	5.32β	20
Phenanthrene	115	3.15α	37	5.45β	21
Cyclobutadiene	?	1.00α	?	0	?

The two methods agree reasonably well with each other and with the relative empirical values for the four known substances, but it will be noted that the two methods are in complete disagreement for the hypothetical cyclobutadiene.   Consequently, it is very important to use both methods wherever possible.   Much more weight can be given to a calculated result if both have been used and are in reasonable agreement.

8q. Conjugation and hyperconjugation.   Organic chemists have long recognized the distinction between a pair of double bonds separated by one single bond, and a more widely separated pair of double bonds.   In the first case they are said to be conjugated (as in 1,3-butadiene) because in many cases they react as a combined unit.   The 1,4 addition reaction (with transfer of the double bond to the 2,3 position) is an example.   Also, the ultraviolet absorption spectrum of a conjugated diene is distinctly different from that of a simple olefin.   However, if the pair of double bonds is separated by two or more single bonds, the chemical and physical properties are just those expected of the individual double bonds.

In Table 8.7 the resonance energy of 1,3-butadiene was too small to be really significant in view of the uncertainty in bond energy calculations. A more accurate estimate can be obtained from the extensive series of precise heats of hydrogenation measured by Kistiakowsky and co-workers.[39] The values are listed in Table 8.9 for mono-olefins and in Table 8.10 for polyolefins. Values for a number of ring compounds are listed but will be discussed at this point only where possible ring strain effects can be eliminated.

On examining the values in Table 8.9 we at once note that, even for the mono-olefins, the heat of hydrogenation is not constant. Rather it appears to depend on the number of alkyl groups adjacent to the double bond. The first two alkyl groups lower the olefin

TABLE 8.9

HEATS OF HYDROGENATION OF MONO-OLEFINS

(In kcal./mole at 355°K for the gas state)

	Substance	Heat of hydrogenation	Hyperconjugation energy
1	Ethylene	32.82	. .
2	Propylene	30.12	2.7
3	1-Butene	30.34	2.5
4	1-Heptene	30.14	2.7
5	*i*-Propylethylene	30.33	2.5
6	*neo*-Pentylethylene	29.53	3.3
7	*t*-Butylethylene	30.34	2.5
8	2-Butene (*cis*)	28.57	4.2
9	2-Butene (*trans*)	27.62	5.2
10	2-Pentene (*cis* and *trans* mixture)	27.95	4.9
11	*i*-Butene	28.39	4.4
12	2-Methyl, 1-butene	28.49	4.3
13	2,3-Dimethyl, 1-butene	28.00	4.8
14	2,4,4-Trimethyl, 1-pentene	27.24	5.6
15	Trimethylethylene	26.92	5.9
16	Tetramethylethylene	26.63	6.2
17	Cyclopentene	26.92	. .
18	Cyclohexene	28.59	. .
19	Cycloheptene	26.52	. .
20	Cyclo-octene	23.52	. .

[39] Kistiakowsky, G. B., and many co-workers, *J. Am. Chem. Soc.*, 1935 to 1939.

TABLE 8.10

HEATS OF HYDROGENATION OF POLYOLEFINS, ACETYLENES, ETC.

(In kcal. per mole at 355°K for the gas state)

	Substance	Heat of Hydrogenation		Reference subst.	Conjugation* energy
		Obs.	Calc.		
21	1,4-Pentadiene	60.79	60.68	3	..
22	1,5-Hexadiene	60.52	60.68	3	..
23	1,3-Butadiene	57.07	60.68	3	3.6
24	1,3-Pentadiene	54.11	58.29	3,10	4.2
25	2,3-Dimethyl-1,3-butadiene	53.87	56.78	11	2.9
26	Benzene	49.80	..	..	..
27	Ethylbenzene	48.92	49.80	26	0.9*
28	o-Xylene	47.25	49.80	26	2.5*
29	Mesitylene	47.62	49.80	26	2.2*
30	Styrene	77.48	82.62	26,1	5.1
			79.26	27,3	1.8
31	Allene	71.28			
32	1,3-Cyclopentadiene	50.87			
33	1,3-Cyclohexadiene	55.37			
34	1,3-Cycloheptadiene	51.26			
35	Hydrindene	45.80			
36	1,3,5-Cycloheptatriene	72.85			
37	Indene	69.91			
38	Acetylene	75.06			
39	Methylacetylene	69.70	75.06	38	5.4*
40	Dimethylacetylene	65.58	75.06	38	9.5*

* The values so designated are hyperconjugation energies.

energy by about 2.5 kcal. each. This effect was discussed by Mulliken, Rieke, and Brown,[40] who named it *hyperconjugation*. The term *hyperconjugation* is used when an alkyl group or other array of several single bonds is involved instead of one of the multiple bonds. Their explanation was in molecular orbital language somewhat as follows. Let us discuss propylene, taking the configuration as shown in Fig. 8.16.

The only orbitals antisymmetric to the plane of the carbon atoms we may take as $2p_z$ for the carbons A, B, and C, and the combination $(1s_D - 1s_E)$ of the hydrogen orbitals on atoms D and E. As an initial approximation these may be combined into bonding molecular orbitals as follows.

[40] Mulliken, R. S., Rieke, C. A., and Brown, W. G., *J. Am. Chem. Soc.*, **63**, 41 (1941).

$$\psi_I = a(2p_{zA}) + b(2p_{zB})$$
$$\psi_{II} = c(2p_{zC}) + d(1s_D - 1s_E)$$

$$(8.48)$$

where ψ_I represents the second or π bond of the C=C double bond, and ψ_{II} is part of the CH_3 bonding system.   In ethylene there would be just the orbital ψ_I.   However, in propylene an interaction is possible between ψ_I and ψ_{II}.

This may be regarded as a resonance calculation with ψ_I and ψ_{II} for the lowest molecular orbital, but it must be remembered that in this case the second pair of electrons must occupy the next higher energy molecular orbital.   Thus in this calculation one should con-

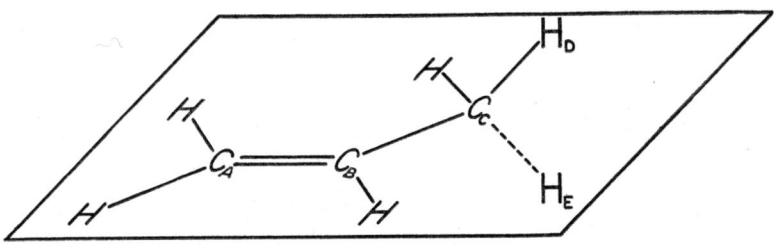

Fig. 8.16.   Configuration of propylene.

sider the four orbitals mentioned above ($2p_z$ for atoms A, B, and C and the combination for D and E) as four components of a linear variation function.   The two lowest energy molecular orbitals are then occupied by pairs of electrons.   The mathematical details will not be given, but one can readily see that in this case there can be some increase of electron density between atoms B and C.   This extra space at low potential energy will lower the total electronic energy for the same reasons that were given for the electron pair bond itself.

Turning now to the diolefins, one finds that the conjugation energy is about 3.5 kcal., which is a little larger than the hyperconjugation energy of an alkyl group with a double bond.   The conjugation energy of a vinyl group with a benzene ring is even less.   The explanation of conjugation is simple enough.   In 1,3-butadiene in planar configuration one has the $2p_z$ orbitals of all four carbon atoms to combine.   Following exactly the same method used above for hyperconjugation, one expects a lowering of energy when all four atoms are considered together (as compared with the two double bonds considered separately). However, one might have expected the interaction of two π bonds to be considerably greater than the interaction of the π bond with the C—H bonds in propylene.

In conclusion, the state of our understanding of these small (1–5 kcal.) irregularities in the energy content of molecules is still far from satisfactory. Since they are largely unexplained in the paraffin molecules, one is not very confident of the present explanation in the olefins. However, for the excited electronic states, conjugation is clearly important (and much more so than hyperconjugation). This is shown by the marked changes in absorption spectra and in chemical reactions. Also it seems probable that conjugation and hyperconjugation may be particularly important when an otherwise vacant orbital is available as in $B(CH_3)_3$ or the carbonium ion $C(CH_3)_3^+$. These molecules appear to be considerably stabilized by interaction of the C—H bond electrons with the vacant orbital on B or C^+, but it is difficult to make quantitative estimates of the effect at present.

8r. Discontinuous change of bond type. In Section 8f we discussed the transition from ionic to covalent bonding in the normal case where there is no change in electron spin. In that case it was shown that there is a continuous transition as the relative electronegativity of the atoms shifts. However, there are certain polyatomic systems, usually complex ions, where the most stable ionically bonded state has a different orientation of electron spins from that of the most stable covalently bonded state. As an example let us consider the complex ions of bivalent nickel of the type NiX_4. Nickel

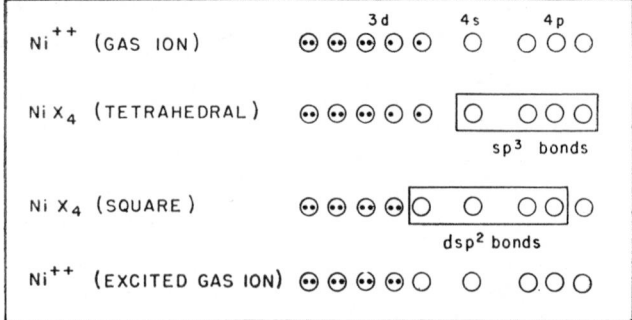

Fig. 8.17. Orbital assignments of electrons in nickel ion and complexes.

has atomic number 28. Consequently there are 8 electrons in the valence shell of Ni^{++} after the $1s$, $2s$, $2p$, $3s$, and $3p$ shells are filled. In the gas ion these eight electrons occupy the five $3d$ orbitals; and, following the usual rules, there will be a pair of electrons in each of three of the orbitals and a single electron each in the other two orbitals. The top line of Fig. 8.17 indicates this situation in a diagram.

If a complex NiX_4 is covalently bonded using pairs of electrons from the X groups, then four additional orbitals are needed. These can be the $4s$ and three $4p$ orbitals as indicated on the second line of Fig. 8.17. In this case the bonds would be based on tetrahedral, sp^3, hybrid orbitals for the nickel. There could be a continuous transition

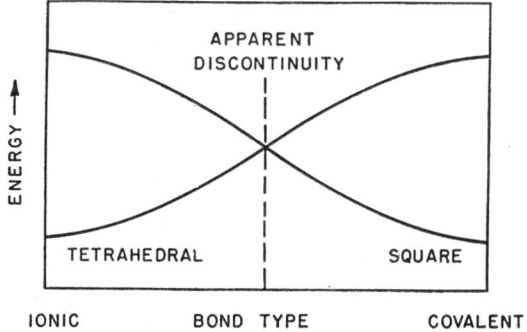

Fig. 8.18. The energy curves for square and tetrahedral nickel complexes as a function of bond type.

between this state and the normal nickel ion as is indicated by the line labeled tetrahedral on Fig. 8.18.

However, in Table 8.3 one sees that four bond orbitals can also be based on dsp^2 hybrids, which have a planar square orientation and a higher bond strength (2.694) than the tetrahedral hybrids (2.000). If the X groups are highly charged, the closer approach required by the square configuration would yield greater electrostatic repulsion than in the tetrahedral configuration. But if the groups are nearly neutral, this difference can be ignored. Consequently, it seems plausible that some covalently bonded complexes will have lower energy with square, dsp^2, bonds. This requires that one $3d$ orbital be available for bonding, which can be attained by placing all eight valence electrons of the Ni^{++} in four $3d$ orbitals. The third line in Fig. 8.17

indicates this situation. Of course, this state does not have to be purely covalent. There will be resonance and therefore a continuous transition with the excited ionic state indicated on line four. This is shown as the line labeled square on Fig. 8.18.

The square and tetrahedral systems do not interact with one another. In terms of the analysis in Section 8f it is because all integrals involving both a tetrahedral wave function and a square wave function are zero. The complete wave functions include factors for electron spin, and since the spin orientations are different in the two cases, the spin factors are orthogonal. Also in this example, but not in all examples of discontinuous change of bond type, the geometrical positions of the groups are grossly different, which would also make these integrals substantially zero. One should remember that the difference of spin orientation is the more generally useful criterion.

Thus if electronegativity and other characteristics of a given X group are such that it falls to the left of the crossing on Fig. 8.18, the stable state of the complex will be tetrahedral, whereas if it falls to the right the stable state will be square. It should be clearly understood that all complexes will be intermediate between ionic and covalent in their bond type, but that one may presume that the square complexes of Ni^{II} are more covalent than the tetrahedral complexes.

In the case of nickel both types are found experimentally, as indicated in Table 8.11. However, the corresponding complexes of bivalent palladium and bivalent platinum are all of the square type.

TABLE 8.11

EXAMPLES OF DISCONTINUOUS CHANGE OF BOND TYPE

Substance	Orientation	Magnetic susceptibility
$K_2Ni(CN)_4$, and $K_2Ni(CN)_4 \cdot H_2O$	Square	Diamagnetic
Nickel dithio-oxalate, etc.	Square	Diamagnetic
$Ni(NH_3)_4SO_4$, $Ni(N_2H_4)_2(NO_3)_2$	Tetrahedral (?)	Paramagnetic
Aqueous Ni^{++}	Tetrahedral (?)	Paramagnetic
$NiCl_2$	Tetrahedral (?)	Paramagnetic
$PdCl_2$	Square	Diamagnetic

The configuration of complexes such as those in Table 8.11 can be determined by x-ray diffraction studies on their crystals. Actually a more convenient experimental criterion is the magnetic susceptibility. The square complexes, with all of their electrons paired, have no magnetic moment and are therefore weakly diamagnetic. All electron clouds with fully paired electrons can be shown to be weakly diamagnetic.

However, the tetrahedral complexes and the simple ion have two unpaired electrons, which according to the Hund rules, Section 5e, will have their spins parallel in the lowest state. This is then a triplet state with a net magnetic moment corresponding to at least that of two electron spins. Since the $3d$ shell is over half full, any orbital magnetic moment should be in the direction of increasing that of the two electron spins. We shall not go through the quantitative relationship of magnetic moment with magnetic susceptibility at this point, since mere paramagnetism is a sufficient criterion. In cases where both of the possible states have unpaired electrons but one has a larger number of net electron spins than the other, it is necessary to use these quantitative magnetic susceptibility relationships. These are given in Section 12e.

8s. Multicenter bonds. Electron pair bonds ordinarily connect two atoms, but in some cases may unite three or more atoms. The simplest possible example is the molecule ion H_3^+. In molecular orbital theory this molecule is easily handled. If the protons A, B, and C are located at the points of an equilateral triangle, the simplest molecular orbital is

$$\psi_{M.O.} = (1s_A + 1s_B + 1s_B)/\sqrt{3} \qquad (8.49)$$

analogous to Eq. (8.33) for H_2. Following calculations similar to those in Section 8h one finds an orbital energy of $E_H + 2\beta$. Placing two electrons in this orbital, one finds for the total bond energy of H_3^+ (compared to $2H + H^+$) of 4β. Also since the bond energy of H_2 on this model is 2β one predicts that the reaction

$$H_2 + H^+ = H_3^+$$

should be exothermic by 2β or roughly the H_2 bond energy.

The bond orbital method treats H_3^+ as a mesomeric system based on the three component structures:

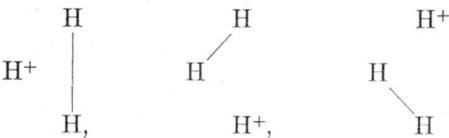

As one expects, the sum combination of the separate bond orbitals yields the ground energy state. The Heitler-London type of ψ is

$$\psi = [1s_A(1)1s_B(2) + 1s_A(2)1s_B(1) + 1s_A(1)1s_C(2) + 1s_A(2)1s_C(1)$$
$$+ 1s_B(1)1s_C(2) + 1s_B(2)1s_C(1)]/\sqrt{6} \qquad (8.50)$$

and carrying out the remaining calculations, the crudest approximation to the total energy is $E_{2H} + \alpha + 2\beta$. Since the energy of H_2 is $E_{2H} + \alpha$ on this approximation, the bonding energy of the proton to H_2 is 2β, which is exactly that given by the molecular orbital treatment. Indeed, the appearance of the molecular orbital exchange integral β in the bond orbital resonance calculation is surprising.

Hirschfelder[41] has studied the H_3^+ ion, using somewhat better wave functions and the variation method. His best result is a bond energy of 184 kcal./mole (without zero point vibrational energy). His method is essentially equivalent to the Wang calculation for H_2 (see Appendix 4) which gives 92.2 kcal./mole. Thus our earlier result, that the additional bond energy of a proton to H_2 (to form H_3^+) is equal to the H_2 bond energy, holds to this higher approximation. While H_3^+ is of little chemical importance, its high bond energy indicates that such multicenter bonds may be generally important.

Probably the most interesting application of multicenter bonds is in diborane, B_2H_6. While most univalent atoms and radicals such as F, Cl, Br, CH_3, etc., form with boron the expected BR_3 type of molecule, BH_3 is unknown and its dimer B_2H_6 is the simplest boron hydride. After a long period of investigation, discussion, and controversy, it is now established[42] that diborane has the structure shown in Fig. 8.19. Presumably the terminal B—H bonds are normal electron pair bonds. This leaves four electrons to bond the two central hydrogens and the borons together. Since each of the boron atoms has two valence shell orbitals available for this central bonding system, there is considerable freedom to the electronic system which constitutes a four-center four-electron system.

Perhaps the simplest description of this system is to put each pair of electrons in a three-center molecular orbital made up of the $1s$

[41] Hirschfelder, J. O., *J. Chem. Phys.*, **6**, 795 (1938).

[42] See Stock, A., *Hydrides of Boron and Silicon*, Ithaca: Cornell University Press, 1933; Bauer, S. H., *Chem. Rev.* **31**, 43 (1942) for reviews of the earlier period. Recent work includes Longuet-Higgins, H. C. and Bell, R. P., *J. Chem. Soc.*, **(1943)**, 250; Pitzer, K. S., *J. Am. Chem. Soc.*, **67**, 1126 (1945); Price, W. C., *J. Chem. Phys.*, **16**, 894 (1948).

orbital from a hydrogen and an s-p hybrid orbital from each boron. The boron atoms can furnish an atomic orbital to each molecular orbital. If these three-center orbitals bind the third particle with an energy at all comparable with that in H_3^+, it is easy to see that this B_2H_6 molecule should be quite stable as compared to two BH_3.

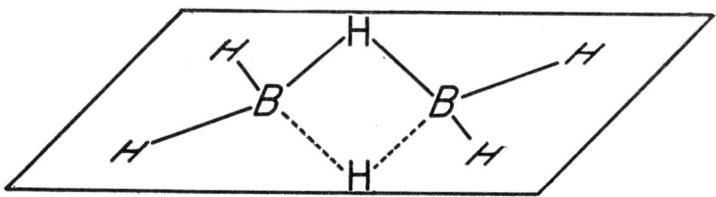

Fig. 8.19.   Configuration of diborane.

A mesomeric description[43] can be given for the central bond in diborane.   Probably the most important components are

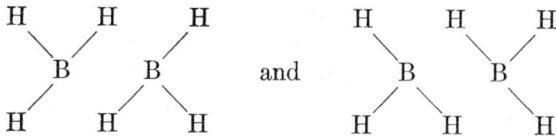

However, this system differs from that discussed for the hypothetical molecule H_4 in that two different orbitals are available for each boron atom, one pointed toward each hydrogen.   The presence of these orbitals also allows the structures

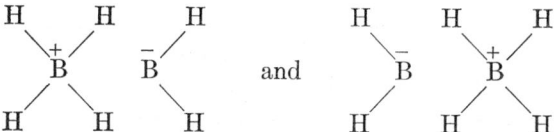

It has been pointed out that[44] a boron-boron double bond structure

$$
\begin{array}{c}
H \qquad\qquad\qquad H \\
\diagdown \;_{-}\;\; H^{+} \;_{-}\; \diagup \\
B\!\!=\!\!=\!\!=\!\!B \\
\diagup \qquad H^{+} \qquad \diagdown \\
H \qquad\qquad\qquad H
\end{array}
$$

[43] Longuet-Higgins and Bell, Ref. 42.
[44] Pitzer, Ref. 42.

actually implies (Section 8j) an electron density extending out around the protons qualitatively similar to that implied by the array of mesomeric structures given above.   Hence the name *protonated double bond* was suggested for this four-electron four-center linkage.

Another similar type of multicenter bond is that appearing in the metal ion-olefin complexes.   In the silver ion-olefin complex

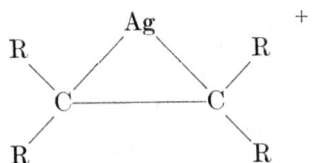

the situation is entirely analogous to that in diborane except that only one three-center orbital is needed, the second pair of electrons forming a normal carbon-carbon bond.

Multicenter orbitals arise for a class of molecules which may be termed *electron deficient*.   When the atoms of such molecules have formed all possible normal electron pair bonds, certain atoms have not completed their valence shells.   Thus in BH_3 there is a vacant valence shell orbital for boron.   Whenever attached atoms have un-shared electron pairs, as in BCl_3, mesomerism of the type

$$+ : \ddot{C}l = \bar{B} \diagup_{Cl}^{Cl}$$

stabilizes the molecule further.   In $B(CH_3)_3$, hyperconjugation of the analogous type occurs.   However, where such stabilizing effects are impossible or insufficient, multicenter bonds may be formed to make use of these low-energy orbitals.   The *important principle* is that *all low-energy orbitals must be employed in the bonding system in some way.*

Atoms with valence shells less than half filled lead to the electron deficiency in molecules.   Substances composed entirely of such atoms are metals, whose binding is thus closely related to multicenter orbitals.   Furthermore, essentially metallic binding is found in the molecule $B_{10}H_{14}$, whose boron atoms show coordination numbers of five and six.[45]

[45] Kasper, J. S., Lucht, C. M., and Harker, D., *J. Am. Chem. Soc.*, **70,** 881 (1948).

8t. Metallic binding. Many qualitative characteristics of metals which were unexplainable in classical mechanics were readily shown to be consistent with quantum mechanical predictions. In particular, the concept of relatively free electrons, which is supported by electric conductivity, etc., had required a high electronic heat capacity of $\frac{3}{2}R$ per mole of electrons in classical mechanics. Actual heat capacities of metals show no such values. The properties of a degenerate Fermi gas, however, are consistent with both the low electronic specific heat and the ready conduction of electricity.

The binding energy of the metal atoms in the crystal cannot be satisfactorily calculated on such a simple Fermi gas model. Some partially successful binding energy calculations have been carried out by more complex methods. They involve mathematical developments which seem more appropriate to Chapter 10, where other properties of solid metals are considered further. Consequently, only a very qualitative discussion of metallic binding will be given here.

Just as for molecular problems, there are two general approaches to metallic bonding: the bond orbital and the molecular orbital. In this case the molecular orbitals are for the entire lattice. This method of attack was started by Bloch,[46] who showed that an appropriate form of molecular orbital for a lattice was

$$\psi = e^{i(k_x x + k_y y + k_z z)} f_k(x,y,z) \tag{8.51}$$

where f_k is a periodic function which returns to the same value at each equivalent point in the lattice. One notes at once that the exponential factor is just that for a free electron, so that the usual Fermi gas result is obtained with f a constant and with appropriate linear combinations of Ψ's to satisfy the boundary conditions.

The remainder of the molecular orbital calculation for a binding energy was supplied by Wigner and Seitz,[47] who developed an approximate method of solving the Schrödinger equation for a Bloch type function. Reasonably satisfactory results were obtained for lithium and sodium, but even potassium gave poor agreement, and atoms with more than one valence electron are much more difficult to handle.

The fundamental reason for binding in metals is the same as in electron pair bonds. There is additional probability of finding electrons in the low-potential energy regions between nuclei.

[46] Bloch, F., *Z. Physik*, **52**, 555 (1928).
[47] Wigner, E. and Seitz, F., *Phys. Rev.* **43**, 804 (1933); **46**, 509 (1934).

The bond orbital method has been applied to metals principally by Pauling.[48] Taking lithium as an example, each atom has eight equivalent neighbors at the corners of a cube, together with six somewhat more distant neighbors. Since each atom has only one valence electron, an ordinary electron pair bond can be formed with only one neighbor at a time. However, the concept of mesomerism or resonance suggests that this bonding electron pair may be first between one pair of atoms, then another, and another. The difference between hydrogen, which is not metallic, and lithium, is that lithium has three $2p$ orbitals available in addition to the $2s$ orbital. This will allow the inclusion in the resonance calculation of structures such as

$$\text{Li—Li}^- \ \text{Li—}$$
$$\hspace{1.8cm}|$$
$$\text{Li} \quad \text{Li} \quad \text{Li}^+$$
$$|$$
$$\text{Li} \quad \text{Li—Li}$$

where there are two bonds to one atom and none to another.

This situation is somewhat analogous to that in diborane, which was discussed in terms of multicenter orbitals. It appears to be safe to conclude that resonance energies are greatly enhanced by the presence of otherwise vacant valence shell orbitals, which allow one electron pair bond to move about independently of the position of others. Electric repulsions will naturally prevent large accumulations of charge. However, the limitation of the Pauli exclusion principle with respect to the orbitals available is absolute. Thus the presence of extra valence shell orbitals is very important for either metallic bonding or the multicenter bonds of electron deficient molecules.

The bond orbital method has not as yet yielded even approximate values of bonding energies. However, it has proven of value in connection with magnetic properties and bond distances.

As indicated at the beginning of this section, some mathematical analysis of the electronic state in metals is presented in Chapter 10 along with that for other types of crystalline solids.

8u. Dipoles and hydrogen bonds. The classical concept of a dipole is a pair of equal and opposite charges a fixed distance apart.

[48] Pauling, L., *Phys. Rev.*, **54**, 899 (1938); *J. Am. Chem. Soc.*, **69**, 542 (1947); *Nature*, **161**, 1019 (1948); and Ewing, F. J., *Revs. Modern Phys.*, **20**, 112 (1948).

The dipole moment μ of a molecule is given by Eq. (6.2) for the x component, and analogous equations for the y and z components, which can be condensed by vectorial notation to

$$\mathbf{\mu} = \int \psi^* \sum_k e_k r_k \psi \, dv \qquad (8.52)$$

where r_k is the vector from the origin to the kth particle of charge e_k, and the sum covers all particles in the molecule.   The usual equations for dipole interaction energies are limited to distances between dipoles large compared to the charge separation within a dipole.   Some molecules, such as CH_3Cl, satisfy this condition fairly well, because large or nonpolar atoms on the outside of the molecule keep the effective dipoles well separated.   Other molecules, such as HF, have the positive charge so exposed that it can come very close to other charges. In the latter case a simple dipole treatment breaks down.

The term *hydrogen bond* is used for the relatively strong attraction of an exposed positive proton for a highly electronegative atom of another molecule (or possibly of a remote portion of the same molecule).   The importance of hydrogen bonds in the physical properties of substances was recognized, particularly by Latimer and Rodebush,[49] before quantum theory had developed very far.   At that time it was supposed that the proton shared an electron pair with each of the atoms next to it.   However, we now know that hydrogen has but one low-energy orbital, and can therefore share only one pair of electrons at a time.   While mesomerism of the type

$$X: \quad H—X \qquad X—H \quad :X$$

undoubtedly makes some contribution, the empirical fact that hydrogen bonds occur only with small, very electronegative atoms, indicates that the electrostatic energy is the important one.   Thus the strongest hydrogen bonds are those connecting two fluoride ions. Oxygen is next best in hydrogen bonding, and nitrogen is the only other atom commonly forming hydrogen bonds of significant strength. The size factor is important, since chlorine is as electronegative as nitrogen but actually does not form hydrogen bonds of any strength.

Furthermore, there is extensive evidence that in most cases the proton is not centrally located between the two electronegative atoms, but rather is bonded and therefore closer to one.   The only known

---

[49] Latimer, W. M. and Rodebush, W. H., *J. Am. Chem. Soc.*, **42**, 1419 (1920).

exception is the F—H—F⁻ ion,[50] where it has been established that the proton is located midway between the fluoride ions. Here the bonding is presumably so largely ionic that the mesomerism is unimportant although undoubtedly present.

Quantitative theoretical calculations of hydrogen bond energies have not been very successful so far, but the experimental values for some examples are given in Table 8.12.

TABLE 8.12

HYDROGEN BONDS

Bond	X—X dist.	Energy in kcal./mole	X—H frequency
F—H—F⁻ in $KHF_2(s)$..........	2.26 A	27 (?)	1450 cm.⁻¹
F—H . . . F in $(HF)_6$...........	2.55	6.7	3440
F—H free gas molecule.........	. .	. .	4140
O—H . . . O in $(HCOOH)_2$......	2.67	7.1	3030
O—H . . . O in ice.............	2.76	4.5	3250
O—H free H_2O molecule........	. .	. .	3650

The longitudinal vibration frequency of the hydrogen is included in Table 8.12.   This is proportional to the square root of the curvature at the potential minimum.   It can be seen that the presence of the second center of attraction decreases this potential curvature, and by an amount roughly in proportion to the bond energy.   Where the proton moves to the mid-point in FHF⁻, the potential curve is enormously flatter.

8v. London forces. Classical mechanics was able to account for the van der Waals attractive forces of molecules with a permanent dipole moment.   Thus the attraction between water molecules was not too difficult to understand.   However, the attractive force between rare gas atoms such as He, Ne, A, etc., remained entirely unexplained until the development of quantum mechanics.   It was London[51] who proposed in 1930 the correct explanation, and it seems appropriate to associate his name with this effect.

The interaction of two helium atoms is the simplest real example of London forces, but being a four-electron problem it is cumbersome

---

[50] Westrum, E. F., Jr. and Pitzer, K. S., *J. Am. Chem. Soc.*, **71**, 1940 (1949); *J. Chem. Phys.*, **15**, 526 (1947); and Ketelaar, J. A. A. and Vedder, W., *J. Chem. Phys.*, **19**, 654 (1951).

[51] London, F., *Z. physik. Chem.*, **B11**, 222 (1930); *Z. Physik*, **63**, 245 (1930).

to carry out the calculations in detail. The forces associated with bond formation between two hydrogen atoms, as given in Section 8b, fall off with increasing distance as a moderate power of D times the exponential of $-2D$, where D is (r_{AB}/a_0). It proves on examination that the London force falls off only as $(1/r_{AB})^6$, so that it is actually the important term at long distances. Consequently, we shall first make the calculation for two hydrogen atoms at very large distances of separation (as compared with the atomic size). For this purpose, the exchange of the electrons between nuclei may be ignored and the basic wave function taken as $1s_A(1)\ 1s_B(2)$. We include all terms in the Hamiltonian, but expand those associated with the interaction between atoms in powers of $1/R$, where R is the internuclear distance (written r_{AB} above), and the coordinates X_1, Y_1, Z_1 and X_2, Y_2, Z_2 of each electron with respect to its own nucleus. The z axis is taken along the line connecting the nuclei.

$$H = H_{OA} + H_{OB} + H'$$

$$H' = -\frac{e^2}{r_{B1}} - \frac{e^2}{r_{A2}} + \frac{e^2}{r_{12}} + \frac{e^2}{R}$$

$$= \frac{e^2}{R^3}(X_1X_2 + Y_1Y_2 - 2Z_1Z_2) + \dots \tag{8.53}$$

where H_{OA} and H_{OB} are the usual Hamiltonian operators for the separate atoms.

One can easily verify that the first-order perturbation theory energy is zero for this function. We follow now a procedure analogous to that of Section 4i, where the polarizability of the hydrogen atom was treated. The corresponding linear variation function in this case is

$$\phi = C_1 f_1 + C_2 f_2$$
$$f_1 = 1s_A(1)1s_B(2) = (\pi a_0^3)^{-1}e^{-(r_{A1}+r_{B2})/a_0} \tag{8.54}$$
$$f_2 = f_1(X_1X_2 + Y_1Y_2 - 2Z_1Z_2)/a_0^2$$

and the necessary integrals are

$$H_{11} = -\frac{e^2}{a_0} \qquad \Delta_{11} = 1$$

$$H_{12} = \frac{6e^2a_0^2}{R^3} \qquad \Delta_{12} = 0$$

$$H_{22} = 0 \qquad \Delta_{22} = 6$$

The secular equation is therefore

$$\begin{vmatrix} -\dfrac{e^2}{a_0} - W & \dfrac{6e^2a_0^2}{R^3} \\[2ex] \dfrac{6e^2a_0^2}{R^3} & -6W \end{vmatrix} = 0$$

with a lower energy solution accurate to R^{-6} as follows.

$$W = -\frac{e^2}{a_0} - \frac{6e^2a_0^5}{R^6} \tag{8.55}$$

The first term is, of course, the energy of the isolated atoms, and the second term is the interaction energy from London forces. Various authors have studied more complex variation functions and have found that the coefficient of the R^{-6} term increases from 6 to about 6.499.

However, the important matter is not the exact value for the case of two hydrogen atoms, but rather the physical ideas about London forces which can be gleaned from this example. It is to be noted that this potential term arises from a coupling of the motion of the electrons in the separate atoms. If one electron is in the region of positive X, the other tends to be in the region of $-X$, etc. In other words this is the same phenomenon implied by the introduction of the term in r_{12} (the distance between the electrons) in the wave functions for either the helium atom or the hydrogen molecule.

Another way of describing this phenomenon is to note that, although the hydrogen atom is spherically symmetrical on the average, at any instant the electron is in a position such that the atom has a dipole moment. This instantaneous dipole has a field, and this field tends to polarize the other atom. While the dipole changes, even reverses, with high frequency, if the polarization of the other atom keeps phase, the net effect is attractive at all times.

Actually, the coulomb force on the electron in an atom does not lead to simple harmonic motion of a single frequency. Rather it must be regarded as having a wide range of frequencies. The atom has, correspondingly, not a single oscillating dipole of one frequency, but effectively an orchestra of dipoles of different frequencies. Consequently, calculations of the London attraction from this point of view must take the polarizability as a function of frequency, and either sum or integrate the net effect over the range of frequencies involved.

Using this approach, London[51] has derived a general formula, which with certain approximations becomes

$$W_{AB} = -\frac{3\alpha_A\alpha_B}{2R^6}\left(\frac{I_A I_B}{I_A + I_B}\right) \qquad (8.56)$$

where I_A and I_B are the ionization potentials of the two atoms involved, and the other symbols have their usual meaning. This formula has the great advantage of involving the experimentally measurable quantities, polarizability and ionization potential, and in consequence can be readily applied to a wide range of systems. However, it should be remembered that it is only a rough approximation which yields a net potential about 18% too large for pairs of hydrogen atoms and about 7% too small for pairs of helium atoms.

One very important property of London forces is that, to the first approximation, they are additive for all the pairs of atoms in an array of many atoms. The reason is simply that the perturbation in an atom is very small, and in consequence that atom can respond to the instantaneous dipoles of more than one nearby atom. This property of additivity makes the forces uniformly cohesive in a crystal lattice of a rare gas.

A second approximation considering the correction to be applied for a triplet of atoms has been given by Axilrod.[52] While the correction was found to be small, it is not necessarily negligible in quantitative calculations.

8w. Repulsive forces. Regardless of the type of attractive force between atoms, we know that the atoms remain a finite distance apart at equilibrium. Thus a repulsive force must set in suddenly at short distances and balance the attractive force at the equilibrium distance between atoms. We have already indicated that such a force is to be expected when the saturated electron clouds of different atoms overlap. According to the basic idea of Fermi statistics, two pairs of electrons can occupy the same region of ordinary space only if one pair has sufficiently greater momentum to be in a different cell in momentum space. However, this additional momentum implies increased kinetic energy and consequently a repulsive interatomic force.

The simplest mathematical form for a potential yielding a sudden repulsive force is

$$V(r) = Br^{-n} \qquad (8.57)$$

[52] Axilrod, B. M., J. Chem. Phys., **19**, 719, 724 (1951).

and this inverse power law has been used extensively in empirical calculations. The values of n which are obtained range from 9 to 15.

Theoretically one may obtain a suggestion as to the most likely mathematical form from the Heitler-London treatment of the hydrogen molecule. According to Eq. (8.5), the coulomb integral H'_c enters into the energy with a positive sign for either the singlet or triplet state, and at small interatomic distances Eq. (8.9) reduces to

$$H'_c = \frac{e^2}{r_{AB}} e^{-2r_{AB}/a_0} \qquad (8.58)$$

Although the r^{-1} factor would predominate at very short distances, the exponential factor is changing most rapidly near the equilibrium distance. Consequently, the suggested form for a general expression for the repulsive potential is

$$V(r) = be^{-r/\rho} \qquad (8.59)$$

where b and ρ are constants appropriate to each specific example.

We note also that the exponential factor in Eq. (8.58) is just the square of the corresponding factor in the wave function for a hydrogen atom. Let us assume the same relationship to hold for hydrogen-like wave functions for complex atoms. Only the outermost or valence electron orbitals will overlap between atoms when the repulsive forces set in. Then we obtain the expression

$$\rho = na_0/2Z^* \qquad (8.60)$$

where n is the principal quantum number and Z^* is the effective nuclear charge for the valence shell orbitals.

Both theory and experiment indicate that ρ is very nearly constant for a considerable range of ion and atom interactions. Using the appropriate screening constants from Pauling and Sherman[53] for a quantity depending on n/Z, one finds that all the ρ values for rare gas interactions lie between 0.17 and 0.21 A. Thus it is reasonable that the repulsive interaction between unlike rare gases or between ions of the rare gas type should also have about the same ρ value.

Empirically, it has been found that a somewhat larger value in the range 0.3 to 0.35 A gives a better fit in the alkali halide crystals. In general, the exponential expression has been found to be more successful in fitting experimental data. Nevertheless, the inverse power law

[53] Pauling, L. and Sherman, J., Z. Krist., **81**, 1 (1932).

is still used occasionally when its form is more convenient mathematically.

These laws of repulsive force will be used in Section 10i in the calculation of the lattice energies of crystals.

GENERAL REFERENCES

Coulson, C. A., *Valence*, New York: Oxford University Press, 1952. An excellent treatment, with more emphasis on the mathematical aspects than some of the following references.

Pauling, L., *The Nature of the Chemical Bond*, Ithaca: Cornell University Press, 1939. An excellent and relatively nonmathematical presentation of Pauling's interpretation of chemical bonds. The emphasis is on the bond orbital methods.

Rice, F. O. and Teller, E., *The Structure of Matter*, New York: John Wiley & Sons, Inc., 1949. An excellent nonmathematical book with chapters on the periodic system, van der Waals forces, and the chemical bond.

Syrkin, Y. K. and Dyatkina, M. E., *Structure of Molecules and the Chemical Bond*, New York: Interscience Publishers, Inc., 1950. This text was translated and revised from a Russian edition of 1946 by M. A. Partridge and D. O. Jordan. It gives somewhat more attention to the mathematical aspects and to the molecular orbital method than Pauling does.

Van Vleck, J. H. and Sherman, A., *Revs. Modern Phys.*, **7**, 167 (1935). This is a review article entitled, *The Quantum Theory of Valence*.

PROBLEMS

8.1 Calculate for both the singlet and triplet states of H_2 the probability per volume element a_0^3 for each electron (the value of $a_0^6 \psi^2$) of finding the electrons located as follows: (a) All particles on the axis in the order electron (1), proton (A), proton (B), electron (2), with the distance between each electron and the nearest proton $0.8a_0$. (b) Both electrons on the plane midway between nuclei and far enough from the axis to make the distance to either proton $0.8a_0$. Take the distance between protons as $1.4a_0$ and use the wave functions of Eqs. (8.1) and (8.2). Remember that these wave functions must be normalized and that the necessary value of Δ is given in Fig. 8.2 or Eq. (8.7).

8.2 Using the result of part (b) above discuss the question, "How much of the time are the two electrons between the nuclei?" An exact quantitative answer is not expected.

8.3 Evaluate the integral in Eq. (8.6) by use of elliptic coordinates.

8.4 Discuss the expected behavior of the parameters in Eq. (8.16) as r_{AB} decreases to zero.

8.5 What would be an appropriate wave function for H_2^+ when r_{AB} approaches infinity? Can this function be obtained with appropriate parameters in Eq. (8.16)?

8.6 Assuming the values of b and r_{AB} in Eq. (8.16), carry through the linear variation method to obtain the values of c and of the energy of H_2^+.

8.7 Use the angular orbitals in Table 3.1 to show that the maximum angular intensity of an sp hybrid orbital is obtained for the $\frac{1}{4}s$ and $\frac{3}{4}p$ ratios. Discuss the approximation involved in neglecting the difference in radial functions at the distances involved in chemical bonds.

8.8 Working from the references cited in Section 8l, obtain the energies of the following bonds: H—Br, Li—Br, C—Br, P—Br.

8.9 In PCl$_5$ all bonds cannot be normal electron pair bonds. Compare the average P—Cl bond energy in PCl$_5$ with that in PCl$_3$.

8.10 Compare the experimental heat of formation of CH$_2$Cl$_2$ with that calculated from bond energies.

8.11 Predict the geometrical structure of PCl$_5$ from the orbitals available and Table 8.6. Assume the unshared electron pair of the normal phosphorus atom is separated and used in bonding.

8.12 Carry through a particle in two-box calculation (Fig. 8.12). For convenience, take a and m such that $E/V_0 = 0.01$ for the particle in one box. This allows terms of the type α^2/β^2 to be neglected as compared with unity. See Section 2h.

8.13 Solve exactly for the lowest energy level of a particle in two boxes (Fig. 8.12) with the two boxes of equal width. Note the symmetry present. The lowest level will be symmetric. The wave function in the central barrier may be expressed as $\cosh \beta x$. See Section 2h for other hints.

8.14 Supply the intermediate steps in the calculation of the bond energy of H$_3^+$ as 4β.

8.15 Show that the orbital, Eq. (8.50), yields the energy $2E_H + \alpha + 2\beta$ for H$_3^+$. This involves dropping a number of integrals which may be shown to be smaller than those retained.

Chapter 9

MOLECULAR SPECTRA AND THERMODYNAMIC
PROPERTIES OF PERFECT GASES

9a. Introduction. In Chapter 8 the electronic energy of molecules was considered. According to the Born-Oppenheimer treatment (Section 3e) this total electronic energy may be taken as a potential energy for the motion of the nuclei. The Schrödinger equation may then be solved for the motion of the nuclei subject to this potential energy, yielding the energy levels for nuclear motion. This procedure was followed in Section 3e for a diatomic molecule. It was there found that, to the first approximation, the rotational energy may be separated from the vibrational energy. The underlying reason is that the forces between nuclei are strong enough to hold the molecule practically rigid. However, the molecular vibration can change slightly the average moment of inertia, so that a second-order correcting term does arise which involves both rotation and vibration.

The same separation of rotational and vibrational energy is possible for polyatomic molecules. While this could be proved in the more mathematical method used for the diatomic molecule, we shall accept it as following from the physical picture of molecular rigidity. The rotational energy levels and thermodynamic functions will be discussed first, followed by the corresponding results for vibrational motion.

9b. Rotation of linear molecules. There exist a number of polyatomic molecules in which all nuclei lie on a straight line. It is convenient to consider the rotation of these linear polyatomic molecules along with our further discussion of the rotation of diatomic molecules.

Strictly speaking, a linear molecule may have a net angular momentum from the electron orbitals and from electron spin which would complicate the treatment of the ordinary molecular rotation. Since almost all stable substances have $^1\Sigma$ ground electronic states, the discussion of these problems will be postponed until excited electronic states are considered in Section 9k, and a *totally symmetric electronic state will be assumed* in this and the immediately following sections.

The rotational energy levels for all linear molecules are given by the formula for diatomic molecules, see Eq. (3.39).

$$E = \frac{h^2 J(J+1)}{8\pi^2 I} \tag{9.1}$$

where I is the moment of inertia which is given more generally by the expression

$$I = \sum_i m_i r_i^2 \tag{9.2}$$

Here m_i is the mass of the ith particle and r_i is the distance of that particle from the center of the mass.

As before, the Jth energy level has a degeneracy of $2J + 1$. The rotational wave functions are those given in Table 3.1 where ϕ and θ define the angular location of the line through the nuclei.

If the linear molecule has a dipole moment, absorption or emission of radiation is possible in connection with transitions between rotation states. Although the magnitude of the radiation coefficients depends on the value of the dipole moment, the selection rules are the same as those obtained in Section 6e for the changes in the rotational quantum numbers of the hydrogen atom. This result follows because the angular wave functions are the same for each problem. One then obtains $\Delta m = \pm 1, 0$, and $\Delta J = \pm 1$. Since the energy is independent of m, one obtains the spectral frequencies by substituting in Eq. (9.1) for absorption $J'' = J' + 1$ and for emission $J'' = J' - 1$.

$$\nu = \frac{\Delta E}{h} = \frac{h}{4\pi^2 I}(J'+1) \qquad \text{(for absorption)} \tag{9.3}$$

Thus the pure rotation spectrum of a linear molecule is a series of equally spaced lines. Spectroscopists have frequently reported results in terms of the quantity $B = h/8\pi^2 I c$, which has the dimension cm.$^{-1}$. Then one has

$$\frac{1}{\lambda} = \frac{\nu}{c} = 2B(J'+1) \tag{9.3'}$$

For ordinary molecules B has a magnitude near 1 cm.$^{-1}$. Thus pure rotation spectra lie in the very far infrared. Only with the development of microwave electronic techniques did it become experimentally practical to investigate pure rotation spectra generally. These microwave spectral data offer by far the most precise values of the moment of inertia of linear molecules. For diatomic molecules the moment of inertia at once yields the interatomic distance. Linear polyatomic molecules have several independent interatomic distances which cannot be evaluated from a single moment of inertia. However, in favorable cases, the moments of inertia of a series of isotopically substituted molecules give enough independent equations to evaluate all the interatomic distances.

The microwave results are commonly reported in terms of the closely related quantity, $B = h/8\pi^2 I$, which is unfortunately given the identical symbol. This quantity has the dimension sec.$^{-1}$ and is usually given in megacycles/sec. (mc.). The two B's differ by just the factor, c, the velocity of light. In these terms

$$\nu = 2B(J' + 1) \tag{9.3''}$$

As an example of the microwave work we take carbonyl sulfide, OCS, which is a linear molecule. Various isotopic species have been studied,[1,2] and the principal absorption lines in the regions measured are listed in Table 9.1 for two of the species. The precise conformance of these data with Eq. (9.3'') is readily noted.

TABLE 9.1

MICROWAVE ABSORPTION SPECTRUM OF OCS

Molecule		ν (mc.)	B_0 (mc.)
$O^{16}C^{12}S^{32}$	$J = 1 \to 2$	24325.92	6081.480
	$3 \to 4$	48651.7	
	$4 \to 5$	60814.1	
$O^{16}C^{12}S^{34}$	$1 \to 2$	23731.33	5932.843
	$3 \to 4$	47462.3	

All the quantities in Table 9.1 are for the ground vibrational state. However, because of zero point vibration, they are not strictly interpretable in terms of a rigid molecule with the atomic nuclei at rest.

[1] Townes, C. H., Holden, A. N., and Merritt, F. R., *Phys. Rev.*, **74**, 1113 (1948).
[2] Hillger, R. E., Strandberg, M. W. P., Wentink, T., and Kyhl, R. L., *Phys. Rev.*, **72**, 157 (1947).

This limitation is significant only because of the extremely high precision of these measurements.

Within this limitation, relating to zero point vibration, one may proceed to interpret these results in terms of interatomic distances. For the linear O—C—S molecule the moment of inertia is

$$I = \frac{1}{m_O + m_C + m_S} [m_O m_C d_{CO}^2 + m_C m_S d_{CS}^2 + m_O m_S (d_{CO} + d_{CS})^2]$$

This equation has the two unknowns d_{CO} and d_{CS}, the C—O and C—S distances. These two unknowns can be obtained from the moments of inertia of any pair of isotopic molecules. The data in Table 9.1 yield $d_{CO} = 1.1647$ and $d_{CS} = 1.5576$ A. Actually there are additional isotopic species of carbonyl sulfide which give additional solutions for the bond distances differing slightly from these values. It is not now clear to what extent these differences arise from the zero point energy effect and to what extent from experimental errors. In any event these uncertainties are small since the differences in bond distance are only a few thousandths A.

If the molecule is symmetrical, one must consider consequences of this symmetry on the acceptability of the wave functions. Not only are all diatomic elementary molecules such as H_2, N_2, O_2, F_2, etc., examples of this type, but also such polyatomic molecules as CO_2(O—C—O), C_2H_2(H—C≡C—H), etc. The symmetry operation of interest is that of turning the molecule end for end. It was mentioned in Section 4c that the rotational wave functions of even J are symmetrical to this operation, whereas those of odd J are antisymmetrical.

Where the atoms exchanged by this operation have zero nuclear spin, the wave function must be symmetric, and only even values of J are acceptable. The molecule CO_2 is of this type.

Where the symmetrically placed atoms have nuclear spin, there will be a wave function factor for nuclear spin analogous to the factors we have employed for electron spin. Let us consider the case of H_2 in some detail. The proton has $\frac{1}{2}$ unit spin, just as the electron, so we may use the same symbols $\alpha(A)$, $\beta(B)$ to indicate nuclear spin $+\frac{1}{2}$ for proton A and $-\frac{1}{2}$ for proton B. The permissible spin factors for the two protons are, as before

antisymmetric: $[\alpha(A)\beta(B) - \alpha(B)\beta(A)]2^{-1/2}$

symmetric: $\begin{cases} \alpha(A)\alpha(B) \\ \beta(A)\beta(B) \\ [\alpha(A)\beta(B) + \alpha(B)\beta(A)]2^{-1/2} \end{cases}$

The total wave function must be antisymmetric to the exchange of the protons. Consequently we may combine the one antisymmetric spin factor with any symmetric rotational function, i.e., one with even J. Similarly one may combine any of the three symmetric spin factors with any antisymmetric rotational function, i.e., one with odd J. Since there are three symmetric spin factors, this gives three times the number of states for any odd rotational level.

No simple perturbation, such as an electric field, will cause the nuclear spins to reorient themselves. Consequently, the forms of hydrogen with parallel and antiparallel nuclear spins may be regarded for some purposes as separate substances; they are called *ortho* and *para* hydrogen, respectively. The transition from one to the other may be catalyzed by inhomogeneous magnetic fields or by dissociation and recombination. Since *para* hydrogen is the species including the state $J = 0$, it becomes the stable form at low temperatures. It is possible to prepare almost pure *para* hydrogen by the use of an appropriate catalyst at the temperature of liquid hydrogen. However, at high temperatures the equilibrium mixture is, of course, three parts *ortho* to one *para* in accordance with the ratio of numbers of spin factors.

The situation with respect to other molecules is similar, except that the three to one ratio applies only to half unit spin. In general the high temperature ratio turns out to be $(S + 1)/S$, where S is the absolute magnitude of the nuclear spin (in unts of $h/2\pi$), and the species with even J is more abundant if S is integral, while the species with odd J is more abundant if S is half integral. The reversal in abundance arises, of course, from the requirement for symmetrical functions if the spin is integral, but antisymmetrical functions if the spin is half integral. The more abundant species is ordinarily called *ortho*, and the less abundant, *para*.

These symmetrical molecules have necessarily zero dipole moment, and hence no pure rotation spectrum. Nevertheless, these considerations are important for thermodynamic properties or for vibration-rotation or electronic-vibration-rotation spectra. We have assumed here that the electronic wave function factor was symmetric to exchange of the nuclei. This is normally the case for the ground state of molecules, but the opposite situation can be readily examined if needed.

The thermodynamic properties related to the rotation of linear molecules may be calculated by substituting these results into the formula for the partition function, Eq. (7.50) or (7.57). Before proceeding further let us define the quantity

$$y = \frac{h^2}{8\pi^2 IkT} = \frac{hcB}{kT} = 1.4387\,\frac{B}{T} \qquad (9.4)$$

where the last expression holds for B in cm.$^{-1}$ and T in degrees K. Then the partition function for rotation is

$$Q_r = \sum_{J=0}^{\infty} (2J + 1)e^{-J(J+1)y} \qquad (9.5)$$

where the sum is over all values of J for an unsymmetrical molecule, or is over just the even or odd values, as appropriate, for the *para* and *ortho* species of a symmetrical molecule.

It is not possible to express the sum for Q_r in simple closed form. If y is large, as in H_2 at moderate temperatures, it is best to sum Eq. (9.5) directly. However, for many substances y is very small, and the sum may be replaced by an integral

$$Q_r = \frac{1}{\sigma}\int_0^{\infty}(2J + 1)e^{-J(J+1)y}\,dJ = \frac{1}{\sigma y} \qquad (9.6)$$

where σ, the symmetry number, is 2 for either species of symmetrical molecules and is 1 for unsymmetrical molecules.

It is also possible to obtain a power series in y for the partition function by the use of the Euler-Maclaurin summation formula.[3] We shall not discuss this in detail but merely state the result,

$$Q_r = \frac{1}{\sigma y}\left(1 + \frac{y}{3} + \frac{y^2}{15} + \ldots\right) \qquad (9.7)$$

which is accurate to 0.1% or better if y is less than 0.3.

In computing the various thermodynamic functions from the partition function, if y is large, it is most convenient to use Eqs. (7.60)

---

[3] Mayer, J. E. and Mayer, M. G., *Statistical Mechanics*, New York: John Wiley & Sons, Inc., 1940. Sec. 7b.

and (7.63) through (7.67). However, if y is small (less than 0.3), the following equations apply to the rotational contribution.

$$\left(-\frac{F}{T}\right)_r = R\left(-\ln y - \ln \sigma + \frac{y}{3} + \frac{y^2}{90} + \dots\right) \tag{9.8}$$

$$\cong R\,[\ln T + \ln (I \times 10^{39}) - \ln \sigma] - 2.7676$$

$$H_r = RT\left(1 - \frac{y}{3} - \frac{y^2}{45} - \dots\right) \tag{9.9}$$

$$S_r = R\left(1 - \ln y - \ln \sigma - \frac{y^2}{90} - \dots\right) \tag{9.10}$$

$$\cong R\,[\ln T + \ln (I \times 10^{39}) - \ln \sigma] - 0.7804$$

$$C_r = R\left(1 + \frac{y^2}{45} + \dots\right) \tag{9.11}$$

where the numerical constants in (9.8) and (9.10) are in cal./deg. mole. It is interesting to note that the term in the first power of y dropped out for the entropy and heat capacity. Consequently these quantities are very accurately given by the first-order terms, which came from Eq. (9.6), provided y is less than 0.1. Few examples arise, other than H_2, where real substances at temperatures of experimental interest give values of y larger than 0.1.

9c. Rotation of nonlinear molecules. For a discussion of the rotational energy levels of nonlinear polyatomic molecules, it is convenient and customary to classify them by the relative magnitude of their principal moments of inertia. If Cartesian axes are taken with their origin at the center of mass, one may calculate the moments and products of inertia as follows.

$$\begin{aligned}
I_x &= \sum m_i(y_i^2 + z_i^2) & I_{xy} &= \sum m_i x_i y_i \\
I_y &= \sum m_i(x_i^2 + z_i^2) & I_{xz} &= \sum m_i x_i z_i \\
I_z &= \sum m_i(x_i^2 + y_i^2) & I_{yz} &= \sum m_i y_i z_i
\end{aligned} \tag{9.12}$$

where m_i is the mass of the ith atom, whose coordinates are x_i, y_i, z_i, and the sum covers all atoms. It may be shown generally[4] that a suitable rotation of these Cartesian axes will reduce the last three quantities, the products of inertia, to zero. The new axes are known as principal axes, and the moments of inertia in terms of these principal axes are commonly used to describe the rotational properties.

[4] Whittaker, E. T., *Analytical Dynamics*, 4th ed., London: Cambridge University Press, 1937. (Also New York: Dover Publications.)

Particularly if a molecule has considerable symmetry, the principal axes are frequently obvious. They will be perpendicular to symmetry planes or identical to rotational symmetry axes. Thus for the water molecule the twofold rotation axis which passes through the oxygen and midway between the hydrogens is one principal axis. A second one passes through the center of mass and is perpendicular to the plane of the molecule. The third axis is perpendicular to the other two, hence lies in the plane of the molecule. The classification scheme is:

1. Spherical top, $\quad I_x = I_y = I_z$
2. Symmetrical top, $\quad I_x = I_y \neq I_z$ $\qquad$ (9.13)
3. Unsymmetrical top, $\quad I_x \neq I_y \neq I_z$

For spherical tops any mutually perpendicular axes are principal axes. Examples are tetrahedral molecules such as CH_4 or $SiCl_4$ and octahedral molecules such as SF_6.

Molecules with one threefold or higher symmetry axis are found to be symmetrical tops. The symmetry axis is customarily the z axis, and has the unique moment of inertia; any axis perpendicular to it has the same moment of inertia as any other. Examples include CH_3Cl, benzene, cyclohexane, and cyclobutane.

Other nonlinear molecules are unsymmetrical tops, although they may accidentally approach the symmetrical or spherical cases.

The quantum mechanical derivation of the energy levels for nonlinear molecules is given in Appendix 17 by matrix methods. The calculation by Schrödinger methods[5] for the spherical and symmetrical cases, although rather lengthy, involves no new principles. Either method leads to the following relatively simple formula for spherical and symmetrical top molecules.

$$E = \frac{h^2}{8\pi^2}\left[\frac{J(J+1)}{I_x} + K^2\left(\frac{1}{I_z} - \frac{1}{I_x}\right)\right] \qquad (9.14)$$

$$J = 0, 1, 2, \ldots$$
$$K = 0, \pm1, \pm2, \ldots, \pm J$$

There is an additional quantum number m, as in the diatomic case, which does not affect the energy. It also has values 0, ±1,

[5] Reiche, F. and Rademacher, H., Z. *Physik*, **39**, 444 (1926); **41**, 453 (1927); Kronig, R. de L. and Rabi, I. I., *Phys. Rev.*, **29**, 262 (1927).

$\pm 2, \ldots, \pm J$. Thus for a given J and K there is a $(2J + 1)$ degeneracy of the energy level.

The wave functions for the symmetric top are moderately complex and are given in the articles[5] where the energy levels are obtained. It is more important here to note some of the wave function properties. The component of angular momentum about the symmetry axis is given (in units of $h/2\pi$) by the quantum number K, while the component of angular momentum on an arbitrary axis in space is given by the quantum number m, which does not affect the energy unless there is some perturbing field. The square of the total angular momentum is $J(J + 1)h^2/4\pi^2$ as in the case of the linear molecules or the two-particle systems. There are various symmetry properties, but it is hardly worth while to discuss them all, since only a selected few are important for a given molecule. For example, in a molecule such as CH_3Cl with a threefold axis, the states with $K = 0, \pm 3, \pm 6, \ldots$ are symmetric to a rotation by $2\pi/3$, which merely interchanges the hydrogen atoms. The states with $K = \pm 1, \pm 2, \pm 4$, etc. have complex symmetry properties depending on the representation used for each degenerate pair.

The rotational energy levels of a real symmetrical top molecule depend, of course, on the symmetry of that particular molecule and on the nuclear spin of each of the equivalent atoms. Where these equivalent atoms have spin other than zero, there will be at least two forms with different net spin for the set of nuclei. Thus for three protons, as in CH_3Cl, all three spins can be parallel, or one can be antiparallel to the other two. These two species, like *ortho* and *para* hydrogen, have different sets of allowed rotational energy levels.

About the simplest example of a symmetrical top is the molecule SO_3, because the oxygen atoms have zero nuclear spin. The complete wave function must therefore be symmetric to any exchange of oxygens. From the wave function property mentioned above, one can limit K to $0, \pm 3, \pm 6$, etc. However, an additional exchange of oxygens can be obtained by a 180° rotation of the planar molecule SO_3 about an axis in the plane passing through an oxygen-sulfur bond. An examination of the properties of the wave functions in this respect leads to the additional limitation of J to the even numbers: 0, 2, 4, etc. for states with $K = 0$, and to either even or odd numbers for any particular state of $K \neq 0$. Thus in all only one-sixth of the rotational states are allowed for SO_3, one-third of the K values, and one-half of the J values.

For the spherical top one notices that the second term in Eq. (9.14) drops out, and with it the effect of the quantum number K on the energy. Then for a given J there is a $(2J + 1)^2$ degeneracy of the energy level.

A spherical top, by symmetry, can have no dipole moment, and consequently no pure rotation spectrum. A symmetrical top can have a dipole moment only along the symmetry or z axis. The resulting selection rules are $\Delta K = 0$, $\Delta J = \pm 1$, which yields the same series of evenly spaced lines as a linear molecule, Eq. (9.3). Actually, in this case there are states of the same initial and final J values but of different K, whose lines should lie on top of one another. Higher order terms, arising from lack of complete rigidity of the molecule, can cause these lines for different K values to be slightly separated.

In addition, there are the molecules which by accident are almost symmetrical tops. In these cases there may be a dipole moment component along any particular axis, and the selection rules must be worked out accordingly.

The energy levels for rotation of an unsymmetrical top are not expressible in simple form, although extensive tables have been calculated which make their computation for any particular example not too difficult. Appendix 8 gives some details about the rotational energy levels of unsymmetrical tops, which are also derived in Appendix 17.

The thermodynamic properties for the rotation of nonlinear molecules can be computed by the usual methods. Since both the temperatures of interest and the moments of inertia for such molecules are usually somewhat larger than for diatomic molecules, the only formulas of practical importance are those for the high-temperature approximation. For symmetrical tops, the partition function can be readily integrated from the energy levels of Eq. (9.14).

$$Q_r = \frac{1}{\sigma} \int_{-\infty}^{+\infty} e^{-(K^2 h^2/8\pi^2 kT)(1/I_z - 1/I_x)} \, dK$$

$$\times \int_{K-\frac{1}{2}}^{\infty} (2J + 1)e^{-J(J+1)h^2/8\pi^2 I_x kT} \, dJ$$

$$= \frac{8\pi^2 I_x kT}{h^2 \sigma} \, e^{-h^2/32\pi^2 I_x kT} \int_{-\infty}^{+\infty} e^{-K^2 h^2/8\pi^2 I_z kT} \, dK$$

Since the integral over J is to be equivalent to a sum containing a full term $J = K$, the selection of the lower limit $K - \frac{1}{2}$ is reasonable. This selection also has the advantage of simplifying the integral over K. We note that the exponent $(h^2/32\pi^2 I_x kT)$ is very small, so that the exponential is approximately unity. Indeed, further study of the errors involved in replacing the sums by integrals indicates that they are of just this order of magnitude. With this further approximation, the partition function becomes

$$Q_r = \frac{\pi^{1/2}}{\sigma} \left(\frac{8\pi^2 kT}{h^2}\right)^{3/2} I_z I_z^{1/2} \tag{9.15}$$

For spherical tops, Eq. (9.15) is obviously applicable, with the two moments of inertia now identical.

It is not convenient to sum (or integrate) over the quantum levels for the unsymmetrical top. However, the classical mechanical expression for the rotational energy can be introduced into the phase integral, Eq. (7.58), and the high-temperature approximation to the partition function calculated thereby. This series of integrations is given in Appendix 9. The result is

$$Q_r = \frac{\pi^{1/2}}{\sigma} \left(\frac{8\pi^2 kT}{h^2}\right)^{3/2} (I_x I_y I_z)^{1/2} \tag{9.16}$$

which can be readily seen to reduce to Eq. (9.15) if $I_x = I_y$.

In Eqs. (9.15) and (9.16) we have inserted the symmetry number σ. On the classical basis (see Section 7o), σ is readily defined as the number of regions of phase space included in the partition function calculation, which differ only by the exchange of indistinguishable particles. Thus for the rotation of nonlinear molecules, σ is the number of equivalent rotational orientations of the molecule. For example, a tetrahedral molecule such as CH_4 has a symmetry number of 12, since any one of the four hydrogens may be placed on top and rotation by one-third of a turn about the axis through the selected hydrogen merely interchanges the others. Similarly, a planar triangular molecule such as SO_3 has $\sigma = 6$, etc.

It should be noted that the maximum symmetry number for a molecule with n equivalent atoms is $n!$, since that is the number of possible interchanges of the n particles. However, it may not be possible to accomplish all these interchanges by rotation. Consequently, the symmetry number for rotation may be less than $n!$.

In one of the examples cited above we have $n! = 24$ for CH_4 but σ is only 12. One interchange of hydrogens in CH_4 can be accomplished by reflection of the molecule through a symmetry plane but not by any rotation. This is equivalent to the conversion from d to l configuration of an asymmetric (optically active) molecule of the tetrahedral type.

In the planar molecule, SO_3, we have $n! = 6$, which is the same as σ. This correctly indicates that all interchanges of the three oxygen atoms can be accomplished by rotations of the molecule.

In quantum theory the symmetry number arises from the fact that only a fraction of the rotational states are actually allowed for a symmetrical molecule. This fraction is $1/\sigma$. We saw above that one-sixth of the states were allowed for the molecule SO_3, which agrees with this statement. As we have already explained, the general case where the nuclei have nuclear spin is very complex, and involves two or more species of the *ortho-para* type. However, for any one species, $1/\sigma$ of the rotational levels will be allowed. For a different species a different set of levels will be allowed, but again they will comprise $1/\sigma$ of the total array of rotational states. The net effect is to divide the partition function computed from all the rotational levels by the factor σ, just as in the classical case, provided the spacing of the energy levels is small compared with kT at the temperatures of interest.

The contributions for molecular rotation to the various thermodynamic quantities are given by the following equations, which apply to all nonlinear molecules regardless of symmetry.

$$\left(-\frac{F}{T}\right)_r = R\left[\frac{1}{2}\ln\left(I_xI_yI_z\right) + \frac{3}{2}\ln T - \ln\sigma + \frac{1}{2}\ln\left(\frac{512\pi^7k^3}{h^6}\right)\right]$$

$$= R\left[\frac{1}{2}\ln\left(I_xI_yI_z \times 10^{117}\right) + \frac{3}{2}\ln T - \ln\sigma\right] - 3.0140 \quad (9.17)$$

$$H_r = \frac{3}{2}RT \qquad\qquad\qquad\qquad\qquad\qquad\qquad\qquad\qquad (9.18)$$

$$S_r = R\left[\frac{1}{2}\ln\left(I_xI_yI_z \times 10^{117}\right) + \frac{3}{2}\ln T - \ln\sigma\right] - 0.0332 \quad (9.19)$$

$$C_r = \frac{3}{2}R \qquad\qquad\qquad\qquad\qquad\qquad\qquad\qquad\qquad\qquad (9.20)$$

9d. Vibration of molecules—normal coordinates. A simple treatment of the vibration of a diatomic molecule was given in

Section 3e. However, if the molecule contains more than two atoms, several distinct modes of vibration are possible. If such a system is given an arbitrary initial displacement, in its ensuing vibration it does not return repeatedly to the initial configuration. Instead, a complex system executes a complicated motion involving numerous frequencies.

A normal mode of oscillation is a very special motion of a complex system in which all particles do return, with frequency ν, to their initial positions. We shall now consider the problem of finding these normal modes of vibration and the normal coordinates which describe them. While this is a classical mechanical problem, we shall see in the next section that the quantum mechanics of such vibrating systems requires these same normal coordinates for its simplification.

A basic assumption in normal vibration theory is that only small amplitudes of motion are involved. Consequently we may expand the complete potential energy expression in a Taylor series in powers of coordinates q_i, which give the displacements of atoms from their equilibrium configurations. In other words, when all q's are zero the molecule is at its lowest potential energy.

$$V(q_1 \ldots q_i) = V_0 + \sum_i (\partial V/\partial q_i)_0 q_i + \frac{1}{2} \sum_i \sum_j b_{ij} q_i q_j + \ldots$$

$$\text{with } b_{ij} = (\partial^2 V/\partial q_i \partial q_j)_0 \qquad (9.21)$$

The subscript zero on the derivatives refers to the fact that these derivatives are evaluated at the point, all q's equal to zero, i.e., the equilibrium configuration. Now since this is the minimum of potential energy, all the first derivatives are zero, and that sum drops out. By definition we may make V_0 zero if we wish. Furthermore the later terms in the series, not given above, will involve the third and higher powers of the q's. Thus if the q's are small they may be neglected as compared with the quadratic terms. We then have as the final expression

$$2V = \sum_i \sum_j b_{ij} q_i q_j \qquad (9.22)$$

Let us consider first a simple example to illustrate the ideas and methods involved. Take a linear $A—B—A$ molecule such as CO_2. Remembering the small amplitudes, we may take an initial orientation of the molecule and treat only infinitesimal displacements from that position. Let us place the central or B atom near the origin with coordinates x_1, y_1, z_1, and the two A atoms near the z axis at $\pm z_0$, with actual coordinates x_2, y_2, z_2 and x_3, y_3, z_3, see Fig. 9.1. For the potential energy we assume an expression of the form of Eq. (9.22), but with certain terms omitted which are believed to be less important.

$$2V = k(z_2 - z_1 - z_0)^2 + k(z_3 - z_1 + z_0)^2 + b\left(x_1 - \frac{x_2}{2} - \frac{x_3}{2}\right)^2$$
$$+ b\left(y_1 - \frac{y_2}{2} - \frac{y_3}{2}\right)^2 \qquad (9.23)$$

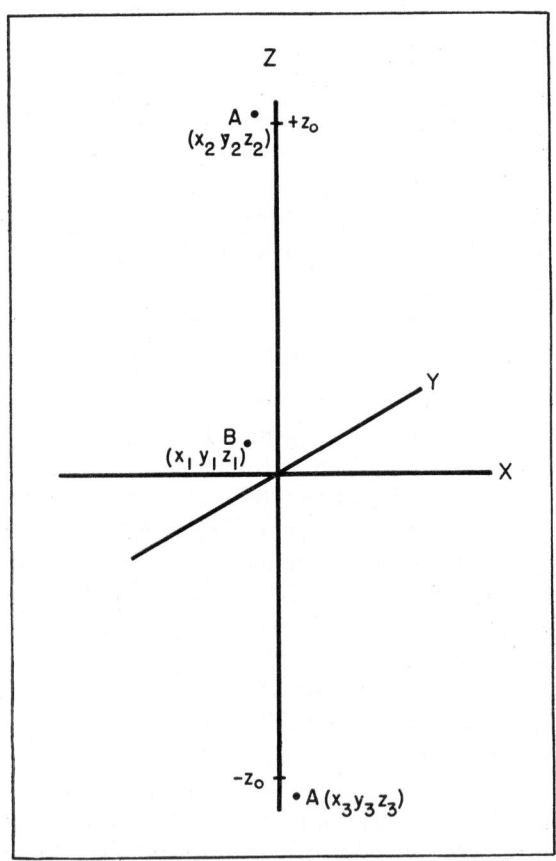

Fig. 9.1. Coordinate system for the vibrations of a linear A–B–A molecule.

Here k is the potential constant for the deviation of the A—B bond length from its equilibrium length z_0, and b is the constant for the bending of the molecule from a linear configuration.

It will be noted in (9.23) that there are no cross terms between the z's and x's or y's. Consequently, in this particular case, one may treat the z motions separately. The usual Newtonian equation of motion is $m_i\ddot{x}_i = F_i = -\partial V/\partial x_i$, where $\ddot{x}_i$ is the second time derivative, the acceleration. These equations in this case, for the z motions, are the following.

$$M\ddot{z}_1 = -2kz_1 + kz_2 + kz_3$$
$$m\ddot{z}_2 = kz_1 - k(z_2-z_0) \qquad (9.24)$$
$$m\ddot{z}_3 = kz_1 - k(z_3+z_0)$$

where M is the mass of B and m the mass of A. Now in a normal mode the molecule executes simple harmonic oscillation, all atoms moving with the same frequency. Thus for a normal mode z_1, z_2, and z_3 must follow the equations

$$z_1 = z_1^0 \cos 2\pi\nu t, \quad (z_2-z_0) = z_2^0 \cos 2\pi\nu t, \quad (z_3+z_0) = z_3^0 \cos 2\pi\nu t \qquad (9.25)$$

where ν is the same throughout, but the amplitude factors z_1^0, z_2^0, z_3^0 will be different. In another normal mode the same equations will hold, but with presumably a new ν and different set of amplitude factors z_1^0, z_2^0, z_3^0. The acceleration is

$$\ddot{z}_i = z_i^0(-4\pi^2\nu^2) \cos 2\pi\nu t \qquad (9.26)$$

and we let $$\lambda = 4\pi^2\nu^2$$

Substituting these results in the equations of motion (9.24) and rearranging, one obtains

$$\begin{aligned}(2k - M\lambda)z_1^0 \qquad\quad -kz_2^0 \qquad\quad -kz_3^0 &= 0 \\ -kz_1^0 \quad +(k - m\lambda)z_2^0 \qquad\qquad &= 0 \qquad (9.27) \\ -kz_1^0 \qquad\qquad\qquad +(k - m\lambda)z_3^0 &= 0\end{aligned}$$

Now this is a set of simultaneous, homogeneous equations for the z^0's, similar to Eq. (4.32) in the linear variation function treatment, and again the determinant of their coefficients must vanish.

$$\begin{vmatrix} 2k - M\lambda & -k & -k \\ -k & k - m\lambda & 0 \\ -k & 0 & k - m\lambda \end{vmatrix} = 0 \qquad (9.28)$$

By various methods (trial and error or manipulation of the determinant) one may show that the roots are

$$\lambda_1 = k/m, \qquad \lambda_2 = k/\mu, \qquad \lambda_t = 0 \qquad (9.29)$$

with $\mu = mM/(2m + M)$.

To find the normal coordinates, we substitute these roots successively in Eqs. (9.27). For $\lambda_t = 0$ one obtains the equations

$$
\begin{aligned}
2kz_1^0 \quad &-kz_2^0 \quad -kz_3^0 = 0 \\
-kz_1^0 \quad &+kz_2^0 \qquad\quad\; = 0 \\
-kz_1^0 \qquad\qquad\; &+kz_3^0 = 0
\end{aligned}
$$

which have the solution $z_1^0 = z_2^0 = z_3^0$. This is clearly a translation of the whole molecule along the z axis (hence the designation λ_t). This is not a vibration, and the zero frequency is thus understandable.

Similar substitution of $\lambda_1 = k/m$ yields $z_1^0 = 0$, $z_2^0 = -z_3^0$, which is a symmetrical vibration of the A atoms relative to a stationary central B atom (see Fig. 9.2). Likewise $\lambda_2 = k/\mu$ yields $z_2^0 = z_3^0 = -(M/2m)z_1^0$, which is an unsymmetrical vibration in which both A atoms move one way and the B atom the other.

While in principle the simple method just followed could be used for normal vibration problems in general, it has serious practical dis-

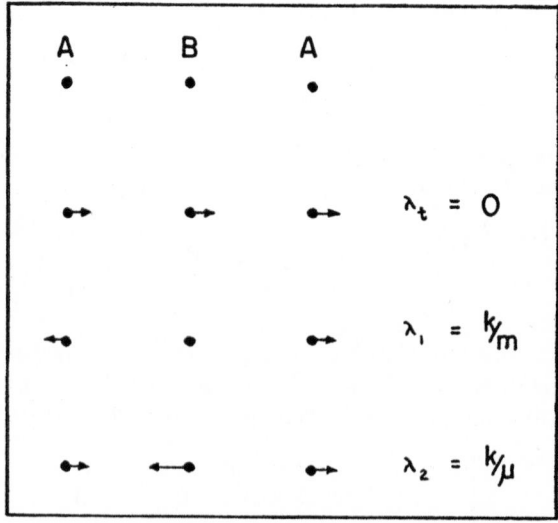

Fig. 9.2.   Longitudinal motions of a linear molecule.

advantages. Even for a nonlinear triatomic molecule the determinant would become ninth-order, because the x, y, and z motions would have to be treated together. However, six of the nine roots would be zero, corresponding to the three translations and the three rotations of such a molecule. Thus it becomes very desirable to set up the problem in such a way as to leave out translation and rotation at the start. If at the same time account is taken of the symmetry of the molecule, even further simplifications occur.

Let us illustrate this by treating the x motions of the A-B-A linear molecule. We define new coordinates corresponding to translation, rotation and vibration, respectively, as

$$q_1 = (Mx_1 + mx_2 + mx_3)/(M + 2m)$$
$$q_2 = x_2 - x_3 \qquad\qquad (9.30)$$
$$q_3 = x_1 - x_2/2 - x_3/2$$

The selection of q_1 and q_2 are easy enough, because q_1 is to give the net translational motion of the center of gravity, and q_2 the beginning of rotation. In this particular case the selection of q_3 is also easy because it is the only combination of x's appearing in the potential energy. In general this procedure of selecting those internal coordinates which appear in the potential energy expression has proven best. Naturally the total number of internal coordinates including translation and rotation (all the q's) must equal the number of Cartesian coordinates involved. In these terms the potential energy is

$$2V = bq_3^2 \qquad\qquad (9.31)$$

and the kinetic energy is

$$2T = (M + 2m)\dot{q}_1^2 + \frac{m}{2}\,\dot{q}_2^2 + \frac{2mM}{M + 2m}\,\dot{q}_3^2 \qquad\qquad (9.32)$$

The transformation to Eq. (9.32) is rather lengthy, since it involves the inverse of Eqs. (9.30), but it may be verified easily by the reverse process, substituting Eqs. (9.30) into Eq. (9.32).

Now since q_1 and q_2 do not appear in the potential energy, they will not give vibratory motion and may be dropped at this point. The equation of motion for q_3 is

$$\frac{d}{dt}\left(\frac{dT}{d\dot{q}_3}\right) + \frac{dV}{dq_3} = 0, \qquad \frac{2mM}{M + 2m}\,\ddot{q}_3 + bq_3 = 0 \qquad (9.33)$$

While the strict derivation of this result comes from the Lagrangian equations of motion (see Appendix 10), anyone unfamiliar with these equations will see the similarity of this result to those found above with Newtonian equations, and can check the correctness of the result in that form if desired. The solution of Eq. (9.33) is clearly simple harmonic motion, with $\lambda_3 = b(M + 2m)/2mM$, or $b/2\mu$ with μ defined as above.

We may recapitulate the results for the A-B-A linear molecule.[6]

$$\left.\begin{array}{l} \lambda_1 = k/m \\ \lambda_2 = k/\mu \end{array}\right\} \; z \text{ motions}$$

$$\lambda_3 = b/2\mu \quad \text{degenerate—} x \text{ and } y \text{ motions}$$

$$\mu = mM/(2m + M)$$

Clearly the y motion is entirely analogous to the x motion, giving the same λ and frequency. These two constitute then a degenerate pair, and any combination of x and y motion will also have the same frequency.

If there had been more than one vibration included in our latter treatment, we would have had kinetic and potential energy expressions of the form

$$2T = \sum_i \sum_j a_{ij} \dot{q}_i \dot{q}_j$$

$$2V = \sum_i \sum_j b_{ij} q_i q_j \tag{9.34}$$

In these general terms the problem is one of transforming to a new set of normal coordinates, Q_i, such that

$$2T = \sum_i \dot{Q}_i^2$$

$$2V = \sum_i \lambda_i Q_i^2 \tag{9.35}$$

where no cross terms appear. In these latter coordinates, the equation of motion (by Lagrangian methods—see Appendix 10) are

$$\frac{d}{dt}\left(\frac{\partial T}{\partial \dot{Q}_i}\right) + \frac{\partial V}{\partial Q_i} = 0$$

$$\ddot{Q}_i + \lambda_i Q_i = 0, \qquad Q_i = Q_i^0 \cos 2\pi\nu_i t \tag{9.36}$$

$$\nu_i = \lambda_i^{1/2}/2\pi$$

---

[6] Many authors use the opposite numbering for modes 2 and 3.

which clearly indicates that the Q's are normal coordinates. Now in any one normal mode the q's must also follow simple harmonic motion of frequency ν. Thus

$$q_i = q_i^0 \cos 2\pi\nu t$$
$$\ddot{q}_i = -4\pi^2\nu^2 q_i^0 \cos 2\pi\nu t = -\lambda q_i$$

However, the equations of motion for the q's are

$$\frac{d}{dt}\left(\frac{\partial T}{\partial \dot{q}_j}\right) + \frac{\partial V}{\partial q_j} = 0 \qquad (9.37)$$

which, upon the introduction of Eqs. (9.34), yield

$$\sum_i a_{ij}\ddot{q}_i + \sum_i b_{ij}q_i = 0$$

Then we assume the motion to be in a single normal mode and introduce the appropriate value of $\ddot{q}$ given above. This yields the series of equations, one for each j, as follows.

$$\sum_i (b_{ij} - a_{ij}\lambda)q_i^0 = 0 \qquad (9.38)$$

Here again is the set of simultaneous, homogeneous linear equations, and the determinant of the coefficients must be zero for there to be a nontrivial solution.

$$\begin{vmatrix} b_{11} - a_{11}\lambda & b_{12} - a_{12}\lambda & \dots \\ b_{21} - a_{21}\lambda & b_{22} - a_{22}\lambda & \dots \\ \dots\dots\dots\dots\dots\dots\dots\dots \\ \dots\dots\dots\dots\dots\dots\dots\dots \end{vmatrix} = 0 \qquad (9.39)$$

Thus the analysis in terms of internal coordinates yields a secular equation as did our first analysis; however, in this case the order is just that of the number of vibrations (and therefore there are no zero roots). Also, if the q's are selected in accordance with the symmetry of the molecule, all off-diagonal terms between different symmetry types are zero. This allows the secular equation to be factored.

Special, more powerful mathematical methods have been developed, particularly by E. B. Wilson, Jr.,[7] which aid in obtaining the a_{ij} and b_{ij} quantities in Eqs. (9.34) and (9.39). The initial steps

---

[7] Wilson, E. B., Jr., *J. Chem. Phys.*, **7**, 1047 (1939); **9**, 76 (1941). For a more elementary introduction, see Meister, A. G. and Cleveland, F. F., *Am. J. Phys.*, **14**, 13 (1946).

of this procedure, yielding the number of modes of vibration of each symmetry type, are given in Appendix 12.

9e. Vibration of molecules—quantum energy levels. While normal coordinates are found in classical mechanics, actual molecular vibrations must be treated by quantum mechanics. We shall assume that we have the normal coordinates Q_i, which are linear functions of the Cartesian displacements x_j of each atom from its equilibrium position.

$$Q_i = \sum_j c_{ij} x_j \tag{9.40}$$

Also the kinetic and potential energies are

$$2T = \sum_i Q_i^2, \qquad 2V = \sum_i \lambda_i Q_i^2 \tag{9.35}$$

The Schrödinger equation is

$$\frac{-h^2}{8\pi^2} \sum_j \frac{1}{m_j} \frac{\partial^2 \psi}{\partial x_j^2} + V\psi = E\psi$$

which on transformation to the Q's becomes

$$\frac{-h^2}{8\pi^2} \sum_j \frac{1}{m_j} \sum_k \sum_l c_{kj} c_{lj} \frac{\partial^2 \psi}{\partial Q_k \, \partial Q_l} + V\psi = E\psi$$

By expansion of the classical kinetic energy equations it is easy to show that

$$\sum_i c_{ij}^2 = m_j \tag{9.41}$$

The additional property

$$\sum_j \frac{1}{m_j} c_{kj} c_{lj} = 0, \qquad \text{if } k \neq l \tag{9.42}$$

may be established from the orthogonality of the transformation which necessarily follows from normal coordinate analysis. However, it would take us too far afield to prove this. The reader can readily verify it in individual cases.

Making use of Eqs. (9.41) and (9.42) and substituting the potential energy expression, the Schrödinger equation simplifies to

$$\sum_i \left(\frac{-h^2}{8\pi^2} \frac{\partial^2 \psi}{\partial Q_i^2} + \tfrac{1}{2}\lambda_i Q_i^2 \psi \right) = E\psi \tag{9.43}$$

This form permits immediate separation of variables by the substitutions

$$\psi = \Pi_i \psi_i(Q_i), \qquad E = \sum_i E_i \qquad (9.44)$$

yielding the individual equations

$$\frac{-h^2}{8\pi^2} \frac{d^2\psi_i}{dQ_i^2} + \tfrac{1}{2}\lambda_i Q_i^2 \psi_i = E_i \psi_i \qquad (9.45)$$

These equations are each of the harmonic oscillator type which was treated in Section 2i. It was found there that the energy levels were $(n + \tfrac{1}{2})h\nu$, and in our present terms $\nu = \lambda^{1/2}/2\pi$. Thus for our polyatomic molecule the total vibrational energy levels are

$$E = \sum_i (n_i + \tfrac{1}{2})h\nu_i \qquad (9.46)$$

where each $n_i = 0, 1, 2, \ldots$, and

$$\nu_i = \lambda_i^{1/2}/2\pi$$

Furthermore, the complete vibrational wave function is just the corresponding product of harmonic oscillator functions.

Experimental determinations of vibrational energy levels by spectroscopic methods have shown these results to be a good first approximation. However, there are appreciable deviations, particularly in the higher energy states, which arise because the amplitude of vibration is not strictly infinitesimal. Thus higher order terms in the potential energy do have an influence. This is known as anharmonicity, and investigation indicates that its effect on the energy levels should appear as additive terms of the type, (const.)$(n_i + \tfrac{1}{2})^2$. It may also appear as cross terms, so that the complete energy level expression becomes

$$\frac{E}{hc} = \sum_i (n_i + \tfrac{1}{2})\omega_i + \sum_i \sum_j (n_i + \tfrac{1}{2})(n_j + \tfrac{1}{2})X_{ij} \qquad (9.47)$$

where we have substituted the frequency in cm.$^{-1}$, $\omega = \nu/c$, and have expressed the anharmonicity in the same units.

As an example let us take two of the normal modes of vibration of the water molecule whose fundamental $(0 \rightarrow 1)$ absorption peaks appear at 1595.0 and 3755.8 cm.$^{-1}$, respectively. The transition to the state with one quantum $(n = 1)$ in each mode appears weakly at 5332.0 cm.$^{-1}$. The sum of the two frequencies above is 5350.8 cm.$^{-1}$, which differs by 18.8 cm.$^{-1}$ because of anharmonicity. Also the $0 \to 2$ overtone of the 1595 vibration is observed at 3151.4 cm.$^{-1}$ In the latter case the anharmonicity is somewhat over one per cent.

The partition function is very easily computed for the harmonic oscillator case.

$$Q_{h.o.} = \sum_{n=1}^{\infty} e^{-nh\nu/kT} = \sum_{n=1}^{\infty} (e^{-u})^n = \frac{1}{1 - e^{-u}} \tag{9.48}$$

with $u = h\nu/kT = hc\omega/kT$. Thus in this case the partition function sums to a simple, closed expression, whether the energy level spacing is large or small compared with kT. The resulting thermodynamic functions were first derived by Einstein (1907) in his classic explanation of the qualitative reason for the decrease of specific heat of crystals at low temperatures. Although sometimes called Einstein functions when computed for $3N_0$ degrees of freedom as in a mole of monatomic crystal, it seems rather better to call them *harmonic oscillator functions* as is usual when they are tabulated for one degree of freedom in N_0 molecules.

$$Q_{h.o.} = \frac{1}{1 - e^{-u}}, \qquad u = \frac{h\nu}{kT} = \frac{hc\omega}{kT}$$

$$-\left(\frac{F}{T}\right)_{h.o.} = -R \ln (1 - e^{-u})$$

$$H_{h.o.} = RT \left(\frac{u}{e^u - 1}\right) \tag{9.49}$$

$$S_{h.o.} = R \left[\frac{u}{e^u - 1} - \ln (1 - e^{-u})\right]$$

$$C_{h.o.} = R \frac{u^2 e^u}{(e^u - 1)^2}$$

Tables of harmonic oscillator functions are given in Appendix 13.

Occasionally one has need of the limiting expressions valid for $u \ll 1$ or $T \gg (h\nu/k)$. The classical mechanical behavior is given by these expressions for $u = 0$.

$$-\left(\frac{F - H_0}{T}\right)_{h.o.} = R \left[\ln \left(\frac{1}{u}\right) + \frac{u}{2} - \frac{u^2}{24} + \ldots\right]$$

$$(H - H_0)_{h.o.} = RT \left[1 - \frac{u}{2} + \frac{u^2}{12} - \ldots\right]$$

$$S_{h.o.} = R \left[1 + \ln \left(\frac{1}{u}\right) + \frac{u^2}{24} - \ldots\right] \tag{9.50}$$

$$C_{h.o.} = R \left[1 - \frac{u^2}{12} + \ldots\right]$$

Thus one obtains the result of R per degree of freedom for the heat capacity of the classical harmonic oscillator. It is also interesting to note that the term $(u/2)$ in the functions where the zero of energy appears has just the effect of shifting the energy zero from the lowest quantum state to the bottom of the potential curve (where classical mechanics would take it).

9f. Vibration-rotation spectra. We have mentioned the selection rules for the absorption (or emission) of radiation for transitions between rotational states. Now let us consider changes between vibrational states, with possible simultaneous change in rotational state. The fundamental equations were derived in Chapter 6, where it was shown that the quantity

$$(\mu_x)_{nm} = \int \psi_n^* \mu_x \psi_m \, dv \tag{6.4}$$

and the corresponding quantities in y and z determine the selection rules. If all are zero, the transition is forbidden; if one or more are not zero, it is permitted. The quantitative probability equations were also given in Chapter 6.

Let us consider an unsymmetrical diatomic molecule, since that will illustrate the important elements in the simplest example. The dipole moment μ is a function of the coordinates of all the particles, including electrons, in the molecule. However, if the electronic state is not changed by the transition, we are really concerned with a dipole moment, $\mu(r)$, for the molecule at its instantaneous internuclear distance r, but averaged with respect to all electronic coordinates. By symmetry, this moment is zero for symmetrical diatomic molecules, and is limited in direction to the axis of the molecule for unsymmetrical diatomic molecules. If $\psi_e(r)$ is the electronic wave function for the nuclear separation, r, then

$$\mu(r) = \int \cdots \int \psi_e^*(r) \mu_x \psi_e(r) \, dv_e \tag{9.51}$$

where μ_x is defined in Eq. (6.1), and we assume the molecule to be oriented along the x axis. The integration in (9.51) is over all the electronic coordinates, and dv_e is the appropriate volume element.

Not very much is actually known about the function $\mu(r)$, but in a typical case it may be presumed to approach zero for both very small and very large values of r and to vary in between in some manner such as the curve in Fig. 9.3. In the region near the equilibrium distance r_0, one can represent $\mu(r)$ by the expansion

$$\mu(r) = \mu_0 + \left(\frac{d\mu}{dr}\right)_{r_0}(r - r_0) + \frac{1}{2}\left(\frac{d^2\mu}{dr^2}\right)_{r_0}(r - r_0)^2 + \ldots \quad (9.52)$$

and for the first approximation we will use only the first two terms.

The vibration-rotation wave functions for a diatomic molecule were given, to the first approximation, in Chapter 3 as

$$\psi = \Theta(\theta)\Phi(\phi)\psi_{HO}(r - r_0)(1/r) \quad (3.40)$$

where Θ and Φ are the angular functions first obtained for the hydrogen atoms, given in Table 3.1, and ψ_{HO} is a harmonic oscillator function given in Section 2i.

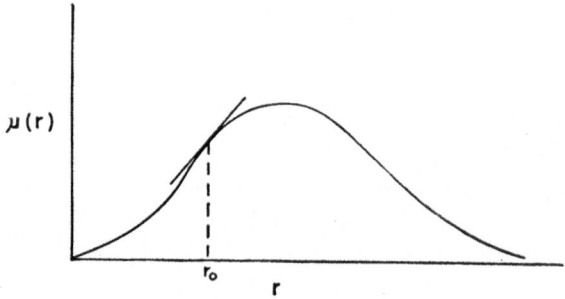

Fig. 9.3.   A possible variation of the dipole moment with interatomic distance in a diatomic molecule.

To compute the transition moment $(\mu_x)_{nm}$, we note that $\mu_x = \mu(r)$ sin θ cos ϕ, and proceed to substitute the wave functions for the nth and mth states, each of which will be defined by three separate quantum numbers. In order to avoid confusion between m and n as designations of quantum numbers and as initial and final states, we change notation to a single prime ($'$) for the initial state, a double prime ($''$) for the final state, and omit the nm from μ_x.   Then

$$\mu_x = \int \Theta^{*''}(\theta)\Theta'(\theta) \sin^2 \theta \, d\theta \int \Phi^{*''}(\phi) \cos \phi \, \Phi'(\phi) \, d\phi$$

$$\cdot \int \psi_{HO}''(r - r_0)\left[\mu_0 + \left(\frac{d\mu}{dr}\right)_{r_0}(r - r_0)\right]\psi_{HO}'(r - r_0) \, dr \quad (9.53)$$

The first two integrals, together with the corresponding ones for y and z, are identical with those considered for the hydrogen atom, and yield the same selection rules $\Delta J = \pm 1$, $\Delta m = 0, \pm 1$.   The third integral, which we will call $R_{n''n'}$, is the same for μ_y and μ_z as for μ_x, and may be simplified by the substitution $q = (r - r_0)$ to

$$R_{n''n'} = \int \psi''_{HO}(q) \left[\mu_0 + \left(\frac{d\mu}{dr} \right)_{r_0} q \right] \psi'_{HO}(q) \, dq \qquad (9.54)$$

The harmonic oscillator functions are normalized and orthogonal. Consequently, if the oscillator quantum number is the same before and after the transition, i.e., $n'' = n'$, we have

$$R = \mu_0, \qquad \Delta n = 0 \qquad (9.55')$$

and if $n'' \neq n$,

$$R = \left(\frac{d\mu}{dr} \right)_{r_0} \int \psi'' \psi' q \, dq, \qquad \Delta n \neq 0 \qquad (9.55'')$$

Of course, if $\Delta n = 0$, there is no change in vibrational energy, and we have the pure rotation spectrum. Its intensity depends on the value of the permanent dipole moment μ_0.

The vibration-rotation spectrum arises if the integral for $\Delta n \neq 0$ has a nonzero value. The harmonic oscillator functions yield a non-zero value if $\Delta n = \pm 1$; consequently, the band of rotational lines based on this vibrational change is permitted. This band for $\Delta n = 1$ is known as the fundamental band, and its quantitative intensity depends on the value of $(d\mu/dr)$. Also, the spectrum usually shows much weaker bands for Δn values greater than one. These can be explained either on the basis of anharmonicity in the potential energy and consequently in the wave functions, or on the basis of higher derivatives of the dipole moment such as $(d^2\mu/dr^2)_{r_0}$. Presumably both effects are of importance.

In the first approximation, the frequencies of the vibration-rotation lines are given by

$$\nu = \nu_0(n'' - n') + \frac{h}{8\pi^2 I_e} [J''(J'' + 1) - J'(J' + 1)]$$

which yields two sets of lines for each Δn, one if $J'' = J' + 1$, and the other if $J'' = J' - 1$. The latter set corresponds to a decrease in rotational energy and is known as the P branch. The former set of lines is called the R branch, and corresponds to increased rotational energy after the transition. The lines of the P branch necessarily lie at lower frequencies than those of the R branch. The equations for the frequencies, in wave numbers ($\omega = \nu/c$), are

$$\omega = \omega_0(n'' - n') + 2B(J' + 1) \qquad R \text{ branch}$$
$$\omega = \omega_0(n'' - n') - 2BJ' \qquad P \text{ branch} \qquad (9.56)$$

In the R branch, J' can have any positive integral value including zero, but in the P branch, $J' = 0$ is excluded because J'' would then be -1, which is impossible. The net result is a spectrum of evenly spaced lines except that the line at $\omega_0(n'' - n')$ is missing, as shown in Fig. 9.4. The missing line would correspond to a pure vibration transition, which is thus seen to be forbidden.

The number of lines actually observed in each branch depends on the temperature. The population N' of the initial state of energy E' is given by the usual Boltzmann expression

$$N' = g'N_0e^{-(E'-E_0)/kT} \qquad (7.13')$$

which is a rearrangement of Eq. (7.13) in terms of the population of the ground state N_0. The a priori probability is unity for the ground state. For the higher states $g' = (2J' + 1)$, and the energy is given by the usual expression. The consequence of the g factor is to make the lines increase in intensity with J for low values of J. However, as the energy exceeds kT, the exponential factor decreases more rapidly, so that the trend reverses, and the last observable lines correspond to energies a few times kT.

This curve of intensity with increasing J has actually been used to estimate the moment of inertia in cases where the individual lines were not resolved but the general contours of the P and R branches were observed. This is, of course, only a crude method.

Actually, the energy level expression used above is only a first approximation and the additional terms given in Eq. (3.41) have a very appreciable effect on the spectrum. The net result is that the lines in the R branch converge to smaller spacing as J increases, while the lines in the P branch diverge. This is also shown in Fig. 9.4, where the actual spectrum of HCl is plotted for the fundamental $(n = 0 \rightarrow 1)$ vibration.

For linear polyatomic molecules all features of the diatomic molecule spectrum arise, but there are some additional possibilities. This is seen most easily by considering the dipole moment as a function of the nuclear coordinates. Figure 9.5 shows the normal vibrations of a symmetrical linear A-B-A molecule, as considered above, together with the possible dipole moment for the distorted molecule.

By symmetry there is, of course, no permanent dipole and therefore no pure rotation spectrum. Also ν_1, like the vibration of a symmetrical diatomic molecule, develops no dipole moment even in the distorted molecule, and is therefore absent in the spectrum. However,

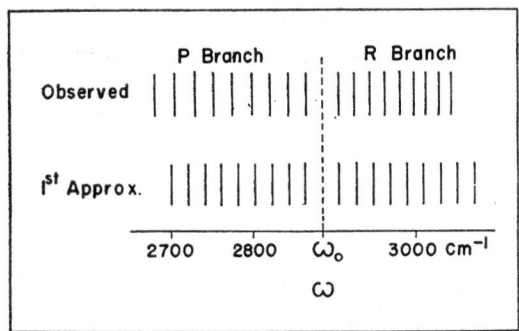

Fig. 9.4.   The vibration-rotation spectrum of a diatomic molecule.

ν_2 destroys the symmetry of the molecule, and hence will have a dipole moment in the distorted configuration. Thus $(d\mu/dq_2)_{q=0}$ will exist, and being oriented along the axis of the molecule, will lead to a vibration-rotation spectrum essentially the same as that described for the unsymmetrical diatomic molecule. This is called a *parallel*

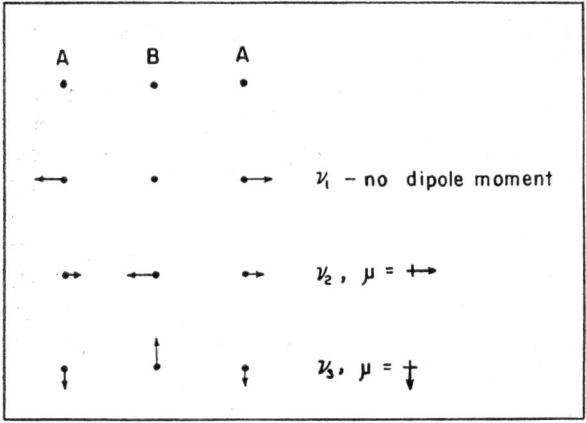

Fig. 9.5.   The normal modes of vibration of a linear A–B–A molecule with the possible instantaneous dipole moment indicated.

band because both the nuclear motions and the dipole moment are parallel to the axis of the molecule.

The third vibration, ν_3, is a *perpendicular* vibration and can cause a change in dipole moment perpendicular to the axis of the molecule. By following through the same sort of calculation given above for the diatomic molecule, one finds that a vibration-rotation spectrum is permitted, but that transitions with $\Delta J = 0$ are allowed in addition to those with $\Delta J = \pm 1$. (There is the exception that the $\Delta J = 0$ line for $J = 0$ is forbidden.) The $\Delta J = 0$ lines for various J values fall on top of one another in the first approximation and hence lead to a very strong central "line" between the P and R branches of the spectrum. This is called the Q branch. The higher terms shift the various lines slightly so that the Q branch is broadened, but the individual lines are not ordinarily resolved in a spectrum.

The spectra of more complex linear molecules differ only in having more than one normal mode of vibration of each of the types discussed.

The principle which applies to the selection rules for vibration-rotation spectra generally is that *a vibration must cause a change in the dipole moment to be active in the absorption or emission spectra.* The exact rotational changes that accompany the vibrational transition depend on the direction of this dipole change and the class of molecule (linear, symmetric top, etc.) and hence are too complex to discuss in detail here. However, for the various symmetry groups, the types of vibration that can cause a change in dipole moment and hence be infrared active are listed in Appendix 12; also the direction of the dipole moment change is indicated.

9g. Raman spectra. The Raman effect has proven to be an important source of information about the structure of molecules. This phenomenon, which had been predicted theoretically by Smekal, was discovered experimentally by Raman in 1928. It can be described as an inelastic scattering of photons by molecules. Thus when an incident photon of frequency ν_0 strikes a molecule, it may be scattered either elastically or inelastically. If it is scattered elastically, its frequency is essentially unchanged because the mass of the molecule is so much greater than that of the photon (note Section 1e on the Compton effect). This scattering of light without frequency change is known as *Raleigh* scattering. However, there is also the possibility of inelastic scattering of the photon. Naturally the photon can transfer to the molecule only such an amount of energy as will leave the molecule in one of its stationary states.   If the energy difference between the initial and final molecular energy levels is ΔE, the frequency of the scattered photon must be $\nu_0 - (\Delta E/h)$.

When the photon loses energy to the molecule, that is when ΔE is positive, the scattered radiation is shifted to lower frequency.   The various spectral lines arising from Raman scattering of reduced frequency are sometimes called Stokes lines.   There is also the possibility that the molecule is initially in an excited state.   Then the molecule can give energy to the photon which will increase its frequency.   Raman lines of frequency greater than the incident frequency are called anti-Stokes lines.

While a more rigorous derivation can be given for the selection rules for the Raman effect, we shall present a semiclassical argument involving the polarizability of the molecule, α.   Now in Section 4i the polarizability was defined by the equation

$$\mathbf{\mu} = \alpha \mathbf{E} \qquad (4.39)$$

where $\mathbf{\mu}$ and $\mathbf{E}$ are the vector dipole moment and electric field, respectively.   It was mentioned that α is in general a tensor, although for spherically symmetrical systems α reduces to a scalar.   Let us expand Eq. (4.39) into its x, y, and z components.

$$\mu_x = \alpha_{xx}E_x + \alpha_{xy}E_y + \alpha_{xz}E_z$$
$$\mu_y = \alpha_{yx}E_x + \alpha_{yy}E_y + \alpha_{yz}E_z \qquad (9.57)$$
$$\mu_z = \alpha_{zx}E_x + \alpha_{zy}E_y + \alpha_{zz}E_z$$

This equation shows the nine scalar components of the tensor α. These quantities are properties of the electron cloud of the molecule and could, in principle, be calculated by appropriate integrals over the complete electronic wave functions.   In practice, however, a less completely deductive approach must be followed.

It may be shown that the off-diagonal elements of the tensor are symmetrical with respect to the main diagonal, i.e., $\alpha_{yx} = \alpha_{xy}$, etc.   In other respects also, the components of α behave very much like the moments and products of inertia.   Thus if the principal axes of the molecule are defined by its symmetry, these same axes will make the off-diagonal components of α vanish.   Similarly, if the z axis is a threefold or higher symmetry axis, $\alpha_{xx} = \alpha_{yy}$, and for molecules such as CH_4 and SF_6, which are spherical tops by symmetry, $\alpha_{xx} = \alpha_{yy} = \alpha_{zz}$, so that α can be regarded as a scalar.[8]

Now let us consider a molecule rotating in the oscillating electric field of the incident radiation of frequency ν_0. If the polarizability is symmetrical to the axis of rotation, α is effectively a constant, and the induced dipole moment is

$$\mu = \alpha E_0 \cos 2\pi\nu_0 t \qquad (9.58)$$

which shows oscillation only with the incident frequency ν_0. Hence only Raleigh scattering will occur.

However, if the polarizability is not symmetrical to the axis of rotation, the dipole moment will show an oscillation depending also on the frequency of rotation. Mathematically,

$$\alpha = a_0 + a_1 \cos (2\pi\nu_r t + \delta) \qquad (9.59)$$

where ν_r is the frequency associated with the rotation and the symbol δ is introduced to signify that the phase of this oscillation is undetermined. Then a component of the induced dipole moment will be given by

$$\mu = a_0 E_0 \cos 2\pi\nu_0 t + a_1 E_0 \cos 2\pi\nu_0 t \cos (2\pi\nu_r t + \delta)$$
$$= a_0 E_0 \cos 2\pi\nu_0 t + \tfrac{1}{2} a_1 E_0 \{\cos [2\pi(\nu_0 + \nu_r)t + \delta]$$
$$+ \cos [2\pi(\nu_0 - \nu_r)t - \delta]\} \qquad (9.60)$$

where the terms showing oscillation with the frequencies $(\nu_0 + \nu_r)$ and $(\nu_0 - \nu_r)$ are apparent. These oscillations of the induced dipole will lead to the emission of radiation at these altered frequencies.

To find the frequencies associated with rotation, we consider the usual quantum mechanical integrals for α. Taking a linear molecule, the polarizability along the axis, α_{zz}, will be different from that perpendicular to the axis, $\alpha_{xx} = \alpha_{yy}$. In an arbitrary direction θ, the instantaneous value of α is

$$\alpha_{\theta\theta} = \alpha_{xx} \sin^2 \theta + \alpha_{zz} \cos^2 \theta = \alpha_{xx} + (\alpha_{zz} - \alpha_{xx}) \cos^2 \theta \qquad (9.61)$$

and for the transition between rotational states indicated by single and double primes, the time-dependent $\alpha_{\theta\theta}$ is

$$\alpha_{\theta\theta}(t) = \int \Psi^{*\prime\prime} [\alpha_{xx} + (\alpha_{zz} - \alpha_{xx}) \cos^2 \theta] \Psi' \, dv \qquad (9.62)$$

Just as we saw in Section 6a for the absorption of radiation, if

---

[8] For further discussion of the tensor of polarizability, see Born, M., *Optik*, Berlin: Julius Springer, 1933; also Ann Arbor, Michigan: Edwards Bros., Inc., 1943.

$E'' = E'$ the time-dependent factors of the two Ψ's cancel, and there is no time dependence in α.

Continuing for a linear molecule, we take E'' different from E'.

$$\alpha_{\theta\theta}(t) = e^{-(2\pi i/h)(E'-E'')t} \int \Phi^{*\prime\prime}(\phi)\Phi'(\phi)\, d\phi$$
$$\cdot \int \Theta^{*\prime\prime}(\theta)\,[\alpha_{xx} + (\alpha_{zz} - \alpha_{xx})\cos^2\theta]\Theta'(\theta)\sin\theta\, d\theta \qquad (9.63)$$

From the factors of Eq. (9.63) the following conclusions can be drawn:[9]

1. The frequency of oscillation of α is $|E' - E''|/h$.
2. To keep the integral in ϕ from vanishing, $(m'' - m') = 0$.
3. To keep the integral in θ from vanishing, $(J'' - J') = 0, \pm 2$.

For the rotational Raman spectrum only the ± 2 values of ΔJ are significant, and they give the frequencies

$$\nu_r = \pm \frac{h^2}{8\pi^2 I}(4J + 6) \qquad (9.64)$$

where J is the quantum number in the lower state. Remembering our result above that the spectrum will show scattered frequencies $(\nu_0 + \nu_r)$ and $(\nu_0 - \nu_r)$, one can now see that the Raman spectrum will consist of a series of equally spaced lines on each side of the unchanged (Raleigh) frequency ν_0. The spacing will be twice that in the absorption spectrum (or $4B$ as defined above) except that the initial interval is larger, actually $6B$. The relative intensities of the lines depend principally on the population of the initial states as given by the Boltzmann distribution law.

The theory for the vibration-rotation Raman spectrum follows very closely that given in the preceding section for the absorption spectrum. The polarizability takes the place of the dipole moment in the various equations. The resulting selection rule for vibration is that *some component of the polarizability must be changed by the given normal vibration for that mode to be active.* Thus for the kth normal coordinate, one considers the derivative

$$\partial \alpha_{ij}/\partial q_k$$

for the six components of α. If any one of these has a nonzero value, the fundamental transition $n_k = 0 \to 1$ is permitted in the Raman

---

[9] Conclusion 2 is readily verified as well as the $(J'' - J') = 0$ result for 3. However, the ± 2 value of $(J'' - J')$ can only be established generally by the use of transformation properties of the Θ's not given above. See Placzek, G. and Teller, E., *Z. Physik*, **81**, 209 (1933).

spectrum. Overtones, which are transitions with Δn greater than one, are relatively very weak in the Raman spectrum, but are observed sometimes. As in the case of the absorption spectrum, these overtones arise from higher derivatives of either the potential energy or the polarizability, and the relationships can be developed in any particular case.

The rotational changes accompanying the vibrational transition follow closely the selection rules for the pure rotation spectrum. Thus for parallel vibrations of linear molecules, the selection rule is just the same: $\Delta J = 0, \pm 2$. A perpendicular vibration of a linear molecule destroys its symmetry axis and hence allows such components of the polarizability as α_{xy} to have a nonzero value. These new polarizability components permit additional rotational changes. Thus for the perpendicular vibrations of a linear molecule the selection rule is $\Delta J = 0, \pm 1, \pm 2$.

The PQR terminology given above is extended for these bands as follows:

ΔJ	-2	-1	0	$+1$	$+2$
Branch	O	P	Q	R	S

Thus parallel Raman bands have O, Q, and S branches. The intensity relations are usually such as to put most into the Q branch, which is, of course, practically a single line. Thus the parallel Raman band for a linear molecule appears to be a sharp line. In the perpendicular vibrations, however, there is little intensity in the Q branch. Also the O and P branches overlap as do the R and S branches. Hence perpendicular bands appear very diffuse.

The relationships for the rotation and vibration-rotation bands for symmetrical tops and unsymmetrical tops are of the same sort as for linear molecules but more complex. Consequently they will not be given here.

Spherical tops are sufficiently simple that some discussion is feasible. Since in that case the equilibrium polarizability is spherically symmetrical, there is no pure rotation Raman spectrum. Also a symmetrical vibration may change the magnitude of α but cannot change its symmetry. Therefore no rotational change is permitted in the vibrational transition. Thus only $\Delta J = 0$ is permitted, yielding just the single line Q "branch." However, an unsymmetrical vibration, if it changes α at all, may do so in an unsymmetrical manner. Consequently the full array of changes, $\Delta J = 0, \pm 1, \pm 2$ become possible in connection with the vibrational transition.

An important additional phenomenon observable in the Raman effect is the *polarization* of the various "lines" or bands. We consider the light scattered at 90° from a perfectly collimated incident beam. If the scattering molecules are spherically symmetrical, the Raleigh scattering must be completely polarized in the plane perpendicular to the incident beam. To see this, one notes that the incident photon can generate only a dipole moment perpendicular to its direction of motion. Thus the generating dipole is necessarily in the plane perpendicular to the incident beam and any photon scattered with its path in this plane will be completely polarized. For the Raman scattering we consider the symmetry of the change in polarizability, $\partial\alpha/\partial q$, in place of the symmetry of the total polarizability.

While in spherically symmetrical systems the induced dipole moment is in the direction of the electric field, this is not generally the case. The components of α, such as α_{xy}, imply a dipole along one axis arising from a field along a different axis. Consequently one expects depolarization of the scattered radiation in at least some cases.

Important conclusions can be drawn concerning the degree of depolarization of the Raman scattering from the symmetry of the molecule and its vibrations. For this purpose the vibrations may be divided into two groups: *totally symmetric vibrations*, which maintain the full symmetry of the molecule, and all other vibrations, which are necessarily antisymmetric to some element of symmetry, and can be called *antisymmetric vibrations*. For the linear, symmetrical molecule A-B-A as shown in Fig. 9.5, ν_1 is totally symmetric, while ν_2 and ν_3 are antisymmetric to one or more symmetry elements.

Now the essential difference between these two types of vibration may be seen by considering the opposite phase of each of the vibrations of the A-B-A molecule. For ν_1 the extreme phases are the maximum extension and compression of the bond lengths. The extended phase is essentially different from the compressed phase. Thus a diagonal (or symmetrical) element of polarizability α_{xx}, α_{yy}, or α_{zz} can behave in a manner such as curve (1) in Fig. 9.6. The derivatives $\partial\alpha_{xx}/\partial q_k$, $\partial\alpha_{yy}/\partial q_k$, $\partial\alpha_{zz}/\partial q_k$ may all have nonzero values for totally symmetric vibrations. If by symmetry these quantities are all equal (as in CH_4), the Raman scattering will be completely polarized. Otherwise these three derivatives may have different values leading to an arbitrary, but frequently very small, degree of depolarization.

However, for an antisymmetric vibration such as ν_2 in Fig. 9.5, the opposite phases represent the same displaced configuration but in a new orientation.   Thus the diagonal polarizability components must behave as curve (2) of Fig. 9.6 in having the same value for equal

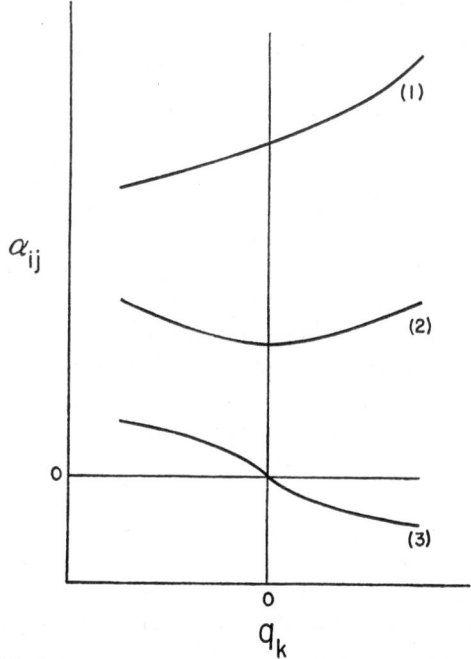

Fig. 9.6.   Possible types of behavior of the polarizability with molecular vibration.

displacements in either direction.   This necessarily leads to a zero slope and to zero values of the derivatives of $\partial\alpha_{ii}/\partial q_k$ at the undisplaced position.   In some cases an off-diagonal component of α can behave as curve (3) in Fig. 9.6, and have a nonzero slope in the undisplaced configuration.

Consequently, antisymmetric vibrations may be either inactive in the Raman effect or active due to only an off-diagonal component of α. However, if the Raman scattering is due to only an off-diagonal component of polarizability, it can be shown that the scattered radiation must be *fully depolarized*. The exact intensity ratio that corresponds to complete depolarization depends on the type of incident radiation and the geometry of the system.

For unpolarized incident light along the z axis and scattered light in the xy plane, one defines ρ as the ratio of intensity polarized perpendicular to the xy plane to that polarized parallel to the plane. Then it can be shown that the maximum value of ρ is $\frac{6}{7}$ for the completely depolarized scattering of antisymmetric vibrations. Totally symmetric vibrations may have any value of ρ less than $\frac{6}{7}$ (except for the spherical cases, where ρ must be zero).

Appendix 12 includes tables showing which antisymmetric types of vibration are active in the Raman effect.

9h. Internal rotation. Molecules such as methanol, ethane, and many others have groups connected by a single bond in such a fashion that one group can rotate with respect to the other within the molecule. Thus in methanol the OH group can rotate with respect to the CH₃ group about the C—O bond. In general such internal rotations will be subject to some forces. The potential energy for an internal rotation involving a methyl group must be a periodic function repeating itself every 120° because of the symmetry of the CH₃ group.

This is the first occasion where the problem of a particle subject to a periodic potential has arisen, but it is not the only one of interest. Crystal lattices constitute periodic potentials also. Consequently the quantum mechanical problem treated here will be of interest in other circumstances.

For an internal rotation one must first make the transformations separating the other coordinates. Although somewhat cumbersome, such transformations are straightforward and have been illustrated already several times. Consequently we omit these details and immediately write the Schrödinger equation for the one-dimensional rotation

$$\frac{d^2\psi}{d\phi^2} + \frac{8\pi^2 I_r}{h^2}[E - V(\phi)]\psi = 0 \tag{9.65}$$

where ϕ is the angle of rotation, and I_r is the reduced moment of inertia. For an internal rotation of two symmetrical coaxial tops, the reduced moment of inertia is

$$I_r = I_1 I_2 / (I_1 + I_2) \tag{9.66}$$

with I_1 and I_2 the moments of inertia of the two tops about the axis of internal rotation. Expressions for the reduced moment of inertia in more complex cases are given in Appendix 16.

The potential energy, $V(\phi)$, in Eq. (9.65) must be a periodic function with a period of 2π. However, if one or both of the rotating groups has symmetry, such as a methyl group, $V(\phi)$ will return to its initial value after rotation of $2\pi/n$, where n is the symmetry number. This may be expressed by

$$V(\phi + 2\pi/n) = V(\phi) \tag{9.67}$$

All the qualitative aspects of the results to be presented apply to any shape of potential barrier, provided it is periodic. Nevertheless it seems preferable to specialize the treatment at this point to the potential function which has been found to be most generally useful.

$$V(\phi) = \tfrac{1}{2}V_0(1 - \cos n\phi) \tag{9.68}$$

With this potential function, the Schrödinger equation can be reduced to the Mathieu differential equation, whose solutions have been studied rather thoroughly. The usual form of the Mathieu equation is

$$\frac{d^2u}{dz^2} + (a + 2\theta \cos 2z)u = 0 \tag{9.69}$$

and in these terms with $\psi = u$, we have

$$2z = n\phi$$
$$\theta = 8\pi^2 I_r V_0/n^2 h^2$$
$$E - \tfrac{1}{2}V_0 = n^2 h^2 a/32\pi^2 I_r$$

It is found that the two solutions of the differential equation can be expressed as

$$\begin{aligned} u_1 &= e^{\mu z}f(z) \\ u_2 &= e^{-\mu z}f(-z) \end{aligned} \tag{9.70}$$

where a general solution is a linear combination, with two arbitrary constants, of these two solutions. Here $f(z)$ is a periodic function and μ is a constant. Furthermore, one finds that μ is a function of a for any given θ. Figure 9.7 shows a typical graph of $\cos \pi i\mu$ as a function of a.

The exact boundary conditions for a wave function for internal rotation are very complicated in most cases. This is because the internal rotation is usually coupled to over-all rotation of the entire molecule. Thus internal rotation by 2π leaves the entire molecule rotated by an angle depending on the relative moments of inertia of the rotating groups. The boundary condition on the internal rotation wave function depends then on this angle and on the wave function for the over-all rotation. However, it is evident that the wave function must remain finite for all ϕ in any case. Now the functions u_1 and u_2 are unacceptable on this basis if μ has any real component. Consequently μ must be a pure imaginary, and cos $\pi i \mu$ must have a value between -1 and $+1$.

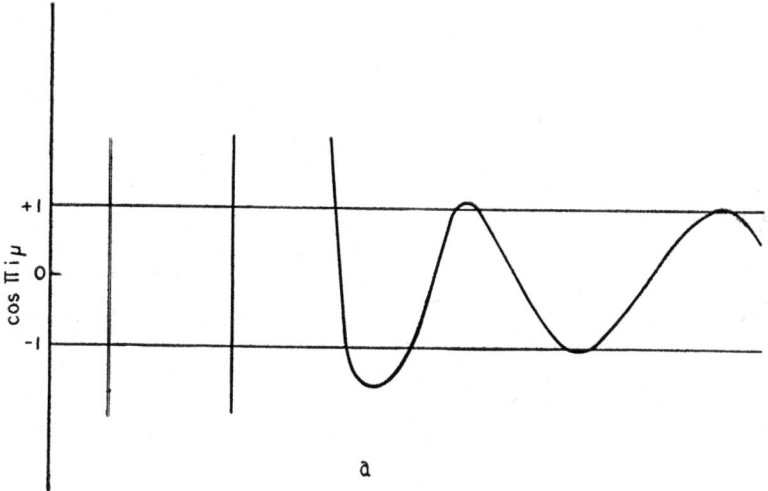

Fig. 9.7.   Typical graph of the function determining internal rotational energy levels.

From Fig. 9.7 it is apparent that this requirement on μ is sufficient to limit the first few a values, and consequently the first few energy levels, within narrow limits. Thus for low resolution spectroscopy and for thermodynamic purposes, one may ignore the exact boundary conditions on the internal rotation wave functions. Any given over-all rotational state will require some particular value for μ. Consequently there will be one internal rotation energy level in each allowed range in Fig. 9.7. For high resolution spectroscopy, one must solve the problem in full detail, as was done for methanol by Koehler and Dennison.[10]

[10] Koehler, J. S. and Dennison, D. M., *Phys. Rev.* **57**, 1006 (1940).

The thermodynamic functions for internal rotation have been computed[11] by numerical calculations from the tabulated a values for acceptable Mathieu functions. The formulas were given in Section 7o. It was necessary to use two independent variables to express the results. One is taken as the ratio (V_0/RT), while the other must include I_r, n, and either V_0 or T. Tables of internal rotation functions are given in Appendix 18.

Before leaving the subject of internal rotation it is desirable to note the transition from vibrational motion at energies well below the top of the potential barrier to rotation at energies above the top of barrier. One can expand the potential function in a power series in ϕ as follows.

$$V(\phi) = V_0 \left(\frac{n^2\phi^2}{4} - \frac{n^4\phi^4}{48} + \frac{n^6\phi^6}{1440} - \cdots \right) \tag{9.71}$$

To the harmonic oscillator approximation one then finds the frequency to be

$$\nu = \frac{n}{2\pi} \sqrt{\frac{V_0}{2I_r}} \tag{9.72}$$

with the usual energy levels. The true restricted rotator energy levels must approach these harmonic oscillator levels at energies near the potential minima.

At high energies, well above the barrier peaks, one can replace $V(\phi)$ by its average value $\frac{1}{2}V_0$. Then the Schrödinger equation is readily solved.

$$\frac{d^2\psi}{d\phi^2} + \frac{8\pi^2 I_r}{h^2} \left(E - \frac{1}{2} V_0 \right) \psi = 0 \tag{9.73a}$$

$$\psi = e^{\pm i\alpha\phi} \tag{9.73b}$$

$$\alpha = \left[\frac{8\pi^2 I_r}{h^2} \left(E - \frac{1}{2} V_0 \right) \right]^{1/2} \tag{9.73c}$$

Here one notes that the wave functions are of the form of Eq. (9.70) but with $f(\phi)$ reduced to a constant (taken as 1). The complicated boundary conditions still apply, but for a simple comparison we will require ψ to be simply periodic in $2\pi/n$, i.e.,

$$\psi(\phi + 2\pi/n) = \psi(\phi) \tag{9.74}$$

---

[11] Pitzer, K. S., *J. Chem. Phys.*, **5**, 469 (1937); Pitzer, K. S. and Gwinn, W. D., *J. Chem. Phys.*, **10**, 428 (1942).

For this example then

$$e^{i\alpha(\phi+2\pi/n)} = e^{i\alpha\phi}e^{2\pi i\alpha/n} = e^{i\alpha\phi} \qquad (9.75)$$

$$\alpha = \pm kn$$

with k any integer including zero. The restricted rotator energy levels of corresponding μ value are selected for comparison in Fig. 9.8.

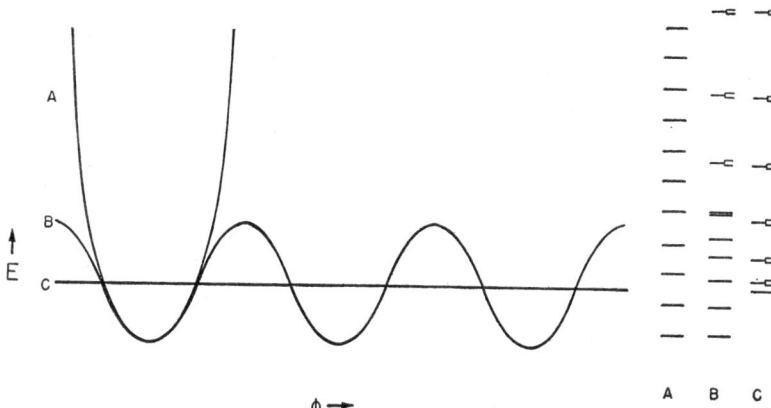

Fig. 9.8. Potential functions, on the left, and energy levels, on the right, for a restricted rotator B and for the harmonic oscillator A and free rotator C approached at low and high energies respectively.

It is apparent in Fig. 9.8 that there is a rather narrow region of transition from vibrational to rotational energy levels near the top of the barrier, but that it is a continuous shift, not any sort of discontinuity.

9i. Double minimum vibrations. The best-known example of a double minimum vibration occurs in the ammonia molecule. This molecule, at equilibrium, has the configuration of a triangular pyramid, but the nitrogen atom is only about 0.38 A out of the plane of the three hydrogen atoms. One normal coordinate is essentially this distance between the nitrogen and the plane of the hydrogen atoms. Clearly positive and negative values of this coordinate correspond to the same electronic energy, so that there must be two minima as indicated in Fig. 9.9.

Double minimum vibrations are common in even moderately complex molecules. In a tetrahedral molecule such as CH_4 one may

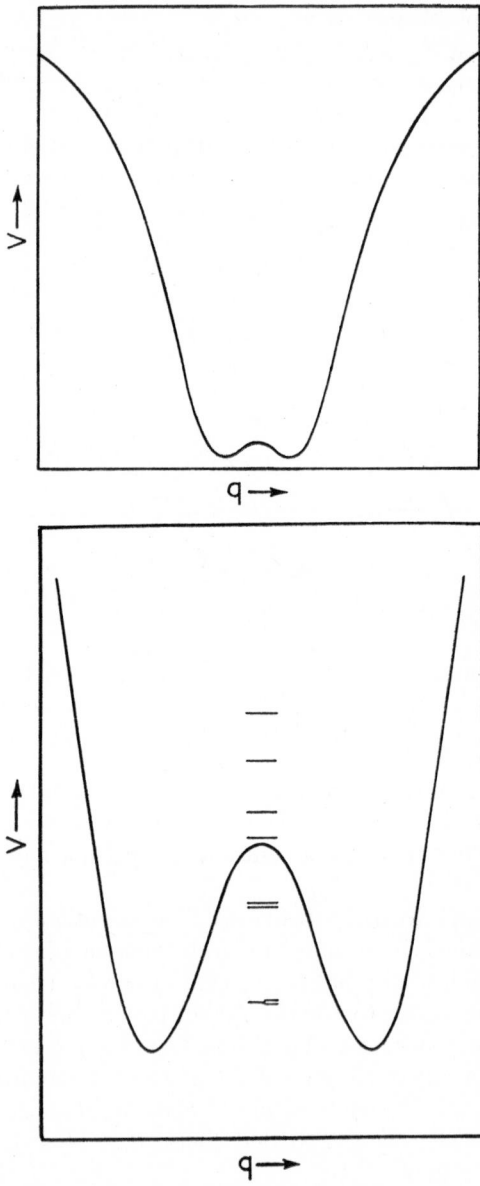

Fig. 9.9. Large and small scale plots of the potential energy for a double minimum vibration together with the lowest few energy levels.

consider the motion of twisting one CH_2 plane with respect to the other. When these are coplanar and the molecule is flat, the potential energy is a maximum, and there are minima for 90° twist in either direction. In an optically active molecule one of these potential minima would correspond to the d configuration, and the other to the l configuration. Nonplanar ring molecules necessarily have double minimum vibrations, since the puckering of the ring can be reversed by moving through the planar configuration.

One approach to the double minimum problem was indicated in Section 8o, where a double box potential was used to illustrate quantum mechanical resonance. Thus whenever the energy levels of interest are sufficiently below the top of the potential peak, one may take the solutions for each single potential valley and combine them by the resonance method. This has been done by Wall and Glockler,[12] using harmonic oscillator functions for the single potential minima.

If one is interested in energy levels near or above the top of the potential peak, it is necessary to use more rigorous methods. Manning[13] has solved the Schrödinger equation exactly for the potential

$$V(x) = A \operatorname{sech}^4 ax - B \operatorname{sech}^2 ax \qquad (9.76)$$

where a, A, and B are constants which can be related to the height of the central potential hill, the distance between minima and the depth of the potential minima below the potential energy at $x = \infty$. The energy levels, in Manning's analysis, appear in continued fractions. While a single solution is readily calculated, handling a variety of problems is difficult. The potential curve and energy levels of Fig. 9.9 are those calculated by Manning for NH_3.

For most molecules with double minimum vibrations, the potential barrier is so high and thick that the first few energy levels are pairs of practically indistinguishable energy. The great interest in ammonia arises because there is a measurable separation of these pairs of levels. This leads to a doubling of the infrared band for this vibration and to an entire spectrum in the microwave region.

For this double minimum vibration the potential is symmetric, i.e., $V(-x) = V(x)$; hence the considerations of Section 4c apply. The wave functions are successively symmetric and antisymmetric in order of increasing energy. Thus, among each pair of energy levels

[12] Wall, F. T., and Glockler, G., *J. Chem. Phys.*, **5**, 314 (1937).
[13] Manning, M. F., *J. Chem. Phys.*, **3**, 136 (1935).

below the top of the barrier, the lower one is symmetric and the upper one is antisymmetric. Transitions involving dipole radiation take place only between states of opposite symmetry. Consequently, one has in the vibration spectrum the transition from the lower state of the lowest pair to the upper state of the next higher pair, and the transition from the upper state of the lowest pair to the lower state of the higher pair. These two transitions are observed at 968.08 and 931.58 cm.$^{-1}$, respectively. The difference of 36.5 cm.$^{-1}$ is the sum of the splittings of the two pairs of levels.

The special microwave spectrum arises from transition from the lower to the upper level of the lowest pair. To the first approximation this spectrum would be a single line. However, the rotation of the molecule causes small changes in this frequency, which are resolved by the remarkably precise microwave spectrometers. Gordy[14] has reviewed microwave spectroscopy, and in particular, measurements of this inversion spectrum up to lines with $J = 16$ and $K = 16$. He gives the formula

$$\nu(\text{mc./sec.}) = 23{,}787 - 151.3J(J + 1) + 211.0K^2$$
$$+ 0.5503J^2(J + 1)^2 - 1.531J(J + 1)K^2 + 1.0555K^4 \qquad (9.77)$$

which is stated to be accurate to 25 mc. To convert to the usual spectroscopic units, cm.$^{-1}$, one divides by 29,979. The inversion frequency for the rotationless state is, therefore, 0.7934 cm.$^{-1}$.

This inversion splitting of the lowest pair of levels has also been measured in the pure rotation spectrum of ammonia. Other molecules where inversion spectra seem likely to be measurable, besides deuterated ammonias, are phosphine, arsine, and ethylene imine.

There has been little need for quantitative tables of thermodynamic functions for the double minimum oscillator. Their qualitative character has been presented[15] elsewhere in some detail. However, if the barrier between minima is even moderately high, as in ammonia, it is a good approximation to take the energy levels for an 'equivalent single minimum oscillator and assume each is double. This simply adds $R \ln 2$ to the entropy and leaves the heat content and heat capacity unchanged.

An alternate, equivalent method is simply to ignore the second potential minimum. Taking ammonia as an example, in the first

[14] Gordy, W., *Revs. Modern Phys.*, **20**, 668 (1948).
[15] Pitzer, K. S., *J. Chem. Phys.*, **7**, 251 (1939).

method $R \ln 2$ is added to the usual harmonic oscillator entropy for the vibration involving inversion. But in this case one must give the molecule a symmetry number of six, because the combination of rotation and inversion can give all six possible interchanges of the hydrogen atoms. In the second method, since inversion is ignored, the symmetry number is three for the triangular pyramid. Clearly $R \ln 2 - R \ln 6 = -R \ln 3$, so that the result is identical by either method.

9j. Accidental degeneracy-resonance. In the complex array of vibrational states for a polyatomic molecule it is not surprising that occasionally two or more different states fall very close together in energy. When this occurs the phenomenon of resonance can arise. Classically one thinks of the molecule first vibrating in one mode but gradually transferring its energy to the other mode, then back again, etc. For the stationary energy states in quantum mechanics, however, one must consider the two component states at the same time and allow for any interaction between them. This phenomenon is also called *Fermi resonance*, after E. Fermi.

The principles and mathematical methods of resonance were given in Section 8o. It is our purpose here to mention examples from molecular spectra. The most famous case is that of carbon dioxide. From Fig. 9.5 and the discussion earlier in this chapter, one recalls that this linear molecule has three fundamental modes of vibration. The first, ν_1, is active and polarized in the Raman effect but inactive in the infrared; ν_2 is infrared active as a parallel vibration; and ν_3 is a doubly degenerate vibration which is active in the infrared as a perpendicular band. Both ν_2 and ν_3 are forbidden in the Raman effect.

The two infrared bands appear very strongly at 2349.3 and 667.3 cm.$^{-1}$, respectively, and each has the proper fine structure of rotational lines for its band type. However, instead of one strong band in the Raman spectrum, there are two bands of nearly equal intensity at 1285.5 and 1388.3 cm.$^{-1}$. To explain this anomaly one notes that twice 667.3 is 1334.6, which is roughly midway between the observed Raman bands. Thus one may assume that a resonance interaction has occurred between the first excited state of ν_1 and the second excited state of the 667.3 cm.$^{-1}$ vibration, ν_3.

For such an interaction to take place the wave functions must be of the same symmetry type. Otherwise one could show that the interaction integral would be zero.   It is convenient to use the symbols of group theory as labels of the various symmetry types.   While a knowledge of group theory is desirable for the study of molecular spectra, the reader can follow the essential arguments without difficulty if he will regard these symbols as mere labels and will accept the correctness of the statements about symmetry types.

In the case of carbon dioxide the first excited state for ν_3 has the symmetry E_{1u}, but the next state with $n_3 = 2$ has two substates (see Appendix 14), one of which has the symmetry A_{1g}.   The Raman active vibration, ν_1, is of the symmetry A_{1g} in all states.   Consequently, the second excited state for ν_3 can interact with the first excited state for ν_1, because the symmetry properties are the same.

The symmetry argument does not prove that a resonance interaction will be appreciable—only that it may.   It is the spectrum itself that clearly indicates that the resonance interaction does occur. The two resulting states are each a mixture of the component states. Since the fundamental ν_1 would be expected to be much more intense in the Raman spectrum than the overtone $2\nu_3$, one can estimate the proportion of ν_1 in the resulting states from the intensity.   With roughly equal intensities observed, we conclude that each state is about half ν_1 and half $2\nu_3$, which is in agreement with the fact that the calculated location for $2\nu_3$ is almost exactly midway between the two observed lines.   We may also conclude that the unperturbed value for ν_1 would be nearly the average of the observed lines or 1337 cm.$^{-1}$.

Other higher vibrational states for CO_2 show similar resonance. Writing the symbol (n_1,n_2,n_3), we have been discussing the states (1,0,0) and (0,0,2).   However, the states (1,1,0) and (0,1,2) will be similarly degenerate.   The three states (2,1,0), (1,1,2), and (0,1,4) yield a similar but more complicated example, the actual states having the energies 4860.5, 4983.5, and 5109 cm.$^{-1}$.

This phenomenon is by no means confined to the molecule CO_2. The methyl group, in almost any organic compound, has a bending vibration near 1460 cm.$^{-1}$.   The symmetrical C—H stretching vibration would be near 2940 cm.$^{-1}$ but interacts with the overtone of 1460 to give a pair of lines at about 2880 and 2970 cm.$^{-1}$.   In many of the more complex molecules, the assignment of the spectrum in terms of the normal modes of vibration is still in doubt, but there are indications of this type of resonance in nearly every example.

Since the effect of this resonance is to split the accidentally degenerate levels symmetrically by a small fraction of their total energy, the contribution of the pair of levels to thermodynamic functions is nearly the same for the real levels as for the hypothetical degenerate levels. Therefore, unless unusual accuracy is required, the calculations can be made in whichever way may be more convenient in a given example. Usually it is easiest to use the fundamental frequencies which would have appeared in the absence of the resonance interaction. However, for rigorously exact results, one must use the real energy levels as observed in the spectrum.

9k. Electronic spectra of diatomic molecules. In addition to the transitions in which only the vibrational and rotational energy of a molecule is changed, there are transitions in which the electronic state changes also. These lead to electronic spectra, which appear at wave lengths from the infrared through the visible far into the ultraviolet. Since changes in both rotational energy and vibrational energy accompany the electronic change, the spectra become highly complex, and there is a very extensive "bookkeeping" problem in tabulating and interpreting such a spectrum. It will be possible here to give only the briefest outline of the principles governing such spectra.

The electronic states of diatomic molecules were considered in Chapter 8, and particularly in Section 8g, where the significance of the term symbols, such as $^1\Sigma_g^+$, $^3\Pi_u$, was explained. The molecular orbital point of view is most useful in considering excited electronic states. One assumes that only one electron is shifted to an excited molecular orbital and usually that it comes from the highest energy orbital which is occupied in the ground state.

The energy of each electronic state depends on the distance between nuclei in its own way. This energy is the potential energy for nuclear motion in that electronic state. Figure 9.10 shows the potential curves for the Li_2 molecule. One should note that the $^1\Sigma_u^+$ and $^1\Pi_u$ states dissociate to one normal lithium atom and one excited (^2P) atom, whereas the normal $^1\Sigma_g^+$ state of Li_2 dissociates to two normal atoms. Also the minima of the various curves do not lie at the same interatomic distance. Consequently, the moment of inertia and the rotational energy constant B will have distinctly different values for the various electronic states.

One finds the spectrum for a single electronic transition in a diatomic molecule to comprise a series of bands, with each band including many closely spaced lines.   One interprets each band as arising from a different change in vibrational energy.   The multitude of lines in the band arises principally from the many possible changes in rotational energy.

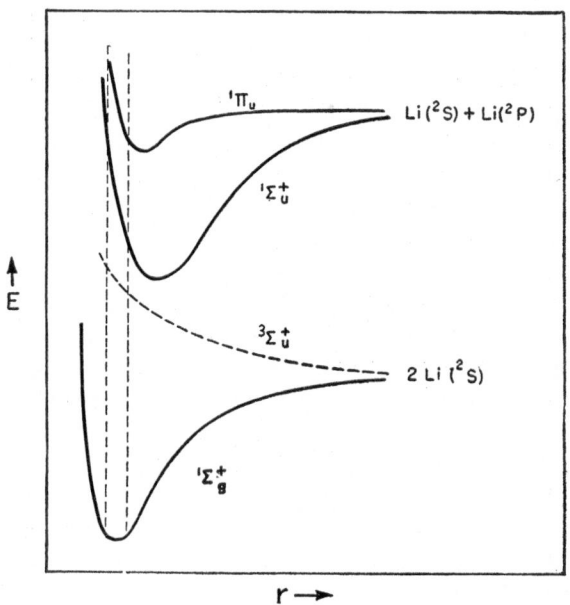

Fig. 9.10.   Potential energy curves for the Li₂ molecule.

Considering first the structure of a single band, one finds a basic rotational energy level pattern similar to that in pure rotation or in vibration-rotation spectra.   Using a single prime for the upper state and a double prime for the lower state, the frequencies of rotational lines should be given by

$$\frac{\Delta E}{hc} = \omega_0 + B'_v J'(J' + 1) - B''_v J''(J'' + 1) \qquad (9.78)$$

where ω_0 includes both the vibrational and electronic energy changes. However, we recall that B'_v and B''_v may have considerably different values.

The selection rules allow $\Delta J = \pm 1$ for transitions between two

$\sum$ states, as in the rotation-vibration spectra. This gives the P and R branches with frequencies

$$\frac{\Delta E}{hc} = \omega_0 + (B_v' + B_v'')m + (B_v' - B_v'')m^2 \qquad (9.79)$$

where $m = -J''$ in the P branch and $m = J'' + 1$ in the R branch. The line corresponding to $m = 0$ is missing. Since $(B_v' - B_v'')$ need not be small, the quadratic term usually causes one of the branches to "turn back" on itself. This will occur at

$$m = -(B_v' + B_v'')/2(B_v' - B_v'') \qquad (9.80)$$

and is called the *band head* because of its appearance, see Fig. 9.11. The more common example has a larger interatomic distance in the higher energy state. Then $(B_v' - B_v'')$ is negative and the band head occurs in the R branch which is at the high-frequency side of the band. In this case the band is *shaded toward the red*. The opposite case does also arise, where the interatomic distance is smaller in the higher energy state and the band is shaded toward the violet.

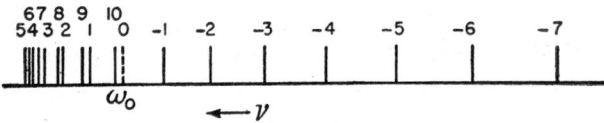

Fig. 9.11. The rotational lines for a typical band with approximately 10% larger interatomic distance in the higher energy electronic state. Note the band head at the left or high frequency end. The m values for the lines are given above.

If one or both of the electronic states have an orbital angular momentum, as in a Π state, then a Q branch is allowed with $\Delta J = 0$. The Q branch may give the appearance of a second band head. Also this electronic angular momentum, which we will call Ω, is along the molecular axis and thus is analogous to the axial rotation of a symmetric top. Replacing the K for the symmetric top by Ω, Eq. (9.14) can be put into the form

$$\frac{E}{hc} = B_v J(J + 1) + A\Omega^2 \qquad (9.81)$$

where B_v has its usual relationship to the moment of inertia of the molecule, but A involves the moment of inertia about the symmetry axis, which is a purely electronic quantity. By transferring the term $A\Omega^2$ to the electronic energy, one has just the usual formula for rotational energy levels, except that J is now limited to the values Ω, $\Omega + 1$, $\Omega + 2$, etc. Thus one or more of the lowest rotational levels are "missing," and the corresponding spectral lines at the beginning of the P and R branches are absent when Ω has a nonzero value.

There are no sharp selection rules as to the change in vibrational quantum number. The theory which applies here is due to Franck and to Condon, and is known as the *Franck-Condon Principle*. In its simplest terms, it states that the electronic change occurs so quickly that there can be no appreciable change in the position or momentum of the nuclei.

Quantitatively one must consider the wave functions which are the products of rotational, vibrational, and electronic factors,

$$\psi' = \psi_e'\psi_v'\psi_r', \qquad \psi'' = \psi_e''\psi_v''\psi_r''$$

and the dipole moment integral for the transition

$$\mu = \int \psi' \mathbf{\mu} \psi'' \, dv \tag{9.82}$$

The integrals involving the rotational factors separate out in exactly the manner found for vibration-rotation spectra in Section 9f, and will not be considered further here. The instantaneous dipole moment $\mathbf{\mu}$ is a sum over both electrons and nuclei, and can be separated into two parts.

$$\mathbf{\mu} = \mathbf{\mu}_e + \mathbf{\mu}_n$$

Then the integral in Eq. (9.82) can be broken down into the one for $\mathbf{\mu}_e$ and the following for $\mathbf{\mu}_n$.

$$\int \psi_v'\mathbf{\mu}_n\psi_v'' \, dv_n \int \psi_e'^*\psi_e'' \, dv_e$$

But this integral is zero because of the orthogonality of the electronic orbitals. The resulting transition moment comes thus entirely from the following.

$$\mu = \int \psi_v'\psi_v'' \, dv_n \int \psi_e'^*\mathbf{\mu}_e\psi_e'' \, dv_e \tag{9.83}$$

The second integral is a constant for any particular electronic transition. The probability of any accompanying vibrational change depends on the first integral. Since the vibrational wave functions ψ_v' and ψ_v'' are solutions of the Schrödinger equation for different potential functions, there is no orthogonality relationship applicable to them.

One can readily see how the first integral in Eq. (9.83) yields the principle stated above. The integral will be zero unless the two vibrational wave functions overlap. In other words, there must be a substantial probability of finding the nuclei in the same location in either state. Also, if one examines the Schrödinger equation more closely, one sees that a large momentum implies a rapidly oscillating wave function. Consequently, if there is a large difference in momentum in the two vibrational states, for the same position, one wave function will be oscillating from positive to negative values rapidly, and the contributions of these regions will largely cancel in the integral.

With reference to Fig. 9.10, one can consider Li_2 molecules initially in the lowest vibrational state of $^1\Sigma_g^+$ as the absorbing species. The vertical dotted lines indicate the approximate limits of zero point vibration in that state. The Franck-Condon principle indicates that the transitions will occur to the $^1\Sigma_u^+$ (or the $^1\Pi_u$) state without change in position, i.e., vertically within the band between the dotted lines. Also, the initial state has only the very small zero point momentum. Consequently, the molecule in the upper state must have a small momentum, which it can have in an excited vibrational state only near the limits of oscillation. These limits of oscillation are, of course, the potential energy curve itself at that energy. Thus the transition can be thought to take place vertically to a point on the potential energy curve of the excited electronic state, after which the molecule begins its oscillation within the region of the potential minimum and bounded by the two branches of the potential curve.

Particularly in emission spectra, the molecules in the initial state may be distributed over a large number of vibrational levels, from each of which a transition can take place to several vibrational levels of the final state. In this event, one obtains a complex sequence of bands. These bands can be arranged in a two-dimensional array, such as Table 9.2, where the entries are the frequencies of the band origins (i.e., the missing $m = 0$ lines), or if the origins are not available, the entries can be the frequencies of the band heads. Such an array is called a *Deslandres table*. The horizontal differences give the vibrational energy level separations in the ground state, while the vertical differences give the corresponding values for the upper state.   These differences for the ground state must be the same regardless of the excited state involved in the transition, hence the columns of horizontal differences must be constant.   Correspondingly the rows of vertical differences must also be constant.   The correct arrangement of the entries can be selected on this basis.   The vibrational quantum numbers n' and n'' are for the upper and lower states, respectively.

TABLE 9.2

A PORTION OF THE DESLANDRES TABLE FOR PN.

(with horizontal and vertical differences)

n' \ n''	0		1		2
0	39,699	1,322	38,377	1,308	37,069
	1,087		1,090		1,087
1	40,786	1,319	39,467	1,311	38,156
	1,073		1,069		
2	41,859	1,323	40,536		. . .
			1,061		
3	. . .		41,597	1,309	40,288
					1,043
4	. . .		. . .		41,331

The data in Table 9.2 for PN come from band heads, so that one cannot expect perfect agreement.   Evidently the vibrational levels in the ground electronic state are spaced at 1321, 1310, . . . cm.$^{-1}$ and those in the excited state at 1088, 1071, . . . cm.$^{-1}$.   These values can be fitted to expressions of the form of Eq. (3.41) if desired.

$$\frac{E}{hc} = \omega_e \left(n + \frac{1}{2} \right) - \omega_e x \left(n + \frac{1}{2} \right)^2 + \ldots \qquad n = 0, 1, 2, \ldots \quad (3.41)$$

As the energy increases, the vibrational energy levels come closer together, so that their separation approaches zero at the dissociation energy.   If Eq. (3.41) holds to this point, the *dissociation energy* can be found by differentiation.

$$\frac{d(E/hc)}{dn} = \omega_e - \omega_e x(2n + 1) = 0$$

$$\left(n + \frac{1}{2}\right) = \frac{1}{2x}$$

$$\frac{D_e}{hc} = \frac{\omega_e}{4x}$$

$$\frac{D_0^\circ}{hc} = \frac{D_e - E_0}{hc} = \omega_e\left(\frac{1}{4x} - \frac{1}{2} + \frac{x}{4}\right) \qquad (9.84)$$

Here D_e is the dissociation energy above the potential minimum, while D_0° is the more generally useful energy above the lowest real quantum state. Usually Eq. (3.41) does not fit the energy levels very accurately near the dissociation limit, and as a result, Eq. (9.84) will give only a very approximate value for the dissociation energy. For example, with the ground state[16] of Li_2^7, $\omega_e = 351.4$ cm.$^{-1}$, $\omega_e x = 2.592$ cm.$^{-1}$, and the calculated $D_0^\circ = 11,730$ cm.$^{-1}$. Herzberg[16] gives 8309 cm.$^{-1}$ for D_0°, while Gaydon[17] prefers the value 8890 cm.$^{-1}$.

Frequently, the series of vibrational bands for an excited state extends much closer to its dissociation limit than the series for the ground state. In Fig. 9.10 one sees that the vertical band between the dotted lines crosses the upper potential curves at energies near or including the dissociation energy. The Franck-Condon principle predicts that the transitions will take place from the ground state to vibrational levels in this range in the excited electronic states. In fact Gaydon's value[17] for the dissociation energy of Li_2 comes from the extrapolation of the vibrational levels of the $^1\Pi_u$ state; where the observed levels extend within about 500 cm.$^{-1}$ from the dissociation limit. For the ground state the highest observed level is about 4000 cm.$^{-1}$ short of dissociation.

Of course, if the dissociation limit of the excited state yields excited atoms, this excitation energy of the atoms must be subtracted to yield the dissociation energy of the normal state. In the lithium case the $(^2P) - (^2S)$ difference is 14,904 cm.$^{-1}$.

A possible pitfall in the calculation of dissociation energies by extrapolation of vibrational energy levels is the chance that there

[16] Herzberg, G., *Molecular Spectra and Molecular Structure, I, Spectra of Diatomic Molecules*, New York: D. Van Nostrand Company, Inc., 1950, p. 546.

[17] Gaydon, A. G., *Dissociation Energies*, London: Chapman & Hall, Ltd., 1947, p. 210.

may be a peak in the potential curve at large interatomic distances, as indicated in Fig. 9.12. In that case the vibrational levels would extrapolate to D', while the true dissociation energy is D_0. Indeed Herzberg[16] accepts the proposal of King and Van Vleck[18] that such a peak occurs in the $^1\Pi_u$ state of Li_2, and that it is the cause of the discrepancy between the two dissociation energies proposed for Li_2.

The spectra of I_2 and Br_2 have each a series of vibrational levels that extends completely to the dissociation limit where continuous absorption begins. Furthermore, in the case of I_2, at least, the re-

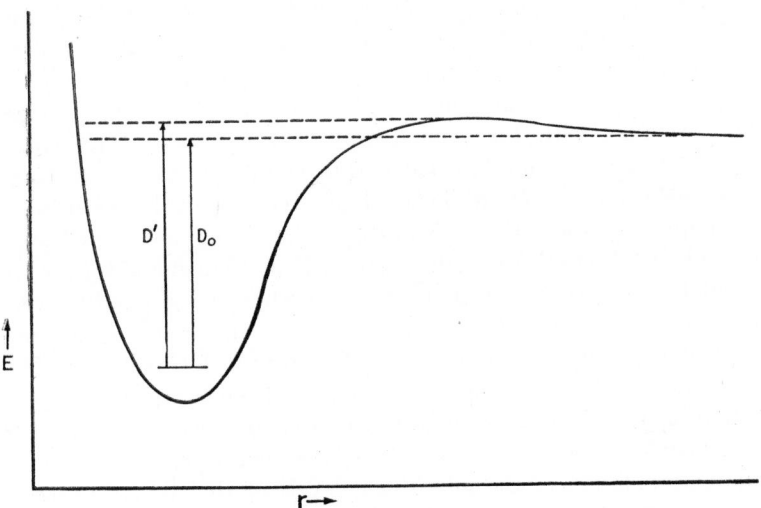

Fig. 9.12. A possible shape of potential curve where an extrapolation of vibrational energy levels would yield a false dissociation energy.

sulting dissociation energy has been confirmed by vapor density measurements[19] to within 0.1%, which proves that no appreciable potential peak can exist in that case.

There are many finer points about electronic spectra which have not been included here, such as interactions with electron spin in states other than singlets, the so-called Λ doubling which occurs in other than Σ states, additional selection rules, and symmetry properties, etc. However, it should be apparent that a full analysis of an

[18] King, G. W. and Van Vleck, J. H., *Phys. Revs.*, **55**, 1165 (1939).
[19] Perlman, M. L. and Rollefson, G. K., *J. Chem. Phys.*, **9**, 362 (1941).

electronic spectrum can yield information about (1) the rotational levels of both electronic states and hence their interatomic distances, (2) the vibrational levels of both electronic states and hence the shape of their potential energy curves, and (3) the total energy separation between the two electronic states. The finer points which we have largely omitted can indicate in addition the character of each electronic state as given in the term symbol, i.e., the net electron spin, the net orbital angular momentum, the manner of coupling of these two, and the various symmetry properties.

91. Electronic spectra of small polyatomic molecules. In this section we shall emphasize the spectra of polyatomic molecules which are sufficiently small that some of the detailed methods of the last section can be applied.

In general one finds far fewer excited electronic states with sharp vibration-rotation line structure in polyatomic molecules than in diatomic molecules. Once the energy is above that required to dissociate some bond in the molecule, there is always the possibility of transition (without radiation) to a repulsive state, such as $^3\Sigma_u^+$ for Li_2 in Fig. 9.10. If such transitions are slow, the individual quantum states live long enough to have sharply defined energies and to yield sharp lines in both absorption and emission spectra. If the radiationless transition to the repulsive state is very rapid, only a continuous absorption is found, while for intermediate times of transition (10^{-11} to 10^{-10} second) one finds the blurred and broadened lines characteristic of *predissociation*. With its number of possible modes of dissociation, the average polyatomic molecule is much more likely to have continuous absorption than sharp line spectra, once the dissociation energy is exceeded.

For the above reason, most of the interest centers in molecules with multiple bonds. Not only do multiple bonds have excited states at lower energies, but also there are more undisturbed electrons to hold the molecule together.

A rapidly converging series of sharp bands, having certain similarity to atomic spectral series, is frequently found for a polyatomic molecule, and is called a *Rydberg series*. The frequencies should fit the formula

$$\frac{\nu}{c} = \omega_I - \frac{R}{(n^*)^2}, \qquad n^* = a,\, a+1,\, a+2,\, \ldots \qquad (9.85)$$

where R is the Rydberg constant from atomic spectra, see Eq. (3.30a), ω_I is the series limit, and n^* is an effective principal quantum number. The value of a will be near that of the principal quantum number of the electron being excited. This is sometimes emphasized by writing $n^* = n + b$, and starting the series of integral values of n with a value appropriate to the molecule concerned. Thus for a series in the CO_2 spectrum $a = 2.21$ or $b = 0.21$ with $n = 2, 3, 4, \ldots$

This formula for a Rydberg series in a molecule is the same formula that is used for similar spectral series in complex atoms, and differs from the formula for the spectrum of the hydrogen atom only in the non-integral quantum numbers. One can understand a simple sequence like this if the electron is excited to an orbital lying almost entirely outside the molecule. The remainder of the molecule then provides merely a singly charged positive center of attraction for the electron, just as the remainder of a complex atom would. Clearly, a series such as this must lead to ionization; the ionization potential is ω_I. Since the ion produced in this manner may be in an excited state, ω_I may not be the minimum ionization potential for the molecule.

From the picture we have of a Rydberg series, it is clear they should occur also for diatomic molecules. They have been observed for O_2, N_2, CO, and a few other molecules in the vacuum ultraviolet. However, Rydberg series constitute such a small portion of the rich spectra of diatomic molecules that they have received relatively little attention.

Frequently a molecule will have two or more Rydberg series. Sometimes they converge to the same limit, as in 2,3-dimethyl-butadiene,[20] where the expressions are

$$\frac{\nu}{c} = 70{,}240 - \frac{R}{(n + 0.90)^2}, \qquad n = 3, 4, \ldots$$

$$\frac{\nu}{c} = 70{,}249 - \frac{R}{(n + 0.50)^2}, \qquad n = 3, 4, \ldots$$

The near equality of ω_I in the two expressions indicates that the two series lead to the same ion, with the ionization potential of 8.668 e.v. in this case. However, for the methyl halides[21] there are in each

[20] Price, W. C. and Walsh, A. D., *Proc. Roy. Soc.* (London), **A174**, 220 (1940).

[21] Price, W. C., *J. Chem. Phys.*, **4**, 539 (1936).

case two series leading to different limits.   The ionization potentials are given in Table 9.3.

TABLE 9.3

IONIZATION POTENTIALS FROM RYDBERG SERIES[21]

	CH_3Cl	CH_3Br	CH_3I
I_1	11.17	10.488	9.490 e.v.
I_2	11.25	10.803	10.115 e.v.
Difference:	0.08	0.315	0.625 e.v.

The separation of the ionization potentials is reasonable as a difference in energy levels for the CH_3X^+ ion in each case. The ion will be in a doublet state and the spin-orbit interaction term, which influences the doublet separation, would be expected to increase in the order Cl, Br, I.

Molecules such as CH_4, where all the outer electrons are in single bonds, show only a continuous absorption at very high frequencies. This absorption leads to decomposition, in the case of methane presumably to $CH_3 + H$.

Symmetry is an important element in electronic spectra, just as it is in vibrational spectra. The electronic states are designated by the symbol for their symmetry type (or in group theory terms, "irreducible representation"). To this is added the usual preceding superscript, $2S + 1$, to indicate the net electron spin S. Thus the ground state of benzene is $^1A_{1g}$, while an excited state might be $^3B_{2u}$. For linear molecules, such as CO_2, the symbols analogous to the diatomic molecule system are sometimes used. Thus $^1\Sigma_g^+$ is equivalent to $^1A_{1g}$, etc., as is indicated in a footnote to the table for $C_{\infty v}$ in Appendix 12. Again we may remind the reader who is not familiar with symmetry group theory that he will be able to follow all the essential arguments if he will regard these symbols as mere labels.

The vibrational state of the molecule also affects the over-all symmetry, because the complete wave function is the product of the electronic wave function and the vibrational wave functions for each of the normal coordinates. The wave function for the lowest vibrational state, $n = 0$, is always totally symmetric, and consequently only excited vibrational wave functions can change the over-all vibrational-electronic symmetry from that of the electronic wave function.

The Franck-Condon principle applies to polyatomic molecule spectra. In this case there are several coordinates fixing the positions of the various nuclei, all of which must remain unchanged at the instant of the transition. A diagram like Fig. 9.10 could be drawn for each normal coordinate, which would indicate the probable quantum state for that vibration after the transition.

The larger moments of inertia of polyatomic molecules give smaller spacing of rotational lines. Thus in many, indeed most cases, the rotational structure is unresolved because of the diffuseness of the lines or the limited resolution of the spectrograph. Exceptions arise with molecules such as CO_2 and CS_2 where bands have been resolved and the rotational constants obtained for both initial and final states.

Benzene has a relatively rich electronic spectrum which will be discussed in some detail. Excitation of one or more of the π electrons is responsible for most of the features, which are shown in the absorption spectrum in Fig. 9.13. The measure of intensity used here is the *molar extinction coefficient* ϵ, defined as follows.

$$\epsilon = \frac{1}{Ct} \log \frac{I_0}{I} \qquad (9.86)$$

where I_0 is the incident light intensity, I is the final intensity after passing through a thickness t cm. of concentration, C moles per liter. This unit can be used for substances in solution with nonabsorbing solvents as well as for gases. While placing a molecule in solution in a solvent, such as n-heptane, grossly changes the rotational line structure, it has only a minor effect on the broader features of the spectrum.

It should be emphasized at once that the extinction coefficient of benzene, in Fig. 9.13, varies over an enormous range. Near 1830 A, where ϵ approaches 50,000, a 1 cm. path through the gas at 0.01 mm. pressure produces considerable absorption; yet at 3300 A the absorption would be less than 0.000001% under these conditions. Of course, one actually uses a path of several centimeters in the pure liquid in the 3000–3500 A region. If the 1830 A transition is a normal, permitted transition, the bands near 2500 A must be "partially forbidden," while those at 3300 A are "highly forbidden." It is interesting, by comparison, to note that the more intense vibrational bands of a molecule such as benzene have extinction coefficients of several hundred, which is rather higher than that for the 2500 A band but

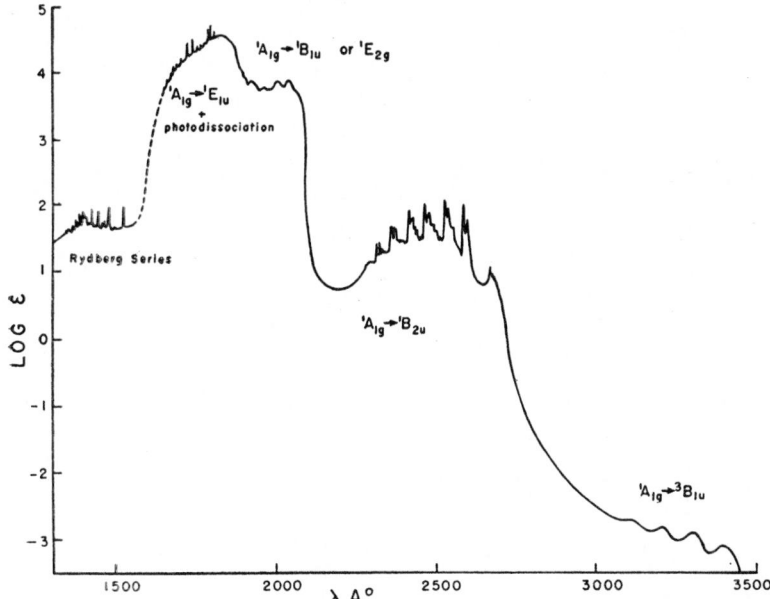

Fig. 9.13. The electronic spectrum of benzene.

considerably less than the extinction coefficient of permitted electronic transitions.

The first excited singlet electronic state in benzene can be described
in the first approximation by the difference combination of the two
Kekulé structures (I and II in Fig. 8.10) just as the ground state is
the sum combination (see Appendix 7, Tables 1 and 2).   It has the
symmetry B_{2u}, while the table for D_{6h} in Appendix 12 shows that
permitted transitions are allowed only to states of A_{2u} and E_{1u} symmetry.   The presently accepted explanation of the 2500 A band
system is that these are transitions to vibrationally excited states
based on the B_{2u} electronic state.   The vibrations which are excited
are just those required to give the complete wave function the symmetry E_{1u}.   Another possibility is absorption by a vibrationally excited molecule in the ground electronic state, but this is less probable
because of the smaller number of such molecules in the thermal distribution at low temperatures.   These bands near 2500 A actually
contain far more fine structure than can be shown on Fig. 9.13, from

which much detailed information concerning the $^1B_{2u}$ state of benzene has been obtained.[22] For example, it is found that the C—C bond stretching force constant is 14% less in the $^1B_{2u}$ state than in the $^1A_{1g}$ normal state, and that the resistance to twisting a $\diagup$C—C$\diagdown$ bond unit from the planar configuration is reduced by 68%. These changes seem very reasonable if the $^1B_{2u}$ state leaves the single bond framework intact, but substantially weakens the bonding of the six π electrons.

The benzene spectrum can be interpreted from the point of view of molecular orbital theory also. The simple, one-electron orbitals were given in Eq. (8.38), with additional details in Appendix 6. The pertinent results are summarized in Table 9.4, where the symmetry characteristics are given for the group D_{6h}.

TABLE 9.4

MOLECULAR ORBITALS FOR BENZENE

	Symmetry	Energy	Designation in Eq. (8.38)
Single orbitals	A_{2u}	$+2\beta$	ψ_1
	E_{1g}	$+\beta$	(ψ_2, ψ_3)
	E_{2u}	$-\beta$	(ψ_4, ψ_5)
	B_{2g}	-2β	ψ_6
States for the molecule	$^1A_{1g}$	$+8\beta$	$\psi_1^2(\psi_2\psi_3)^4$
	$^{3,1}B_{2u}$	$+6\beta$	
	$^{3,1}B_{1u}$	$+6\beta$	$\psi_1^2(\psi_2,\psi_3)^3(\psi_4,\psi_5)$
	$^{3,1}E_{1u}$	$+6\beta$	

The individual E_{1g} orbitals, ψ_2 and ψ_3, are degenerate, as are the E_{2u} orbitals, ψ_4 and ψ_5; consequently, linear combinations of these are equally valid, and no attempt is made to indicate just what combination is appropriate in any particular state. The ground state fully occupies all of the A_{2u} and E_{1g} orbitals. The first excited state is obtained by moving one electron from an E_{1g} orbital to an E_{2u} orbital. However, because of the degeneracy, four complete wave functions are possible, of which one pair is degenerate (E_{1u}). Also, since two electrons are alone in orbitals, their spins can be parallel as well as antiparallel, yielding both triplet and singlet states. More highly excited states also exist, of course.

[22] See a series of 12 papers by Ingold, C. K., Garforth, F. M., and Poole, H. G., *J. Chem. Soc.*, 1948, pp. 406–517.

To the initial approximation of the sum of the one electron orbital energies, the six states $^3B_{2u}$, $^1B_{2u}$, $^3B_{1u}$, $^1B_{1u}$, $^3E_{1u}$, $^1E_{1u}$ all have the same energy. However, as we know, the repulsion between electrons and possibly other effects will vary among these states, giving them different energies in reality. Many calculations[23] have been made in attempts to obtain quantitative energies for these states but only limited success has been achieved as yet. The results do indicate quite definitely that the $^1B_{2u}$ state is the lowest singlet, in agreement with the bond orbital method. Our discussion above of the transition to the $^1B_{2u}$ state is not affected by the substitution of the molecular orbital wave function.

The selection rules for benzene yield allowed electronic transitions to $^1A_{2u}$ and $^1E_{1u}$ states with the dipole perpendicular to and in the plane of the ring, respectively. Among the states in Table 9.4, we find $^1E_{1u}$, which we then identify with the very intense bands near 1800 A. A calculation of the transition probability, using the appropriate molecular orbitals, confirms the high extinction coefficient.

The bond orbital method does not give a $^1E_{1u}$ state (Table 2, Appendix 7) in its ordinary form. By introducing ionic, or polar, structures, Craig[24] has obtained an appropriate $^1E_{1u}$ state. New empirical constants were introduced for these new structures, but these new constants can be carried over from one molecule to another with some success.

The very weak absorption near 3300 A arises from transition to a triplet state. The molecular orbital and bond orbital calculations[23] favor $^3B_{1u}$ for the symmetry of the lowest excited triplet state, but this assignment must be regarded as somewhat tentative yet.

It has been proposed that the intense, continuous absorption underlying the sharp bands in the 1850 A region may be associated with a photo-decomposition in which a C—H bond is broken. The energy is more than adequate at this wavelength (1800 A is equivalent to 160 kcal./mole). In any event, two absorption processes are probably involved.

The sharp bands in the 1350–1550 A range have been interpreted as two Rydberg series converging to the same ionization limit. The rather diffuse bands near 2000 A are believed to be an electronically

[23] See (a) Geoppert-Mayer, M. and Sklar, A. L., *J. Chem. Phys.*, **6**, 645 (1938) for the original paper; and (b) Parr, R. G., Craig, D. P., and Ross, I. G., *J. Chem. Phys.*, **18**, 1561 (1950) for a later calculation.

[24] Craig, D. P., *Proc. Roy. Soc.* (London), **A200**, 401 (1950).

forbidden transition to a singlet state, which becomes allowed by combination with excited vibrational states, just as in the case of the $^1A_{1g} \rightarrow {}^1B_{2u}$ transition. Presumably, the proximity to the permitted 1800 A transition allows a resonance interaction with the states in the 2000 A range which lends intensity to the latter. The results in Table 9.4 suggest that the electronic state involved in the 2000 A bands is the $^1B_{1u}$ state, but arguments have been presented [23b,24] for a $^1E_{2g}$ state on the basis of the more elaborate calculations.

Before closing this section, some attention must be given to the reverse of the absorption process. The violent discharges used to

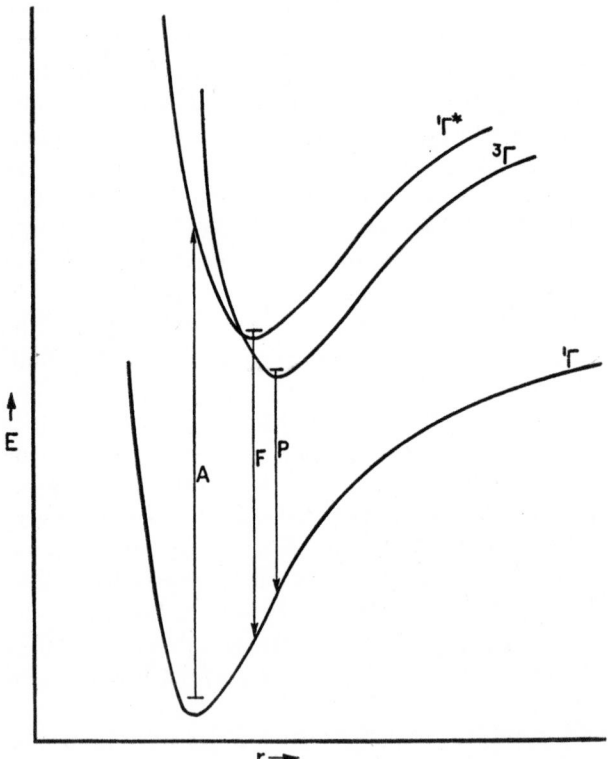

Fig. 9.14. A potential energy diagram illustrating absorption A, fluorescence F and phosphorescence P. Only the ground vibrational levels are indicated. The radiationless conversion to the triplet state occurs in the area where the two upper curves cross.

excite atomic and diatomic emission spectra would decompose poly-atomic molecules, hence a more delicate and selective excitation process must be used. This is commonly irradiation by light of only moderately higher frequency than the emission desired. If the transition is permitted (or only "partially forbidden"), one obtains a fluorescence in which the light is emitted within about 10^{-8} second after absorption. However, even this short time is sufficient for the excited molecules to lose most of the extra vibrational energy they may have received in the excitation process. Hence the fluorescence emission usually takes place from the ground vibrational state of the excited electronic state to excited vibrational states of the ground electronic state. This is illustrated in Fig. 9.14.

In some cases, benzene included, a radiationless conversion[25] occurs from the excited singlet state to a triplet state. This conversion is pictured as taking place at a crossing of potential curves as indicated in Fig. 9.14. The "forbidden" emission from the triplet to the ground singlet may have a half time as long as a few seconds, although values near 10^{-2} second are equally common. This delayed emission is called *phosphorescence*. In the cases of long half times, it is necessary to place the active substance in solution in a glassy state. Apparently this delays other processes by which the triplet molecules can lose their energy and preserves the energy for light emission.

This phosphorescence in benzene is, of course, the reverse of the absorption near 3300 A to the triplet state.

9m. Electronic states in dyelike molecules. Certain types of organic molecules are characterized, not only by having an absorption band in or near the visible spectrum, but also by very high intensities of absorption. The electronic states associated with these intense bands will be considered in this section.

First let us explore the general character of intensity-frequency relationships for a very simple model by calculating the absorption coefficient for a three-dimensional harmonic oscillator of electronic mass and charge. We want the quantity $(\mu_x)_{nm}$, defined in Eqs. (6.4) and (6.1).

$$(\mu_x)_{nm} = \int \psi_n^* e x \psi_m \, dx \tag{9.87}$$

where we will take the harmonic oscillator wave functions ψ_0 and ψ_1 as given in Eqs. (2.67) for ψ_n and ψ_m. Substitution yields

---

[25] Kasha, M., *Chem. Rev.*, **41**, 401 (1947); also papers by G. N. Lewis, cited by Kasha.

$$\mu_x = \left(\frac{2}{\pi}\right)^{1/2} \alpha e \int_{-\infty}^{+\infty} e^{-\alpha x^2} x^2 \, dx = \frac{e}{\sqrt{2\alpha}}$$

$$= e(h/8\pi^2 m\nu_0)^{1/2} \tag{9.88}$$

with identical values for μ_y and μ_z. The Einstein coefficient for absorption is

$$B = \frac{8\pi^3}{3h^2} (\mu_x^2 + \mu_y^2 + \mu_z^2) = \frac{\pi e^2}{h m \nu_0} \tag{9.89}$$

Since the actual absorption band is spread over some frequency range, we consider the integral of the extinction coefficient over the frequency range of the absorption, and after several steps obtain

$$\int \epsilon \, d\omega = \frac{h N_0 \nu_0 B_{nm}}{(2.303)1000 c^2} = \frac{\pi e^2 N_0}{2303 m c^2} = 2.31 \times 10^8 \tag{9.90}$$

where ω is the frequency in cm.$^{-1}$, i.e., ν/c, and ϵ is the extinction coefficient as defined in Eq. (9.86).

Now if we take this transition probability as a basis, we can give the probability for other examples as a ratio to this ideal case. We define the *oscillator strength* f as the ratio of the experimental transition probability to that given by Eq. (9.90). Since the reciprocal of 2.31×10^8 is 4.33×10^{-9}, we have

$$f = 4.33 \times 10^{-9} \int \epsilon \, d\omega$$

Similarly we may define f as the ratio of the theoretical transition probability to the theoretical value for our ideal case. Using the value found in Eq. (9.88) for the ideal case, we obtain

$$f = \frac{8\pi^2 m\nu_0}{3he^2} [(\mu_x)_{nm}^2 + (\mu_y)_{nm}^2 + (\mu_z)_{nm}^2] \tag{9.91}$$

One can draw certain conclusions quickly concerning the f values for simple examples. For a one-dimensional harmonic oscillator, one finds $f = \frac{1}{3}$; for two-dimensional, $f = \frac{2}{3}$; if two electrons are available to make the transition, the f value is doubled, etc.

Experimentally, the integration over the 1800 A absorption band of benzene yields about 0.7. A value such as this in the vicinity of 1 is to be expected for a fully allowed transition.

While electrons are normally subject to coulomb forces rather than Hooke's law forces, nevertheless we can use this harmonic oscillator model for a qualitative discussion of the nature of electronic transitions.

If an electron is bound by the usual forces so that it is held within a single atom, its fundamental frequency of oscillation is very high, and strong absorption occurs only in the far ultraviolet. Although the color of such substances as hydrated copper sulfate might seem to be intense, the f values for the absorption bands in these cases are far less than unity. To move the frequency of an intense, fundamental band down near the visible spectrum, the restoring force on the electron must be reduced and the amplitude of its motion correspondingly increased. Except for the possibility of extra large atoms, this increased amplitude can be had only by permitting motion through the space of several atoms. This extended motion can occur in inorganic substances, such as triiodide ion, but our discussion will be confined to organic molecules.

The cyanine dyes and their related polymethine types best illustrate this principle. There follow a few examples, with the two principal bond structures of these mesomeric molecules.

A
$$\begin{cases} (CH_3)_2N^+{=}CH(-CH{=}CH)_n-\ddot{N}(CH_3)_2 \\ (CH_3)_2\ddot{N}-(CH{=}CH-)_nCH{=}N^+(CH_3)_2 \end{cases}$$

Here A is a simple amidinium ion extended by n vinylene groups, while B is a typical cyanine with heterocyclic rings as terminal units. It will be noted that the essential mesomeric system is the same in each case. The two structures entering the resonance descriptions are equivalent, consequently the C—C bonds down the chain are of equal length. To shift from the lower structure to the upper structure in each case, the unshared electron pair on the left nitrogen moves to the right to form the double bond; each pair of electrons forming a double bond in the chain moves one bond to the right; and finally the electron pair from the right C=N moves onto the nitrogen as an unshared pair.

It is not implied that all these electrons must move in unison. Intermediate structures, such as the following, contribute also.

$$(CH_3)_2\overset{..}{N}-\overset{+}{C}H(-CH=CH)_n-\overset{.}{N}(CH_3)_2$$

$$(CH_3)_2\overset{+}{N}=CH-\overset{..}{C}\overset{-}{H}(-CH=CH)_{n-1}-CH=\overset{+}{N}(CH_3)_2$$

While these forms, with the charge on a carbon atom, are undoubtedly of higher energy, nevertheless they contribute significantly, as do the Dewar structures in the case of benzene. Furthermore, these intermediate structures allow a change from one of the extreme forms to the other, with a shift of only one electron pair at a time.

With this description, we see that the connecting chain of the polymethine dye is essentially just an electric conductor, a copper wire if you wish. Each $-\overset{.}{C}H-$ unit of the chain can be considered to have all but one of its valence electrons fixed in single bonds, but that last electron is essentially metallic; it is free to move along the chain from one unit to another. This suggests the simple model[26] of electrons free to move along the chain but confined in other directions and at the ends of the chain. The analogous free electron gas model has had considerable success in explaining metallic properties (Section 71; also Chapter 10).

In applying this free electron model to a polymethine dye, one uses the one-dimensional particle in a box equation of Section 2h. Although the molecule chain is actually of a zigzag configuration, it is not too far from straight, and the differences introduced by the kinks in the path are of a secondary character. The length of the box should be the sum of the bond lengths down the conducting chain, plus a terminal length at each end to represent the effective space available to the electrons beyond the nitrogen nuclei. We will leave this terminal length C as an adjustable parameter, because we do not wish to vary the potential energy near the ends to account for the differences in end groups. If there are N electrons in our system, there will be $N-1$ atoms along the chain and $N-2$ bonds. The length will then be $(N-2)L + 2C$, where L is the C—C bond length. Any small difference between C—N and C—C bond lengths can be absorbed in the end effect term C. Since there are N electrons, the

[26] (a) Bayliss, N. S., *J. Chem. Phys.*, **16**, 287 (1948); (b) Kuhn, H., *J. Chem. Phys.*, **16**, 840 (1948), *Helv. Chim. Acta*, **31**, 1441 (1948); (c) Simpson, W. T., *J. Chem. Phys.*, **16**, 1124 (1948).

first $N/2$ energy levels must be filled. The absorption band will correspond to the excitation of one of the electrons in the top or $N/2$ level to the next higher level. The frequency is

$$\nu = \frac{h}{8m} \cdot \frac{(N/2 + 1)^2 - (N/2)^2}{[(N-2)L + 2C]^2}$$

$$= \frac{h}{8mL^2} \cdot \frac{N+1}{(N-2+2C/L)^2} \qquad (9.92)$$

Converting to the wave length, one obtains, after division

$$\lambda = \frac{8mc}{h} \cdot L^2 \left[N + \left(4\frac{C}{L} - 5 \right) + \frac{(2C/L - 3)^2}{N+1} \right] \qquad (9.93)$$

By trial, the ratio C/L is found to be between 1 and 2 in most cases, so that the last term within the brackets is always small, and one finds the wave length to increase linearly with the number of units in the chain. This agrees with the empirical rule of 1000 A increase in λ per vinylene unit, which has been found to hold very generally for the cyanine type dyes, provided L has the value 1.24 A. The actual bond distance in these dyes is not known but is presumably near the 1.39 A value found for the same $\frac{3}{2}$ bonds in aromatic ring molecules. While this is not perfect agreement,[27] it is unexpectedly good for so crude a theory. Formula (9.93) becomes then,

$$\lambda = 500(N + 4C/L - 5) \quad A \qquad (9.94)$$

For the simple amidinium ion dyes, A above, the absorption maxima[26c] come at 3090, 4090, and 5110 A, respectively, for molecules with $N = 6, 8,$ and 10. Thus for this series, a precise fit is obtained if $C/L = 1.3$ or $C = 1.6$ A. While this seems a little large for a nitrogen atom, the greater electronegativity of the nitrogen atoms indicates a tendency to hold more than their share of electrons, as compared to carbon atoms. This effect manifests itself in the present theory by increasing C above its proper geometrical value.

For the cyanine[28] ions of series B above, the maxima come at 5575, 6500, and 7580 A for the molecules with $N = 8, 10,$ and 12, respectively. Again, a good fit is obtained by adjusting C, which is

---

[27] One might properly claim that the calculation yields the average of the excitation energies to the lowest singlet and triplet states. This correction would certainly improve the calculated L, but the refinement is hardly appropriate in such a crude theory.

[28] Brooker, L. G. S., Sprague, R. H., Smyth, C. P., and Lewis, G. L., *J. Am. Chem. Soc.*, **62**, 1116 (1940).

2.5 A for this series.   Considering the aromatic rings, which are not really insulated from the main oscillating system in these molecules, the C value of 2.5 A is quite reasonable.

The intensities for the transitions can also be calculated on the free electron model by the method given above for the harmonic oscillator. Now the zigzag character of the chain has a first-order effect, and it is very important to know whether the chain may have a *cis* instead of *trans* orientation about any bond.   For the all *trans* chain with a bond angle α and $C = L$, Kuhn[29] gives the formula

$$ f = \frac{4}{3\pi^2} \left(1 - \cos \alpha\right) \frac{N^2(N + 2)^2}{(N + 1)^3} \tag{9.95} $$

The oscillator strengths calculated with this formula are about 1.5 times the observed values for various dyes of the polymethine type.

In addition to the symmetrical cyanine type dyes, which make all bonds along the chain equivalent, there are several types which destroy this equivalence of successive bonds.   Within the cyanine type, the terminal groups can be different.   In the merocyanines, the dye is not an ion but a neutral molecule with a very basic group on one end and an acidic group on the other.   An example, C, is a dye with quinoline as a basic group and rhodanine as an acidic group.

In the dye C one structure is electrically quite neutral, while the other has an enormous dipole moment, since the charges are so widely separated.   Increasing the dielectric constant of the solvent lowers

[29] Kuhn, H., *J. Chem. Phys.*, **17**, 1198 (1949).

the energy of the dipolar form as compared with the neutral form. Thus the relative importance of the resonance forms can be varied, not only by changing the end groups, but also in these cases by changing the solvent.

As the other limit of these intermediate types, there are the polyenes themselves, where there are no end groups. Hexatriene is an example.

$$D \begin{cases} H_2C{=}CH{-}CH{=}CH{-}CH{=}CH_2 \\ H_2\overset{\cdot}{C}{-}CH{=}CH{-}CH{=}CH{-}\overset{\cdot}{C}H_2 \\ H_2\overset{+}{C}{-}CH{=}CH{-}CH{=}CH{-}\overset{\cdot\cdot}{\underset{}{C}}\overset{-}{H}_2 \\ \overset{-}{H_2}\overset{\cdot\cdot}{C}{-}CH{=}CH{-}CH{=}CH{-}\overset{+}{C}H_2 \end{cases}$$

Although there are three of the lower structures which shift the double bonds, all are of high energy as compared with the normal structure at the top. Thus the double bonds are in very definite positions, although they are conjugated. While the excited state may tend to place the π bonding electrons in other positions, because of the Franck-Condon principle, the electronic energy must be calculated for the position of the nuclei in the normal molecule.

For a treatment of the polyenes, Kuhn[29] introduced a sine wave potential between infinite barriers as a first approximation to the potential for π electron motion. The potential minima along the sine curve correspond to the double bonds where the nuclei are closer together. Since we shall be taking the height of the potential peaks V_0 as an adjustable parameter, we eliminate all others by taking the observed bond distances, 1.35 and 1.46 A for conjugated C=C and C—C, respectively, and by assuming an extra half bond length at each end. In the treatment of internal rotation in Section 9h we discussed the Schrödinger equation for a periodic potential. For our present purpose, we take the approximate solutions of Kuhn,[29] valid well above the potential peaks, which yield for the absorption frequencies

$$\omega = 153{,}000(N + 1)^{-1} + \tfrac{1}{2}V_0(1 - N^{-1}) \qquad (9.96)$$

where N is the number of π electrons, as before, and V_0 is the height of the potential peaks in cm.$^{-1}$. The first term in Eq. (9.96) is that for the free electron model, and the second term arises from the potential peaks within the box.

Although one might assume the same V_0 for all polyenes, a further consideration of the ground state indicates that this is unlikely. In addition to the mesomeric structures shown above for hexatriene, there are forms where the charges or odd electrons are on intermediate atoms, such as

$$H_2C=CH-\overset{..}{C}\overline{H}-CH=CH-\overset{+}{C}H_2$$

$$H_2\overset{.}{C}-CH=CH-\overset{.}{C}H-CH=CH_2$$

The number of these forms increases rapidly as the length of the polyene chain increases; hence the nominally single bonds should take on more double bond character. Consequently, the bond lengths should become more nearly equal, and the effective V_0 should decrease with increase in chain length. While one could investigate this variation in detail, it is more in keeping with our simple theory to assume that $V_0(1 - N^{-1})$ is a constant which we shall call V_∞. This implies that the V_0 for butadiene is 33% higher than that of an infinite chain. Equation (9.96) then simplifies to

$$\omega = 153,000(N + 1)^{-1} + \tfrac{1}{2}V_\infty \tag{9.97}$$

The experimental absorption frequencies are compared in Table 9.5 with the values calculated from Eq. (9.97), taking V_∞ as 30,000 cm.$^{-1}$.

TABLE 9.5

ABSORPTION FREQUENCIES OF THE POLYENES

Substance	N	ω (exper.)	ω (calc.)
Butadiene	4	46,100	45,600 cm.$^{-1}$
Hexatriene	6	38,500	36,850
Octatetraene	8	33,100	32,000
Axerophtene	10	28,900	28,900
Anhydro vitamin A	12	27,100	26,750
β-Carotene	22	22,150	21,650
Dehydro-β-carotene	24	21,050	21,120
Dehydrolycopene	30	19,850	19,950

(Kuhn[29] gives references for these experimental values.)

The agreement found in Table 9.5 offers strong support for Eq. (9.97), even though some of the assumptions made in its derivation are very crude.

Formula (9.97) for the polyenes gives a frequency of about 15,000 cm.$^{-1}$ for an infinite chain, whereas the formula for the cyanine type dyes predicted a zero frequency for an infinitely long molecule.

Probably this difference is spurious in that V_0 in Eq. (9.96) should have been assumed to approach zero for an infinite chain. Rather than pursue the behavior of V_0 further, however, it is more important to note that the periodic potential has given a finite separation of certain energy levels, even though the particle is unbounded in the sense that it has sufficient energy to surmount all potential peaks over an infinite distance. This is an apparent contradiction of our conclusion in Section 2j that an unbound particle can have any energy. We shall postpone a thorough discussion of this important point until we consider metals in Chapter 10, but will remark that this finite energy level separation is precisely the characteristic of an electric insulator. By contrast, the zero frequency difference of the infinite symmetrical polymethine dye is characteristic of an electric conductor.

There are many other classes of dyes, and several can be treated by obvious variations of the methods used above. Even benzene can be considered as a ring around which the six π electrons are free to move. The radius of the ring calculated from the absorption frequency is nearly correct.

The now familiar methods of bond orbitals and molecular orbitals have been applied to dye molecules also. Of course, the "particle in a box" orbitals used above are molecular orbitals of a sort. The bond orbital method has not been particularly convenient for the polar states necessarily involved in a strong electronic absorption. The conventional molecular orbital method, which is based on atomic orbitals, has proven[26c] to be capable of explaining most of the same phenomena discussed here, but with more complex formulas in most cases. Since we have already presented other examples of the molecular orbital method, we will omit further discussion of it here.

9n. Isotope effects. Although the effect of nuclear mass on vibrational and rotational energy levels has been included in all the equations in this chapter, nevertheless the importance of isotopes in interpreting spectra is so great as to deserve special attention. First let us consider the qualitative effects.

The purely electronic energy, which is a function of interatomic distances, is unaffected by the masses of the nuclei. However, both vibrational energy levels and the rotational energy levels are very dependent on atomic masses. Thus one has a means of distinguishing between electronic effects and vibrational or rotational energies. In this connection one must carefully distinguish between the electronic energy of the potential minimum for vibrational motion and the lowest real quantum state which includes zero point vibrational energy.

A simple example might be an electronic spectrum which shows a doublet structure with a separation of the magnitude 1000 cm.$^{-1}$. This could be either a pair of vibrational bands or an electronic doublet, such as $^3\Pi_0$, $^3\Pi_1$ or two unrelated electronic levels accidentally near one another. An appropriate isotopic substitution will shift the vibrational frequency substantially but will leave an electronic doublet unchanged.

The penetration of a potential barrier is even more sensitive to mass than the vibrational or rotational energy levels. Thus in the spectrum of ammonia, the energy level separation arising from the inversion through the potential barrier decreases from 0.79 cm.$^{-1}$ for NH_3 to practically zero for ND_3 in the ground vibrational state. In the first excited vibration state, the figures are 35.7 cm.$^{-1}$ for NH_3 and 3.4 cm.$^{-1}$ for ND_3. By comparison, the largest factor by which a rotational energy level spacing can be reduced by deuterium substitution is 2. Since mass enters the vibration frequency as the square root, the maximum factor there is $\sqrt{2}$.

Another qualitative effect is the reduction of symmetry by partial isotopic substitution. This is particularly useful in bringing into the vibration spectrum frequencies which are inactive in the most symmetrical molecules, such as benzene.

The quantitative effect of isotopic substitution on rotational energy levels is readily computed in most cases from the bond angles and distances in the molecule. However, a detailed picture of the isotope effect on vibrational energy levels can be had only from a complete solution of the normal coordinate problem. For a complex molecule, a complete normal coordinate calculation is very difficult, consequently any method which is easier to apply is of great interest.

If a full normal coordinate analysis is not made for a molecule, it is still possible to apply the *Teller-Redlich product rule* to the frequencies of isotopic species. This rule concerns the ratio of the product of all frequencies of a given symmetry type to the corresponding product for the isotopically substituted molecule. This ratio is related to another ratio involving the atomic masses, the total molecular weight, and the moments of inertia of the substituted and of the unsubstituted molecule. The importance of this product rule is that it does not involve the potential constants—only the assumption that they are unaffected by isotopic substitution. The product rule also involves the assumption of a quadratic potential function as in all normal coordinate analyses; thus it will fail to the extent that anharmonicity enters.

A very simple illustration of the product rule can be given for the parallel vibrations of HCN. The two internal coordinates can be taken as q_1, the displacement of the H—C distance, and q_2, the displacement of the C—N distance. The complete quadratic potential function for these coordinates can be taken as

$$2V = k_1 q_1^2 + k_2 q_2^2 + 2k_3 q_1 q_2 \tag{9.98}$$

and the frequencies are given by the equations,

$$\lambda_1 + \lambda_2 = k_1 \left(\frac{1}{m_{\mathrm{H}}} + \frac{1}{m_{\mathrm{C}}} \right) + k_2 \left(\frac{1}{m_{\mathrm{C}}} + \frac{1}{m_{\mathrm{N}}} \right) - \frac{2k_3}{m_{\mathrm{C}}}$$

$$\lambda_1 \lambda_2 = (k_1 k_2 - k_3^2) \frac{M}{m_{\mathrm{H}} m_{\mathrm{C}} m_{\mathrm{N}}} \tag{9.99}$$

$$\lambda_i = 4\pi^2 \nu_i^2, \qquad M = m_{\mathrm{H}} + m_{\mathrm{C}} + m_{\mathrm{N}}$$

One notes easily that in the first equation for $\lambda_1 + \lambda_2$ the force constants and masses are intermixed, but in the equation for $\lambda_1 \lambda_2$ there is simply a product of a force constant factor times a mass factor. Therefore one may derive by division the following equation for the ratio of the products of ν_1 and ν_2 for HCN and DCN,

$$\frac{\nu_1' \nu_2'}{\nu_1 \nu_2} = \left(\frac{M'}{M} \cdot \frac{m_{\mathrm{H}}}{m_{\mathrm{H}}'} \right)^{1/2} \tag{9.100}$$

where the prime refers to the isotropically substituted molecule. Inserting the data for HCN and DCN yields

$$\frac{1906 \times 2629}{2089 \times 3312} = 0.7242$$

$$\left(\frac{28.03}{27.02} \times \frac{1.0081}{2.0147} \right)^{1/2} = 0.7205$$

where the directly observed spectral frequencies ω_0 are used. The use of strictly harmonic ω_e values should make the agreement exact.

The general formulation of the product rule involves the use of group theory and is given in Appendix 12. It has proved of the utmost value in checking assignments of vibration frequencies in complex molecules, particularly those of high symmetry.

It is also important to note that the potential function for HCN, Eq. (9.98), contains three constants, but only two vibration frequencies are involved. Consequently it is impossible to evaluate all three constants from the two vibration frequencies of HCN. As a practical matter, it is common practice to neglect the cross term k_3 in such a case. However, this can yield spurious values of k_1 and k_2 unless k_3 was really negligible.

The spectrum of DCN contributes two additional data. Thus, although the DCN data are not completely independent in view of the product rule, nevertheless the isotopic substitution provides a means of evaluating the complete potential energy expression. To apply this method one needs the true harmonic frequencies ω_e, which are in exact accord with the product rule.

9o. Summary for thermodynamic properties of perfect gases. The results of Section 7o, when combined with those of the present chapter, complete the theory needed to calculate the thermodynamic properties of any substance as an ideal gas. Our only purpose in this section is to collect a few of the most useful formulas in the most convenient form. Here we consider only the rigid rotator, harmonic oscillator approximation, except for simple internal rotations. The further refinements are discussed in Appendix 14. Also we assume a single electronic state which is totally symmetric and has all electron spins paired.

The thermodynamic functions of principal interest are the heat capacity at constant pressure C_p, the heat content or enthalpy $H - H_0$, the entropy S, and the (Gibbs) free energy, which is best calculated from the function $(F - H_0)/T$. If we represent any of these functions by G, the complete function is the sum of contributions for translation, rotation, and vibration, together with internal rotation if present in the molecule.

$$G = G_t + G_r + G_v + G_{ir} \qquad (9.101)$$

The contribution for internal rotation may be taken from the tables of Appendix 18 if it is within the range of types for which the tables were prepared. If more than one internal rotation is present, the contribution is the sum of terms for each rotation.

The contribution of molecular vibrations are obtained by summing the appropriate harmonic oscillator function G_{ho} from Appendix 13 over all the normal modes of oscillation of the molecule. For degenerate vibrations the term must be doubled or tripled as appropriate. Thus we have

$$G_v = \sum_i d_i G_{ho}(u_i) \tag{9.102}$$

where d_i is the degeneracy, $u_i = hc\omega_i/kT$, and the sum covers all the normal modes.

The contributions for translation and rotation can be combined into two sets of formulas, one for linear molecules and one for nonlinear molecules.

For linear molecules

$$C_{p,t+r} = \tfrac{7}{2}R = 6.955$$
$$(H - H_0)_{t+r} = \tfrac{7}{2}RT = 6.955T \tag{9.103}$$

$$-\left(\frac{F - H_0}{T}\right)_{t+r} = R[-\ln P + \tfrac{7}{2}\ln T + \tfrac{3}{2}\ln M \\ + \ln (I \times 10^{39}) - \ln \sigma] - 10.050$$

$$S_{t+r} = R[-\ln P + \tfrac{7}{2}\ln T + \tfrac{3}{2}\ln M \\ + \ln (I \times 10^{39}) - \ln \sigma] - 3.095$$

where the numerical constants are in cal./degree mole and P is in atm., T in degrees Kelvin, M in atomic weight units, and I in gm. cm.². The symmetry number is σ.

For nonlinear molecules

$$C_{p,t+r} = 4R = 7.949$$
$$(H - H_0)_{t+r} = 4RT = 7.949T \tag{9.104}$$

$$-\left(\frac{F - H_0}{T}\right)_{t+r} = R[-\ln P + 4\ln T + \tfrac{3}{2}\ln M \\ + \tfrac{1}{2}\ln (I_xI_yI_z \times 10^{117}) - \ln \sigma] - 10.296$$

$$S_{t+r} = R[-\ln P + 4\ln T + \tfrac{3}{2}\ln M \\ + \tfrac{1}{2}\ln (I_xI_yI_z \times 10^{117}) - \ln \sigma] - 2.347$$

where the units are the same as for linear molecules.

GENERAL REFERENCES

Fowler, R. and Guggenheim, E. A., *Statistical Thermodynamics*, London: Cambridge University Press, 1939. Most of these statistical problems are considered and comparisons with experimental data of various types are included.
Herzberg, G., *Molecular Spectra and Molecular Structure, I Diatomic Molecules*, also, *II Infrared and Raman Spectra of Polyatomic Molecules*, New York: D. Van

Nostrand Company, Inc., 1945. These two volumes are the standard works on molecular spectra but do not include the electronic spectra of polyatomic molecules.

Lewis, G. N. and Calvin, M., "The Color of Organic Substances," *Chem. Rev.*, **25**, 273 (1939).

Maccoll, A., "Color and Constitution," *Quart. Revs.* (London), 1, 16 (1947).

Mayer, J. E. and Mayer, M. G., *Statistical Mechanics*, New York: John Wiley & Sons, Inc., 1940. This book gives greater detail on some of the statistical problems.

Sponer, H. and Teller, E., "Electronic Spectra of Polyatomic Molecules," *Revs. Modern Phys.*, **13**, 75-170 (1941).

PROBLEMS

9.1 The microwave spectra of HCN and DCN yield, respectively, $B_0 = 44300.8$ and 36207.4 mc. Calculate the moment of inertia for each molecule and the values of the C—H and C—N distances consistent with these moments of inertia.

9.2 Show that $\lambda = k/\mu$ gives the result $z_2^0 = z_3^0 = -(M/2m)z_1^0$ when substituted into Eqs. (9.27).

9.3 Treat the z motion for an A-B-A linear molecule by selecting two internal vibrational q's in addition to the translational $q = (Mz_1 + mz_2 + mz_3)/(M + 2m)$. If you wish, try to make use of the symmetry of the molecule in selecting the q's.

9.4 Add the term, $k'(z_2 - z_1 - z_0)(z_3 - z_1 + z_0)$, to the potential energy, Eq. (9.23), and obtain the corresponding expression for the λ's.

9.5 Calculate the mean square amplitude $\overline{q_3^2}$ for CO_2 in its ground vibrational state. The frequency of this vibration is 667 cm.$^{-1}$. For this purpose one may ignore the degeneracy of this motion. Is this amplitude very small compared with interatomic distances?

9.6 Use the full energy level expression, Eq. (3.41), together with the constants given there for HCl, to obtain an accurate expression for the lines in the $n = 0 \rightarrow 1$ band which are plotted in Fig. 9.4. It is convenient for this purpose to define a quantity $m = J' + 1$ for the R branch and $m = -J'$ for the P branch. Then m takes all integral values both $+$ and $-$ except zero.

9.7 Herzberg gives the following expression for the vibrational energy levels of Li_2^7 with one term in addition to that considered in Section 9k: $(E/hc) = 351.43(n + \frac{1}{2}) - 2.592(n + \frac{1}{2})^2 - 0.0058(n + \frac{1}{2})^3$ cm.$^{-1}$. Calculate the dissociation energy from this formula and compare it with the values in the text.

9.8 The free electron model can be applied to the π electrons in benzene by confining these electrons within a ring or annulus of average radius R, but leaving them free from any restriction to rotational motion around the ring. Relate the calculated energy difference between the ground state and the first excited state to the electronic spectrum of benzene. Does this give a reasonable R value? Neglect repulsion between electrons. The energy differences are in the kinetic energy of angular motion.

Chapter 10

CRYSTALLINE SOLIDS

10a. Introduction. A crystal can always be regarded as a giant molecule. Consequently, the properties of crystals can be calculated, in principle, by the same methods that are used for the individual molecules in a perfect gas. In practice the vastly larger number of particles in a crystal makes many of these methods impractical. Nevertheless, a sufficient number of the molecular concepts can be carried over to crystals to make crystalline solids the logical topic to follow molecules.

There are four general types of bonding in solids:

1. Metallic as in Li, Cu, etc.
2. Covalent (nonmetallic) as in diamond, red phosphorus, etc.
3. Ionic as in NaCl, BaO, etc.
4. van der Waals (London and dipole forces including H bonds) as in Ne, CH_4, H_2O, etc.

There are, of course, intermediate cases which fall between these ideal types. Thus SiO_2 is intermediate between (2) and (3).

While types (3) and (4) differ widely in the strength of the bonds, they are basically similar in that all electrons can be regarded as localized in single ions or molecules. Once one understands the laws governing the forces between pairs of ions or molecules, the total energy and other properties of the entire crystal can be calculated without further consideration of the electrons.

In crystals of the covalent type (2) the electrons can be regarded as localized in individual bonds; hence the treatment of a crystal is not significantly different than that of a small molecule.

Thus we need consider in detail only the electronic motion in crystals of the metallic type. This will be done in the early sections of this chapter. In certain later sections, the lattice energy of nonmetallic crystals will be considered, as well as the motion of the nuclei in any sort of crystal.

10b. Electronic states in a one-dimensional lattice. Before proceeding to three-dimensional problems it is well to illustrate certain principles with one-dimensional examples. Let us consider a regular linear array of attracting centers (such as nuclei) along which electrons may move. Depending on the exact force law, the potential curve may have a form such as one of the lower curves in Fig. 10.1. If we neglect the oscillations in potential energy, we have the top curve as the limit. It is that of a free particle.

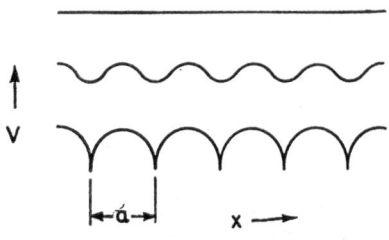

Fig. 10.1. Possible potential curves for a one-dimensional metal.

The general form of wave function for such a potential has been indicated in Eq. (8.51) and again in Eq. (9.70). In a convenient notation for the present purpose, we have

$$\psi = e^{2\pi i k x} f_k(x) \tag{10.1}$$

where $f_k(x)$ is a function which is periodic in the same interval, a, as the lattice. We note at once that for the free particle f becomes a constant. Then the energy is simply

$$E = \frac{h^2 k^2}{2m} = (\text{const.})k^2 \tag{10.2}$$

Thus a plot of the energy for the free particle as a function of k gives just a parabola. This is shown in A of Fig. 10.2.

Although the mathematics is somewhat complicated, it is found that regardless of the shape of the potential curve, a small periodic perturbation will give the result shown in B in Fig. 10.2. The energy levels take a sudden upward jump at $k = \pm 1/2a$. Additional discontinuities will occur at multiples of this critical k value.

If the periodic potential has a large amplitude, the resemblance to the parabola A is lost and the energy dependence on k becomes like that of curve C in Fig. 10.2. The break at $k = \pm 1/2a$ becomes more pronounced, and the energy varies less with k in the continuous regions.

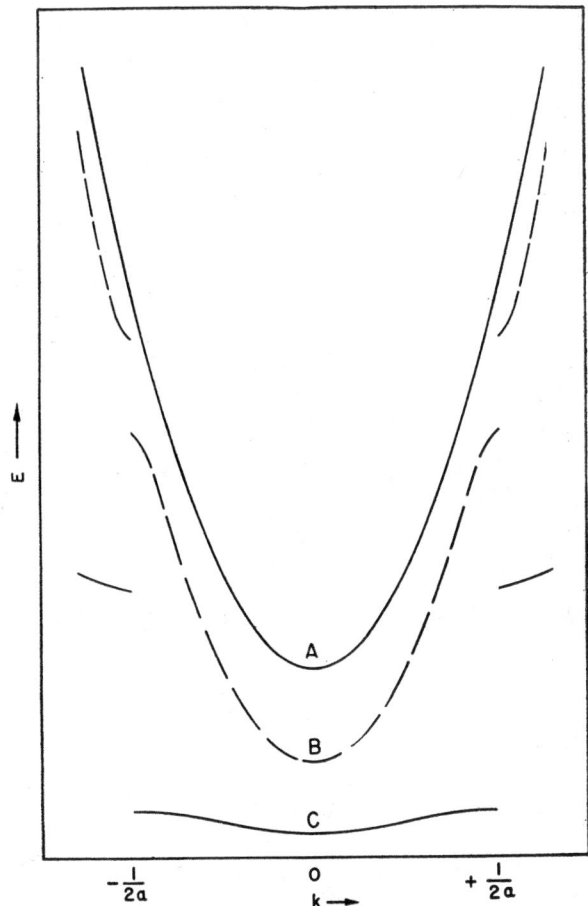

Fig. 10.2.   The energy levels of a particle in one-dimensional periodic potentials
of three types.

In the extreme case of deep and widely separated potential minima,
we may consider simply the wave functions and energy levels for the
particle in a single minimum.   If one does not know in which potential well the particle is located, one must take linear combinations
of the wave functions for the various potential wells.   However, if
the wave function goes substantially to zero between wells, i.e., in the
potential maxima, then the energy is not appreciably affected by these

combinations. Actually, Eq. (10.1) is still an appropriate form. Now substantially all the variation is in $f_k(x)$, which is independent of k. The exponential factor merely varies the coefficient of $f(x)$ from one potential well to the next, giving in effect the various linear combinations of the individual well wave functions.

Up to this point we have assumed an infinite range of motion in the x direction. However, a crystal is finite and has a finite number of atoms which correspond to the potential minima. Consequently we must introduce some boundary condition. For an isolated crystal the potential energy for an electron should rise suddenly at the crystal face. This gives us the particle in the box type of boundary condition as discussed in Section 2h. An ordinary electric current cannot flow through the boundaries of such an isolated crystal. Thus for some purposes it is preferable to consider a block of a larger crystal and to impose periodic boundary conditions. In the linear case the block may contain N atoms and hence have a length Na. Then the condition is

$$\psi(x) = \psi(x + Na) \tag{10.3}$$

which on substitution of (10.1) becomes

$$e^{2\pi ikx}f(x) = e^{2\pi ik(x+Na)}f(x + Na)$$
$$1 = e^{2\pi ikNa}$$
$$kNa = l \quad \text{or} \quad k = l/Na \tag{10.4}$$

where the periodicity of $f(x)$ is used, as well as the properties of an imaginary exponential. Thus l is an integer, positive or negative. One can show that box type boundary conditions give the same general pattern of energy levels even though the exact wave functions are different.

Now if there are only N atoms in the crystal, there will be just N potential minima. Thus if we take combinations of the lowest energy wave functions for the single minima, there will be just N final functions. However, we see from Eq. (10.4) that there are just N values of l in the range

$$-\frac{N}{2} \leqslant l \leqslant +\frac{N}{2}, \quad -\frac{1}{2a} \leqslant k \leqslant +\frac{1}{2a}$$

This range corresponds exactly with the central segment of curve C

in Fig. 10.2. This section represents the N wave functions based on the lowest energy level for each single well. Then the next section represents a second set of N wave functions based on the first excited state for each single well, etc. This explains the reason for the break in the energy level curve.

We see that there is a continuous variation from the free particles at one extreme to particles tightly bound in deep potential minima at the other. However, regardless of this variation, there is an essentially continuous *band* of N energy levels, followed by a sharp break in energy (except for the perfectly free particles). These are the essential features we wish to carry forward for further consideration.

Before proceeding to three-dimensional examples, let us indicate the relationship of these results for a one-dimensional lattice to the discussion of dyelike molecules in section 9m.

In the cyanine type molecules each C—C bond down the chain was equivalent and each —ĊH— group contributed one electron to the π bond system. Thus, ignoring end groups, a chain of N units has N equivalent potential minima and N electrons. According to our theory of this section, there will be N energy levels in the lowest band of π states, but with two electrons in each state only the lower half of the band will be occupied in the ground state.

The long wave length absorption arises from the excitation of one electron from the highest occupied level to the lowest vacant level. Since the band is only half filled, these are adjacent levels in a band. Thus as N approaches infinity and the band becomes truly continuous, the separation of these levels decreases to zero as given in Eq. (9.94).

The model assumed for the polyenes differed in that alternate C—C bonds were assumed to be shorter and therefore of lower energy. This changed the basic periodicity to that of a —CH=CH— unit which has two π electrons. Consequently, for N units and a band of N energy levels, there are $2N$ electrons which fully occupy the band. The transition must move one electron from the highest state in this band to the lowest state in the next band. We see that this will require a finite energy even as N approaches infinity, which again is in agreement with the earlier result.

10c. Electronic states in a three-dimensional lattice. The three-dimensional problem is not essentially different from the one-dimensional problem, although one expects some complications. The basic wave function can be retained, provided we adopt vector notation.

$$\psi = e^{2\pi i \mathbf{k} \cdot \mathbf{r}} f_k(\mathbf{r}) \tag{10.5}$$

Now $f_k(\mathbf{r})$ must be periodic in any lattice interval.

For the free particle, $f_k(\mathbf{r})$ becomes a constant as before, and the energy is given by the same expression in terms of the vector $\mathbf{k}$.

$$E = \frac{h^2 \mathbf{k}^2}{2m} = \frac{h^2}{2m}(k_x^2 + k_y^2 + k_z^2) \tag{10.6}$$

We have also written the result in terms of the components of $\mathbf{k}$ along the x, y, and z axes.

Thus the energy level curve for the free particle model is a parabola just as it was in the one-dimensional case. However, the points at which a periodic potential causes a break in the curve are not so simple, because they vary with the direction of motion. The region in space appropriate for the $\mathbf{k}$ vector which corresponds to the central segment in Fig. 10.2 is known as the first *Brillouin zone* after L. Brillouin, who investigated these problems in 1930.

The essential ideas related to this difference of direction in $\mathbf{k}$ space can be illustrated in two dimensions as well as in three. In either case if one defines a set of reciprocal vectors $\mathbf{K}$, such that for any $\mathbf{K}$ the function

$$e^{2\pi i \mathbf{K} \cdot \mathbf{r}}$$

has the same periodicity as the lattice. Then the boundaries of the Brillouin zones are defined by planes which satisfy the equation

$$\mathbf{k} \cdot \mathbf{K} = \mathbf{K}^2/2 \tag{10.7}$$

This equation gives a plane perpendicular to and bisecting each $\mathbf{K}$ vector.

In the one-dimensional lattice of spacing a, the $\mathbf{K}$ vector is in that direction and of magnitude $\pm 1/a$. Then the values of $\mathbf{k}$ satisfying Eq. (10.7) are $\pm 1/2a$ as found above.

Next we consider a two-dimensional square lattice with interval a, as shown in Fig. 10.3. The smallest $\mathbf{K}$ vectors have the components $\pm 1/a$, 0; or 0, $\pm 1/a$ for k_x and k_y, respectively. One can readily verify that these vectors satisfy the condition given above. Then the first Brillouin zone is the area within the boundary planes given by $k_x = \pm 1/2a$ and $k_y = \pm 1/2a$.

If in the planar crystal under consideration there are N atoms in each direction, or N^2 in all, then the periodic boundary conditions on k_x and k_y are each identical with Eqs. (10.4) for the linear lattice. Following through the calculation, one obtains just N^2 energy levels

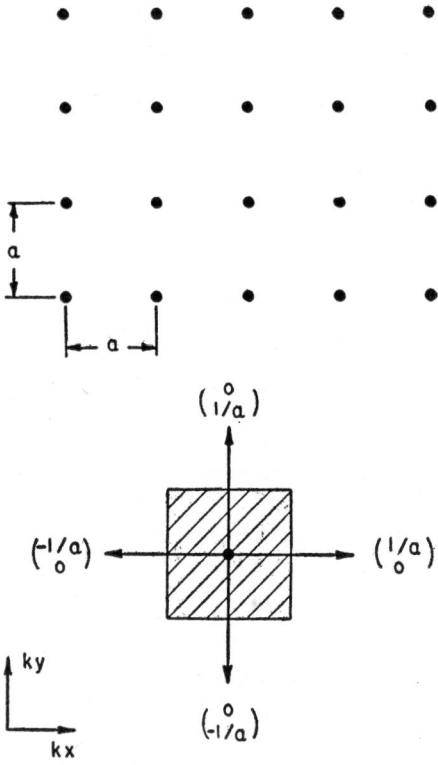

Fig. 10.3. Top, a square lattice of interval a. Bottom, the k vector space for this lattice. The K vectors are indicated with their components given in parentheses. The first Brillouin zone is the shaded area.

in the first Brillouin zone, or one per lattice cell as would be expected. If there is one atom per unit cell in the lattice, there will be just one energy level per atom in this first Brillouin zone.

A regular hexagonal lattice is shown in Fig. 10.4, together with the other quantities discussed above. The first Brillouin zone is a regular hexagon in k space and contains, as always, the same number of

translational energy levels as there are cells in the lattice.   Other
lattice patterns would give similar results.

Let us return now to a plot of the energy as a function of **k**, such
as Fig. 10.2.   The break in energy will come at a different |**k**| value
for different directions in the **k** space.   In Fig. 10.5 we show a similar

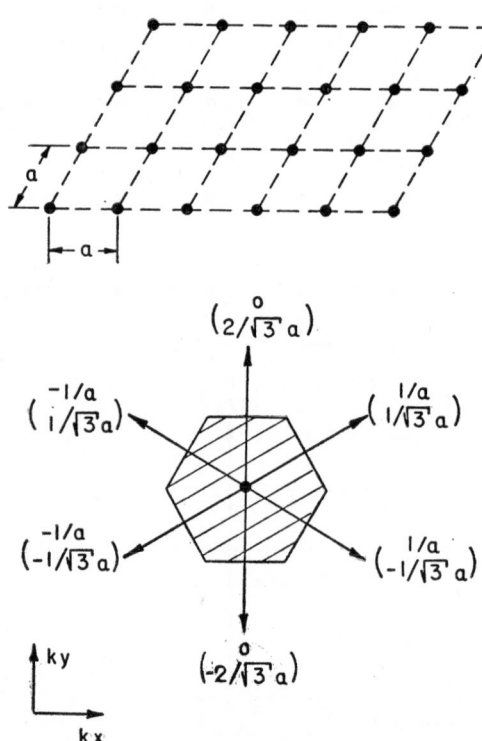

Fig. 10.4.   Top, a hexagonal lattice of interval, a.   Bottom, the k vector space
for this lattice.   The K vectors are shown with their components in parentheses.
The first Brillouin zone is the shaded area.

plot for our square lattice, but give just the curves for directions along
the axes in **k** space in Fig. 10.3 and the diagonal directions, i.e., at
45° to the axes.   In the diagonal direction the zone boundary comes
at $\pm 1/\sqrt{2}a$ while along the axes it is at $\pm 1/2a$.   Curve A gives
just the parabola of Eq. (10.6) for the energy of a free particle.
Curve B gives the energy where the periodic potential of the lattice

has only a small effect. Here we see that the energy levels of the first Brillouin zone actually overlap those of the second zone. This arises because of the $|\mathbf{k}|$ value in the direction of the zone diagonals is sufficiently greater than that along the axes, that the energy levels in the corners of the first zone are higher than the lowest energy levels of the second zone.

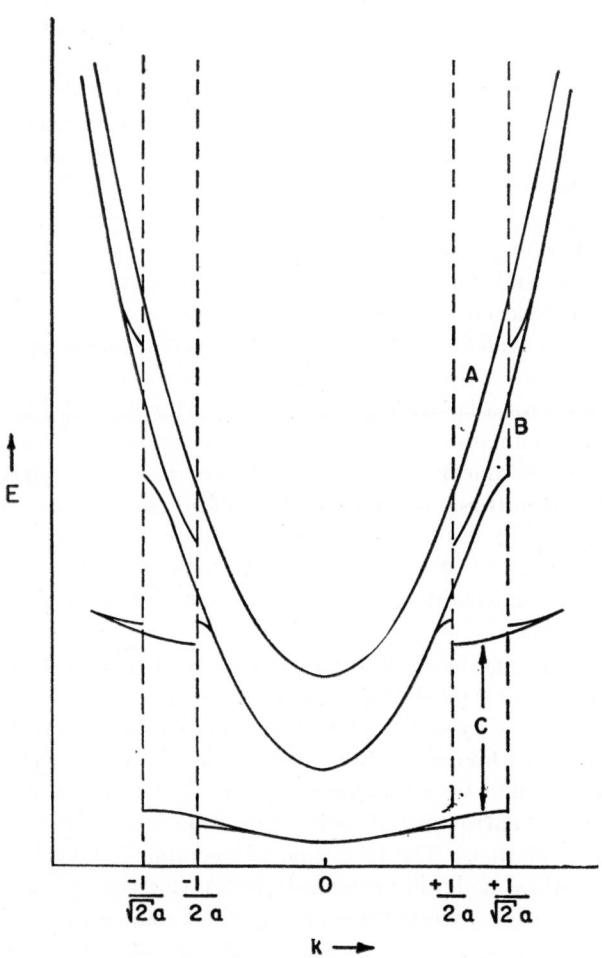

Fig. 10.5. The energy levels of a particle in a square lattice. The curves are for k values along the axes and diagonals.

Curve C represents an example where the potential wells of the lattice are large and the wave function drops to a small value in the space between wells. In this case there is a wide energy interval between levels of the first and second zone regardless of the difference in value of $|k|$ at the boundary.

We may now recapitulate our essential conclusions. In a two- or three-dimensional lattice of N atoms there will be essentially continuous bands of N energy levels per band. In contrast to the linear case, these bands may overlap one another in energy even though there is an appreciable potential energy associated with the lattice. However, if the potential wells are large enough, the bands will be separated from one another in energy even in the two- or three-dimensional case.

In the paragraph above we have assumed an essentially atomic lattice where each atom is equidistant from a considerable number of neighbors and where the unit cell of the crystal can be defined so as to include only one atom. This is the case with the simple metallic and covalent lattices. A molecular lattice necessarily has at least one whole molecule in a unit cell and hence has bands of N energy levels for a lattice of N molecules. The difference between a molecular and an atomic lattice is similar to that between the polyene and the cyanine linear molecules which were discussed above.

10d. Conductors, semiconductors and insulators. We are now prepared to discuss the essential distinction between typical metals, which are electric conductors, and covalent crystals which are insulators. Semiconductors arise in intermediate cases and will be considered also.

If we have a crystal of N atoms, there will be in all ZN electrons. We assume some typical atomic lattice with one atom in a unit cell. The potential energy of the nuclei has a profound effect on the inner shell electrons, whose wave functions rapidly decrease to very small values in the region between atoms. Hence the bands of these energy levels are very narrow, since they are extreme cases of the C type in Figs. 10.2 and 10.5. The first zone will contain N levels based on $1s$ atomic states and will accommodate $2N$ electrons by pairing all spins. Similarly, any other inner shells will accommodate their usual number of electrons. Thus for our present purpose, we may ignore all inner shells and consider only the valence electrons.

We have said nothing about the repulsive energy between electrons in this chapter. While this term would have a very considerable effect on quantitative calculations, it has no primary qualitative effect. Also, in principle, we should construct completely antisymmetric wave functions by the use of determinants of ZN order. Again it is found that the same qualitative results are obtained from the more precise procedure as from the simple sum of one-electron energy levels. Consequently, we will continue to ignore these refinements in this section.

In an alkali metal there is one valence electron per atom. The first Brillouin zone for valence electrons contains N energy levels and can accommodate $2N$ electrons. Therefore this band is only half filled, and there are vacant energy levels only infinitesimally higher than the highest filled energy levels. This is the situation characteristic of a *metal—the presence of a partially filled band of electronic energy levels.*

It will be recalled from Section 2c and those following it, that the quantity k_x corresponds qualitatively with the component of momentum of the electron in the x direction. One will normally have equal numbers of electrons with positive and negative k_x, and therefore no net electric current. However, if the band is partially filled, then in an electric field a few electrons can have their direction of motion changed without great increase in kinetic energy. Thus one can have electric conductivity. Indeed, on this simple model one would have infinite conductance because the electrons moving down the field would continue to gain speed indefinitely. To explain electric resistance one must introduce a means of transfer of electron kinetic energy to the thermal vibrations of the lattice of atomic nuclei.

An insulator is obtained when the valence electrons just fill a band which is well separated from higher energy bands. In this case there are precisely the same number of electrons moving in each direction from the symmetry of Brillouin zones in **k** space. Since a large energy is required to excite an electron to the next higher band, no electric conductivity is observed.

Let us consider now the elements with two-valence electrons. The lowest valence shell band is based on s orbitals and holds $2N$ electrons. Thus one might expect these elements to be insulators, as is indeed the case with helium, which has no valence shell p orbitals. However, for the remaining elements, the alkaline earths, the p orbital bands evidently overlap the s band, because these elements are metals. Such quantitative calculations as are feasible all agree that the s and p energy level bands for typical alkaline earth lattices should overlap, while the $1s$ band for helium should be widely separated from the $2s$ or $2p$ bands. Thus helium is an example of type C in Fig. 10.5, while the alkaline earths are examples of type B.

The two allotropic forms of carbon, diamond and graphite, offer an interesting example of these effects. In diamond we have an atomic lattice where each atom has four equidistant neighbors in

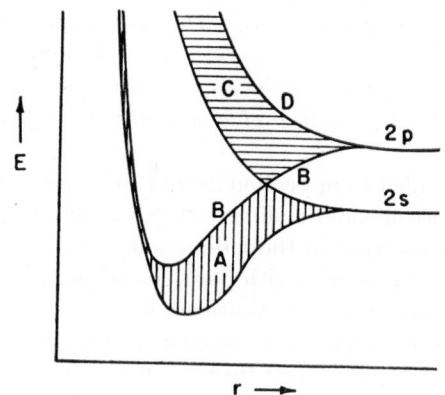

Fig. 10.6.　The energy level bands for diamond.

tetrahedral directions. The simplest unit cell contains two atoms, which complicates matters slightly but does not change the general picture.

Kimball[1] has carried out a semiquantitative zone treatment of diamond. Figure 10.6 shows his results, except for some minor details. At large distances there are very narrow $2s$ and $2p$ bands holding two and six electrons per atom, respectively. As the lattice spacing is reduced, these bands widen and eventually overlap. However, instead of remaining overlapped at still shorter distances, the bands separate again and then each set has capacity for four electrons per atom.

Actually, in Kimball's approximation the $2p$ bands include a lower band, B, of zero width, a middle band, C, of substantial width,

[1] Kimball, G. E., *J. Chem. Phys.*, **3**, 560 (1935).

and an upper band, D, of zero width. At the smaller lattice distances, the lower $2p$ band, B, leaves the upper group and joins onto the lower energy band, A. Probably a more accurate treatment would give bands B and D finite width, but it seems reasonable that the main features of the pattern are correct.

Thus at the lattice spacing for minimum energy, as in an actual diamond crystal, the lower bands, A and B, are just filled with the four valence electrons per atom, and there is a wide energy interval above, which contains no energy levels. This is in agreement with the fact that diamond is an electric insulator.

This separation of energy level bands at shorter distances, after the s and p levels have begun to overlap, appears to be characteristic of the tetrahedral lattice. The calculations that have been made for typical metallic lattices, such as the body-centered cubic lattice of the alkali metals, show no such effect.

Graphite has a layer lattice and can be treated as a two-dimensional problem. Each atom has three nearest neighbors at 120° angles. Thus we may assume a set of three σ bonds per carbon atom just like the C—H and two C—C bonds in benzene. Presumably the energy level diagram for these σ bonds would be similar to that of diamond in that the lower energy level bands would be completely filled.

As in the case of benzene, we may consider separately the π electron system, since all its wave functions are antisymmetric to the plane of the lattice, while the σ functions are all symmetric. Each carbon atom has one p_z function and one electron to contribute to the π system. However, as can be seen in Fig. 10.7, there are two atoms per unit cell. The calculations[2] indicate that the energy level band arising from the first Brillouin zone just touches but does not overlap the second zone. Also there is a zero density of energy levels at the point of contact. With two electrons per unit cell, the first zone is completely filled at the absolute zero. At any higher temperature there will be vacancies in the first zone, and electrons in the second zone which will yield conductivity. However, the behavior of graphite will be abnormal in that the conductivity will approach zero at low temperatures because of the zero density of energy levels at the top of the first zone.

Some substances show an electric conductivity far smaller than

[2] Wallace, P. R., *Phys. Rev.*, **71**, 622 (1947); Coulson, C. A., *Nature*, **159**. 265 (1947).

that of typical metals but still distinctly measurable. In such cases the conductivity commonly increases with temperature, while that of normal metals decreases. These substances of low conductivity can be subdivided into two general groups. In some cases the current is carried by the gross migration of ions in the crystal, as indicated by transference experiments (and by the absence of a measurable Hall effect—see Section 10f). In other cases, the current is carried by electrons, and these are called *semiconductors*.

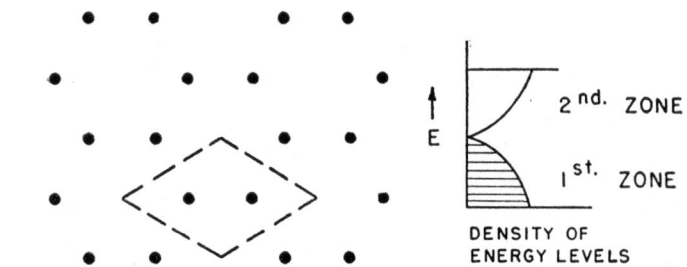

Fig. 10.7. Left, the structure of one layer of graphite showing the hexagonal unit cell containing two atoms. Right, the energy level bands arising from the first two Brillouin zones. At 0°K. the first zone is filled and the second empty as shown.

The conductance σ of a typical semiconductor follows an exponential law with respect to temperature as follows.

$$\sigma = Ae^{-E/kT} \tag{10.8}$$

Evidently the conductance must arise from some sort of thermal excitation, with E the energy required to move one electron into the excited state.

In almost all cases it is believed that the semiconductor obtains its conductivity from some sort of lattice defect. In some cases, probably including silicon, there is an actual impurity present. In substances such as zinc oxide there is a slight deviation from the exact composition. Possibly, in some cases there is just a thermally excited disorder in an otherwise perfect crystal.

In any event the defect in the lattice will have one or more special electronic energy levels associated with it. These special levels may lie in the otherwise forbidden region between the filled band and the next higher empty band of an insulator.

Figure 10.8 illustrates this situation and indicates the two possibilities. Diagram B shows an electronic semiconductor, such as ZnO with a slight excess of Zn atoms. The special defect levels are filled with electrons, but some of these electrons may be thermally excited to the vacant band above. In the regular lattice band the electrons can conduct in the usual manner.

Diagram C typifies the opposite type, of which Cu_2O is an example. In this case there is an excess of the nonmetal atom, oxygen. Thus we may expect the special levels to be vacant. However, if they are

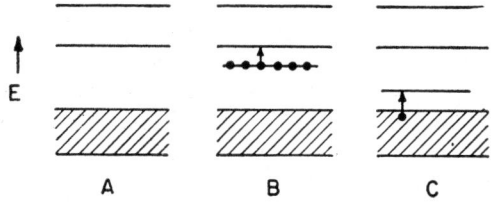

Fig. 10.8. Electronic energy levels for an insulator (A), and electronic semiconductor (B), and a "hole" semiconductor (C).

near enough to the top of the filled band, thermal excitation may occur to these special levels. Then the regular lattice band is not quite full and can yield conduction. In this case one can consider that the conduction arises from the "holes" in the filled band; hence substances of this type are called hole semiconductors.

The wave functions of the special levels are normally localized about the defect and therefore have no part in the conduction.

From the above discussion we see that graphite is a special case of a semiconductor—one with zero excitation energy.

10e. Binding energies in metals. Only in the very simplest cases has it been possible to calculate binding energies of metallic crystals that have quantitative significance. The examples are lithium and sodium. These substances have but a single valence electron per atom and have such large atomic volumes that in much of the space the metallic electrons are virtually free. In order to obtain this "free electron" state, it is essential that the inner shell electrons be confined, effectively, to a small fraction of the total volume surrounding the nuclei.

While various methods might be used to obtain electronic wave functions for the crystal, the successful calculations have used numerical integrations of a type analogous to the Hartree method for isolated atoms (see Section 5d). Indeed the potential function for the valence electron, corresponding to the net effect of the nucleus and inner shell electrons, can be taken from such calculations for the isolated atoms. However, the wave function for the valence electron itself must be obtained by a new calculation which employs boundary conditions appropriate to the crystal.

In principle one should integrate the Schrödinger equation throughout the crystal, using the net potential obtained by summing this Hartree potential for each atom. However, in practice this is neither feasible nor necessary. One can divide the crystal up into cells containing single atoms. It is then found to be a good approximation to integrate the wave equation within each cell, using only the potential arising from the nucleus and inner shell electrons of the atom within that cell.

Recalling the Bloch wave function,

$$\psi = e^{2\pi i \mathbf{k} \cdot \mathbf{r}} f_k(\mathbf{r}) \tag{10.5}$$

we first seek the solution for $k = 0, f_0(\mathbf{r})$. In this case the exponential is a constant so that the usual Schrödinger equation is directly applicable to f_0.

$$\frac{-h^2}{8\pi^2 m} \nabla^2 f_0 + [V(r) - \epsilon_0] f_0 = 0 \tag{10.9}$$

Here $V(r)$ is the Hartree potential function for the valence electron, and ϵ_0 is the electronic energy level.

The logical way to divide the crystal into cells is to place planes midway between atoms and perpendicular to the lines connecting them. The alkali metals have the body-centered cubic structure. Thus each atom has eight nearest neighbors at the corners of a cube. The planes just defined yield an octahedral cell about each atom. However, in this structure there are six more neighbors only 15% farther removed. Bisecting these additional bonds with planes as before has the effect of cutting off each of the six vertices of the octahedral cell. Thus the final cell is a fourteen-sided figure which is of nearly spherical shape.

Since the function f_0 is to be periodic in the lattice, one can show that its derivative should be zero on a cell boundary with respect to the coordinate perpendicular to the boundary plane. While this condition can be fulfilled, it is much simpler to replace the nearly spherical cell by a sphere of the same volume and make the radial derivative zero at the surface of the sphere.   In the case of the alkali metals, convincing arguments have been given to the effect that this approximation introduces little error.   Then Eq. (10.9) reduces to the one-dimensional equation

$$\frac{-h^2}{8\pi^2 m r^2} \frac{d}{dr}\left(r^2 \frac{df_0}{dr}\right) + [V(r) - \epsilon_0]f_0 = 0 \qquad (10.10)$$

with the simple boundary condition

$$\frac{df_0}{dr} = 0 \quad \text{at} \quad r = r_s$$

where r_s is the radius of the sphere containing one atomic volume. Solution of this equation yields a value of ϵ_0, or more generally, a curve of ϵ_0 vs. r_s such as is shown in Fig. 10.9 for lithium.

It has not been feasible to solve the Schrödinger equation so directly

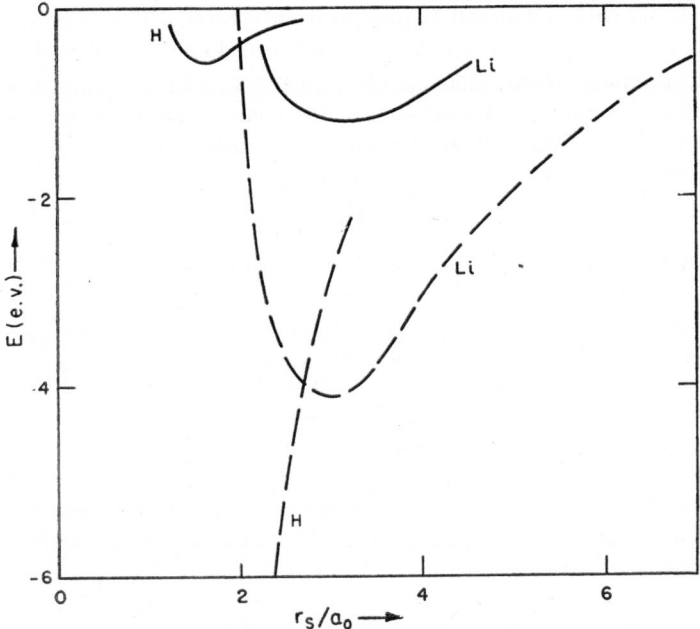

Fig. 10.9.   Values of ϵ_0 (broken) and of the total binding energy (solid) for lithium and for a hypothetical metallic hydrogen.

for the remaining functions where $\mathbf{k}$ is not zero. However, these f_k functions can be calculated by perturbation methods if they do not differ too much from f_0. We shall omit these details but state the essential conclusion that their energies are given by

$$\epsilon(\mathbf{k}) = \epsilon_0 + \frac{h^2}{2m^*}\,\mathbf{k}^2 \qquad (10.11)$$

where m^* is an effective electronic mass. For perfectly free electrons m^* becomes exactly the electron mass. In other cases it depends on a sum of integrals, each involving the wave function for an excited state of the atom. However, this complex expression is independent of $\mathbf{k}$. For lithium m^*/m is found to have the value 1.53, and for sodium it is accidentally very very close to unity, actually 0.94.

To this one-electron orbital approximation, one may now calculate the total electronic energy of the valence electrons by summing $\epsilon(\mathbf{k})$ over the range of $\mathbf{k}$ values necessary to accommodate all the electrons. In accordance with the Pauli exclusion principle, one allows two electrons with antiparallel spins to each orbital. This corresponds exactly to the calculation for the degenerate Fermi gas in Section 71. The occupied volume of $\mathbf{k}$ space is a sphere of radius k_0. The number of discrete states is proportional to the volume of this sphere and to the physical volume of the crystal. The expression for k_0 is

$$k_0 = \left(\frac{3N}{8\pi V}\right)^{1/3} \qquad (10.12)$$

where N and V are the number of valence electrons and the volume, respectively.

The excess energy of the electronic system above that for all electrons in the state ϵ_0 is commonly called the Fermi energy. The mean Fermi energy per electron, ϵ_F, is then

$$\epsilon_F = \overline{(h^2\mathbf{k}^2/2m^*)} = \frac{3}{5}\cdot\frac{h^2 k_0^2}{2m^*} \qquad (10.13)$$

Since the radius r_s is that of a sphere containing one atom and one valence electron (in an alkali metal), Eq. (10.13) may be rearranged to give

$$\epsilon_F = \frac{3h^2}{10m^*}\left(\frac{9}{32\pi^2}\right)^{2/3}\frac{1}{r_s^2} = 1.105\left(\frac{e^2}{a_0}\right)\left(\frac{m}{m^*}\right)\left(\frac{a_0}{r_s}\right)^2 \qquad (10.14)$$

where a_0 is the usual radius of the first Bohr orbit.

The remaining elements in the calculation involve the potential energy terms arising from the repulsion between electrons. It is readily shown that, if each cell is electrically neutral, there will be no net electrostatic interaction between cells. However, the usual coulomb and exchange integrals (as in Eq. 5.9) can be taken for the various pairs of orbitals over a single cell. We have also found in any multiple electron problem that the explicit interelectronic coordinates must be introduced into the wave function in order to obtain a good approximation. This is frequently called *correlation*, and the energy reduction obtained, the *correlation energy*. The correlation energy is the energy reduction when the wave function is modified so as to keep the individual electrons away from one another. It is clearly not practical to introduce all the interelectronic coordinates explicitly in a calculation such as this. Wigner[3] has given a rough formula for the correlation energy in systems of this type with essentially uniform density of free electrons.

$$\epsilon_{cor.} = -\frac{0.288e^2}{a_0} \cdot \frac{1}{5.1 + (r_s/a_0)} \tag{10.15}$$

Here r_s is, as defined above, the radius of a sphere containing one electron, and a_0 is the usual radius of the first Bohr orbit.

The various terms in the calculation of the binding energy, or cohesive energy, of sodium and lithium are summarized in Table 10.1. The calculations were actually made[4] for several interatomic distances. The values given in Table 10.1 are for r_s values of 3.21 a_0 and 4.12 a_0 for lithium and sodium, respectively, which are approximately the calculated potential minima. The value for lithium agrees with the experimental crystal structure parameter within about 1%, but the calculated value for sodium is about 7% larger than the experimental value.

It is interesting to note that the net effect of the last three terms is almost exactly zero. This means that the net electrostatic effect on one valence electron of all the other valence electrons is just balanced by that of all the atomic kernels (nuclei plus inner electron shells) except the closest one.

Another method of calculation has been proposed by Löwdin[5] which

[3] Wigner, E., *Phys. Rev.*, **46**, 1002 (1934); *Trans. Faraday Soc.*, **34**, 678 (1938).

[4] For a more detailed account and references, see Seitz, F., *The Modern Theory of Solids*, New York: McGraw-Hill Book Company, Inc., 1940, Sec. 78.

[5] Löwdin, P. O., *J. Chem. Phys.*, **19**, 1570, 1579 (1951).

Table 10.1

The Binding Energy of Li and Na
(energy unit: kcal./mole)

	Li	Na
Ionization of atom, ϵ_I	123.4	118.7
Lowest crystal orbital, ϵ_0	−206.0	−185.9
Mean Fermi energy, ϵ_F	43.6	42.9
Subtotal, $(\epsilon_I + \epsilon_0 + \epsilon_F)$	−39.0	−24.3
Coulomb term, ϵ_c	114.8	89.6
Exchange term, ϵ_x	−90.2	−69.2
Correlation term, ϵ_{cor}	−21.7	−19.6
Total, calculated	−36.1	−23.5
Experimental	−37.3	−26.

avoids the new integration of the Schrödinger equation in the lattice cell. It is more analogous to the usual molecular orbital method and it appears to yield interesting results when these molecular orbitals are constructed from linear combinations of atomic orbitals. Lowdin has made some very clever mathematical transformations involving what he calls *combined atomic orbitals*, and these permit him to avoid some of the difficult integrations which would otherwise arise. His result for the binding energy of sodium seems almost too good when one remembers that the correlation energy between valence electrons has not been considered.

Binding energy calculations have been attempted for several other metallic elements. However, even in the case of potassium the results are disappointing. Presumably it is the increased magnitude of inner shell interactions which causes the method used for sodium to fail for potassium. The other obvious difference is the presence of low energy d orbitals for potassium, and this may be important too.

An interesting calculation of Wigner and Huntington[6] concerns a hypothetical metallic hydrogen with the body-centered lattice like the alkali metals. The cellular method was used as described above for lithium and sodium. The calculation correctly gives for this hypothetical metallic hydrogen a much higher energy than for molecular hydrogen. From Fig. 10.9 one notes that good binding is obtained between hydrogen atoms only at much smaller interatomic distances than for lithium. However, in a metallic lattice this small

[6] Wigner, E. and Huntington, H. B., *J. Chem. Phys.*, **3**, 764 (1935).

distance yields a very large Fermi energy, which makes the metallic hydrogen less stable than molecular hydrogen.

10f. The free electron model. The model of a gas of free electrons was discussed in Section 7l in connection with the Fermi-Dirac statistics which such a gas must follow. The more detailed approach of the last section was required to calculate the binding energy, but it was found that the Fermi energy, the zero point kinetic energy of the electrons, is given by essentially the same formula as that for free electrons. Consequently, it is worth while to apply the free electron model to some other problems, such as the magnetic susceptibility, the thermionic emission of electrons, the electronic specific heat, the thermal electromotive force, and the electric conductivity.

The results for the electronic specific heat were given in Section 7l but are repeated here.

$$C_{el.} = R \frac{\pi^2}{2} \frac{kT}{\epsilon_m} = \gamma T \qquad (10.16)$$

where $C_{el.}$ is the electronic specific heat per mole of free electrons and ϵ_m is the upper limit of the Fermi energy. The coefficient of T is commonly given the symbol γ. It will be recalled that the mean Fermi energy is three-fifths of ϵ_m. The simple expression for ϵ_m based on the electron density n_0 in particles per cc. was given as Eq. (7.46).

$$\epsilon_m = \frac{h^2}{8m} \left(\frac{3n_0}{\pi} \right)^{2/3} \qquad (7.46)$$

Equation (10.16) sometimes holds over a substantial temperature range even though the value of ϵ_m is different from that in Eq. (7.46). Some examples are given in Table 10.2.

TABLE 10.2
ELECTRONIC SPECIFIC HEAT IN METALS

	$\gamma \times 10^4$ (obs.)	Metallic e^- per atom	ϵ_m from Eq. (10.16)	ϵ_m from Eq. (7.46)
Cu:	1.80 cal. deg.$^{-2}$	1	4.7 e.v.	7.0 e.v.
Mg:	3.25	2	5.2	7.1
Al:	3.46	3	7.3	11.6
Zr:	6.92	4	4.9	11.1

Since the derivations are rather lengthy, we shall merely describe the ideas involved in the calculation of these other electronic properties and then state the results.[7] For the *magnetic susceptibility* of the free electron gas one remembers that, in the absence of a magnetic field, half of the electrons will have positive spin and half negative. The application of a magnetic field will reduce the energy of those electrons with the favorable spin orientation because of their magnetic moment. Thus a new distribution will be set up with somewhat more than half of the electrons having their magnetic moment parallel with the field. Correspondingly less than half of the electrons must have their magnetic moment antiparallel. The net effect is to induce a magnetic moment parallel to the field which yields a paramagnetic contribution.

The magnetic susceptibility arising from spin for a free electron gas is

$$\chi = \frac{3}{2} \mu_0^2 \frac{n_0}{\epsilon_m} \qquad (10.17)$$

where n_0 is the number of electrons per cc., and μ_0 is the magnetic moment of the electron, $eh/4\pi mc$.

On the simplest analysis, the orbital motions of an electron gas confined to a definite volume make no contribution to the magnetic susceptibility. A more refined calculation of Landau yields a small diamagnetic effect. In addition, even moderate deviations from the free electron gas cause considerable variation from Eq. (10.17) for the spin contribution. Also, the completed inner electron shells of the ions contribute a diamagnetic effect. Consequently, numerical comparisons, even for the alkali metals, of experimental susceptibilities with calculations from Eq. (10.17) would have little significance.

The phenomenon of electron emission from heated metal surfaces is well known and of great practical importance. Figure 10.10 shows: (a), the initial assumption of a square potential barrier for a free electron at the edge of the metal and then with the solid line; (b), the net barrier after one considers the image force. This is the force which arises because a charge near the surface of the metal induces an opposite charge in the metal surface. Finally curve (c) shows the effect of an electric field on the potential barrier.

Actually if the field is strong enough, one gets some *cold emission*

---

[7] Derivations are given, among others, by Seitz, F., *The Modern Theory of Solids*, New York: McGraw-Hill Book Company, Inc., 1940, Chap. 4.

or *field emission* because electrons at the top of the Fermi distribution can penetrate the potential barrier as is indicated by the arrow (1).

The usual *thermionic emission* arises from process (2) in which the electrons are thermally excited and pass over the potential barrier.

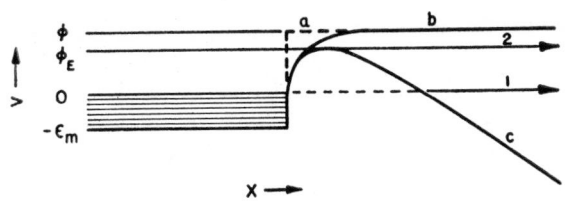

Fig. 10.10.   Energy diagram for field emission (1) and thermionic emission (2) of electrons from metals.

By considering the number of electrons colliding with the surface with sufficient velocity to surmount the barrier, one can calculate the emitted current.   The result is

$$I = AT^2(1 - r)e^{-\phi/kT}e^{\mathbf{E}e^{3/2}/kT} \qquad (10.18)$$

where I is the current emitted per sq. cm., r is the fraction of the electrons having sufficient energy to pass over the barrier which are reflected back, ϕ is the work function as indicated in Fig. 10.10, and $\mathbf{E}$ is the electric field.   Also

$$A = \frac{4\pi mek^2}{h^3} = 120 \quad \text{amp./cm.}^2\text{deg.}^2 \qquad (10.19)$$

These equations describe the thermionic emission process quite well, although as may be expected for any free electron model calculation, some deviations occur.   The work function ϕ has the magnitude of a few electron volts for most metals.

It is clear from the very nature of a free electron gas that it will be capable of conducting electricity.   The difficulty arises in the source of the resistance—why the conductance is not infinite.   The observed magnitude of electric resistance requires some mechanism of transfer of electronic kinetic energy to the lattice vibrations.   Since this mechanism involves the lattice, it is clearly beyond pure Fermi gas theory to account for electric resistance.

Nevertheless, it has been possible to treat *electric conductance* by adding to the Fermi gas theory the concept of a mean free path for the motion of an electron before it comes again into thermal equilibrium with the lattice. The result is

$$\sigma = \frac{e^2 n_0 l(T)}{(2m\epsilon_m)^{1/2}} \tag{10.20}$$

where σ is the conductance and $l(T)$ is this mean free path, which is indicated to be a function of the temperature. It is the mean free path for the electrons at the top of the Fermi distribution which is significant. Equation (10.20) indicates, as we expected, that if the mean free path should become infinite, the resistance would disappear.

Even though we are unable to estimate the mean free path theoretically on this model, it is interesting to insert the appropriate values in Eq. (10.20) and evaluate $l(T)$ numerically. For lithium at room temperature it is close to 10^{-6} cm. The mean 'free path varies inversely with the temperature and is somewhat longer in good conductors, such as copper and silver, than it is in the alkali metals.

Theories have been developed concerning the probability of energy transfer from moving electrons to lattice vibrations, which confirm roughly both the magnitude and temperature dependence of this electronic mean free path. However, these theories involve quantum methods beyond the scope of this chapter.

While heat can be conducted by lattice vibrations as well as electronic motion, in some metals the latter is the predominant term. By a derivation analogous to that for electric conductance, the *heat conductivity* is calculated to be

$$\kappa = \frac{\pi^2}{3} \frac{k^2 n_0 l(T)}{(2m\epsilon_m)^{1/2}} \cdot T \tag{10.21}$$

where κ is the heat conductivity, and k and T are the usual Boltzmann constant and temperature.

We note that $l(T)$ appears in both Eqs. (10.20) and (10.21). Eliminating it between the two expressions, we obtain

$$\frac{\kappa}{T\sigma} = \frac{1}{3}\left(\frac{\pi k}{e}\right)^2 \tag{10.22}$$

which indicates that $(\kappa/T\sigma)$ should be a constant for all substances where the heat conductance is due principally to a free electron gas. This sort of relationship was first observed by Wiedemann and Franz in 1853. The ratio in Eq. (10.22) is now called *Wiedemann-Franz ratio*.

Table 10.3 shows the value of the Wiedemann-Franz ratio for a number of substances at room temperature. The theoretical value, converted to practical units, is 2.45×10^{-8} watt ohm/deg.^{2}. Only for metals such as antimony and bismuth are large deviations found, and in such cases the value depends considerably on the physical state, i.e., crystal size, etc.

TABLE 10.3

WIEDEMANN-FRANZ RATIO FOR PURE METALS
AT ROOM TEMPERATURE (all $\times 10^{-8}$)

Mg	Al	Fe	Ni	Cu
2.3	2.2	2.9	2.4	2.2

Rh	Ag	Sb	Pb	Bi
2.6	2.4	2.6–3.8	2.5	2.7–4.6

The general term, *electrothermal* effects, includes the thermal emf and the Thomson heat. The latter is the heat produced by an electric current flowing through a temperature gradient (besides the heat due to resistance). Also when a current passes from one metal to another there is a heat effect known as the Peltier heat. These quantities are interrelated by thermodynamics.[8]

The free electron theory yields for the *Thomson heat* the expression

$$\sigma_T = -\frac{\pi^2 k^2 T}{3e}\left[\frac{1}{\epsilon_m} + \frac{l'}{l}\right] \tag{10.23}$$

where σ_T is the Thomson heat, l is our familiar electron mean free path, and l' is the derivative of l with respect to energy in the Fermi distribution.

The other electrothermal quantities can be obtained by integrations with respect to temperature of the difference between the Thomson heat for the two metals involved. Actually to perform these integrations, some assumption must be made with respect to the term l'/l. While some authors have regarded it as negligible, we shall merely assume it to be constant with respect to temperature (or more strictly that its temperature variation is negligible). Then one finds for the emf of a thermocouple with junctions at T_1 and T_2

$$\text{emf} = \frac{\pi^2 k^2}{6e}(T_2^2 - T_1^2)\left[\left(\frac{1}{\epsilon_m} + \frac{l'}{l}\right)_A - \left(\frac{1}{\epsilon_m} + \frac{l'}{l}\right)_B\right] \tag{10.24}$$

[8] See Bridgman, P. W., *The Thermodynamics of Electrical Phenomena in Metals*, New York: The Macmillan Company, 1934.

where the subscripts A and B refer to the two metals making up the thermocouple.

The dependence of the emf on the difference of squares of temperatures is quite well verified for a number of substances at low temperatures. Figure 10.11 shows the emf of copper-constantan thermocouples plotted against T, T^2, and T^3, and indicates that the T^2 dependence is correct.

Finally we shall mention briefly the *Hall effect*. It is well known that a charged particle moving through a magnetic field suffers a force perpendicular to both the field and the direction of motion. This force applies, of course, to the electrons moving in a wire in a

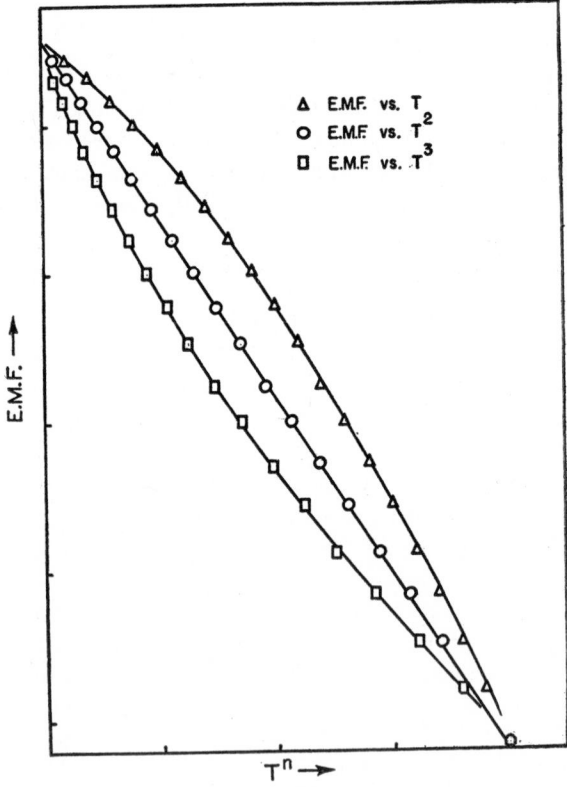

Fig. 10.11. The E.M.F. of copper-constantan thermocouples plotted against T, T^2 and T^3.

magnetic field.   Since the electrons must remain within the wire, an electric potential difference is developed perpendicular to both the current and magnetic field, i.e., across the wire.   In practice a metal strip is more convenient.   Then the Hall constant, R_H, is defined by

$$E_y = R_H H_z I_x/t \tag{10.25}$$

where t is the thickness of the strip, and the other symbols have their usual significance.

On the degenerate Fermi gas theory of free electrons the Hall constant is found to be

$$R_H = -c/n_0 e \tag{10.26}$$

where n_0 is the number of free electrons per unit volume, c is the velocity of light, e is the magnitude of the charge in e.s.u., and R_H is in abs. e.m.u.-c.g.s. units.   The negative sign arises from the sign of the charge on the conducting particle.

Table 10.4 lists the observed values of the Hall constant for some metals, together with the calculated values for those examples where the free electron gas theory might be expected to apply.

TABLE 10.4

VALUES OF THE HALL CONSTANT

$R \times 10^4$ abs. e.m.u.

Substance	Observed	Calculated
Li	−17.0	−13.5
Na	−25.0	−24.6
Al	−3.0	−3.5
Cu	−5.5	−7.4
Ag	−8.4	−10.4
Au	−7.2	−10.5
Be	+24.4	. . .
Fe	+100.	. . .

The positive sign of the Hall constant for beryllium and iron would require positive conducting particles on the free particle theory.   This difficulty disappeared when it was found that an almost full Brillouin zone yielded a positive Hall constant for electron conduction. Roughly, the electron vacancies behave as positive holes in the otherwise filled zone of electronic levels.

The magnitude of the Hall effect for a semiconductor depends on the concentration of impurity atoms or other lattice defects.   However, it is in qualitative agreement in that the Hall constant is negative for electronic semiconductors and positive for hole semiconductors.

Sometimes the Hall constant is too small to measure. This is generally true for substances conducting by ion migration, but it may also arise for an equal mixture of electronic and hole conductivity where both types are combined in a single substance.

10g. The specific heat of solids. The specific heat of solid substances has played a large role in the development of atomic theory. The law of *Dulong and Petit* (1818) stated that the heat capacity per gram atom of solid elements was slightly over 6 cal. per degree. It was recognized that certain light elements such as carbon, boron, beryllium, and silicon were exceptions in that their heat capacity at room temperature was much less than six. However, it was also found that the heat capacity of these substances was rising rapidly with temperature, whereas that for substances obeying the Dulong and Petit law was substantially constant. Thus one presumed that all substances would follow the law at higher temperatures.

Kopp (1864) extended this law to compounds by showing that the molar heat capacity was the sum of the atomic heat capacities of the elements in the compound. The law of Dulong and Petit, particularly as extended by Kopp, was widely used to check atomic weights or to decide which multiple of an equivalent weight should be selected for the atomic weight.

When heat capacities were measured at low temperatures it was found that the values for all substances dropped below the Dulong and Petit value. Indeed it appeared that heat capacities approach zero at the absolute zero.

In the meantime the law of Dulong and Petit had received an explanation in classical statistical mechanics. By assuming that each atom is restrained by Hooke's law forces, one finds for the classical energy for motion in the x direction,

$$\epsilon = \frac{p_x^2}{2m} + \frac{b}{2} x^2 \tag{10.27}$$

if we take the potential minimum as the zero for x, and b as the force constant. Then in Eq. (7.58) we find the integral for the partition function, yielding

$$Q_x = \frac{1}{h} \int_{-\infty}^{+\infty} e^{-p_x^2/2mkT} \, dp_x \int_{-\infty}^{+\infty} e^{-bx^2/2kT} \, dx = \frac{2\pi kT}{h} \left(\frac{m}{b}\right)^{1/2} \tag{10.28}$$

Taking the appropriate derivatives of Eq. (7.55) to obtain the heat capacity yields the value R per mole. Now the y and z directions will make equal contributions, so that the total classical heat capacity for a gram atom of solid is

$$C_v = 3R = 5.962 \quad \text{cal./degree} \qquad (10.29)$$

Since the measured heat capacities are at constant pressure, one must add the difference $(C_p - C_v)$, which is commonly a few tenths calories per degree at room temperature. Thus the Dulong and Petit value, a little over six, is confirmed.

The explanation of the decrease in heat capacity below this classical value was one of the next triumphs of quantum theory to follow after Planck's original treatment of blackbody radiation and Einstein's interpretation of the photoelectric effect. In 1907 Einstein suggested that the oscillational energy of atoms in a crystal would be quantized and limited to the values $nh\nu$, where ν is the classical frequency and n is a positive integer. Except for the omission of the half unit of zero point energy, this is just the expression we found in Section 2i for the harmonic oscillator.

We have already applied this energy level system to the specific heat of molecules, obtaining the results of Eq. (9.49). Making Einstein's assumption that all frequencies are the same, one has $3N_0$ modes of oscillation, and the heat capacity is

$$C_v = 3R \frac{u^2 e^u}{(e^u - 1)^2} \qquad (10.30)$$

$$u = h\nu/kT$$

Sometimes the quantity $(h\nu/k)$ is called the characteristic temperature θ, whereupon u is the ratio θ/T.

The Einstein expression yields a qualitatively correct decrease of heat capacity toward zero as the temperature is reduced and the correct limit of $3R$ at high temperatures. But it does not fit the experimental data quantitatively.

Both Debye[9] and Born and von Karman[10] independently laid the remaining groundwork for a quantitative theory in 1912 by pointing out that the vibrations of a crystal were really normal modes of vibration and would have a broad distribution of frequencies. In

[9] Debye, P., *Ann. Physik*, **39**, 789 (1912).
[10] Born, M. and von Karman, T., *Physik. Z.*, **13**, 297 (1912); **14**, 15 (1913).

this sense a crystal is just a giant molecule and the equations of Sections 9d and 9e are applicable. However, any crystal of reasonable size will have such an enormous number of normal vibrations (3 per atom) that a direct solution of the secular Eq. (9.39) is impractical. One must find some additional principle to aid in the solution.

Debye used the vibrations of a continuous isotropic medium as a model for a crystal but retained the proper total number of modes, $3N_0$ for a gram atom.

Waves in a solid body are, of course, sound waves. As compared with a gas, however, there can be transverse waves in a solid, in which the motion is perpendicular to the direction of propagation. These are in addition to the usual longitudinal or compressional waves. Thus in an isotropic solid there are two separate velocities of sound, c_t for transverse waves and c_l for longitudinal waves. Also for waves moving in the x direction the transverse motion can be in either the y or the z direction. Hence there are two transverse modes for each longitudinal mode.

The selection of the proper normal modes of oscillation for any particular shape of solid body is a very complex problem. There are simplified assumptions which give results that are correct statistically, although erroneous in certain details. One procedure is to assume a block out of an infinite crystal and to apply periodic boundary conditions[11] just as were applied in Sections 10b and 10c. The displacement from equilibrium position of the point at x,y,z is

$$q_l = A_l \cos 2\pi(\mathbf{k} \cdot \mathbf{r} - \nu_l t)$$
$$= A_l \cos 2\pi(k_x x + k_y y + k_z z - \nu_l t) \qquad (10.31\text{a})$$
$$q_t = A_t \cos 2\pi(\mathbf{k} \cdot \mathbf{r} - \nu_t t)$$
$$= A_t \cos 2\pi(k_x x + k_y y + k_z z - \nu_t t) \qquad (10.31\text{b})$$

As before, $\mathbf{k}$ is the vector whose direction gives the direction of the wave, and whose magnitude gives the number of waves per centimeter. The expansion of the vectors into scalar components is also given. The A's are the amplitude constants, and the ν's are the frequencies of the longitudinal and transverse vibrations.

---

[11] In an isolated block of solid with either rigid surfaces or free surfaces, the vibrations must be some sort of standing waves rather than the traveling waves assumed in the text. However, some of these standing waves are not purely longitudinal or transverse vibrations. This problem of the true normal modes of a finite solid is very complex and was discussed in detail for a sphere in Debye's original paper.[9]

Under the periodic boundary conditions for a cube of edge length L, the allowed values of the k_x components are n_x/L, where n_x is any integer, positive or negative. The conditions on k_y and k_z are similar. The velocity of a wave is obtained by holding $(\mathbf{k} \cdot \mathbf{r} - \nu t)$ constant, hence is $(\nu/|\mathbf{k}|)$. Thus the expressions for the frequencies are

$$\nu_l = c_l|\mathbf{k}| = c_l(k_x^2 + k_y^2 + k_z^2)^{1/2}$$

$$= (c_l/L)(n_x^2 + n_y^2 + n_z^2)^{1/2} \tag{10.32a}$$

$$\nu_t = (c_t/L)(n_x^2 + n_y^2 + n_z^2)^{1/2} \tag{10.32b}$$

where the relations between n and k have been introduced also.

From Eqs. (10.32) we see that the frequency is proportional to the radial distance from the origin to the point n_x, n_y, n_z in a space where the latter are the three Cartesian coordinates. We have a vast number of modes of oscillation; hence the number of n's is large, and we may treat this space as a continuum. The number of points (modes of vibration) in a narrow frequency range between ν and $\nu + d\nu$ is related to the volume of a spherical shell in n space. We note that the points are spaced a unit distance apart in each direction, hence the volume per point is also unity. Then if the radius is r,

$$r = (n_x^2 + n_y^2 + n_z^2)^{1/2}$$

we have $\qquad \nu_l = r(c_l/L) \quad \text{and} \quad \nu_t = r(c_t/L) \tag{10.33}$

and in the spherical shell the number of points is

$$\rho(\nu)\, d\nu = 4\pi r^2\, dr \tag{10.34}$$

Then we find for the densities of frequencies ρ_l and ρ_t,

$$\rho_l = 4\pi r^2 \frac{dr}{d\nu} = \frac{4\pi L^3}{c_l^3} \nu_l^2 \tag{10.35a}$$

$$\rho_t = 2 \cdot \frac{4\pi L^3}{c_t^3} \nu_t^2 \tag{10.35b}$$

where the two transverse modes for each point give the factor (2) in Eq. (10.35b). Also the total density of frequencies is the sum of these,

$$\rho = \rho_l + \rho_t = 4\pi L^3 \left(\frac{1}{c_l^3} + \frac{2}{c_t^3}\right) \nu^2 \tag{10.36}$$

If we define a mean velocity of sound c by the expression

$$\frac{3}{c^3} = \left(\frac{1}{c_l^3} + \frac{2}{c_t^3}\right) \tag{10.37}$$

then Eq. (10.36) simplifies to

$$\rho = \frac{12\pi L^3}{c^3} \nu^2 \qquad (10.38)$$

Debye realized that there would be deviations from these equations as the wave lengths of motion approached interatomic distances in the crystal. Nevertheless, he suggested that it might be a good approximation to continue the frequency distribution of Eq. (10.38) to some maximum frequency ν_m selected so that the total number of frequencies would have the correct value $3N_0$ (for one gram atom). This yields

$$3N_0 = \int_0^{\nu_m} \rho(\nu)\, d\nu = \frac{4\pi L^3}{c^3} \nu_m^3 \qquad (10.39)$$

or, solving for ν_m, one has

$$\nu_m = c(3N_0/4\pi V)^{1/3} \qquad (10.40)$$

where we have introduced the volume V of a gram atom in place of the equivalent quantity L^3.

Now all that remains to calculate the heat capacity or some other thermodynamic function is to integrate the appropriate expression for the contribution of a single frequency over the full distribution of frequencies. The contributions for a single harmonic oscillator are obtained by the substitution of k for R in Eq. (9.49). Then the heat capacity of a crystal is

$$C_v = k \int_0^{\nu_m} \rho(\nu) \frac{u^2 e^u}{(e^u - 1)^2}\, d\nu$$

But with $u = h\nu/kT$, this simplifies to

$$
\begin{aligned}
C_v &= k \cdot \frac{12\pi L^3}{c^3} \left(\frac{kT}{h}\right)^3 \int_0^{h\nu_m/kT} \frac{u^4 e^u\, du}{(e^u - 1)^2} \\
&= 9R \left(\frac{kT}{h\nu_m}\right)^3 \int_0^{h\nu_m/kT} \frac{u^4 e^u\, du}{(e^u - 1)^2} \qquad (10.41)
\end{aligned}
$$

The integral in Eq. (10.41) does not yield a simple result, except as the upper limit of integration is small or approaches infinity. However, it has been evaluated numerically and the results tabulated. We give in Appendix 19 the values for the heat capacity and other common thermodynamic functions from this Debye theory. It is common to define a Debye characteristic temperature

$$\theta_D = \frac{h\nu_m}{k} = \frac{hc}{k}\left(\frac{3N_0}{4\pi V}\right)^{1/3} \qquad (10.42)$$

and to regard the variable in the Debye functions as (θ_D/T).

While we shall not derive the relationship between the velocities of sound and other elastic constants, the equations for an isotropic solid in terms of the compressibility β, Poisson's ratio σ, and the density ρ are

$$c_l^2 = \frac{3(1-\sigma)}{\beta\rho(1+\sigma)}, \qquad c_t^2 = \frac{3(1-2\sigma)}{2\beta\rho(1+\sigma)} \qquad (10.43)$$

From these expressions θ_D can be calculated independently of heat capacity measurements.

At low temperatures, the upper limit of integration $h\nu_m/kT$ in Eq. (10.41) becomes large, and one can see that the integrand then approaches zero. Thus for sufficiently small T the integral approaches a definite limit, yielding the well-known T^3 law.

$$C_v = \left(\frac{12\pi^4}{5}\right) R \left(\frac{T}{\theta_D}\right)^3, \qquad T \ll \theta_D \qquad (10.44)$$

The heat capacity in this low temperature region arises from the low-frequency vibrations which are those of long wave length. For wave lengths which are long compared with interatomic distances, the solid will behave as a continuum. Consequently we can depend on the T^3 law as being rigorous at sufficiently low temperatures for large crystals. Of course, if the solid is not isotropic, Eq. (10.43) must be replaced by more complex expressions.

The Debye equation has had great success both as an approximate formula for all temperatures and as an exact equation in the T^3 region. It is very useful as a method of extrapolation to the absolute zero of experimental heat capacity data. Table 10.5 compares the θ_D values from various sources, while Fig. 10.12 shows a typical heat capacity curve. A curve from the Einstein formula is shown dashed in Fig. 10.12 to illustrate the failure of that theory at very low temperatures.

TABLE 10.5

A COMPARISON OF DEBYE θ VALUES

	Al	Cu	Ag
θ_D from general $C_v - T$ curve....................	389	313	213
θ_D from T^3 law at very low T......................	419	338	225
θ_D from elastic data at 290°K.......................	394	342	212
θ_D from estimated elastic const. at 0°K..............	406	351	218

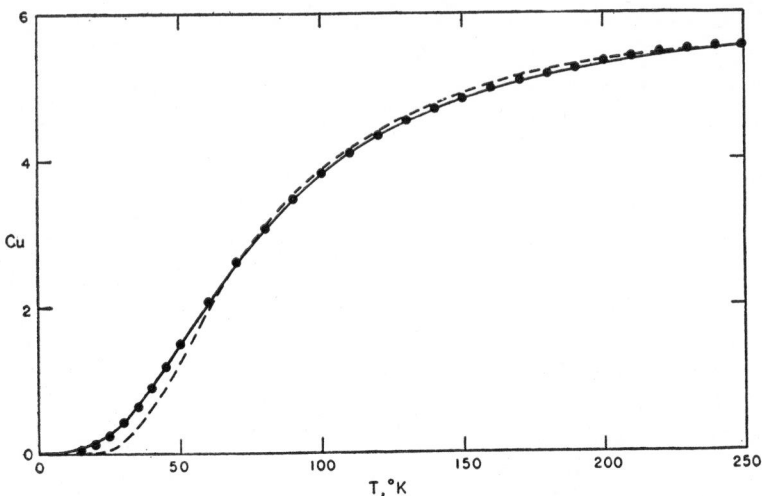

Fig. 10.12. The heat capacity of copper (points) compared with curves from the Debye theory (solid) and the Einstein theory (broken).

From Table 10.5 one notes that the θ_D values drop by several per cent between the T^3 region and the higher temperature region. This emphasizes the approximate nature of the Debye function. We also note that reasonable agreement is obtained with θ_D values from elastic constants.

The zero point vibrational energy of a Debye crystal is readily calculated. It is, of course, $\frac{1}{2}h\nu$ for each normal mode of oscillation. Then

$$E_0 = \frac{1}{2}h\int_0^{\nu_m} \rho(\nu)\nu \, d\nu = \frac{6\pi hL^3}{c^3} \times \frac{\nu_m^4}{4} = \frac{9}{8}R\theta_D \qquad (10.45)$$

for one gram atom of a monatomic crystal.

The Born and von Karman[10] method avoids the errors of the Debye method in the high-frequency region of the spectrum, but it is sufficiently more complex that actual calculations were carried out only in crude approximation until many years after the basic theory was developed. Indeed, in 1912 when Born and von Karman and Debye proposed their theories, few heat capacity data were precise enough to establish the existence of any difference from the Debye equation.

Equations (10.31) yield a similar approximation to normal modes of vibration of a crystal lattice as of a continuous medium, provided one realizes that the displacement has meaning only at an atom site, and provided the forces within the crystal are harmonic. As we have seen before, any reasonable potential function yields harmonic forces for small displacements. Thus within the limitations discussed above[11] we may accept Eqs. (10.31) without change, but we must examine the maximum values of n_x, n_y, n_z because these will be determined from the nature of the lattice. The assumption of a wave length less than the interatomic distance in that direction is meaningless, since the equation for wave motion has actual meaning only at atom sites.

A comparison of Eqs. (10.5) and (10.31) for electronic wave functions and normal vibrational coordinates, respectively, shows the basic similarity in the functions. Consequently it is plausible that the allowable values of k_x, k_y, and k_z should lie within a volume similar to the Brillouin zone described above. Such a result is obtained from a detailed analysis.

The actual frequencies of vibration for a given k_x, k_y, k_z can be calculated only after a definite system of interatomic forces has been assumed. For each set of k's a third-order secular equation is obtained, corresponding to the one longitudinal and two transverse vibrations of the continuum.

It is a long and cumbersome task to calculate these frequencies numerically as a function of the k's for any given force system and

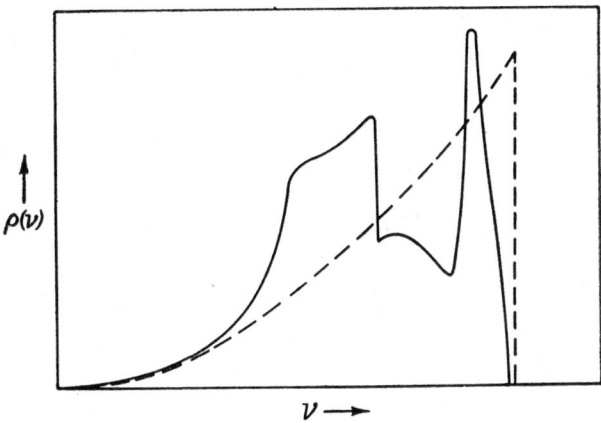

Fig. 10.13. The distribution of normal modes of vibration of a face-centered cubic lattice (solid line) compared with the distribution assumed in the Debye theory (broken line).

lattice. The most interesting example is that of the face-centered cubic lattice which was worked out by Leighton.[12] He assumed a harmonic force system with one constant for the twelve nearest neighbor interactions and a second constant for the six next nearest neighbors of a given atom.

Figure 10.13 shows the frequency distribution found by Leighton as compared with the Debye distribution for the same macroscopic elastic constants. One can see how the Debye theory gives a fair average of the higher frequency region besides being exactly correct in the limit at low frequencies.

Because the heat capacity itself varies so rapidly with temperature, it is convenient to make precise comparisons in terms of Debye θ_D values. At any given temperature the θ_D value can be found that yields either the observed heat capacity or that calculated on the lattice theory. These θ_D values can then be compared, as a function of temperature. Also if the Debye theory held, θ_D would be a constant; hence the variation in θ_D is a measure of the deviation from the Debye theory. Figure 10.14 shows these values for copper. The variation of about 9% in θ_D in the region 4–30°K corresponds to approximately 25% variation in the heat capacity from the Debye theory.

All the theories give $3R$ for the limiting heat capacity at high temperatures. Consequently the use of θ_D as a means of comparison in this region is impractical.

Born[13] also discussed the heat capacity of solid compounds. It is found that the vibrations divide themselves roughly into an *acoustic branch* and one or more *optical branches*. The acoustic branch consists of the vibrations in which all the different atoms of a single molecule move essentially together. Thus its characteristics are just those of the vibrations of an atomic lattice such as we have been discussing so far. These vibrations have a broad distribution, and are determined essentially by the velocity of sound in the medium—hence the name, acoustical branch.

The internal vibrations of molecules in a crystal may interact somewhat between molecules. Consequently the vibration frequencies which would all have precisely the same value in separated gas molecules spread out into a band in a solid. However, in molecular

[12] Leighton, R. B., *Revs. Modern Phys.*, **20**, 165 (1948).
[13] Born, M., *Dynamik der Kristallgitter*, Leipzig: B. G. Teubner, 1915.

crystals these bands are usually very narrow and yield sharp Raman or infrared spectra. Hence they are called optical branches.

In ionic lattices such as NaCl there are, of course, no single definite molecules. Nevertheless it is found that the same general pattern arises. There is an acoustic branch in which the adjacent Na^+ and Cl^- ions move together, and an optical branch in which adjacent Na^+ and Cl^- ions move in opposite directions. While the optical branch in this sort of crystal is broader than it is in molecular crystal, it is still fairly narrow. The optical branch is responsible for the infrared spectrum of an ionic crystal.

Crystals such as $CaCO_3$ constitute examples including the features of both the molecular and ionic types. The internal vibrations of the $CO_3^=$ ion will interact only slightly and give a sharp spectrum like that of a molecular lattice. Then there are also broader bands of frequencies arising from rotational oscillations of $CO_3^=$ ions and vibrations in which Ca^{++} and $CO_3^=$ ions move opposed to one another.

It has proven quite satisfactory to approximate the heat capacity

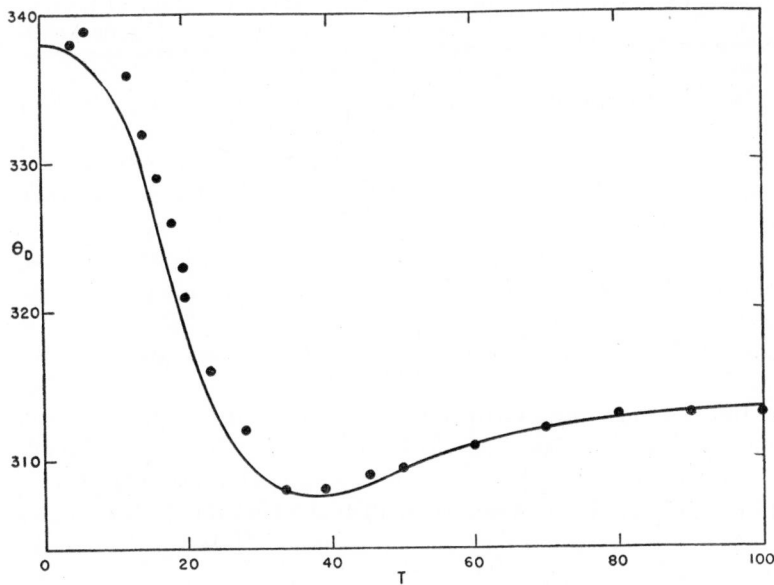

Fig. 10.14. Values of θ_D from the heat capacity measurements on copper (points) and the curve calculated from the lattice theory by Leighton.

contribution of each optical branch of a solid compound by an Einstein or harmonic oscillator function. This takes a single, average frequency for all the vibrations in the narrow band. These functions are tabulated in Appendix 13. Then one may take a Debye function for the frequencies of the acoustical branch. Thus we have for the molal heat capacity of a solid compound

$$C_v = 3Rf_D \left(\frac{\theta_D}{T}\right) + \sum_{j=1}^{3s-3} Rf_{ho}(h\nu_j/kT) \tag{10.46}$$

where f_D is the Debye function tabulated in Appendix 19, f_{ho} is the harmonic oscillator function tabulated in Appendix 13, and s is the number of atoms in the molecular unit. The frequencies ν_j are those of the various optical branches, and may be observable spectroscopically.

In molecular crystals the torsional motions of whole molecules have frequencies closely related to those of the translational motions of the acoustical branch. Also there is usually no measure of the frequency of these torsional motions except from the heat capacity itself. Therefore it has been necessary to lump the $3N_0$ torsional motions with the $3N_0$ translational vibrations to constitute a low-frequency branch of $6N_0$ frequencies. One approximates this heat capacity by doubling the contribution of the usual Debye function. The θ_D is obtained by fitting the experimental heat capacity values.

Lord, Ahlberg, and Andrews[14] applied this method to solid benzene with considerable success. With twelve atoms in the molecule there will be 30 optical branches in addition to the six torsional and translational motions placed in an expanded acoustical branch. The frequencies of these 30 intramolecular vibrations are almost the same in the solid as in the gas or liquid. Consequently frequencies from the spectrum of the gas can be used if the solid spectrum is unavailable.

10h. Superconductivity. Of all the physical phenomena occurring outside the atomic nucleus in simple substances, superconductivity has proven most resistant to quantum theoretical treatment. It was only after the discovery in 1950 of the isotope effect[15] on the transition temperature that the correct type of theoretical approach was clearly indicated.

[14] Lord, R. C., Jr., Ahlberg, J. E., and Andrews, D. H., *J. Chem. Phys.*, **5,** 649 (1937).
[15] Maxwell, E., *Phys. Rev.*, **78,** 477 (1950); **79,** 173 (1950); Reynolds, C. A., Serin, B., Wright, W. H., and Nesbitt, L. B., *Phys. Rev.*, **78,** 487, 813 (1950).

While the resistance of any pure metal approaches a very small value at the absolute zero, in superconductors there is a sudden drop to zero resistance at a definite, finite transition temperature. By contrast, in other metals the resistance decreases gradually and continuously. In the superconductors, mercury, tin, and thallium, it has been shown that the transition temperature varies as $M^{-1/2}$ in samples of varying isotopic composition.

This isotope effect shows that the superconductive transition is associated in some way with lattice vibrations, because a purely electronic phenomenon would not depend on the nuclear masses. The most probable interaction between electrons and lattice vibrations at these extremely low temperatures would be one depending on the zero point vibrational motion. From the equations of Section 2i one can readily verify that the mean square amplitude of a harmonic oscillator in its lowest state is proportional to α^{-1} or to $M^{-1/2}$. Consequently, we may expect that some interaction energy of electronic motion with lattice vibrations will be proportional to this mean square amplitude, and that the transition ending superconductivity will occur when kT becomes comparable with this energy. This interaction could depend on the fluctuations of density of positive ions, which would cause corresponding fluctuations in the potential energy of the metallic electrons.

The precise electromagnetic properties of a superconductor also indicate necessary characteristics of a satisfactory theory. In particular the Meissner effect requires a superconductor to be an ideal diamagnetic as well as a perfect conductor. This means that there is no magnetic field within a superconductor, although a sufficiently strong field destroys the superconductivity even at the absolute zero.

London[16] has developed the macroscopic electromagnetic equations for a superconductor, and has inferred the probable consequences for a microscopic theory. It would take us too far afield to discuss this in detail. London's conclusion is that there must be some fixed and definite distribution of the conduction electrons in momentum space.

Fröhlich and Bardeen[17] have indicated possible detailed theories, but their validity is still under discussion. Their principal requirement for superconductivity is a large interaction between lattice vibrations and electronic motion. But it is just this same type of

[16] London, F., *Superfluids*, Vol. 1, New York: John Wiley & Sons, Inc., 1950
[17] For a review see Bardeen, J., *Revs. Modern Phys.*, **23**, 261 (1951).

interaction which yields ordinary electric resistance at higher temperatures. Thus one has the peculiar conclusion that poor electric conductors are more likely to be superconductors.

The experimental evidence supports this conclusion. Such good electric conductors at higher temperatures as copper, silver, gold, and the alkali metals do not become superconducting, while metals such as mercury, lead, and titanium do. Bardeen has suggested the quantitative criterion for superconductivity, $n_0\rho > 10^6$, where ρ is the room temperature resistivity in e.s.u., and n_0 is the usual number of metallic electrons per cc. This criterion works in most cases but has several exceptions.

10i. Lattice energies for nonmetals. Where the electrons are all localized in individual atoms or ions or in particular bonds between atoms, it is possible to calculate the lattice energy without a quantum mechanical treatment of the entire crystal. Of course, a quantum treatment of the entire crystal will give the correct result, as Löwdin[18] has shown for an ionic crystal. Nevertheless, it is usually simpler to solve the quantum mechanics for the electronic motion of an appropriate component of the crystal and then sum the proper terms over the entire crystal.

In the case of a diamond crystal one assumes the same basic C—C single electron pair bond as in the paraffin hydrocarbons. Since there are four bonds about each carbon atom and each bond connects two atoms, the lattice energy is twice the bond energy. This result is included in Table 8.4. Similar calculations can be made for other purely covalent crystals.

In molecular crystals the forces between molecules are presumably the same as in the gas phase, i.e., van der Waals forces. Such forces are discussed in Sections 8u, 8v, and 8w. The simplest example of this type of crystal is a rare gas such as argon. Except for helium, where the zero point energy and other quantum effects predominate, the rare gases crystallize in the face-centered cubic structure which is also called the cubic closest packed structure. As the latter term indicates, it is one of several structures which are examples of the closest possible packing of rigid spheres. The pattern is that of twelve atoms around a given central atom, i.e., a coordination number of twelve.

[18] Löwdin, P. O., Dissertation, Upsala (1948); *Ark. Mat. Astrom. Fysik*, **35A**, No. 9 (1947).

The potential for interaction of each pair of argon atoms in the crystal will include the London force attraction and the ever-present repulsive forces. From Eqs. (8.56) and (8.57) the simplest intermolecular potential for rare gas atoms is

$$\epsilon(r) = -ar^{-6} + br^{-n} \tag{10.47}$$

The value of a may be estimated from Eq. (8.56), but only rough agreement can be expected in view of the approximations in the theory of London forces.

It is true, of course, that the inverse sixth power term is just the leading term of an inverse power series. Some authors include also an inverse eighth power term which corresponds to dipole-quadrupole interactions. Actually this refinement is of doubtful value as long as simple additivity of pair interactions is being assumed in a crystal. The corrections to the additivity relationship are very likely greater than the effect of additional attractive terms after the inverse sixth power term.

It is convenient to rearrange the potential expression of Eq. (10.47) in terms of the interatomic distance at the potential minimum r_0, and the depth of that minimum, ϵ_0. These quantities are illustrated in Fig. 10.15. The expression now becomes

$$\epsilon(r) = \epsilon_0 \left[\frac{6}{n-6} \left(\frac{r_0}{r} \right)^n - \frac{n}{n-6} \left(\frac{r_0}{r} \right)^6 \right] \tag{10.48}$$

The three constants in Eq. (10.48), ϵ_0, r_0, and n, can be evaluated from the heat of sublimation of the crystal at $0°K$, the interatomic distance, and one other appropriate datum. The most convenient procedure is to assume a few reasonable values of n and evaluate ϵ_0 and r_0 from the crystal data in each case. Then various other properties can be calculated and the best n value selected.

Following this procedure, the potential energy of the entire crystal is

$$V = \frac{N_0 \epsilon_0}{2} \left(\frac{6 r_0^n}{n-6} \sum_i r_i^{-n} - \frac{n r_0^6}{n-6} \sum_i r_i^{-6} \right) \tag{10.49}$$

where the sums are to cover all of the other atoms around a given central atom. The factor N_0 allows each atom to be counted as a central atom, but this includes each interaction twice—hence the division by 2. For any given lattice, one of the sums will bear a

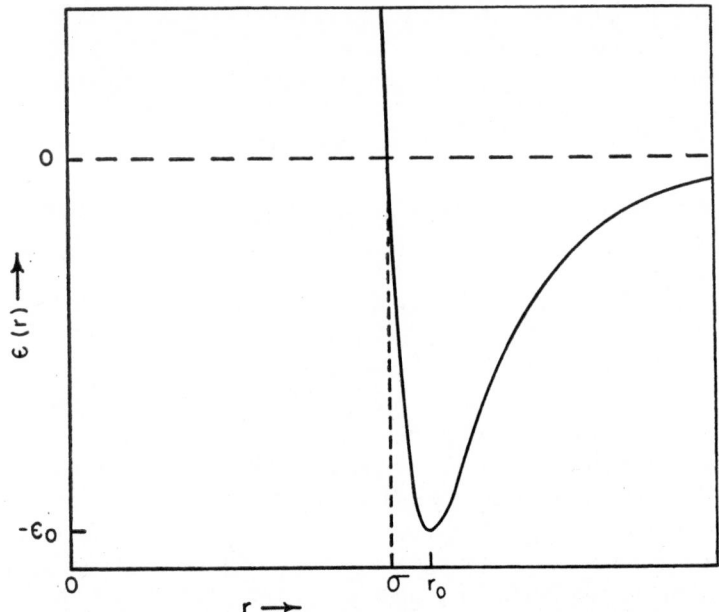

Fig. 10.15. A potential curve for the interaction of pairs of rare gas atoms such as argon. The potential minimum at r_0 and the collision diameter σ are shown.

fixed ratio to a single term. This ratio may be defined as

$$C_n = R^n \sum_i r_i^{-n} \tag{10.50}$$

where R is the nearest neighbor distance, and has been calculated[19] for the face-centered cubic lattice for various n values as follows.

n:	6	8	10	12	14
C_n:	14.4539	12.8019	12.3112	12.1318	12.0590

Now we may rewrite the total potential energy,

$$V = \frac{N_0 \epsilon_0}{2} \left[\frac{6 C_n}{n-6} \left(\frac{r_0}{R} \right)^n - \frac{n C_6}{n-6} \left(\frac{r_0}{R} \right)^6 \right] \tag{10.51}$$

At the equilibrium distance the potential energy must be a minimum; consequently

[19] Jones, J. E. and Ingham, A. E., *Proc. Roy. Soc.* (London), **A107,** 636 (1925).

$$\frac{dV}{dR} = \frac{N_0\epsilon_0}{2r_0}\left(\frac{-6n}{n-6}\right)\left[C_n\left(\frac{r_0}{R}\right)^{n+1} - C_6\left(\frac{r_0}{R}\right)^7\right] = 0$$

$$(r_0/R) = (C_6/C_n)^{1/n-6} \tag{10.52}$$

Substitution of this value of (r_0/R) in Eq. (10.51) yields, after simplification.

$$V = -\frac{N_0\epsilon_0 C_6^{n/n-6}}{2C_n^{6/n-6}} \tag{10.53}$$

Equations (10.52) and (10.53) now permit the evaluation of both ϵ_0 and r_0 in the example proposed above, where V and R are known experimentally and n is assumed.

In the calculation just completed we have neglected the zero point vibrational energy. The zero point energy is readily calculated from the experimental θ_D by Eq. (10.45), but the effect of zero point energy on the apparent equilibrium distance in the crystal represents a more complex problem. Corner[20] has given a formula for estimating this correction,

$$R_0 - R_e = 4(MT_c)^{-1/2} \text{ A} \tag{10.54}$$

where M is the molecular weight, T_c is the critical temperature, and R_0 and R_e are the interatomic distances with and without zero point energy, respectively.

Applying this method to neon and argon yields the results shown in Table 10.6. Corner[20] used the second virial coefficient of the gas as the principal additional data on which to base the selection of n. For neon the best value was 12.0, while for argon the result was 12.3. However, even in the case of argon the integral value 12 is almost

TABLE 10.6
LATTICE ENERGY CALCULATIONS FOR NEON AND ARGON

	Neon	Argon
R_0, observed	3.20	3.81 A
$(R_0 - R_e)$, Eq. (10.54)	0.13	0.05 A
R_e	3.07	3.76 A
ΔH_0, observed	449	1852 cal./mole
E_0, Eq. (10.45)	140	178 cal./mole
$-V = \Delta H_0 + E_0$	589	2030 cal./mole
r_0 for $n = 12$	3.16	3.87 A
ϵ_0 for $n = 12$	4.8×10^{-15}	1.65×10^{-14} erg
(ϵ_0/k)	34.5°	119°K

[20] Corner, J., *Trans. Faraday Soc.*, **44**, 914 (1948).

as satisfactory and much more convenient. The second virial coefficient calculations are discussed in the next chapter.

In addition to these calculations using the inverse power repulsive potential, Corner and others have made calculations using the exponential repulsive term of the type indicated in Eq. (8.59). Corner found slightly better agreement with the exponential term, but it is questionable whether the additional mathematical difficulty in its use would be justified in most applications.

For ionic crystals the principal energy term is just the electrostatic potential energy of the array of positive and negative charges. However, as compared with the inverse sixth or higher power potential terms, this potential falls off so slowly with distance that its summation over an entire crystal is a problem of some consequence. It has been solved by Madalung and others[21] for each of the simple ionic lattices. The resulting energy per ion pair is

$$\Phi = - \frac{A z^2 e^2}{R} \tag{10.55}$$

where A is a numerical constant known as the Madelung constant, and R is some characteristic distance in the lattice, usually the shortest anion-cation distance. Ordinarily A is given for the case where the most numerous ion has a single charge (A^+B^-, $A^{++}B_2^-$, etc.). If in the actual crystal this ion has a multiple charge, this value must be introduced as z in equation (10.55). The Madelung constants for a few simple crystal lattices are given in Table 10.7.

TABLE 10.7

MADELUNG CONSTANTS FOR A FEW LATTICES

Structure	A
Sodium chloride, A^+B^-	1.747558
Cesium chloride, A^+B^-	1.762670
Sphalerite, A^+B^-	1.63806
Wurtzite, A^+B^-	1.641
Fluorite, $A^{++}B_2^-$	5.03878
Rutile, $A^{++}B_2^-$	4.816
β-Quartz, $A^{++}B_2^-$	4.4394

In addition to the electrostatic forces between the ions, the same forces that were present in a molecular lattice must be present in an

[21] For a summary of this and other work on ionic crystals, see Sherman, J., *Chem. Rev.*, **11**, 93 (1932).

ionic crystal.   In this case the London attractive forces are of secondary importance, although they are not necessarily negligible. · In any case the repulsive forces must balance the sum of all attractive forces at the equilibrium distance.

Since the relative sizes of the positive and negative ions vary from one crystal to another, the relative importance of the repulsive forces between ions in close contact varies similarly.   The more complete treatments of Born, Mayer, Helmholz, and Huggins[22] consider all possible terms and are as a result cumbersome.   Let us take as a simplified example the crystal KF where the ions are of about the same size.   Thus we will be justified in including only the repulsive term for the six nearest neighbor K-F interactions.

For the inverse sixth power London force terms in the sodium chloride type lattice, the quantities analogous to C_n in Eq. (10.50) have been computed.   The results are for unlike ion interactions, 6.595, and for like ion interactions, 1.807, both values being based on the nearest neighbor distance in the lattice.   One can readily see that the first constant should be a little over six because there are six nearest neighbors in the sodium chloride structure, and the more distant neighbors make only a small contribution.   For the like ion interactions the shortest distance is greater by $\sqrt{2}$, but there are 12 equivalent neighbors.   This gives a contribution of 1.5 toward the second constant.

The lattice potential energy for KF per ion pair is then

$$\Phi = -\frac{Ae^2}{R} - \frac{C}{R^6} + 6be^{-R/\rho} \qquad (10.56)$$

$$C = 6.595c_{+-} + 1.807(c_{++} + c_{--})/2$$

where the constants for the various London force terms have been combined as indicated and the exponential form of the repulsive potential is used.

The Madelung constant was given in Table 10.7. Eq. (8.56) is used for the London force terms together with the data given below.

Polarizability in cc.

$$\alpha = 0.88 \times 10^{-24} \text{ for } K^+; \quad \alpha = 1.05 \times 10^{-24} \text{ for } F^-$$

[22] Born, M. and Mayer, J. E., Z. Physik, **75**, 1 (1932); Mayer, J. E. and Helmholz, L., Z. Physik, **75**, 19 (1932); Huggins, M. L., J. Chem. Phys., **5**, 143 (1937).

Ionization energy in ergs.

$$I = 50 \times 10^{-12} \text{ for } K^+; \quad I = 6.5 \times 10^{-12} \text{ for } F^-$$

Constants for Eq. (10.56) in erg cm.

$$c_{+-} = 8.0 \times 10^{-60}; \quad c_{++} = 29 \times 10^{-60}; \quad c_{--} = 5.4 \times 10^{-60}$$

$$C = 84 \times 10^{-60}$$

At the equilibrium distance the derivative of the potential energy is zero.

$$\frac{d\Phi}{dR} = \frac{Ae^2}{R^2} + \frac{6C}{R^7} - \frac{6b}{\rho} e^{-R/\rho} = 0$$

$$\frac{6b}{\rho} e^{-R/\rho} = \frac{Ae^2}{R^2} + \frac{6C}{R^7} \tag{10.57}$$

This gives one equation for the determination of b and ρ. Another may be obtained from the second derivative of Φ, which can be related to the compressibility β, and the molal volume. The molal volume of a sodium chloride type lattice is $2N_0R^3$. Then we find

$$\frac{d^2\Phi}{dR^2} = -\frac{2Ae^2}{R^3} - \frac{42C}{R^8} + \frac{6b}{\rho^2} e^{-R/\rho} = \frac{18R}{\beta} \tag{10.58}$$

The values for KF at $0°K$ are $R = 2.67$ A and $\beta = 3.2 \times 10^{-12}$ cm.²/dyne.

Equations (10.57) and (10.58) may now be solved simultaneously for ρ and b, yielding $\rho = 0.30 \times 10^{-8}$ cm. and $b = 2.26 \times 10^{-9}$ erg. We then obtain the results in Table 10.8 for the lattice energy of KF.

TABLE 10.8

LATTICE ENERGY OF KF

	erg $\times 10^{12}$	kcal./mole
Electrostatic, $-Ae^2/R$	-15.09	-217.2
London forces, $-C/R^6$	-0.23	-3.3
Repulsive, $6be^{-R/\rho}$	$+1.85$	$+26.6$
Zero pt. vibr., $9R\theta_D/8$	$+0.15$	$+2.1$
Total lattice energy	-13.32	-191.8

10j. Molecular rotation and disorder in solids. We conclude our consideration of the crystalline state with a discussion of two related phenomena which cause very similar anomalies in the heat capacity curve of a solid. Several types of heat capacity curve are indicated in Fig. 10.16. Such anomalies have been attributed either to the rather sudden beginning of molecular rotation in the crystal, for substances such as N_2 or CH_4, or the introduction of some sort of positional disorder, such as the shift from an ordered to a random arrangement of Cu and Zn atoms in a copper-zinc alloy. Another sort of order is that of the magnetic moment vectors in a ferromagnetic material. At the Curie transition, which is usually of the gradual type illustrated at C in Fig. 10.16, these magnetic moments become disordered, i.e., randomly oriented. The substance is then paramagnetic.

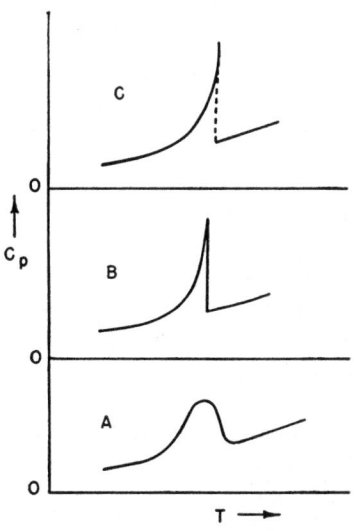

Let us take the problem of molecular rotation first. It is similar to the problem of restricted rotation within molecules, which was considered in Section 9h, but usually involves two or possibly three axes of rotation. Also the potential barrier restricting the rotation is not a constant but depends on the neighboring molecules and the density of packing. As neighboring molecules begin to rotate, the crystal expands and the potential barrier to rotation decreases for the central molecule. This increased ease of rotation, when the neighboring molecules begin to rotate, is called the *cooperative* effect, and leads the transition to complete itself rather quickly once it is well begun.

Fig. 10.16. Three types of heat capacity curves associated with gradual transitions such as the initiation of molecular rotation in solids or the introduction of disorder of atomic location or magnetic moment orientation. In transitions of type C the heat capacity curve may have an essentially infinite slope at the peak or it may have a definitely finite slope.

For the two-dimensional free rotation of a linear molecule we have the rotational states considered in Sections 3e and 9b. The energy levels are

$$E = \frac{h^2 J (J + 1)}{8 \pi^2 I}$$

and there is a $2J + 1$ degeneracy of the Jth level. Levels with J even are symmetric to exchange of the nuclei (or to turning the molecule end for end), while levels of odd J are antisymmetric.

If the rotation is highly restricted, so that it comprises essentially small amplitude oscillations, one can construct the energy level pattern from the levels of a harmonic oscillator. Let us assume that the two ends of the molecule are either identical, as in H_2, N_2, or CO_2, or extremely similar, as in HD, CO, or N_2O. Then as a first approximation, at least, we can assume the potential energy to depend only on the orientation of the axis of the molecule without regard for the two ends of the molecule. If we assume the equilibrium orientation of the linear molecule is along the z axis, then in polar coordinates V is an even function of $(\theta - \pi/2)$, with potential minima at $\theta = 0$ and $\theta = \pi$. Also, if the crystal is reasonably symmetrical, oscillations in the x and y directions will be restricted by about the same potential barrier; consequently we may regard V to be independent of ϕ in the polar system of coordinates.

This restricted rotation is essentially a double minimum vibration, such as was discussed in Section 9i. There will be two wave functions corresponding to the lowest harmonic oscillator level, one for each orientation of the molecule. We may designate these $u_0(\theta)$ and $u_0(\pi - \theta)$. The question now arises whether these are appropriate wave functions by themselves, since they imply information as to the end for end orientation of the molecule. If the ends of the molecule are distinguishable, and if one has experimental information (in principle, at least) as to the orientation, one or the other of these functions would be appropriate. However, if the molecule is strictly symmetrical, or if the orientation is unknown, because the molecule can turn (possibly by penetration of the potential barrier) within the time of observation, one must replace these wave functions by their symmetrical and antisymmetrical linear combinations.

$$u_S = [u_0(\theta) + u_0(\pi - \theta)]/\sqrt{2}$$
$$u_A = [u_0(\theta) - u_0(\pi - \theta)]/\sqrt{2}$$

The reasoning here is exactly analogous to that introduced in Section 5a in connection with a two-electron atom and the Pauli exclusion principle. Now the states represented by u_S and u_A are not necessarily of exactly the same energy, but if the potential barrier is high, they will be at least approximately degenerate.

The excited oscillational states will have additional degeneracy because of the equivalence of the x and y directions of oscillation. Such a vibration is discussed in some detail in Appendix 14. It is sufficient here to note that the degeneracy of the nth level is $n + 1$. Furthermore, there will be the end for end degeneracy in addition, so that there will be $2n + 2$ states in all for the nth energy level.

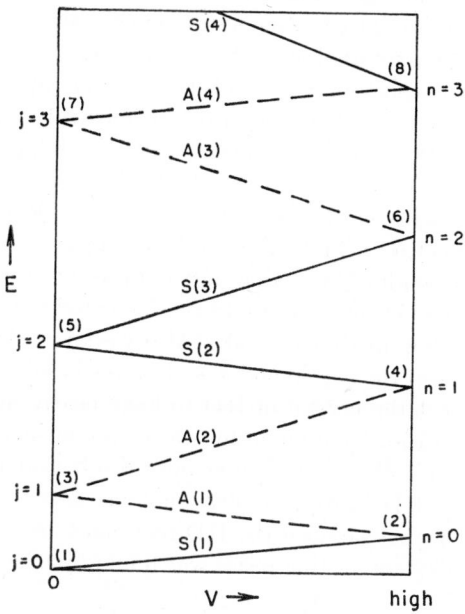

Fig. 10.17. A correlation diagram for the energy levels of torsional oscillation or rotation for a diatomic molecule in a crystal. Free rotation is shown on the left and a high potential barrier on the right. The energy scale is only qualitative.

Let us now draw a qualitative correlation diagram for energy levels with intermediate heights of potential barrier. We will use the symmetric and antisymmetric wave functions throughout. The result is shown in Fig. 10.17.

As was explained in Section 9b, there will be *ortho* and *para* species for homonuclear diatomic molecules (and for such other linear molecules as CO_2 and C_2H_2). Thus only the symmetric or antisymmetric states will have significance for any single molecule. We note that for intermediate or high potential barriers, there is a single lowest

S state and a single lowest A state. Thus such molecular crystals should conform to the third law of thermodynamics. The only exception is H_2 (or D_2) where the potential barrier is so low at $10°K$ that the *ortho* molecules are randomly distributed over the three rotational states for $J = 1$. Presumably there is some potential affecting rotation even in hydrogen, so that this triplet of states is slightly split. Thus at some lower temperature the *ortho* hydrogen should settle down into the single lower component of the $J = 1$ triplet (which is associated with the $n = 0$ vibrational state).

Molecules with nonequivalent ends have both S and A states available. If their ends differ only by isotopic substitution, such as HD, Cl^{35}—Cl^{37}, etc., they would be expected to be randomly oriented in the solid. If the potential barrier is high, the molecules will be randomly distributed over the two states, with $n = 0$. This will contribute the expected ($R \ln 2$) term to the entropy, even at low temperatures, corresponding to random mixing of the isotopes.

However, the evidence from hydrogen indicated that the potential barrier is very low in that crystal. Also we know that the energy difference between the $J = 0$ and $J = 1$ states is substantial. Thus one would expect the crystal of HD to have nearly all molecules in the *single* lowest rotational quantum state, even at several degrees K. Consequently, one obtains the anomalous result that the entropy of mixing of H and D isotopes is lost—not because they are located regularly, but rather because the HD molecules are still rotating in the crystal. This interesting result was found by Clusius, Popp, and Frank.[23]

Where the two ends of the molecule are composed of different atoms, such as HCl or ICl, the potential energy is usually so different for the two orientations of the molecule that it is lined up regularly in the crystal. However, in CO and N_2O (N—N—O), which have practically no dipole moment, there is evidence for random orientation. These substances have too much entropy, by almost $R \ln 2$, at $15°K$. This would correspond to random end for end orientation of the molecules or to random distribution over the two $n = 0$ states, which is equivalent.

The rotation of nonlinear molecules in crystals is naturally a more complex problem. Also the number of equivalent orientations depends on the particular molecule. If the potential barrier is high,

23 Clusius, K., Popp, L., and Frank, A., *Physica*, 4, 1105 (1937).

the results are entirely equivalent to those for the diatomic molecule, i.e., single lowest states for strictly symmetrical molecules but random mixing of isotopes. The nonlinear molecule most likely to show the peculiarities of hydrogen is methane. However, it undergoes a gradual transition at 20.4°K, and the third law entropy calculation indicates that the methane molecules settle down into single quantum states. Also measurements[23] on CH_3D yield the result that the entropy of mixing of the hydrogen isotopes remains at low temperatures. While the limiting state approached at low temperatures in methane is clearly that of a high potential barrier, there are some peculiar properties associated with the beginning of molecular rotation in the 15 to 30°K range. Both CD_4 and CH_3D show two transitions in this range, while CH_4 shows only one. This difference must arise in some way from either the differences in moment of inertia or more probably the different *ortho-para* like species associated with the different nuclear spin orientations. Heavier tetrahedral molecules such as $C(CH_3)_4$ show only a single transition.

If the potential barrier to rotation were a constant, the heat capacity would follow the curve defined in Appendix 18 or a similar curve for two or three axes of rotation. Such curves show such a slight bump as vibration goes over to rotation that no anomaly would be noticed in most cases. It is difficult to define quantitatively the behavior when the effective barrier for one molecule depends on what its neighbors are doing. However, one can see that such cooperative behavior will tend to sharpen up the transition. A mild degree of interaction leads to a heat capacity curve showing a clear anomaly, but one which is continuous throughout. An example is $C_2H_4Cl_2$ which gives a curve such as A in Fig. 10.16. If the cooperative interaction is larger, the heat capacity climbs to a very high value. Indeed it is experimentally difficult to distinguish between isothermal heat absorption (analogous to heat absorption in fusion) and an extremely high specific heat. Also it is usually impossible to decide whether the heat capacity drops discontinuously from a peak value or has an extremely steep but continuous drop on the high-temperature side. These are illustrated by curves B and C in Fig. 10.16.

As a simple illustration of order-disorder phenomena, let us mention β-brass, which in the ideal case is 50% Cu-Zn alloy. This is a body-centered cubic lattice. In the ordered state the copper atoms constitute a simple cubic lattice, and there is a zinc atom at the center of each unit cube of copper atoms. This places the zinc atoms in a simple cubic lattice also, so it is arbitrary which element one places at the cube corners and which at the body center. In this ordered state each atom has eight nearest neighbors, all of the opposite type.

In the completely disordered state there is an equal chance that any lattice site is occupied by a copper atom or a zinc atom. Thus on the average four of the nearest neighbors of a copper atom are other copper atoms and four are zinc atoms.

One can readily see why such a disorder phenomenon should be cooperative. If a given unit cube of eight atoms are all of one kind, say copper, it makes a great deal of difference whether one places a zinc or a copper atom at the center. In the one case there are eight Cu-Zn nearest neighbor bond energy terms, while in the other case there are eight Cu-Cu terms. Since the structure becomes ordered at low temperatures we assume the former contribute the greater bond energy. However, if a unit cube has four copper and four zinc atoms at its corners, it makes no difference whether a copper or a zinc atom is placed in the center. In either case there are equal numbers of like and unlike bond terms. Strictly, the Zn-Zn interactions will be different from the Cu-Cu terms, but since all atoms must be placed somewhere in the lattice, this difference does not enter in the final energy.

Except for this complication of the cooperative aspect, we see that order-disorder transitions in solids are quite simple. However, an adequate accounting of the cooperative interactions involves the consideration of a large number of atoms at once and as a result leads to very difficult mathematics. Hence we shall merely state that order-disorder transitions are usually of the type of curves B and C in Fig. 10.16.

GENERAL REFERENCES

London, F., *Superfluids, I. Macroscopic Theory of Superconductivity*, New York: John Wiley & Sons, Inc., 1950.

Seitz, F., *The Modern Theory of Solids*, New York: McGraw-Hill Book Company, Inc., 1940.

Chapter 11

IMPERFECT GASES AND LIQUIDS

The properties of the individual molecules constitute sufficient data for the calculation of the properties of a perfect gas, but molecular interactions must also be considered in calculations for solids, liquids, or imperfect gases. While in dilute gases the interactions may be confined to pairs and triplets, in solids, liquids, and very dense gases these intermolecular forces effectively link all the molecules into a single assemblage or giant molecule.

The regularity of a crystal lattice provides a basis for simplifications in the theory of solids, but this regularity is not present for liquids. As a consequence, statistical calculations from molecular properties have not proved very fruitful for liquids. Most of our present working knowledge arises from experimentally measured properties, interrelated in accordance with thermodynamics. These limitations on the effective use of basic theory will indicate the reason that the present chapter is a series of special topics rather than a comprehensive treatment.

11a. Equilibria among clusters of molecules. In Chapter 7 the elements of statistical mechanics were developed for systems of many molecules which were assumed to interact only at trivial moments of collision. We could now consider the fundamental statistics of a system where the particles interact substantially all the time. However, a simpler approach, which assumes chemical equilibria between single molecules and clusters or polymers of two or more molecules, will serve our purpose as well. Molecules of NO_2 have an attractive interaction which tends to hold them together into molecules of N_2O_4. The attractive force between argon atoms is weaker but its effect is similar at a correspondingly lower temperature in that it holds pairs of argon atoms together. There is a major difference in that a molecule of NO_2 can form a chemical bond with just one other molecule of NO_2, while an atom of argon has a London force attraction for as many other argon atoms as may be nearby. Consequently we will expect larger clusters of argon atoms to form under appropriate conditions.

One of the principal methods of investigating the NO_2—N_2O_4 equilibrium is by measurement of the P-V-T behavior of the gas. The N_2O_4 molecules are assumed to contribute to the total pressure as single molecules. We shall make the same assumption—that a cluster acts as a single molecule in contributing to the pressure. This leaves it undetermined just how close together a pair of molecules must be if they are to be regarded as having formed a cluster.

If we let A represent any molecule, the reactions to be considered are

$$2A = A_2; \quad 3A = A_3; \quad \ldots ; \quad nA = A_n$$

with the usual equilibrium constants (in concentrations)

$$K_2 = \frac{C_2}{C_1^2}, \quad \ldots , \quad K_n = \frac{C_n}{C_1^n} \tag{11.1}$$

The number of clusters of size n is

$$N_n = C_n V \tag{11.2}$$

Now the total number of molecules remains fixed at N_0. By combining the equations above, we find

$$C_n = K_n C_1^n, \qquad K_1 = 1$$
$$N_0 = \sum_n n N_n = V \sum_n n C_n$$
$$= V \sum_n n K_n C_1^n \tag{11.3}$$

We shall make no detailed assumptions about the K's. However, the effect of adding one molecule to a large cluster must eventually cease to depend on the size of the cluster. In other words, for the reaction,

$$A_{n-1} + A = A_n$$

the equilibrium constant will be the same for all large clusters. Thus

$$C_n / C_{n-1} C_1 = K_0 = K_n / K_{n-1} \tag{11.4}$$

where K_0 is independent of n. Consequently, we may write for large n

$$K_n = \kappa K_0^n \qquad (11.5)$$

where κ is like an equilibrium constant, a function only of temperature. If Eqs. (11.4) and (11.5) first begin to hold for $n = n'$, then

$$\kappa = K_{n'} K_0^{-n'}$$

Let us now write Eq. (11.3) in expanded form.

$$N_0 = V[C_1 + 2K_2 C_1^2 + 3K_3 C_1^3 + \ldots + n\kappa (K_0 C_1)^n + \ldots] \qquad (11.6)$$

This is a polynomial equation which, in principle, can be solved for C_1. At low pressures, V is large, C_1 is small, and the successive terms become rapidly smaller. Then

$$C_1 = \frac{N_0}{V}\left(1 - \frac{2K_2 N_0}{V} - \ldots\right) \qquad (11.7)$$

As the volume is decreased, C_1 increases, and the second and a few additional terms gradually become more important, but nothing drastic happens unless the product $(K_0 C_1)$ approaches unity. At this point the series fails to converge, and effectively all the molecules go into a single giant cluster, the liquid phase.

At the point of condensation C_1 is $(1/K_0)$, and this value can be used to calculate the concentration of small clusters of two and three, etc., in the saturated vapor. Likewise the vapor pressure equation, together with these first few K's are sufficient to give an expression for K_0.

Above the critical temperature it is evident that the product $(K_0 C_1)$ never reaches unity, since no condensation occurs. This can arise if the terms for intermediate sized clusters become larger than the initial term, C_1. Then, as the volume is decreased, C_1 needs increase only very slowly and may approach $(1/K_0)$ only at infinite density.

Before carrying this general analysis further, let us consider the relatively dilute gas where only the very small clusters exist. The pressure of a perfect gas was derived in Section 7e. We may assume our present mixture of clusters to be a perfect gas mixture, where the pressure is the sum of the partial pressures which each component would exert if it were alone. However, if two single molecules come close enough, we must consider them to be a cluster of two. Hence we must reduce the total volume by some amount b, corresponding to this distance at which we assume cluster formation to have taken place.

$$P_n = N_n kT/(V - b) = C_n kTV/(V - b)$$

$$P = \sum P_n = \frac{kTV}{V - b} \sum K_n C_1^n \tag{11.8}$$

Now we have not defined b exactly nor have we indicated whether it will depend on the distribution of molecules in clusters. However, if we assume that b is constant and much smaller than V, the equation for the pressure can be rearranged to

$$P = kT \left(1 + \frac{b}{V} + \ldots\right)(C_1 + K_2 C_1^2 + \ldots)$$

$$= N_0 kT \left[\frac{1}{V} + (b - N_0 K_2)\left(\frac{1}{V}\right)^2 + \ldots\right] \tag{11.9}$$

where the expression for C_1 in Eq. (11.7) was used.

An equation expressing the pressure as an inverse power series in the volume was first obtained from considerations of the virial theorem (Section 8e), and is commonly written

$$P = A \left(\frac{1}{V} + \frac{B}{V^2} + \frac{C}{V^3} + \ldots\right) \tag{11.10}$$

The constants $A, B, C, \ldots$ are known as *virial coefficients*. A is the first virial coefficient, B the second virial coefficient.

It is also possible to express the volume as a power series in the pressure. One obtains

$$V = \frac{A}{P} + B + C'P + D'P^2 + \ldots \tag{11.10'}$$

where A and B are the same quantities as in Eq. (11.10), while C', D', etc. are different as is indicated by the prime marks.

From our theory of clusters, we obtained an equation for the pressure as a series of inverse powers of the volume. It is evident that the first virial coefficient concerns just the perfect gas law. It is the *second virial coefficient*, which gives the initial departure from the perfect gas behavior, to which we turn our attention.

11b. The second virial coefficient. A comparison of Eqs. (11.9) and (11.10) gives the expression

$$B = b - N_0 K_2 \tag{11.11}$$

for the second virial coefficient, which shows clearly that it is to be associated with interactions of pairs of molecules. For complex molecules the calculation of B from molecular data would be very difficult.

It is feasible to calculate B for molecules where the interaction energy depends only on the distance between the molecule centers. This is strictly true only for atoms, with the rare gases, He, Ne, A, etc., the principal examples of interest. For molecules the interaction energy will depend on the angular orientation of each molecule, but in CH_4 and a few other cases this effect is so small as to be almost negligible.

Although we shall consider the quantum mechanical calculation of the second virial coefficient in the next section, the classical calculation is adequate for most substances and will be given first.

The equilibrium constant K_2 can be related to the partition functions for single and double molecules. This can be done either by considering the free energy change or by direct statistical calculation. The former is a straightforward thermodynamic calculation from Eq. (7.60). To illustrate the statistical method, we choose the same energy zero for both single and double molecules.

Then following the procedure of Section 7b, one obtains for single molecules

$$n_i = g_i e^{-\alpha} e^{-\epsilon_i/kT} \tag{11.12a}$$

and for double molecules (designated by primed quantities)

$$n_i' = g_j' e^{-2\alpha} e^{-\epsilon'_i/kT} \tag{11.12b}$$

where the factor 2 in the exponent involving α arises from the fact that the constant total of molecules as single units must count the double molecules twice.

Now the total number of single and double molecules are computed

$$N_1 = e^{-\alpha} \sum g_i e^{-\epsilon_i/kT} = e^{-\alpha} Q_1$$
$$N_2 = e^{-2\alpha} \sum g_j' e^{-\epsilon'_i/kT} = e^{-2\alpha} Q_2$$

and the equilibrium constant in concentrations becomes

$$K_2 = \frac{N_2 V}{N_1^2} = \frac{V Q_2}{Q_1^2} \tag{11.13}$$

Next we use the classical or integrated expression for the partition function for translation from Section 7o,

$$Q_t = V(2\pi mkT/h^2)^{3/2} \qquad (11.14)$$

which then yields

$$K_2 = \frac{V^2(2\pi \cdot 2mkT/h^2)^{3/2}}{V^2(2\pi mkT/h^2)^3} Q_i = \left(\frac{h^2}{\pi mkT}\right)^{3/2} Q_i \qquad (11.15)$$

where Q_i is the internal partition function for the double molecules, and m is the mass of a single molecule.

The classical, or phase integral, form of Q_i from Eq. (7.58) is

$$Q_i = \frac{1}{\sigma h^3} \int \cdots \int e^{-\epsilon(q,p)/kT} \, dq_1 \ldots dq_3 \, dp_1 \ldots dp_3$$

The integrations over the momenta are easiest in Cartesian coordinates, in which

$$\epsilon(q,p) = \frac{1}{2\mu} (p_x^2 + p_y^2 + p_z^2) + \epsilon(r) \qquad (11.16)$$

where $\epsilon(r)$ is the potential energy and μ is the reduced mass for internal motion.

From Eq. (3.1) we have

$$\mu = m_1 m_2/(m_1 + m_2) = m/2$$

Then each momentum integral is

$$\int_{-\infty}^{+\infty} e^{-p^2/mkT} \, dp = (\pi mkT)^{1/2}$$

and

$$Q_i = \frac{1}{2}\left(\frac{\pi mkT}{h^2}\right)^{3/2} \int \cdots \int e^{-\epsilon(r)/kT} \, dq_1 \ldots dq_3 \qquad (11.17)$$

where σ, the symmetry number, has been given the value 2. It is now best to shift to spherical coordinates, since the potential energy is then a function only of r. The integrations with respect to angles yield the usual value, 4π, and

$$Q_i = 2\pi \left(\frac{\pi mkT}{h^2}\right)^{3/2} \int_0^{r_0} e^{-\epsilon(r)/kT} r^2 \, dr \qquad (11.18)$$

Combining this result with Eqs. (11.15) and (11.11), one finds

$$K_2 = 2\pi \int_0^{r_0} e^{-\epsilon(r)/kT} r^2 \, dr \qquad (11.19)$$

$$B = b - N_0 2\pi \int_0^{r_0} e^{-\epsilon(r)/kT} r^2 \, dr \qquad (11.19')$$

However, b represented the volume excluded from a single molecule, because such a molecule was assumed to have formed a cluster if it approached another molecule too closely. If r_0 is this distance at which the molecules are assumed to have formed a cluster, one might think that b should have the value $\frac{4}{3}\pi r_0^3 N_0$. This value is actually twice the correct value because it would associate the entire excluded volume with each of the two interacting single molecules rather than dividing it between them. Then we find

$$B = N_0 \left(\frac{2}{3}\pi r_0^3 - 2\pi \int_0^{r_0} e^{-\epsilon(r)/kT} r^2 \, dr \right)$$

$$= N_0 2\pi \int_0^{r_0} (1 - e^{-\epsilon(r)/kT}) r^2 \, dr \qquad (11.20)$$

In the equations prior to this one, it appeared as if r_0 would have to be specified exactly; yet with a potential falling off continuously there would be no precise distance at which it could be neglected. However, in Eq. (11.20) we see that as ϵ approaches zero, the quantity in parentheses also approaches zero. Expanding the exponential for $\epsilon \ll kT$ yields

$$(1 - e^{-\epsilon/kT}) = \frac{\epsilon}{kT} + \cdots$$

Thus if ϵ is proportional to r^{-6}, as was found in Section 8v, the integral will converge rapidly with increasing r, and one may shift the upper limit to infinity.

Our final classical expression for the second virial coefficient is then

$$B = 2\pi N_0 \int_0^\infty (1 - e^{-\epsilon(r)/kT}) r^2 \, dr \qquad (11.21)$$

To proceed further we need some expression for the potential energy. In Section 10i the corresponding potential expression for molecular interaction was discussed, and Eq. (10.48) was applied to the calculation of the lattice energy of a molecular crystal. Taking this same expression with the repulsive exponent 12, one obtains

$$\epsilon(r) = \epsilon_0 \left[\left(\frac{r_0}{r} \right)^{12} - 2 \left(\frac{r_0}{r} \right)^6 \right] \qquad (11.22)$$

Some authors prefer to use as a characteristic distance the collision diameter σ, at which the potential is zero (see Fig. 10.15), instead of the distance to the potential minimum, r_0. Then

$$\epsilon(r) = 4\epsilon_0 \left[\left(\frac{\sigma}{r} \right)^{12} - \left(\frac{\sigma}{r} \right)^6 \right] \qquad (11.22')$$

and
$$r_0 = 2^{1/6}\sigma \qquad (11.23)$$

The actual integration of Eq. (11.21) with these inverse power formulas is rather troublesome and will not be given here. Lennard-Jones[1] has published the resulting equations, and several authors[2] have given some calculated values.   Table 11.1 presents the resulting values of the second virial coefficient for the potential (11.22) in terms of B/β, where

$$\beta = 2^{1/2}\pi N_0 r_0^3/3 = 2\pi N_0 \sigma^3/3 \qquad (11.24)$$

TABLE 11.1

THE SECOND VIRIAL COEFFICIENT FOR THE POTENTIAL
$$\epsilon(r) = \epsilon_0[(r_0/r)^{12} - 2(r_0/r)^6]$$

ϵ_0/kT	B/β	ϵ_0/kT	B/β	ϵ_0/kT	B/β
0.0025	0.32	0.20	0.243	0.7	−1.323
0.005	0.39	0.25	0.115	0.8	−1.704
0.01	0.46	0.30	−0.021	0.9	−2.108
0.02	0.51	0.35	−0.164	1.0	−2.538
0.03	0.525	0.40	−0.313	1.1	−3.00
0.04	0.53	0.45	−0.467	1.2	−3.48
0.06	0.515	0.50	−0.628	1.3	−4.00
0.08	0.49	0.55	−0.793	1.4	−4.55
0.10	0.46	0.60	−0.964	1.5	−5.13
0.15	0.36	0.65	−1.141	1.6	−5.75
0.20	0.243	0.70	−1.323		

Values for (ϵ_0/kT) from 0.2 to 1.0 are from Ref. (2b); others are interpolated from Ref. (2a).

Of course, if the second virial coefficient is known as a function of temperature, then by using also the heat capacity of the ideal gas one can calculate the Joule-Thomson coefficient or the heat capacity of the real gas in the range of moderate pressures.

Also we note from Eq. (11.22) that the coefficient of the r^{-6} term is $2\epsilon_0 r_0^6$, which is then the constant C in the London force formula.

$$W_{AB} = V = -Cr^{-6} \qquad (11.25)$$

In Section 8v the approximate theoretical expression for the constant C was found to be

$$C = 3\alpha^2 I/4 \qquad (11.26)$$

[1] Lennard-Jones, J. E., Proc. Roy. Soc., **A106**, 463 (1924).

[2] (a) Hirshfelder, J. O., McClure, F. T., and Weeks, I. F., J. Chem. Phys., **10**, 201 (1942); (b) Stockmayer, W. H. and Beattie, J. A., J. Chem. Phys., **10**, 476 (1942).

where α is the polarizability and I is the ionization potential. These various quantities[3] are given in Table 11.2 for a few simple substances where the assumption of spherical symmetry is plausible. The formula of this section, Table 11.1, fits the observed second virial coefficient satisfactorily in these cases except for helium and hydrogen, where the quantum effects are important. Also it will be noted that the constants for neon and argon are substantially the same as those found from the lattice energies in Table 10.6.

TABLE 11.2

INTERMOLECULAR FORCES BETWEEN GAS MOLECULES

SUBST.	ϵ_0/k (°K)	$r_0 \times 10^8$ (cm.)	$\alpha \times 10^{24}$ (cm.^{3})	I (e.v.)	$2\epsilon_0 r_0^6 \times 10^{48}$ (e.v. cm.^{6})	$\frac{3}{4}\alpha^2 I \times 10^{48}$ (e.v. cm.^{6})	RATIO
He	10.2*	2.88*	9.20	24.5	1.0	0.74	1.3
Ne	35.7	3.08	0.39	21.5	5.2	2.5	2.1
A	119	3.84	1.63	15.4	66	31	2.1
Kr	172	4.03	2.46	13.3	128	61	2.1
Xe	224	4.56	4.00	11.5	350	140	2.1
H$_2$	37.0*	3.28*	0.81	16.4	7.9	8.0	1.0
N$_2$	95.6	4.14	1.74	17	83.5	39	2.1
CH$_4$	145	4.27	2.58	14.5	153	73	2.1

* These values come from the quantum mechanics of the second virial coefficient; see next section.

It is evident from Table 11.2 that the approximate theoretical formula (11.26) gives about the correct result for helium and probably by accident an accurate result for hydrogen, but that it gives much too small a constant for the larger atoms or molecules. The last column gives the ratio of the constant observed from the virial coefficient and that calculated. The constancy of the ratio 2.1 for all but hydrogen and helium suggests the use of this number as an empirical correction factor for Eq. (11.26).

It must be realized that many of the figures in Table 11.2 are very approximate and depend on the particular assumptions made. For example, the use of a value of the repulsive exponent other than 12 would affect the values of ϵ_0/k and r_0 appreciably. Also the theory of London forces yields the r^{-6} term as merely the first of a series and it has been found that the r^{-8} term is not entirely negligible. How-

[3] Taylor, H. S. and Glasstone, S., *A Treatise on Physical Chemistry*, 3d ed., Vol. 2, New York: D. Van Nostrand Company, Inc., 1951, p. 328; London, F., *Trans. Faraday Soc.*, **33**, 8 (1937).

ever, these refinements do not change the general picture. The r^{-6} potential for attractive London forces and their general dependence on polarizability and ionization potential are well verified by the second virial coefficients of these real gases.

11c. Quantum effects in the second virial coefficients. In gases of very light molecules, deviations from the classical treatment of the last section arise because of quantum effects. Two essentially independent types of deviations are possible. First there is the divergence from Boltzmann statistics by the Bose-Einstein or Fermi-Dirac statistics, whichever is applicable. Second, the phase integral expression, Eq. (11.21), assumes a large number of individual quantum states for the vibration of a double molecule, while in some cases there may be only one or two quantum states with energies below the dissociation limit for the molecule pair.

It is found that substantial quantum deviations are found only for the two gases helium and hydrogen. Since the full mathematical analysis is tedious and complicated, it will not be given in detail.

Deviations from Boltzmann statistics arise when the fractional occupancy of the lowest quantum state for translational motion approaches unity. In the Fermi-Dirac case, this value of unity is a maximum. However, in the Bose-Einstein case, which applies to He and H_2, an unlimited number of molecules can occupy the lowest quantum state. Nevertheless, the distribution differs from the Boltzmann formula when this probable occupancy approaches one. From Chapter 7 we find that if we assign zero energy to this lowest state, then this probable occupancy is (see Eq. 7.34)

$$e^{-\alpha} = \frac{n}{V}\left(\frac{h^2}{2\pi mkT}\right)^{3/2} \tag{11.27}$$

In Section 7h, we verified that even for H_2, $e^{-\alpha}$ is small. The value is 0.0714 at the boiling point. However, for helium at its boiling point, 4.3°K, we find for $e^{-\alpha}$ the value 1.17, which indicates clearly that deviations from Boltzmann statistics will arise.

The contribution of this Bose-Einstein degeneracy to the second virial coefficient has been shown to be[4]

$$B_{B.E.} = -\frac{N_0}{16}\left(\frac{h^2}{\pi mkT}\right)^{3/2} \tag{11.28}$$

[4] Uhlenbeck, G. E. and Gropper, L., *Phys. Rev.*, **41**, 79 (1932).

which has the value -7.8 cc. at the boiling point of helium, $4.3°K$. Since the molal volume of an ideal gas is only 350 cc. at this temperature, it can be seen that this contribution to gas imperfection is appreciable.

The Schrödinger equation is not easily solved for the inverse power potential function used in the last section. It has been integrated by numerical methods in a few specific cases. However, we can estimate the number of discrete states below the dissociation energy by a method which is essentially equivalent to the old quantum theory of Bohr and Sommerfeld. In our most elementary considerations, we had the wave length for a particle, $\lambda = h/p$, or the wave number, $k = p/h$. But we saw that for a bound particle the lowest quantum state has essentially a half wave in its wave function, the next state has a full wave, etc. Thus the number of discrete states up to a given energy can be estimated from the number of half waves in the available path at that energy,

$$n = 2\int k \, dq = \frac{2}{h} \int p \, dq \qquad (11.29)$$

where the integration is to cover the coordinate q from one limit of its classical motion to the other. (The old quantum theory equation was equivalent in that the integral covered a full cycle and the factor 2 was omitted.)

This estimate of the number of discrete quantum states can be made as well from the area in phase space, together with the unit of area h assigned to each quantum state. In our case, the accessible region of phase space would be symmetrical, with equal sections involving positive momenta and negative momenta. The integral in Eq. (11.29) covers only the half area with positive momenta; hence the factor of 2 is needed to yield the correct total area, and the identical final answer is obtained by this method.

Applying Eq. (11.29) to our problem of the molecule pair, we take the dissociation energy as our total energy level. Then the kinetic energy is just the negative of the potential energy at any point, and we have

$$p = [-2\mu\epsilon(r)]^{1/2} = 2(\mu\epsilon_0)^{1/2} x^{-3} (1 - \tfrac{1}{2} x^{-6})^{1/2}$$

where x is r/r_0 and μ is the appropriate reduced mass, $\tfrac{1}{2}m$. A good approximation is obtained by expanding the final square root, which yields for the integral

$$n = \frac{2r_0}{h} \int_{2^{-1/6}}^{\infty} 2(\mu\epsilon_0)^{1/2}(x^{-3} - \tfrac{1}{4}x^{-9} - \tfrac{1}{32}x^{-15} - \ldots) \, dx$$

$$= 2.16(\mu\epsilon_0)^{1/2} r_0/h \tag{11.30}$$

The lower limit of the integral is, of course, the collision diameter, where the potential energy is zero. For convenience in calculation, Eq. (11.30) may be rearranged to involve the full mass of a single molecule in atomic weight units M; the distance, r_0 in A; and the ratio ϵ_0/k in °K. We then have

$$n = 0.0350 r_0 M^{1/2}(\epsilon_0/k)^{1/2} \tag{11.31}$$

Taking the values from Table 11.2 we find for helium, $n = 0.65$. Actually, numerical integrations of the Schrödinger equation for various potential functions have given either one discrete level or none depending on the exact potential assumed. For hydrogen one finds $n = 1.0$.

If the number of quantum states is small, as in the case of He and H_2, the second virial coefficient must be calculated by quantum mechanical methods even if the deviations from Boltzmann statistics are small. Actually the quantum effects arise also for energies above the dissociation energy if the wave length is of the order of the linear dimensions of the molecules. However, one can readily see that this will be the case if there are only one or two discrete states below the dissociation limit.

The second virial coefficients for hydrogen and helium have been calculated[5] by methods considering all these phenomena. With the potential constants in Table 11.2, good agreement with the experimental data is obtained.

11d. The critical region—fluctuations. The critical region represents an interesting phenomenon both experimentally and theoretically. Quantum mechanics enters only for the few substances where it was important for the second virial coefficient, and will not be considered further. We will focus our attention on the dissociating cluster theory of Section 10a. The reaction of addition of one molecule to a cluster

$$A_{n-1} + A = A_n$$

was considered, and it was assumed that eventually a size would be reached after which the equilibrium constant would become inde-

[5] De Boer, J. and Michels, A., *Physica*, **5**, 945 (1938); **6**, 409 (1939); also Gropper, L., *Phys. Rev.*, **55**, 1095 (1939).

pendent of n.   Now let us consider the significance of surface tension in this connection.   The effect of surface tension is to make droplets or clusters of intermediate size less stable than either a large body of liquid or a gas of single molecules and very small clusters.

However, above the critical temperature we found that intermediate sized clusters must be more stable than the large body of liquid.   This is in agreement with the fact that the surface tension vanished at the critical point.   Also it is reasonable to expect that this trend of relative stability of different sized clusters with temperature should continue steadily past the critical point.   These concepts are illustrated in Fig. 11.1.

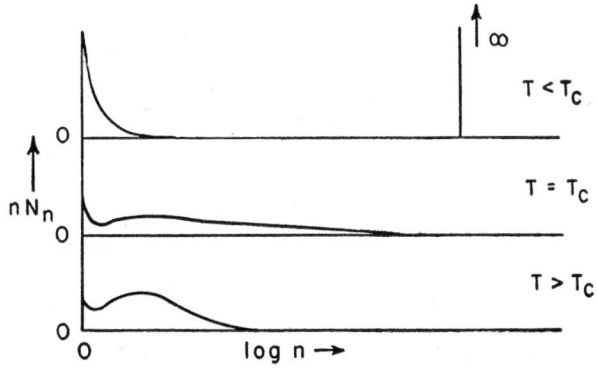

Fig. 11.1.   The total number of single molecules in clusters of size n, nN_n, for various temperatures.   These curves are strictly qualitative.

Mathematically, one could introduce the surface tension into the formulas for the cluster equilibrium constants.   It would take the form of a parameter raised to the power $n^{2/3}$.   However, all experimental quantities can be treated as well by regular thermodynamic methods.

In Section 7b we mentioned the subject of fluctuations from the most probable distribution, and pointed out that if the probable number of a given species in a distribution is n_i, the probable fluctuation in that quantity is $\sqrt{n_i}$.   It was correctly stated that ordinarily the most probable distribution has properties indistinguishable from all other distributions of appreciable probability.   The only exception for simple systems arises in the critical region.   Here, as we see in

Fig. 11.1, there are substantial numbers of molecules in a distribution of very large clusters. However, the mere fact that the clusters are very large means that the number of such clusters is small and therefore subject to significant fluctuation. This manifests itself experimentally in opalescence or light scattering.

It must be realized that our theory of clusters is a crude one. The precise definition of the distance at which a molecule is regarded as entering a cluster is troublesome in the general theory, although it caused no real difficulty in the calculation of the second virial coefficient. More complex theories have been presented but none has as yet been adequate to yield reliable predictions concerning the critical region. Thus it seems best for our purposes to use the simple theory which illustrates the qualitative phenomena.

11e. The theory of corresponding states. The idea of corresponding states arose from the equation of state proposed by van der Waals, and was suggested by him in 1873. The theory of corresponding states is of course more general than the equation and holds that in terms of reduced temperatures $(T/T_{crit.})$, volumes, etc., the behavior of all substances should be the same. At that time the available knowledge of the properties of individual molecules was insufficient for a really satisfactory theoretical derivation in these terms, or to indicate what substances should follow this theory. With our present knowledge of van der Waals forces we are in a position to show that strict corresponding states behavior will arise when certain conditions are met. These conditions are given in the next paragraphs.

First, classical statistical mechanics must be a good approximation (i.e., quantum effects must be negligible) so far as the translational motion of whole molecules is concerned. As an example, this assumption for a harmonically vibrating solid gives the Dulong and Petit value of the heat capacity. Since most solids attain this condition before melting, this assumption should be acceptable for their liquids. However, this will exclude hydrogen and helium from consideration and make doubtful a few other cases, including neon.

Second, it will be assumed that the molecules are spherically symmetrical, either actually or by virtue of rapid and free rotation.

Third, the nature of any intramolecular vibrations will be assumed to be the same whether the molecules are in the liquid or gas states.

The experimental spectra indicate that this is a good approximation for nonpolar molecules.

Fourth, the potential energy of an assemblage of molecules will be taken as a function only of the various intermolecular distances. This condition eliminates polar substances because the intermolecular force then depends also on the relative angular orientation of the molecules. Also it eliminates any substances tending to form a limited number of valence bonds. However, this assumption is consistent with the London attractive forces and the repulsive forces i.e., with nonpolar van der Waals forces.

Fifth, the potential energy for a pair of molecules must be given by an expression of the type,

$$\epsilon = \epsilon_0 \phi(r/r_0) \tag{11.32}$$

where ϵ_0 and r_0 are constants specific to each substance but ϕ is a universal function. This sort of potential is shown in Fig. 10.15. We have considered such potential functions in earlier sections, and the results expressed in Eqs. (10.48) and (11.22) conform to the type assumed here. The success of these equations indicates that the rare gases should conform to this condition (although He and Ne fail on condition 1). In all probability the important consideration is whether the attractive potential is inverse sixth power in terms of the distance between molecular centers. While this is probably a good approximation for molecules such as CH_4 and N_2, it is not so likely to hold for CCl_4 or $C(CH_3)_4$. In the latter molecules the principal attractive forces center in the chlorine atoms or the methyl groups, which are not at the center of the whole molecule. So long as the repulsive branch of the potential curve is steep, minor variations in shape are of secondary importance.

For the theory of corresponding states, we do not need to define the exact nature of the function ϕ; the only requirement is its universality.

Before giving a mathematical derivation, a simple explanation is helpful. One can consider two different systems obeying these five conditions and containing the same number of molecules. If they are enclosed in boxes whose respective linear dimensions are proportional to the r_0 values (and volumes proportional to r_0^3), spatial correspondence is achieved. Since energies of motion are proportional to the temperature, we must make the temperatures proportional to the ϵ_0 values if we are to keep kinetic and potential energies on a corresponding basis. Thus if our two systems are placed in volumes bearing the same ratio to their r_0^3 values and at temperatures having the same ratio to their ϵ_0 values, the two systems should exhibit corresponding behavior.

Turning to the mathematical derivation, we note that we have not developed a rigorous general theory of statistical mechanics for condensed systems. However, if we regard an entire volume of liquid as a single molecule, we can see that the thermodynamic properties should be related to a partition function in which the energy levels are those of the entire system. With classical behavior one may use the integral form, Eq. (7.58),

$$Q = \frac{1}{\sigma h^{3n}} \int \cdots \int e^{-E(q,p)/kT} \, dq_1 \ldots dq_{3n} \, dp_1 \ldots dp_{3n} \qquad (11.33)$$

but with $\epsilon(q,p)$ changed to $E(q,p)$ to indicate that we are now taking the energy of a whole mole of material. We shall be interested in relative properties of the liquid or the imperfect gas where the base value can be the corresponding property of the ideal gas. Thus if the internal motions within molecules are the same in all states, they can be ignored. Also, if the molecules are effectively spherical, there are no angular coordinates which need enter the equation. The coordinates in Eq. (11.33) are thus reduced to the translational coordinates of the centers of the molecules.

In proceeding with the analysis, one notes that it is the complex potential energy which makes it impossible to factor out a contribution from each molecule. The kinetic energy can, of course, be written

$$K.E. = \frac{1}{2m} \sum_{i=1}^{n} (p_{x_i}^2 + p_{y_i}^2 + p_{z_i}^2) \qquad (11.34)$$

The integration over each momentum involves a factor

$$\int_{-\infty}^{+\infty} e^{-p^2/2mkT} \, dp = (2\pi mkT)^{1/2}$$

Hence the integration over all the momenta yields

$$Q = \frac{(2\pi mkT)^{3n/2}}{\sigma h^{3n}} \int_0^{X_0} \cdots \int_0^{Z_0} e^{-\Phi/kT} \, dx_1 \ldots dz_n \qquad (11.35)$$

where the limits of integration correspond to the dimensions of a
rectangular box containing the gas.

The potential energy is given by

$$\Phi = \frac{\epsilon_0}{2} \sum_{i=1}^{n} \sum_{j=1}^{n} {}' \phi\,(r_{ij}/r_0) \tag{11.36}$$

in which r_{ij} is the distance between molecules i and j, the prime indicates the omission of terms with i and j equal, and the division by 2
arises because the sums include each term twice. The integral for Q
is thus extremely complex, and no attempt will be made to evaluate
it. What we can do is rewrite it as follows.

$$Q = \left[\frac{2\pi m k \epsilon_0}{h^2}\left(\frac{T}{\epsilon_0}\right)\right]^{3n/2} \frac{r_0^{3n}}{\sigma} \int_0^{(X_0/r_0)} \cdots \int_0^{(Z_0/r_0)}$$
$$\times\, e^{-(\epsilon_0/T)(1/2k)\Sigma\Sigma\phi(r_{ij}/r_0)}\, d\left(\frac{x_1}{r_0}\right) \ldots d\left(\frac{z_n}{r_0}\right) \tag{11.37}$$

The multiple integral now depends only on the value of the ratio
(ϵ_0/T) and upon the upper limits of integration, the latter amounting
to the ratio of the volume $(X_0 Y_0 Z_0)$ to r_0^3, since the shape of the
container should not be significant. We may then write

$$Q = \frac{(2\pi m k \epsilon_0 r_0^2)^{3n/2}}{\sigma h^{3n}}\, F(V/r_0^3,\ T/\epsilon_0) \tag{11.38}$$

where the factor (T/ϵ_0) before the integral in Eq. (11.37) is included
in F along with the integral.

As we said above, we are concerned with properties relative to those
of the ideal gas. Since this derivation would also hold for the ideal
gas state, we are interested in ratios of Q for some other state to Q
for the ideal gas. In these ratios the factor before F will cancel.
Thus we have proven that these relative properties will depend only
upon the reduced variables, V/r_0^3 and T/ϵ_0. Since the critical point
is certainly a corresponding point, we may substitute the variables
V/V_c and T/T_c if we prefer.

Actually a corresponding states behavior could arise under some
other circumstances than those given above, although the detailed
behavior would be different. The most obvious possibility would be
a different shape of potential function ϕ. Thus if a second group of
molecules followed all these conditions but with a different ϕ, corresponding states behavior would arise among the second group of

substances, but it would be different for each ϕ. Similarly, if a group of nonspherical molecules had the same shape factor, i.e., the same proportional dependence of potential on angular orientation, corresponding states behavior would follow for this group within itself. Thus the five conditions above are not all necessary, but are sufficient to define the simplest circumstances where corresponding states will apply.

Once the molecular criteria for conformance to corresponding states were recognized, it was found[6] that the substances which might be expected to follow the theory did follow it. The heavier rare gases A, Kr, Xe, and CH_4 follow the theory very accurately, while N_2 comes fairly close. The vapor pressures of all except N_2 follow very closely the equation

$$\log \pi = \frac{4.29810}{\theta} - 12.55400 \log \theta + 0.63158 + 3.66652\theta \qquad (11.39)$$

where $\pi = P/P_c$ and $\theta = T/T_c$. These vapor pressures and some other properties are listed in Table 11.3.

TABLE 11.3

THE CORRESPONDING STATES BEHAVIOR OF A PERFECT LIQUID

$\theta = T/T_c$	$-\log \theta$	$-\log \pi$ ($\pi = P/P_c$)	ΔS_{vap}	$C_{s(tr)}$	ϕ_{liq} ($\phi = V/V_c$)	$\frac{V_{gas}}{V_{liq}} = \frac{d_{liq}}{d_{gas}}$
0.56	0.25181	1.8291	18.68	10.7	0.376	335
0.57	0.24413	1.7542	18.20	10.7	0.379	290
0.58	0.23657	1.6825	17.72	10.7	0.382	250
0.59	0.22915	1.6134	17.25	10.7	0.385	215
0.60	0.22185	1.5469	16.82	10.7	0.387	187
0.62	0.20761	1.4213	15.95		0.392	142
0.64	0.19382	1.3044	15.18		0.398	110
0.66	0.18046	1.1953	14.42		0.404	84
0.68	0.16749	1.0933	13.73		0.410	67
0.70	0.15490	0.9974	13.11		0.417	53
0.75	0.12494	0.7808			0.437	31
0.80	0.09691	0.5912			0.461	19
0.85	0.07058	0.4224			0.490	12
0.90	0.04576	0.2697			0.531	7.3
0.95	0.02228	0.1298			0.596	4.2
1.00	0.00000	0.0000			1.000	1.0

$P_c V_c/T_c = 23.9$ cc. atm. per deg. Kelvin.

[6] Pitzer, K. S., *J. Chem. Phys.*, **7**, 583 (1939); Guggenheim, E. A., *J. Chem. Phys.*, **13**, 253 (1945)

The term *perfect liquid* has been proposed for this simplest type of substance which is subject to corresponding states theory, because its behavior represents a useful basis from which to measure the deviations of other substances. Deviations can arise from polarity, nonspherical shape, or other variations in the intermolecular potential, or from quantum mechanical effects. The criterion for quantum mechanical deviation will involve Planck's constant, and may be taken from the factor ahead of F in Eq. (11.38). The essential ratio is $(m\epsilon_0)^{1/2}r_0/h$, which is equivalent to $(MT_c)^{1/2}V_c^{1/3}/h$. The value of $(MT_c)^{1/2}V_c^{1/3}$ for argon is 328, for nitrogen 266, and for methane 256. This is about the lower limit for classical behavior. The substances with lower values are neon, 104, hydrogen 32.6, and helium 17.6. These show deviations increasing in the order indicated. The behavior of helium as a quantum liquid will be considered further below.

11f. Liquids. While the theory of corresponding states gives a theoretical framework within which liquid behavior must lie, it does not calculate the actual properties of any liquid. On the other hand, the rigorous statistical calculations of liquid properties clearly demand some more powerful mathematical methods than the direct integration of Eq. (11.35) with a potential such as the inverse sixth and twelfth power expression of Eq. (11.22). Born and Green,[7] and Kirkwood[8] have proposed such methods, but the mathematical approximations required to obtain numerical results have been so severe as to make the results[8] of less than full quantitative significance.

The principal characteristics of the structure of a liquid are given by the radial distribution function, which can be obtained from the x-ray diffraction pattern, as well as from the theories mentioned above. We let $\rho(r)$ be the density of atoms at a distance r from a given atom. Then the number of atoms in a spherical shell of radius r and thickness dr will be $4\pi r^2\rho(r)\,dr$. We let the average density of atoms in the liquid be ρ_0.

It has been shown[9] that ρ is related to the x-ray scattering intensity I by the equations

$$s = 4\pi \sin \theta/\lambda \tag{11.40}$$

[7] Born, M. and Green, H. S., *A General Kinetic Theory of Liquids*, London: Cambridge University Press, 1949.

[8] Kirkwood, J. G., *J. Chem. Phys.*, **7**, 919 (1939); Kirkwood, J. G., Lewinson, V. A., and Alder, B. J., *J. Chem. Phys.*, **20**, 929 (1952).

[9] See Gingrich, N. S., *Revs. Modern Phys.*, **15**, 90 (1943) for a general review on x-ray diffraction by liquids.

where θ is half of the scattering angle and λ is the wave length;

$$i(s) = (I/N_0 f^2) - 1 \qquad (11.41)$$

where f is the atomic scattering factor for x-rays, and I is the coherent scattered intensity in electron units; and finally

$$4\pi r^2 \rho(r) = 4\pi r^2 \rho_0 + (2r/\pi)\int_0^\infty si(s) \sin rs \, ds \qquad (11.42)$$

The accuracy of the final result is limited both by the experimental accuracy and by the fact that the experimental measurements cannot cover the full range of s from zero to infinity.

Frequently it is more convenient to use the relative radial distribution function, $W = \rho/\rho_0$. The results for argon[9] are shown at the top of Fig. 11.2. The curve is for the liquid at 91.8°K and 1.8 atm. For comparison, the interatomic potential curve for argon is given in Fig. 11.2. It is clear that the first shell of neighboring atoms comes at just the distance of the minimum of the potential curve.

The intermolecular potential can be combined with the distribution function to calculate the potential energy of a liquid if the potential depends only upon the distances between pairs of atoms. The number of molecules at a distance r from a central molecule is

$$n(r) \, dr = 4\pi \rho(r) r^2 \, dr = 4\pi \frac{N_0}{V} W r^2 \, dr \qquad (11.43)$$

since the mean density of atoms is (N_0/V). However, any of the N_0 molecules can be a central molecule; hence the total number of pairs at a distance r from one another is $(2\pi N_0^2/V)W r^2 \, dr$. Then if the potential for a pair at a distance r is $\epsilon(r)$, the total potential energy of the liquid is

$$\Phi = \frac{2\pi N_0^2}{V}\int_0^\infty \epsilon W r^2 \, dr \qquad (11.44)$$

The application of this equation to argon is illustrated by the bottom section of Fig. 11.2. The area under the curve gives the integral in Eq. (11.44). The principal difficulty arises in the region of r less than the maximum in W. Here in the repulsive branch the potential curve is so steep that a small error in W can lead to a gross error in the energy. In the present case the distribution actually extends down to values of r where the potential is large and positive. Since this is probably spurious, it seems best to terminate the integral at the point where the potential curve crosses the axis.

The intermolecular potential used was that found from the sublimation energy of the solid and the second virial coefficient of the gas, see Tables 10.6 and 11.2.   The resulting potential energy of the liquid, referred to zero for all molecules at infinite distance, is 1200 cal. per mole.   This should equal the energy of vaporization to the ideal gas,

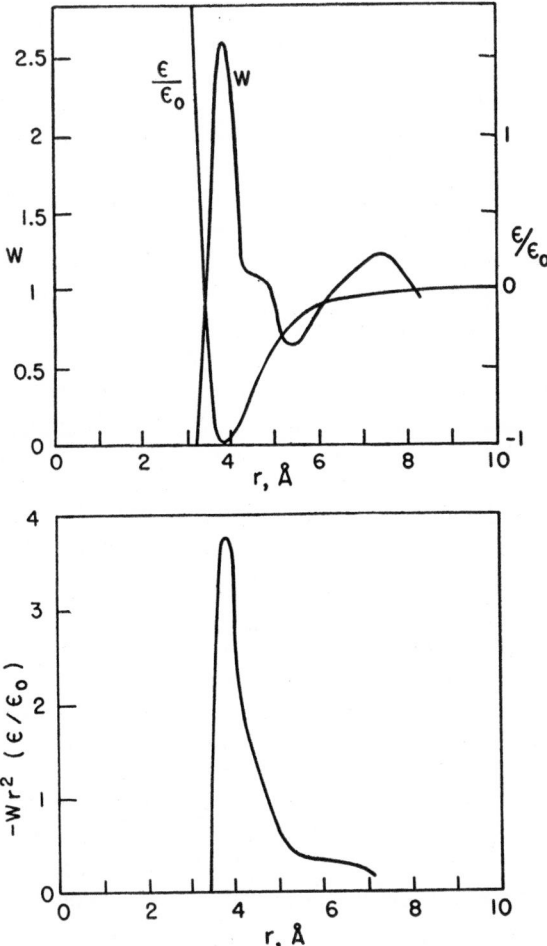

Fig. 11.2.   Top, the radial distribution function W for liquid argon at 91.8°K., together with the intermolecular potential for argon.   Bottom, the graphical integration of the total potential energy of the liquid.

which at the same temperature is 1350 cal. per mole. While the agreement is not very close, it is to be remembered that no parameters were adjusted, and that the distribution function gave indications in itself of some inaccuracy.

The kinetic energy of a liquid can be shown readily to be the same as for the ideal gas. This can be seen from Eq. (11.35), where the kinetic energy terms were integrated for the liquid with the same result as for the gas. Then the total energy content per mole is

$$E = \Phi + 3RT/2 \tag{11.45}$$

In addition to the relatively exact relationship just derived, there have been a number of approximate theories of liquids, such as the theory of holes and the free volume theory. Also the deviation of the entropy of vaporization from the normal value serves as a useful measure of the restriction of rotation or of internal motions in the liquid state. These theories are helpful in understanding the nature of more complex liquids, at least until the more rigorous theory has developed further.

11g. Liquid helium. While the quantitative properties of liquid hydrogen and liquid neon show some effects of quantum deviations from classical mechanics, no new qualitative phenomena arise. However, in helium such new phenomena do appear. Also, in recent years the availability of He^3 has made it possible to investigate the effects of Fermi-Dirac statistics as compared with the Bose-Einstein statistics of He^4.

The complete description of the interesting experimentally measured properties of condensed helium would require more space than can be allowed here.[10] These paragraphs give but a very brief outline.

The first peculiarity is that mere cooling never solidifies either He^3 or He^4. The liquid state continues to the lowest temperatures studied so long as the pressure is low. A solid is obtained by increasing the pressure, as is indicated in Fig. 11.3.

The second peculiarity, in He^4 only, is the λ point transition at 2.186°K. This is a gradual transition of the type mentioned in Section 10j in connection with order-disorder or molecular rotation problems in solids. The heat capacity curves in Fig. 11.4 illustrate the λ point transition in He^4 and the absence of such an effect in He^3.

[10] See general references on liquid helium at the end of the chapter.

Liquid He⁴ below the λ point is known as liquid He II, while that above the λ point is called He I.

The additional qualitative peculiarities are associated with He II. These include essentially frictionless flow in very thin films, which

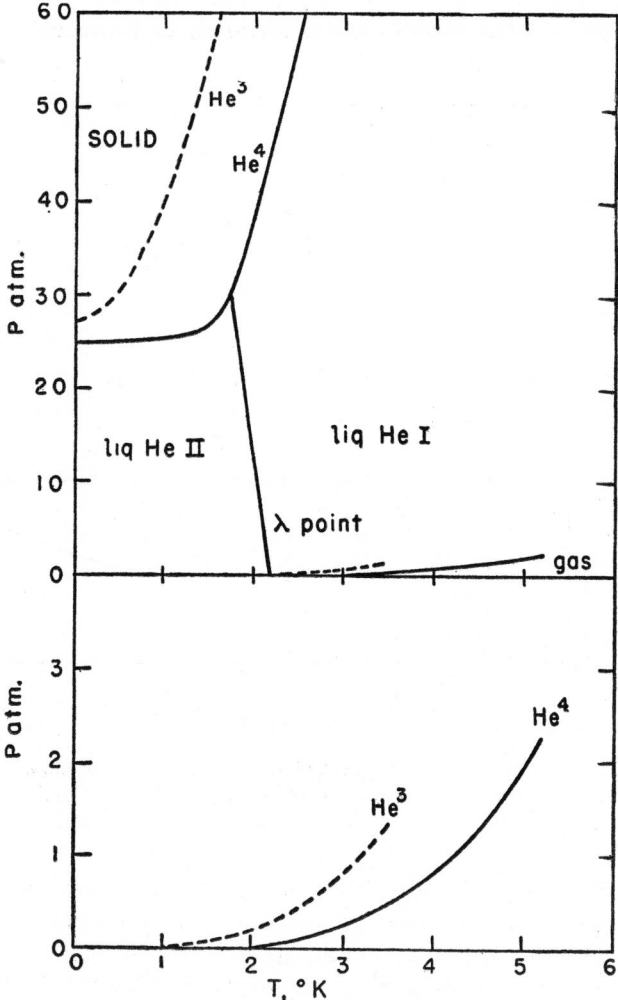

Fig. 11.3.   The phase relationships of helium.   Solid lines are for He⁴, broken lines for He³.   The lower section is an expanded diagram of the vapor pressure curves up to the respective critical points.

introduces gross deviations from normal viscosity; heat flow proportional to the cube root of the temperature gradient instead of the first power; the so-called fountain effect wherein pressure differences are generated by temperature gradients, etc.

Ordinary liquids, if supercooled, approach a nonzero entropy at 0°K. This is attributed to the randomness or irregularity of the

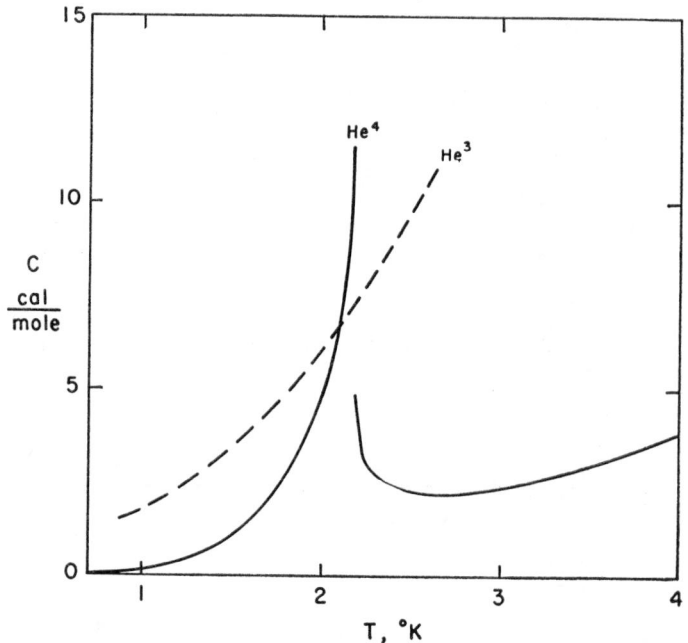

Fig. 11.4. The heat capacity curves of He³ and He⁴ showing the λ point for the latter. The data for He³ are from indirect sources and are subject to considerable uncertainty.

liquid or glassy structure, which implies that a vast number of different quantum states are equally consistent with the glass at 0°K. On the contrary, liquid He appears to approach zero entropy at 0°K just like a crystal. Indeed the heat capacity of He⁴ follows a T^3 law up to about 0.6°K, and again for a short range above the λ transition. To give this result, the energy levels for vibrational motion of the atoms in the liquid must follow the Debye formula. Since He³ follows

Fermi statistics, we might expect the linear C vs. T plot found for conduction electrons in metals. Indeed this interpretation has been given the very limited data available for that substance. At higher temperatures the Fermi degeneracy will be lost. If this occurs before the classical state is reached, an intermediate region of heat capacity proportional to T^3 might be expected. This appears to arise in the region 2–3°K, see Eq. (11.46) below.

We have come to associate zero point energy with any quantum mechanical system where the particles are confined to small volume. Indeed we shall expect the zero point energies to be large for both He^4 and He^3. The Debye law behavior of He^4 allows us to estimate the zero point energy in that case by Eq. (10.45). The heat capacity indicates θ_D to be about 30°K, which yields an E_0 value of $9R\theta_D/8$, or about 60 cal./mole. Since the heat of vaporization of He^4 is only about 20 cal./mole, one can see that the zero point energy is a major effect.

Because zero point energy is reduced by increasing the volume available to the particle, we can understand that the molal volume of liquid He should be much larger than that of normal liquids, in relation to the r_0 of the potential function in each case. This is illustrated in Table 11.4. It is this expanded volume caused by zero point energy which presumably prevents solidification on cooling.

Table 11.4
Comparative Data on Liquid Helium, Neon, and Argon

	He^3	He^4	Ne	A
$T_c k/\epsilon_0$	0.33	0.51	1.24	1.27
$\Delta H_{vap}/N_0\epsilon_0$	0.5	1.0	6.1	6.6
$V_{liq}/N_0 r_0^3$	2.7	1.9	0.96	0.84
$V_c/N_0 r_0^3$	5.0	4.0	2.4	2.2
$h/r_0\sqrt{m\epsilon_0}$	2.74	2.37	0.53	0.16

Before He^3 became available, there was much speculation as to whether it would show a liquid state at all. Not only would the smaller mass increase the zero point energy for a liquid, as compared with He^4, but the shift to Fermi statistics would also have an additional effect in the same direction. Thus, unless the zero point energy could be reduced by further expansion of the molal volume, it seemed likely that the zero point energy would be so large that no liquid could exist. However, de Boer plotted the ratio of the critical temperature to the molecular potential constant $T_c k/\epsilon_0$, against the quantum parameter $h/r_0\sqrt{m\epsilon_0}$, which was mentioned at the end of Section 11e. Such a plot would account only for the effect of mass on the zero point energy at the critical point, not for any effect of change of statistics. Figure 11.5 is a plot of this type, and shows that He³ fits reasonably on the curve through A, Ne, H₂, and He⁴.

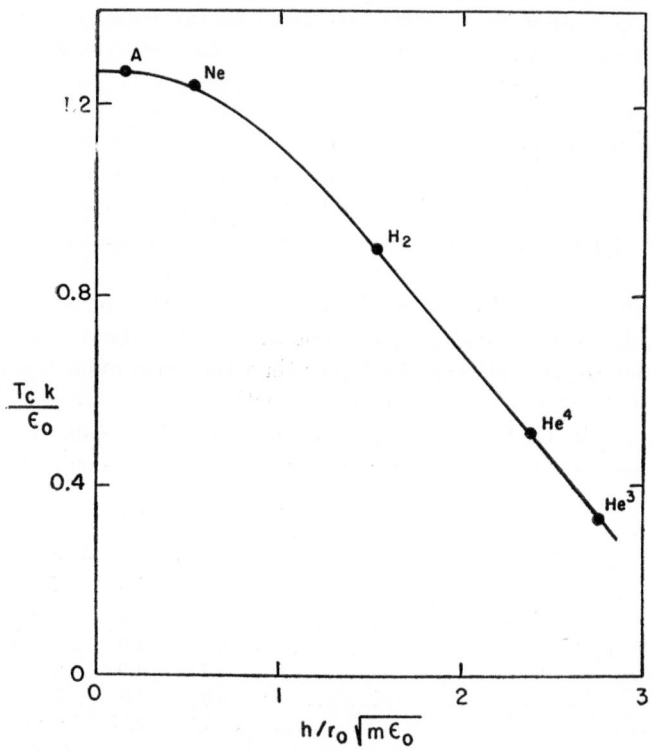

Fig. 11.5.   The quantum effect on the critical temperature of liquids.

The indication from Fig. 11.5 that the Boltzmann statistics are applicable at the critical point of He³ may be confirmed by some rough calculations based on the theory of the ideal degenerate Fermi gas. At the critical density of He³, 0.042 gm./cc., the upper limit of the Fermi energy ϵ_m is 4.4×10^{-16} erg (or $\epsilon_m/k = 3.2°K$). The total Fermi energy is then $\frac{3}{5}N_0\epsilon_m$, or 3.8 cal./mole. The thermodynamic data on liquid He³ have been interpreted in terms of a heat capacity equation

$$C = 0.68RT + 0.2RT^3 \qquad (11.46)$$

which, upon integration, yields

$$H_T - H_0 = 0.34RT^2 + 0.05RT^4 \qquad (11.47)$$

This equation is valid only up to 2.5°K. Nevertheless it is clear that the total thermal energy absorbed at the critical temperature, 3.34°K, is in the range 15–20 cal./mole. Since this thermal energy is four to five times the Fermi gas zero point energy, it is reasonable to assume that the deviation from Boltzmann statistics is small at the critical temperature.

Nevertheless, at 1°K the situation has so changed that liquid He³ approaches a highly degenerate state. The density has increased to 0.0792, which raises ϵ_m/k to 4.9°K. Then application of Eq. (7.49) for the heat capacity of a highly degenerate Fermi gas yields $1.0RT$, in rough agreement with Eq. (11.46).

In contrast to a degenerate Fermi gas, where there is but one molecule to a quantum state, a degenerate Bose gas places all molecules in the lowest quantum state. We must assume that the peculiar properties of He II (liquid He⁴ below the λ point) are in some way related to this Bose-Einstein degeneracy. This conclusion seems practically certain now that it is known that He³ has no λ point above 0.25°K. Indeed, an accurate analysis of the statistics for a Bose gas of intermediate degeneracy yields a break in the heat capacity at

$$T_\lambda = \frac{h^2}{2\pi mk}\left(\frac{n_0}{2.162}\right)^{2/3} \qquad (11.48)$$

where n_0 is the number of particles per cc., and the other quantities have their usual meaning. This temperature is 3.14°K for a gas of the mass and density of liquid He⁴. The agreement of 3.14 with 2.186°K is quite close for such a crude theory. Similarly, the entropy at the λ point is calculated to be 1.3R as compared with 0.8R observed experimentally. The other features of the heat capacity curve agree less well with the Bose gas theory.

Various attempts have been made to develop a theory of a Bose-Einstein liquid, but the intrinsic complications of the liquid state have made this exceedingly difficult. While quantitative agreement has never been obtained, it seems plausible that weaknesses in the

theory account for the discrepancies.   Under the requirement of symmetric wave functions, the angular momentum of a pair of He^4 atoms
must be either zero or an even multiple of $h/2\pi$.   At the interatomic
distance corresponding to the potential minimum r_0, a pair of He
atoms have a moment of inertia of $\frac{1}{2}mr_0^2$.   The temperature ϵ/k,
corresponding to the second rotational level, $J = 2$, of such a diatomic molecule is

$$\frac{\epsilon}{k} = \frac{2 \times 3h^2}{8\pi^2 Ik} = \frac{3h^2}{2\pi^2 mr_0^2 k} \qquad (11.49)$$

which has the value 8.7°K for He^4.

   At temperatures much smaller than this 8.7°K all pairs of He atoms
are in the $J = 0$ state.   This is the ideal case of He II, the superfluid.
Since adjacent atoms are forbidden from acquiring small amounts of
angular momentum, they are, in a sense, locked together, and the
usual frictional effects of viscosity do not arise.   In the region just
below the λ point, the extra specific heat is associated with the introduction into the liquid of *rotons*, which are local regions where a pair
of atoms have the excited angular momentum of a $J = 2$ state.   The
term *roton* was introduced by Landau, who developed a quantum
hydrodynamics.   The term *phonon* is the corresponding term for a
quantum of linear motion, i.e., an excited state for a vibration such as
the longitudinal motions of the Debye theory for crystals.   The
phonons account for the normal T^3 term in the heat capacity.

   For some purposes it is a satisfactory model to assume He II to be
composed of two interpenetrating fluids: a superfluid containing no
rotons, and a normal fluid.   Such a peculiarity as the abnormal heat
flow is now explained as a flow of normal fluid to the cold region and
an opposite flow of superfluid to the hot region.   The dependence of
heat flow on the cube root of the temperature gradient arises from a
friction between countercurrent flows of normal and superfluids,
which is taken as proportional to the cube of the relative velocity.
If the flow is through very small channels in a porous material, the
normal flow is impeded by ordinary viscosity.   Thus the free flow of
the superfluid constitutes a net material flow toward the cold region.
If this flow is restricted, a pressure difference arises.

   Solutions of He^3 in He^4 have been investigated extensively.   The
primary conclusion is that the He^3 always associates itself with the
normal fluid of He^4, and never with the superfluid.   Thus, if one
generates a superfluid flow through very small channels at tempera-

tures below the λ point, the He³ is left behind and is concentrated in the He⁴ which does not pass through the channels. Similarly, He³, by diluting the normal fluid of He⁴, stabilizes the normal fluid with respect to the superfluid. This has the effect of lowering the temperature of the λ transition. It is found that T_λ is approximately proportional to the mole fraction of He⁴ in the solution.

The vapor-liquid equilibrium constants have been studied. The constant K is defined as the ratio of mole fraction of He³ in the gas to that in the liquid. If these solutions followed Raoult's law, we would have

$$K = P_3^\circ / P_4^\circ \tag{11.50}$$

where the P° values are the vapor pressures of the pure liquids at that temperature.

In the region above the λ point, we might expect conformity to Eq. (11.50). Although the measured values of K run a little higher, it is not certain that the difference is beyond experimental error. Below the λ point we would expect the K values to exceed those calculated from Eq. (11.50) if the He³ is dissolving only in the normal portion of the liquid He⁴. The experiments definitely confirm this general idea.

GENERAL REFERENCES

Dingle, R. B., Atkins, K. R., and Daunt, J. G., *Advances in Physics*, **1**, 111, 169, 209 (1952). These three review articles summarize more recent theory of liquid helium and work on the isotope He³.

Hildebrand, J. H. and Scott, R. L., *The Solubility of Nonelectrolytes*, New York: Reinhold Publishing Corp., 1950; see the chapters on "Intermolecular Forces" and "The Liquid State."

Keesom, W. H., *Helium*, New York: The Elsevier Press, Inc., 1942. This is the general reference work on ordinary helium: gas, liquid, and solid.

Taylor, H. S. and Glasstone, S., *Treatise on Physical Chemistry*, 3d ed., Vol. 2, New York: D. Van Nostrand Company, Inc., 1951; see Chapter 2 by Beattie, J. A. and Stockmayer, W. H., "The Thermodynamics and Statistical Mechanics of Real Gases," and Chapter 3 by Kimball, G. E., "The Liquid State."

Chapter 12

MISCELLANEOUS TOPICS

12a. Electric and magnetic susceptibilities. The effects of electric and magnetic fields on atoms and molecules have been mentioned at numerous points throughout the preceding chapters. We have considered both static fields and the rapidly oscillating field associated with photons or radiation. However, there are a few additional topics which have not been included in the natural order at an earlier state and which seem worth including here.

We hasten to add that this is far from a comprehensive treatment. The general electric and magnetic theories are given in many places. Also there are several treatises[1] which give comprehensive accounts in terms of molecular properties. Let us first review some of the basic relationships of electromagnetic theory of matter. The dielectric constant ϵ and the magnetic permeability K are defined by the equations

$$\epsilon = \mathbf{D}/\mathbf{E}, \qquad K = \mathbf{B}/\mathbf{H} \qquad (12.1)$$

where the vectors $\mathbf{E}$, $\mathbf{D}$, $\mathbf{H}$, and $\mathbf{B}$ are the electric field strength, the electric displacement, the magnetic field strength, and the magnetic induction, respectively. We must be careful to distinguish ϵ from molecular energy levels, which we have sometimes given the symbol ϵ_i.

We also have

$$\mathbf{D} = \mathbf{E} + 4\pi\mathbf{P}, \qquad \mathbf{B} = \mathbf{H} + 4\pi\mathbf{M} \qquad (12.2)$$

where $\mathbf{P}$ and $\mathbf{M}$ are the electric and magnetic polarizations (or in the latter case, the intensity of magnetization). Then the electric and magnetic susceptibilities are

---

[1] Van Vleck, J. H., *Electric and Magnetic Susceptibilities*, New York: Oxford University Press, 1932; Stoner, E. C., *Magnetism and Matter*, London: Methuen & Co., Ltd., 1934; Fowler, R. and Guggenheim, E. A., *Statistical Thermodynamics*, London: Cambridge University Press, 1939, Chap. 14.

$$\chi_e = \frac{\mathbf{P}}{\mathbf{E}} = \frac{\epsilon - 1}{4\pi}, \qquad \chi_m = \frac{\mathbf{M}}{\mathbf{H}} = \frac{K - 1}{4\pi} \qquad (12.3)$$

The total polarizations are the sums of the molecular polarizations. If $\mathbf{u}_e$ and $\mathbf{u}_m$ are the electric and magnetic dipole moments, respectively, of a molecule, and we have n_0 molecules per unit volume,

$$\mathbf{P} = n_0 \overline{\mathbf{u}_e}, \qquad \mathbf{M} = n_0 \overline{\mathbf{u}_m} \qquad (12.4)$$

where the bar indicates the average value.

A calculation of the effective electric field, $\mathbf{e}(loc)$, inside a small spherical cavity in a dielectric medium yields the result

$$\mathbf{e}(loc) = \mathbf{E} + 4\pi \mathbf{P}/3 \qquad (12.5)$$

Then the use of the expression for the polarizability of a molecule yields

$$\overline{\mathbf{u}_e} = \alpha \mathbf{e}(loc) = \alpha(\mathbf{E} + 4\pi \mathbf{P}/3) \qquad (12.6)$$

Now we combine Eqs. (12.3) and (12.4) with (12.6) to obtain

$$\frac{\epsilon - 1}{\epsilon + 2} = \frac{4\pi}{3} n_0 \alpha \qquad (12.7)$$

which is readily converted to a molal basis by multiplication by M/ρ, the ratio of the molecular weight to the density. There results

$$\left(\frac{\epsilon - 1}{\epsilon + 2}\right)\frac{M}{\rho} = \frac{4\pi}{3} N_0 \alpha \qquad (12.8)$$

which is known as the Clausius-Masotti equation. The quantity given by either side of Eq. (12.8) is sometimes called the *molar polarization,* or better, the *molar polarizability.* It would seem better to have taken that quantity to be smaller by the factor $3/4\pi$, but that was not done.

It should be realized that the derivation of Eq. (12.8) considered no specific interaction between neighboring molecules, and assumed spherical cavities. Also the mean dipole moment was assumed to be proportional to the field. Thus these several equations cannot be expected to be valid for highly polar liquids or solids, such as water and ice.

Optical theory gives for the refractive index n the relationship $n^2 = \epsilon K$, but K is almost always very close to unity for the dilute systems we shall be considering. Consequently, we may set $\epsilon = n^2$ and obtain the polarizability at optical frequencies from the equation

$$\frac{4\pi}{3} N_0\alpha(op) = \frac{M}{\rho}\left(\frac{n^2 - 1}{n^2 + 2}\right) \tag{12.9}$$

By optical frequencies we mean the frequencies of the light used in refractive index measurements which might extend well down into the infrared but which would still be very high frequencies from the point of view of electrical measurements. Also for gases at low pressures, neither n^2 nor ϵ differ appreciably from unity, hence we have the following simplified equations.

$$\alpha(op) = (n^2 - 1)M/4\pi N_0\rho \tag{12.9'}$$

$$\alpha = (\epsilon - 1)M/4\pi N_0\rho \tag{12.8'}$$

$$\overline{\mathbf{\mu}}_e = \alpha\mathbf{E} = (M/N_0\rho)\chi_e\mathbf{E} \tag{12.10}$$

Similar equations could be developed for the magnetic properties. However, it is usually found that specific interactions between molecules arise if the magnetic susceptibility becomes of the order of unity. For dilute systems we have the equation analogous to (12.10).

$$\overline{\mathbf{\mu}}_m = (M/N_0\rho)\chi_m\mathbf{H} \tag{12.11}$$

Finally, let us state without derivation the expressions to be used for the perturbing energy, i.e., the extra term in the Hamiltonian, arising from an electric field or a magnetic field, in either case along the z axis. In conformity with Chapter 4, we will use F for the intensity of the electric field and $\mathcal{3C}$ for the magnetic field strength.

$$H'_e = -\sum_i Fe_i z_i \tag{12.12}$$

$$H'_m = -\sum_i \frac{\mathcal{3C}e_i}{2m_i c} M_{z_i} + \sum_i \frac{\mathcal{3C}^2 e_i^2}{8m_i c^2}(x_i^2 + y_i^2) \tag{12.13}$$

$$M_z = xp_y - yp_x = \frac{h}{2\pi i}\left(x\frac{\partial}{\partial y} - y\frac{\partial}{\partial x}\right)$$

where M_z is the familiar angular momentum about the z axis.

The z components of the electric and magnetic moments may be derived by differentiations.

$$\mu_e = -\frac{\partial H'_e}{\partial F} = \sum_i ez_i \tag{12.14}$$

$$\mu_m = -\frac{\partial H'_m}{\partial\mathcal{3C}} = \sum_i \frac{e_i}{2m_i c} M_{z_i} - \sum_i \frac{\mathcal{3C}e_i^2}{4m_i c^2}(x_i^2 + y_i^2) \tag{12.15}$$

As indicated above, this section is not intended to be an initial presentation of these topics but only a reminder of electromagnetic theory to one having a general understanding of the subject and a summary of the equations to be needed in the next few sections.

12b. Dipole moments. In Eqs. (12.8) and (12.9) we have expressions for the total polarizability, and for that remaining at "optical" frequencies, respectively. This distinction is arbitrary but very practical. We can classify molecules into those with permanent dipole moments and those without. For the latter group the polarizability arises entirely from distortions of the molecule from its equilibrium configuration, both electronic and nuclear. Thus as long as the frequency is well below that of the lowest molecular vibration, the polarizability should approach a constant value. In the next sections we shall discuss these polarizability terms, but for the present we shall assume we have this $\alpha(op)$ for frequencies below all molecular vibrations.

However, for molecules with permanent dipole moments an additional polarization can arise from nonrandom orientation of these dipoles. This effect will be associated with the frequencies of molecular rotation, which are much lower than those of internal oscillations. Also these low frequencies imply energy levels spaced at intervals comparable with thermal energies; hence the dipole effect will be temperature dependent. It is this effect of dipole orientation which we now desire to calculate. Since molecular rotation is essentially classical at temperatures of interest, we shall use classical statistics.

We let the permanent dipole moment of the molecule be μ. It makes no difference whether the molecule is a linear or nonlinear molecule, because rotation about the axis of the dipole moment will have no effect. The component of the dipole moment in the direction of the field is

$$\mu_z = \mu \cos \theta \qquad (12.16)$$

and the perturbing energy from the electric field is

$$\epsilon' = -F\mu \cos \theta \qquad (12.17)$$

Now the relative population of molecules of varying orientation will be given by the usual Boltzmann factor

$$e^{-\epsilon'/kT} = e^{F\mu \cos \theta/kT}$$

Consequently, we write for the mean dipole moment

$$\bar{\mu} = \frac{\int_0^{2\pi} \int_0^{\pi} \mu \cos \theta e^{F\mu \cos \theta / kT} \sin \theta \, d\theta \, d\phi}{\int_0^{2\pi} \int_0^{\pi} e^{F\mu \cos \theta / kT} \sin \theta \, d\theta \, d\phi} \qquad (12.18)$$

These integrals are not difficult to evaluate, and yield

$$\bar{\mu} = \mu \, (\coth y - y^{-1})$$
$$y = F\mu/kT \qquad (12.19)$$

For almost all practical conditions of measurement the value of $F\mu/kT$ is very small. Then the approximate expression is

$$\bar{\mu} = \mu y/3 = F\mu^2/3kT \qquad (12.20)$$

and the dielectric constant, Eq. (12.8), becomes

$$\left(\frac{\epsilon - 1}{\epsilon + 2}\right) \frac{M}{\rho} = \frac{4\pi}{3} N_0[\alpha(op) + \mu^2/3kT] \qquad (12.21)$$

This can be simplified in the same fashion as Eq. (12.8′) for gases where ϵ is close to unity.

The polarizability from high frequency motions, $\alpha(op)$, is not affected by temperature; hence we may plot the molar polarizability, $M(\epsilon - 1)/\rho(\epsilon + 2)$, against the reciprocal of the temperature, as is shown in Fig. 12.1. If, as we have assumed, the dipole moment μ is a constant, we should find a straight line whose slope is $4\pi N_0\mu^2/9k$ and whose intercept is $4\pi N_0\alpha(op)/3$. This is illustrated by the data for HCl in Fig. 12.1.

For very simple molecules this behavior is found. Also the intercept usually agrees quite well with the value calculated from Eq. (12.8) or (12.8′) by extrapolation of the refractive index to zero frequency from the measurements in the visible region.

In more complex molecules two effects become important. The polarizability found from a plot like Fig. 12.1 is higher than that obtained by extrapolating the refractive index from visible frequencies. The difference is the polarizability arising from molecular vibrations whose frequencies lie in the infrared. This will be the subject of Section 12d. The other complication, which is less common, is a failure to obtain a linear dependence of the molar polarizability on the reciprocal temperature. A variation of the dipole moment with temperature will cause this behavior, which is illustrated in Fig. 12.1 by the data for dichloroethane.

While all infrared active vibrations must have an effect on the dipole moment, their excitation usually causes little change in the average dipole moment. If the dependence of the moment on the coordinate of vibration is linear, and the amplitude of vibration is symmetrical with respect to the equilibrium position, the average over the vibrational coordinate will yield exactly the same moment as that calculated for a static model in the equilibrium configuration. Either asymmetry of the vibrational motion or nonlinearity of the moment will give some effect, but in most cases this is negligible.

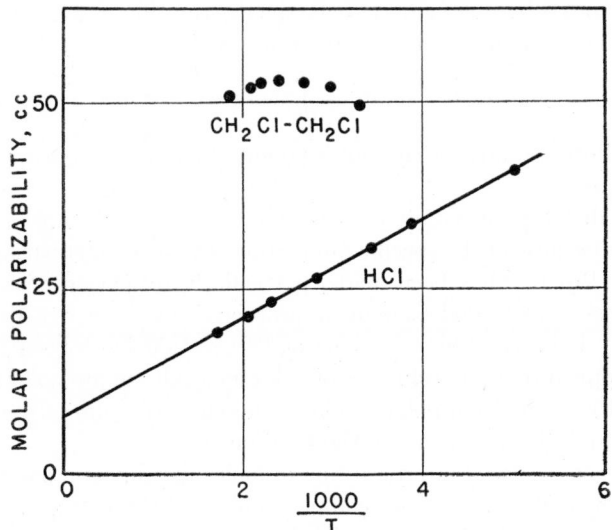

Fig. 12.1.   The molar polarizability as a function of the reciprocal of the temperature.

However, if the dipole moment in the equilibrium position is at a minimum, possibly zero, and increases with either direction of vibrational distortion, a very significant effect can arise. Also there may be a rapid equilibrium between tautomeric forms of the molecule or between a variety of geometrical isomeric configurations. If this equilibrium is shifted with temperature, the apparent dipole moment of the molecule will change.

A favorite example is dichloroethane, CH_2Cl—CH_2Cl. Here it is the rotation of the dipoles of the CH_2Cl groups with respect to one another about the C—C bond which causes the peculiar behavior.

The minimum energy configuration is found to be *trans*, planar with respect to the Cl—C—C—Cl skeleton. Since this position has a center of symmetry, it can have no dipole moment. However, small oscillations of a torsional nature will yield an average moment. More important is the thermal equilibrium with a skew or gauche configuration obtained by rotation of one CH_2Cl group by $\pm 120°$ with respect to the other. There is a potential minimum in that position which is about 1.4 kcal./mole higher than that of the *trans* position. The effective dipole moment squared for the substance at a given temperature is found by averaging μ^2 over the distribution of molecular configurations. Thus in the case of an internal rotation ϕ, one has

$$\mu^2 \text{ (effective)} = \int_0^{2\pi} \mu^2(\phi) e^{-\epsilon(\phi)/kT} \, d\phi \qquad (12.22)$$

where both μ^2 and the molecular potential energy ϵ are expressed as functions of ϕ.

The dielectric constant of polar liquids is a much more complex subject because of the specific interactions between neighboring molecules. Progress has been made, particularly by Onsager,[2] with the consideration of models more appropriate than the one discussed above. However, the equations of this section have been successfully applied to dilute solutions of polar molecules in nonpolar liquids. In that case the total polarizability is taken as the sum of the contributions of all components of the solution.

The conventional interpretation of molecular dipole moments is in terms of *bond moments*. In complex molecules the various bond moments are added vectorially. Thus the substitution of hydrogen in benzene by Cl or CN, respectively, yields a dipole moment of 1.55 or 3.92D. The common unit of dipole moment is 10^{-18} e.s.u., and is labeled D after Debye, who contributed much to this subject. If we assume in each case that the substituent is negative, then vectorial addition yields 4.88, 3.42, and 2.37D for the *ortho*, *meta*, and *para* C_6H_4ClCN compounds, respectively. The experimental values are 4.75, 3.38, and 2.53D. These values indicate reasonable additivity in this case. This accuracy of additivity is actually rare among aromatic compounds because of the likelihood of mesomeric effects.

Mesomeric molecules show deviations from the calculated dipole moments of the expected sort. In the absence of mesomerism one

---

[2] Onsager, L., *J. Am. Chem. Soc.*, **58**, 1486 (1936).

might expect each of the dipole moments of H_3CCl, $H_2C{=}CHCl$, and $HC{\equiv}CCl$ to be just the difference between the C—Cl and C—H bond moments.   The values are 1.92, 1.44, and 0.44D.   These variations can be understood in terms of the net effect of the structures:

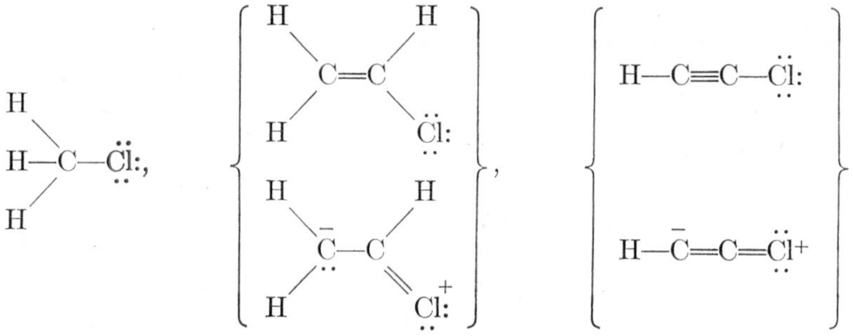

One assumes that the normal C—Cl bond makes the carbon positive and the chlorine negative, in accord with their electronegativity difference.   This can be thought of as a further resonance with a C^+ Cl^- ionic structure if desired, see Section 8f.   Then methyl chloride should display a normal C—Cl bond.   With the multiple carbon-carbon bonds, the opportunity arises to engage the otherwise unshared electrons of the chlorine in bonding.   However, this necessarily makes the chlorine more positive and decreases the moment of the whole molecule.   We may also note that the dipole moment of chlorobenzene, mentioned above, is close to that of chloroethylene.   This indicates that the contributions of the charged structures are about the same in these two cases.

Recently it has been emphasized that dipole moments are greatly influenced by bond hybridization in cases where the molecule contains unshared pairs of electrons in valence shells.   All hydrogen-like atomic orbitals yield electron distributions which are symmetrical with respect to the nucleus.   Thus if unshared pairs are in unhybridized orbitals, they contribute nothing to the dipole moment.   However, hybrid orbitals, such as a tetrahedral sp^3 hybrid, yield an electron distribution whose center of gravity is well removed from the nucleus.   The most striking example is found in the pair of nitrogen compounds NH_3 and NF_3.   Both are symmetrical pyramids with bond angles at the nitrogen atom of 106.8° and 102.5°, respectively.   The electronegativity difference is about one unit in each case, but with hydrogen less than nitrogen, while fluorine is more electronegative than nitrogen. Thus, from a bond moment viewpoint, one might expect about the same magnitude of dipole moment in each case (although of opposite orientation); actually the moment for ammonia is 1.5 D while that of NF_3 is only 0.2 D. The difference must arise primarily from the unshared pair of electrons on nitrogen which appears to contribute a moment of about 0.7 D. This moment adds to the N—H moments in ammonia but subtracts from the N—F moments in NF_3.

Before closing this section we should remark that our selection of a classical treatment of dipole orientation was optional. We could have given a treatment based on quantum mechanical functions for molecular rotation. Such treatments are given in many treatises[1] (although sometimes limited to linear molecules), and have one very interesting result. The net polarization arises from molecules in the lowest rotational state, at least for small fields. The net dipole from all higher rotational states averages to zero. Then the inverse temperature dependence of the total polarization comes from the decrease in population of the lowest rotational state with rise of temperature. The quantum result is the same as the classical one for the total polarization, as would be expected.

12c. Electronic polarizability and the refractive index. Let us now turn to the portion of the polarizability which arises from other sources than permanent dipoles. An example is the polarizability of the normal hydrogen atom which was calculated in Section 4i.

The polarizability is of interest in a number of ways. We have been considering the dielectric constant and refractive index most recently, but recall also that the formula for London forces involved this quantity. The Raman effect selection rules involved changes in the polarizability. We wish to point out now that there is a close relationship between the probabilities for light absorption and the polarizability. This relationship comes from second-order perturbation theory, which is given in Appendix 20. The result is

$$\alpha = \frac{2}{3} \sum_i' \frac{(\mu_x)_i^2 + (\mu_y)_i^2 + (\mu_z)_i^2}{E_i - E_0} \tag{12.23}$$

where α is the polarizability averaged over all orientations, E_i and E_0 are the energies of the ith and the ground states, respectively, and the sum covers all states except the ground state. The quantities

$(\mu_x)_i$, etc., are just the dipole transition integrals which we have used repeatedly,

$$(\mu_x)_i = \int \psi_i^* \mu \psi_0 \, dv \tag{6.4}$$

and which were seen in Chapter 6 to control the absorption and emission of radiation. Since the original state is always the ground state, the second subscript is omitted for the (μ)'s.

The sum in Eq. (12.23) covers all excited states of the molecule, including the continuum lying above dissociation or ionization limits. Thus it is not very useful for the computation of the total polarizability, although it is valuable in giving the contribution of any particular excited state. The total optical polarizability is better found from the refractive index. For a dilute gaseous system we have Eq. (12.9')

$$\alpha(op) = (n^2 - 1)M/4\pi N_0 \rho \tag{12.9'}$$

From the phenomenon of dispersion we know that the refractive index varies with frequency. The theory requires a complex perturbation calculation for the forced oscillations of a molecule under the influence of an oscillating electromagnetic field of frequency ν_0. The resulting[3] polarizability for molecules in their ground state is

$$\alpha(\nu) = \frac{2}{3h} \sum_i{}' \frac{\nu_i}{\nu_i^2 - \nu_0^2} [(\mu_x)_i^2 + (\mu_y)_i^2 + (\mu_z)_i^2] \tag{12.24}$$

$$\nu_i = (E_i - E_0)/h$$

and the conversion to refractive index is obvious from the equation above. One can easily see that Eq. (12.24) reduces to Eq. (12.23) if the field frequency drops to zero. Also it is apparent that anomolous dispersion will occur near frequencies of absorption where $\nu_i = \nu_0$ because the denominator of that term will become zero.

However, once the frequency of the light is well below any particular absorption frequency, the contribution of that term decreases smoothly until zero frequency is reached. Thus for a substance with no absorption near the visible spectrum it is quite practical to extrapolate the refractive index or the polarizability to an apparent limit for

---

[3] This formula was obtained originally by Kramers. Its derivation is given in Eyring, H., Walter, J., and Kimball, G. E., *Quantum Chemistry*, New York: John Wiley & Sons, Inc., 1944, p. 332.

zero frequency.   Figure 12.2 shows the small change of polarizability
with frequency in the near infrared and visible ranges for the carbon
dioxide molecule.   At still lower frequencies the polarizability varies
widely because of the effect of molecular vibrations.

A molecular vibration with a frequency of about 10^3 cm.$^{-1}$ makes
a small negative contribution to the polarizability at the frequencies
of visible light.   It is negative because $\nu_0^2 > \nu_i^2$, and it is small be-

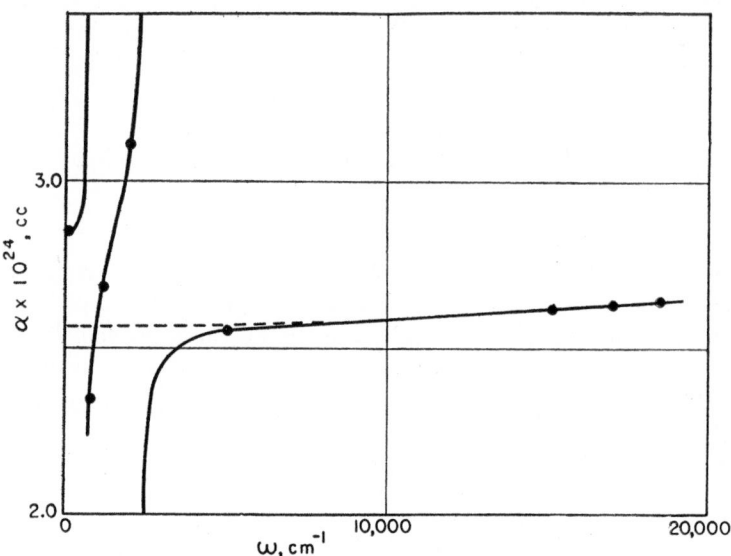

Fig. 12.2.   The polarizability of carbon dioxide as a function of frequency.
The effects of infrared active overtones are ignored—they would be small.   The
experimental points are shown.   The remainder of the curve is qualitatively
drawn with respect to the known absorption frequencies.   The dotted line indicates the course of an extrapolation from the visible frequency range.

cause the effective charges and amplitudes of vibration are small for
the motion of whole atoms as compared with electrons.   Nevertheless, as the frequency is reduced, the denominator in Eq. (12.24)
becomes small for these atomic motions, and their contribution may
become very significant.   Figure 12.2 indicates this behavior qualitatively for the two infrared active fundamental vibrations of carbon
dioxide.   If the molecule had a dipole moment, its effect would
appear at still smaller frequencies.   Before considering atomic polari-

zation in the next section we shall make a few further remarks concerning electronic polarizabilities.

The molar polarizability (also called the molar refraction) arising from electronic motions is frequently discussed as a measure of the amplitude of motion of electrons in atoms and molecules. The molar polarizability of a large molecule can be estimated with considerable accuracy as the sum of the contributions of the various bonds or other component units. Another interesting application concerns ionic compounds. Tables of ionic refractivities (on a molar basis) have been constructed by various authors. It is found that the molar refractivities of some compounds are close to the sums for their component ions. These are exactly the compounds which would be regarded as highly ionic on other grounds. The reduction in the molar refractivity of other compounds below the sum for the ions has been considered an indication of the deviation from purely ionic bonding.

12d. Atomic polarization and the intensity of vibration spectral bands. In the last section the relationship was given between a spectral intensity and the contribution of that excited state to the total polarizability. Let us apply this to molecular vibration spectra and the *atomic polarizability* which is attributed to such motions.

The basic equations for spectral intensities were given in Chapter 6, and in Section 9m the oscillator strength was defined as

$$f = \frac{8\pi^2 m\nu}{3he^2} \left[(\mu_x)_{nm}^2 + (\mu_y)_{nm}^2 + (\mu_z)_{nm}^2 \right] \tag{9.91}$$

The relationship of the oscillator strength to the extinction coefficient as commonly defined for solutions was also given. Let us supplement these equations with definitions of the quantities usually used for work in the gas phase.

The *absorption coefficient* is defined as

$$k = \frac{1}{PL} \ln \frac{I_0}{I} \tag{12.25}$$

where P is the pressure in atm. (reduced to 0°C), L is the optical path length in cm., and I_0 and I are the incident and transmitted intensities. This expression should make k a function only of frequency. Then the integrated intensity for the ith absorption band is

$$A_i = \int_{band} k(\nu) \, d\nu = c \int_{band} k(\omega) \, d\omega \qquad (12.26)$$

where alternate expressions are given in terms of the true frequency and the practical spectroscopic measure, $\omega = \nu/c$, in cm.$^{-1}$. By relating these quantities to the more absolute basis of Chapter 6 and to the quantities defined in Section 9m, the following equations are obtained.

$$A_i = \frac{8\pi^3 \nu_i n_0}{3hc} \left[(\mu_x)_i^2 + (\mu_y)_i^2 + (\mu_z)_i^2 \right] \qquad (12.27)$$

$$A_i = \frac{\pi c^2 n_0}{mc} f_i = 1.599 \times 10^{22} f_i \qquad (12.28)$$

where n_0 is the number of molecules per cc. in the gas at 0°C and 1 atm. pressure, and the subscript i refers to the ith transition throughout.

For transitions involving molecular vibration (but no electronic change) we may obtain some further relationships for the μ's by considering the normal coordinates. Since we assume harmonic oscillation in each normal coordinate Q, we may use the results of Section 2i to obtain for the $0 \to 1$ transition

$$Q_i^{1,0} = \int \psi_1 Q_i \psi_0 \, dQ_i = (h/8\pi^2 m_i \nu_i)^{1/2} \qquad (12.29)$$

where m_i is the effective reduced mass for the normal coordinate. If we use the definition of Eq. (9.35), wherein the normal coordinates are adjusted to make the effective mass unity, m_i will drop out.

Now we may assume that the magnitude of any normal coordinate is very small, essentially a differential quantity. Consequently we may expand the dipole moment vector $\mathbf{\mu}$ as follows.

$$\mathbf{\mu} = \mathbf{\mu}_0 + \sum_i \frac{\partial \mathbf{\mu}}{\partial Q_i} Q_i \qquad (12.30)$$

Then we have for the $0 \to 1$ transition of the ith vibration

$$(\mu_x)_i = \frac{\partial \mu_x}{\partial Q_i} \int \psi_1 Q_i \psi_0 \, dQ_i = (h/8\pi^2 m_i \nu_i)^{1/2} \frac{\partial \mu_x}{\partial Q_i} \qquad (12.31)$$

$$A_i = \frac{\pi n_0}{3 c m_i} \left[\left(\frac{\partial \mu_x}{\partial Q_i} \right)^2 + \left(\frac{\partial \mu_y}{\partial Q_i} \right)^2 + \left(\frac{\partial \mu_z}{\partial Q_i} \right)^2 \right] \qquad (12.32)$$

These last equations make it possible to draw conclusions about the charge distribution within molecules. For example, the symmetry of carbon dioxide gives it zero dipole moment. However, each C=O bond may have a dipole associated with it. Then in the bending vibration ν_3, as illustrated in Fig. 9.2 and 9.5, these dipoles are shifted so that they no longer cancel one another exactly. By a detailed calculation the dipole moment for the C=O bond may be related to the quantities, $(\partial\mu/\partial Q_i)$, in Eq. (12.32).

Measurements of the absolute intensity of the 670 cm.$^{-1}$ band of carbon dioxide, which is the ν_3 band, permit a calculation of the magnitude of this C=O bond moment. The value $1.17D$ has been obtained, which is much smaller than the value of $2.3D$, which is commonly assigned the C=O bond in aldehydes and ketones. There is in carbon dioxide a mesomerism involving the structures,

$$O=C=O, \quad {}^+O\equiv C-O^-, \quad {}^-O-C\equiv O^+, \quad {}^-O-\overset{+}{C}=O, \quad O=\overset{+}{C}-O^-$$

while in an aldehyde or ketone there can only be the structures

$$\begin{matrix}\diagdown\\ \diagup\end{matrix}C=O, \quad \begin{matrix}\diagdown\\ \diagup\end{matrix}\overset{+}{C}-O^-$$

The presence of the triple bonded structures with positive charges on the oxygen atoms presumably reduces the net negative charge on those atoms in carbon dioxide.

For many years there was a disagreement between the absolute infrared intensity data and the contributions of those same infrared bands to the total polarizability. This was resolved by Wilson and Wells,[4] who showed the intensity measurements had been erroneous. The individual vibration-rotation lines of a vibrational band are so sharp that the available spectrometers had insufficient resolving power to measure the true absorption coefficient. The correct integrated intensities were obtained by adding a pressure of inert gas which broadened the individual lines. There is agreement now with the refractive index data. Also it seems likely that true spectral intensities will yield a considerable body of data on the charge distribution within molecules.

12e. Paramagnetism. Just as substances with a large dielectric constant obtain that property from molecular dipoles free to orient in the electric field, likewise large magnetic susceptibilies arise only

---

[4] Both the method and the results for several compounds are given in a series of papers by Wilson, E. B., Jr., Wells, A. J., and Thorndike, A. M., *J. Chem. Phys.*, **14**, 578 (1946); **15**, 157, 868 (1947).

from substantial molecular magnetic moments which can orient themselves in the magnetic field. If classical mechanics were a good approximation in the magnetic case, we could adopt the results of Eqs. (12.19) and (12.20) directly. However, large magnetic moments arise only from electron spin and electron orbital angular momentum, and these effects are far from classical. Another statement of this difference is that molecules with single lowest quantum states can have an electric moment, but magnetic moments are always associated with degenerate electronic states.

Let us assume that the magnetic moment is associated with a quantum number J. Then the component M in the field direction can have the values $-J$, $-J + 1$, . . . , $J - 1$, J, or $2J + 1$ in all. If the magnetic moment arises purely from electron orbital motion (see Section 4e), its magnitude is

$$\mu_m = M\mu_0 \quad \text{(orbital only)} \tag{12.33}$$

with μ_0 the Bohr magneton.

$$\mu_0 = |e|h/4\pi mc = 0.9271 \times 10^{-20} \text{ erg/gauss}$$

If the magnetic moment arises purely from spin, the result is twice as great. For mixed cases we get more complex results which can be expressed as

$$\mu_m = Mg\mu_0 \tag{12.34}$$

where the Lande g factor is 1 for pure orbital motion, 2 for pure spin. The expression[5] for atoms with LS coupling is

$$g = 1 + \frac{J(J + 1) + S(S + 1) - L(L + 1)}{2J(J + 1)} \tag{12.35}$$

where S, L, and J were defined in Section 5e.

In complex cases there may be several sets of energy levels within the thermal range. Thus a ground state might be $^2P_{1/2}$ but the $^2P_{3/2}$ level might be of low energy compared with kT. We shall not consider these complex cases but will assume just one degenerate energy level. Then a magnetic field destroys the degeneracy and yields a single set of energy levels given by the $2J + 1$ values of M in the equation

$$H'_m = -\mathcal{3C}\mu_m = -\mathcal{3C}Mg\mu_0 \tag{12.36}$$

[5] Van Vleck, J. H., *Electric and Magnetic Susceptibilities*, New York: Oxford University Press, 1932, p. 173; Herzberg, G., *Atomic Spectra and Atomic Structure*, New York: Prentice-Hall, Inc., 1937, p. 109 (reprinted, Dover Publications, 1944).

The mean magnetic moment is

$$\bar{\mu}_m = \frac{\displaystyle\sum_{M=-J}^{M=J} M g\mu_0 e^{M\mathcal{3C}g\mu_0/kT}}{\displaystyle\sum_{M=-J}^{M=J} e^{M\mathcal{3C}g\mu_0/kT}} \qquad (12.37)$$

We let

$$x = \mathcal{3C}g\mu_0/kT \qquad (12.38)$$

and expand the exponentials on the assumption that Mx is small for all values of M. Then we have

$$\bar{\mu}_m = g\mu_0 \frac{\sum M(1 + Mx + \ldots)}{\sum (1 + Mx + \ldots)}$$

$$= g\mu_0 \frac{\sum M + x \sum M^2 + \cdots}{2J + 1 + x \sum M + \cdots} \qquad (12.39)$$

where all of the sums run from $-J$ to $+J$. The sums over any odd power of M are zero, hence the leading term in the numerator is that in M^2, while the denominator has just the value $2J + 1$.

The sum of squares of integers up to N is known to be

$$\sum_0^N n^2 = N(N + 1)(2N + 1)/6$$

By appropriate manipulations and the use of this formula one eventually obtains

$$\bar{\mu}_m = \frac{\mathcal{3C}g^2\mu_0^2}{kT} \cdot \frac{J(J + 1)}{3} \qquad (12.40)$$

which is just the classical average of Eq. (12.20), if we take the magnitude of the magnetic moment to be

$$\mu_m = \sqrt{J(J + 1)}g\mu_0 \qquad (12.41)$$

This seems very reasonable because we have become used to the $J(J + 1)$ type of expression for the total angular momentum.

The magnetic property commonly reported from experimental measurements is the molal susceptibility. It is defined as the ratio of the magnetic polarization of a gram mole to the field strength. Then from Eq. (12.4) one obtains

$$\chi_{mol} = N_0\bar{\mu}_m/\mathbf{H} \qquad (12.42)$$

which on combination with Eq. (12.40) yields

$$\chi_{mol} = \frac{N_0 J(J+1)g^2\mu_0^2}{3kT} \tag{12.43}$$

Curie's law (P. Curie, 1895) was obtained empirically and gave the dependence of the magnetic susceptibility on T^{-1}. Thus this feature of our result is in agreement with experiment. There are relatively few examples upon which we may fully test Eq. (12.43). There are no paramagnetic atomic gases. It is found that the rare earth ions follow this equation in most cases at room temperature. Here the magnetic effects are associated with the incomplete 4f shell, which is well inside the atom and not much influenced by crystalline fields or chemical bonds.

The rare earth ions, whose energy levels within the thermal range comprise the simple set of states assumed above, are listed in Table 12.1, together with the experimental results, which are averages of reasonably concordant values from hydrated sulfates, aqueous solutions, etc. The unit, *effective magneton number*, is used. This is defined as

$$\mu_{eff} = (3kT\chi_{mol}/N_0\mu_0^2)^{1/2} \tag{12.44}$$

Equation (12.43) then gives for the theory

$$\mu_{eff} = g\sqrt{J(J+1)} \tag{12.45}$$

Table 12.1
Paramagnetism of Rare Earth Ions

Ion	No. 4f e^-	Normal state	S	L	J	g	μ_{eff} theory	μ_{eff} exp.
La^{+++}	0	$^1S_0$	0	0	0	—	0	0
Ce^{+++}	1	$^2F_{5/2}$	$\frac{1}{2}$	3	$\frac{5}{2}$	$\frac{6}{7}$	2.54	2.4
Pr^{+++}	2	$^3H_4$	1	5	4	$\frac{4}{5}$	3.58	3.5
Nd^{+++}	3	$^4I_{9/2}$	$\frac{3}{2}$	6	$\frac{9}{2}$	$\frac{8}{11}$	3.62	3.5
Gd^{+++}	7	$^8S_{7/2}$	$\frac{7}{2}$	0	$\frac{7}{2}$	2	7.94	8.0
Tb^{+++}	8	$^7F_6$	3	3	6	$\frac{3}{2}$	9.72	9.5
Ds^{+++}	9	$^6H_{15/2}$	$\frac{5}{2}$	5	$\frac{15}{2}$	$\frac{4}{3}$	10.65	10.7
Ho^{+++}	10	$^5I_8$	2	6	8	$\frac{5}{4}$	10.61	10.3
Er^{+++}	11	$^4I_{15/2}$	$\frac{3}{2}$	6	$\frac{15}{2}$	$\frac{6}{5}$	9.58	9.5
Tu^{+++}	12	$^3H_6$	1	5	6	$\frac{7}{6}$	7.56	7.3
Yb^{+++}	13	$^2F_{7/2}$	$\frac{1}{2}$	3	$\frac{7}{2}$	$\frac{8}{7}$	4.54	4.5
Lu^{+++}	14	$^1S_0$	0	0	0	—	0	0

It is seen that the agreement in Table 12.1 is quite good. Also Van Vleck[1] obtained agreement in the cases of Sm^{+++} and Eu^{+++} by considering the complete array of energy levels within the thermal range. This calculation for the rare earths was first performed by Hund, and the accord of the spectroscopic states with his rules is apparent.

At very low temperatures and for very high magnetic fields the assumption that Mx is small breaks down. Under these conditions one can saturate the material by lining up almost all the individual magnetic moments. Frequently other complications arise, since the low-temperature experiments are necessarily performed with solids. These are minimized in cases where the entire magnetic moment arises from spin, i.e., when L is zero and $J = S$. The exact equation for the intensity of magnetization for a mole is

$$M_{mol} = N_0 g \mu_0 \left[\frac{2J + 1}{2} \coth \frac{(2J + 1)x}{2} - \frac{1}{2} \coth \frac{x}{2} \right] \qquad (12.46)$$

$$x = \mathfrak{IC} g \mu_0 / kT$$

This equation fits the low-temperature measurements on hydrated gadolinium sulfate very satisfactorily from low fields up to 95% of maximum magnetization. Also one can easily see that it yields the correct saturation magnetization of $N_0 g \mu_0 J$ when x becomes infinite.

If these same methods are applied to the ions in the transition region with incomplete d shells, no agreement is found. It was Stoner who emphasized that the orbital contributions for the d electrons are "quenched" by the fields of surrounding molecules. We know that d electrons participate in chemical bonding in these elements; consequently it is not unreasonable that the d orbits should be disturbed. Table 12.2 gives the data for the iron series elements. The theoretical values for pure spin are readily obtained by substituting S for J and $g = 2$ in our various formulas. The effective magneton numbers are $2\sqrt{S(S + 1)}$. Except for Mn^{++} and Fe^{+++} which have $^6S_{5/2}$ states, the theoretical effective magneton numbers in Table 12.2 would be different if orbital magnetic effects had been included.

The values in Table 12.2 show good agreement with the theory for pure spin paramagnetism except for Co^{++} and Ni^{++}. In these cases the theory, including orbital effects, would yield 6.5 and 5.5, respectively. Possibly the quenching of orbital magnetic moment is incomplete in these two cases. There are some hydrated solid salts

TABLE 12.2

PARAMAGNETISM OF AQUEOUS IONS OF THE FIRST TRANSITION SERIES

ION	No. $3d$ e^-	State of gas ion	$2\sqrt{S(S+1)}$	μ_{eff}, exp.
K^+, ..., V^{+5}	0	$^1S_0$	0	0
V^{+4}, etc.	1	$^2D_{3/2}$	1.73	1.75
V^{+3}	2	$^3F_2$	2.83	2.76–2.85
V^{++}, ..., Mn^{+4}	3	$^4F_{3/2}$	3.87	3.68–4.0
Cr^{++}, Mn^{+++}	4	$^5D_0$	4.90	4.8
Mn^{++}, Fe^{+++}	5	$^6S_{5/2}$	5.92	5.96, 5.94
Fe^{++}	6	$^5D_4$	4.90	5.3
Co^{++}	7	$^4F_{9/2}$	3.87	4.6–5.0
Ni^{++}	8	$^3F_4$	2.83	3.23
Cu^{++}	9	$^2D_{5/2}$	1.73	1.8–2.0
Zn^{++}, Cu^+	10	$^1S_0$	0	0

containing these ions that fit the spin theory better. In both the rare earth compounds and this first transition series, measurements have been made over a temperature range on hydrated salt crystals. These confirm the approximate conformance to Curie's law.

We recall from Section 8r the discussion of covalently bonded complexes of the transition elements wherein the number of unpaired spins is reduced. The use of magnetic susceptibility to determine the predominant bond type was discussed there. The equations of this section are obviously applicable to obtain the quantitative susceptibilities to be expected in terms of the number of unpaired electrons.

The second and third transition series elements are even more inclined to form covalent complexes than the iron series. Thus it is not too surprising that general agreement of the type shown in Table 12.2 has not been obtained for these other series.

A considerable number of values[6] are becoming available for the ions with incomplete $5f$ shells, which are sometimes called the actinides. The values follow those for the corresponding rare earth ions quite closely in most cases. There are uncertainties in the exact theoretical values to be expected, because these heavy elements show a tendency toward jj coupling (and away from LS coupling). For example, in U^{+4} there are two $5f$ electrons. The expected effective

---

[6] See Seaborg, G. T., paper on "Electronic Structure of the Heaviest Elements," in *The Transuranium Elements*, ed. Seaborg, G. T., Katz, J. J., and Manning, W. M., New York: McGraw-Hill Book Company, Inc., 1949, p. 1492.

Bohr magneton number for LS coupling is 3.58 with a $^3H_4$ state, while jj coupling would yield 3.84. The experimental values range from 3.52 to 3.75. Thus there is good support for the basic assumption of two $5f$ electrons well shielded from the electric fields that usually quench orbital effects except in the case of f electrons. Similar agreement is obtained for some other actinide ions.

The results we have discussed for the first transition series characterize nonlinear molecules generally. The exact quantization of angular electronic motion arises only where there is no angular dependence on the potential energy of interaction with the nuclei. Thus in linear molecules one still has exactly quantized angular momentum about the molecule axis. In particular, NO has a $^2\Pi$ ground state. The two components of the doublet, $^2\Pi_{1/2}$ and $^2\Pi_{3/2}$, are separated by only 121 cm.$^{-1}$. Consequently, the calculation of the susceptibility becomes a special problem, but one which has yielded excellent agreement with experimental magnetic data.

The oxygen molecule has a $^3\Sigma$ ground state; hence its paramagnetism arises purely from spin. The magnetic susceptibility of gaseous oxygen follows accurately the theory for $S = J = 1$, $L = 0$ in the equation above.

Returning to nonlinear molecules, we expect substantial paramagnetism only from unpaired electron spins. Indeed Jahn and Teller[7] have proved that the stable ground state of a nonlinear molecule must be orbitally nondegenerate. Consequently any permanent magnetic moment in such a molecule must arise purely from spin. The formulas given for the transition series ions apply generally to cases where only spin is involved. These methods have been applied successfully to such examples as triphenylmethyl radical as well as inorganic compounds of the types we have mentioned.

If the atoms with permanent magnetic moment are located close to one another, as in metals and some solid compounds, there may be large specific interactions between neighboring magnetic atoms. The effect of these interactions may be to orient the magnetic moments parallel to one another, which will yield *ferromagnetism*. In other cases the interaction may have the opposite effect, and there may be established a definite pattern of antiparallel magnetic moments. This situation is called *antiferromagnetism*. MnO and FeO show antiferromagnetism. The magnetic properties of an antiferro-

---

[7] Jahn, H. A. and Teller, E., *Proc. Roy. Soc.* (London), **A161**, 220 (1937).

magnetic substance are not so striking as those of a ferromagnetic. However, they have been recognized by experiments near the Curie point, which is the temperature at which either ferro- or antiferro-magnetism breaks down to paramagnetism.   This transition is caused by the increase in thermal energy, which overcomes the tendency of the magnetic moments to take an ordered distribution.

The development of neutron diffraction has produced a new tool for the investigation of antiferromagnetism.   The magnetic moment of the neutron represents an important element in its interaction with atoms.   Consequently, the scattered neutron beam intensity in a diffraction experiment depends on the orientation of any permanent magnetic moments associated with atoms in the crystal.

There are many paramagnetic solids where the interactions between magnetic atoms are sufficient to cause deviations from Curie's law, but not large enough to yield a ferromagnetic or an antiferromagnetic material.   Above their respective Curie points, ferromagnetic sub-stances fall into this category.   Weiss has generalized Curie's law in the form

$$\chi_{mol} = (\text{const.})/(T + \Delta) \tag{12.47}$$

This expression fits a considerable amount of magnetic data on sub-stances of the type we have mentioned.

The salts $MnSO_4$ and $FeSO_4$ exist in both anhydrous and hydrated form, and their behavior offers an excellent example of the increased interaction between metal ions as they are brought closer together. The hydrated crystals, $MnSO_4 \cdot 4H_2O$ and $FeSO_4 \cdot 7H_2O$ obey Curie's law quite accurately.   If the Weiss expression is used, the values of Δ are $1°K$ or less.   However, if the water is removed, the Δ values rise to $24°$ for $MnSO_4$ and $31°$ for $FeSO_4$.   In some other cases, such as $FeCl_2$ and $NiCl_2$, negative values of Δ are obtained by fitting the Weiss expression to data near room temperature.

Throughout this section we have ignored the second term in Eqs. (12.13) and (12.15), together with any second-order perturbation effects from the first term.   These effects usually yield a net diamag-netic contribution.   Also there may be other diamagnetic substances present in the sample, such as water and negative ions in the aqueous solutions or hydrated rare earth crystals.   We have assumed that any of these diamagnetic terms of significant magnitude have been taken into account in computing the experimental paramagnetic susceptibility.   However, typical gram diamagnetic susceptibilities are of the order of 10^{-6} or less, while paramagnetic susceptibilities at room temperature are frequently in the vicinity of 10^{-4}. Thus the diamagnetic correction is often negligible.

12f. Diamagnetism. We wish now to consider cases where there is no permanent magnetic moment. Such substances are normally diamagnetic in that they are repelled by a magnetic field. In atoms the orbital angular momentum about the z axis is exactly quantized in the sense that the application of the angular momentum operator to the wave function yields a numerical constant times the unchanged wave function. If that constant is zero, the orbital angular momentum and magnetic moment are both zero. We assume also that the net electron spin is zero. Then the application of Eqs. (12.13) and (12.15) yields a nonzero result only for the second term. Thus for diamagnetic atoms, we have

$$\chi_{mol} = -\frac{e^2 N_0}{4mc^2} \sum_i (\bar{x}_i^2 + \bar{y}_i^2) = -\frac{e^2 N_0}{6mc^2} \sum_i \bar{r}_i^2 \qquad (12.48)$$

where in the second equality the equivalence of the three directions in space for a spherical atom is used. The mean values in the sums are, of course, the quantum mechanical averages involving integrals over the probability distribution indicated by the wave function.

We see that the diamagnetic susceptibility offers a measure of the mean radius of the electronic orbitals in atoms. A calculation of the mean value of r^2 for hydrogen-like orbitals yields for a single electron the result,

$$\chi_{mol} = -\frac{e^2 N_0 a_0^2}{6mc^2}\left[\frac{5n^4 - 3n^2 l(l+1) + n^2}{2Z^2}\right] \qquad (12.49)$$

While this equation is not directly applicable to stable atoms whose susceptibility may be measured, it can be used in connection with a screening constant type of treatment. In that case Z is replaced by Z^* or $(Z - S)$ as indicated in Section 5d. Since the contribution of an electron depends on $n^4/(Z^*)^2$, it is apparent that the outer shell of electrons will make the predominant contribution to the susceptibility.

Let us pass over the case of linear molecules, whose intermediate character will be apparent, and turn to nonlinear molecules. Now we have no exact quantization of orbital angular momenta. In addition to the contribution of the term discussed in the preceding paragraphs, a second-order contribution is obtained from the first term of Eq. (12.13) or (12.15). The net result can then be expressed formally as

$$\chi_{mol} = -\frac{e^2 N_0}{6mc^2} \sum_j \bar{r}_j^2 + \frac{2}{3} N_0 \sum_i{}' \frac{(m_x)_i^2 + (m_y)_i^2 + (m_z)_i^2}{E_i - E_0} \tag{12.50}$$

where the magnetic moment transition integrals are of the type

$$(m_x)_i = \int \psi_i^* \left[\sum_j (e_j/2m_j c) M_{x_j} \right] \psi_0 \, dv \tag{12.51}$$

The sums in j cover all particles in the molecule, and the M's are angular momentum operators. Random orientation of the molecules with respect to the field has been assumed. It will be noted that the second term in Eq. (12.50) is exactly analogous to Eq. (12.23) for the electric polarizability. Its derivation follows an exactly similar pattern to that given in Appendix 20 for the polarizability.

These magnetic moment transition integrals are not readily evaluated, but it may be seen that some such quantities must be present. The first term in Eq. (12.50) is dependent on a selection of the origin of coordinates, which is not self-evident for a polyatomic molecule. However, Van Vleck[1] shows that the change in the two terms of Eq. (12.50) exactly cancel one another for a change in the origin.

The diamagnetic susceptibility of molecules has been treated empirically, principally by Pascal.[8] The results are somewhat similar to those obtained for the electronic molal refractivities of molecules. A general approximate additivity relationship is found, but there are many situations requiring additional correction constants.

The aromatic hydrocarbons are sometimes pictured as allowing π electrons to move freely around their rings. This would give an anisotropy, because, with the molecules in the xy plane, the mean

TABLE 12.3

ANISOTROPIC DIAMAGNETISM OF AROMATIC RINGS
(Molal susceptibilities $\times 10^6$ along the axes indicated)

	x	y	z
Benzene:	37.3	37.3	91.2
Naphthalene:	53.9	56.1	169.0
Anthracene:	62.6	75.8	251.8

[8] Pascal, P., in *Traite de chimie organique*, Vol. 2, ed. V. Grignard, Paris: Masson et C., 1936, pp. 515–573.

values of x^2 and y^2 would be much larger than that of z^2. This effect is substantial, as is indicated by the data in Table 12.3. In the cases of naphthalene and anthracene the several rings are along the x axis.

Pauling[9] and London[10] have both discussed the theory of this sort of diamagnetism, which is sometimes called large orbit diamagnetism.

Before closing these sections on magnetic effects it is desirable to emphasize again the essentially quantum nature of atomic and molecular magnetism. There exists a theorem of Miss van Leeuwen which proves that an assemblage of charged particles moving classically with thermal energy will have zero magnetic susceptibility. The general proof, while not difficult, would require additional development of classical equations of motion for particles in an electromagnetic field. The reader may find it in Van Vleck[1] or elsewhere. However, we can easily demonstrate the cancellation of the two terms of Eq. (12.15) for a simple model.

Suppose that we have a singled charge particle held at a fixed distance R from a point in space, but otherwise free to rotate. The moment of inertia is mR^2, and at the temperature T, the angular momentum will be

$$M^2 = 2IkT = 2mR^2kT \tag{12.52}$$

Strictly, this is the average of a thermal distribution, but it may be used as a single value. Then the square of the magnetic moment is

$$\mu^2 = \frac{e^2}{4m^2c^2} M^2 = \frac{e^2R^2kT}{2mc^2} \tag{12.53}$$

The orientation of this magnetic moment with respect to the field will be subject to exactly the same equations as applied to electric dipole orientation. Then Eq. (12.20) yields

$$\bar{\mu}_1 = \frac{\mathcal{K}\mu^2}{3kT} = \frac{\mathcal{K}e^2R^2}{6mc^2} \tag{12.54}$$

where the subscript 1 was added to indicate that this is a value for only the first term of Eq. (12.15). For the second term in that equation, we have

$$\bar{\mu}_2 = -\frac{\mathcal{K}e^2}{4mc^2} (\bar{x}^2 + \bar{y}^2) \tag{12.55}$$

but the mean values of the squares of x, y, and z must all be the same

9 Pauling, J., *J. Chem. Phys.*, **4**, 673 (1936).
10 London, F., *J. phys. radium*, **8**, 397 (1937).

and equal to $R^2/3$. Then we have

$$\bar{\mu_2} = - \frac{5Ce^2R^2}{6mc^2}$$ (12.56)

which exactly cancels the first term.

Paramagnetism arises from unpaired spins or from the nonzero quantization of orbital angular momentum of charged particles. Diamagnetism occurs in the absence of a quantized magnetic moment. But again quantum effects are important, because, if there were excited states with magnetic moment accessible in the thermal energy range, the sort of cancellation illustrated in Eqs. (12.54) and (12.56) would occur. Thus both para- and diamagnetism have an essentially quantum origin.

12g. Statistical theory of reaction rates. While the theory of thermodynamics is incapable of treating the rates of chemical reactions, the combined theories of quantum mechanics and statistical mechanics do yield a theory of chemical kinetics. The Arrhenius equation

$$k = Ae^{-E/RT}$$ (12.57)

breaks the rate expression into two principal factors, the activation energy E, and the constant A, which is variously called the collision number, frequency factor, etc. Although in principle the quantum statistical theory is a single unit, in its practical approximation it divides into two broad sections which treat these two factors somewhat independently. Eyring, M. G. Evans, and Polanyi have made major contributions to statistical rate theory.

To calculate the rate of the reaction

$$A + B + \ldots = M + N + \ldots$$

one must have the complete expression for the energy of the combined system, including all the nuclei in the reacting molecules, as a function of the various internuclear coordinates. Following the usual Born-Oppenheimer approximation, it is assumed that the electronic motion is rapid as compared with the motion of the nuclei. Consequently it is appropriate to regard the total electronic energy, together with the internuclear potential terms, as the effective potential energy for nuclear motion. This potential function can be visualized as a surface in which the energy is the vertical coordinate and the internuclear distances are horizontal coordinates.

In principle, there will usually be more than one possible arrangement of electron spins for the entire system.   Thus there will be a separate potential function for each electronic state of different net spin.   Usually one of these potential surfaces is the lowest in all important regions, and as a consequence the others may be ignored. However, this is not always the case, and the possibility of a chemical reaction proceeding through an intermediate state of different spin must be kept in mind at all times.

Let us now choose a simple type of reaction as an example—that

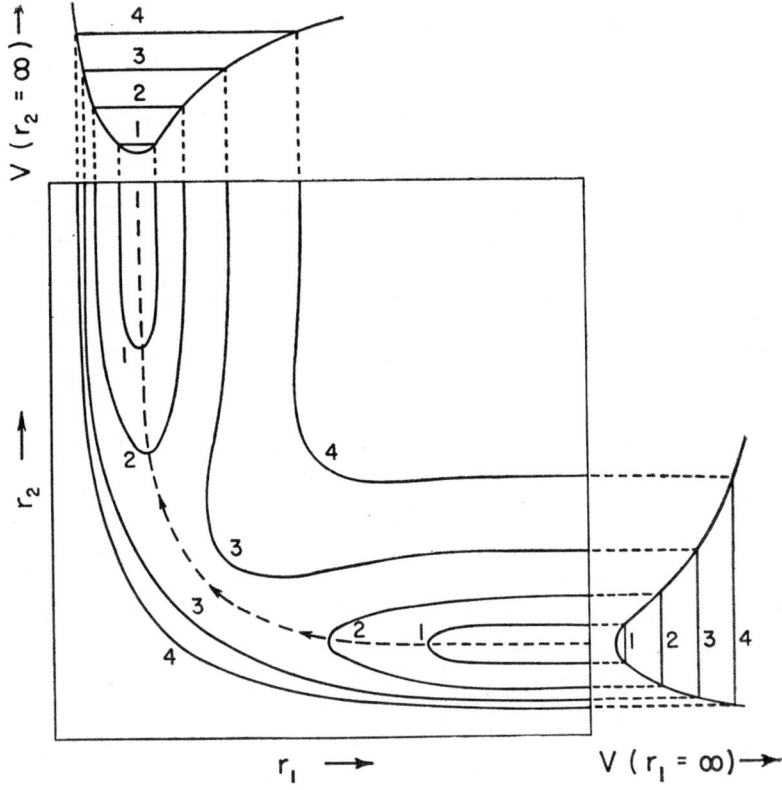

Fig. 12.3. A contour map of a potential energy surface for the linear system A–A–A as a function of the two shorter A–A distances, r_1 and r_2. The potential curves are also shown for the diatomic molecules (where the third atom is at infinite distance).

of an atom A with a diatomic molecule A_2.

$$A + A_2 = A + A_2$$

the net change which one can measure may be a redistribution of isotopic species, as in

$$H + D_2 = D + HD$$

or a rearrangement of nuclear spins as in the conversion of *para* H_2 to *ortho* H_2.

In this case the combined system is the triatomic unit A_3. The potential energy is a function of three variables which may be taken as either the three interatomic distances, r_{12}, r_{13}, and r_{23} or the two shorter distances and the angle between these two "bonds." Three-dimensional space allows us to represent a potential surface as a function of only two of these variables at a time. Thus Fig. 12.3 represents a possible potential surface for a linear A-A-A system as a function of the two shorter A-A distances. The minimum energy path for the reaction is also indicated by the line with the arrowheads on it.

We can expect that the characteristics of the "summit of pass," through which this reaction path proceeds, will be the determining factors in the reaction rate. Consequently we focus our attention on a region of length δ, along the reaction coordinate at the summit. This is illustrated further in Fig. 12.4, where the energy is plotted

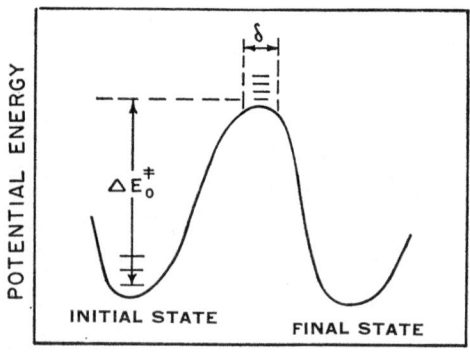

Fig. 12.4.   Potential energy curve along the reaction path or reaction coordinate showing the hypothetical region of length δ containing the activated state.

as a function of the reaction path as a linear coordinate. The region of length δ at the summit represents the system in the *activated state* or the *activated complex*. The actual length δ is arbitrary, and will be shown eventually to cancel out of the rate expression. However, quantum mechanics does not allow us to discuss the system at a precise value of a coordinate when we are to consider the simultaneous momentum.

Now the general argument proceeds in the following manner. First we consider a state of complete equilibrium. The ratio of systems in the initial and final states will be given by the usual principles of statistical thermodynamics. In such a calculation the very small number of activated complexes is ignored. However, for our present purpose we shall also calculate the number of systems in the activated state. We also note that systems in the activated state will have either a positive or negative velocity for the reaction coordinate. For such a simple potential system as we are assuming here, it is reasonable to assume that every molecular system in the activated state with a positive velocity started in the initial state and will move on into the region of the final state. Similarly, every activated system with negative velocity started in the "final" state and will move on to the "initial" state.

Next we remove all molecules in the final state. We assume that this will eliminate all those activated complexes with negative velocities along the reaction coordinate, but that the number of complexes with positive velocities will remain unchanged. Then we need only to calculate the number of systems passing from left to right through the activated state per second in order to have the rate of reaction.

The equilibrium concentrations of systems in different states are given by the ratio of the complete products of the partition functions divided by the volume. This can be derived readily from thermodynamics and the equations of Section 7n, or from pure statistical arguments such as the one used in Section 11b. Then for the reaction

$$A + B + \ldots = M + N + \ldots$$

we have for the over-all equilibrium

$$K = \frac{C_M C_N \ldots}{C_A C_B \ldots} = \frac{(Q_M/V)(Q_N/V) \ldots}{(Q_A/V)(Q_B/V) \ldots} e^{-\Delta E_0/RT} \qquad (12.58)$$

where ΔE_0 is the energy difference, per mole, between the initial and final states at $0°K$, i.e., the energy difference between the systems

388   MISCELLANEOUS TOPICS   [Chap. 12

in their lowest quantum states. This allows us to base each partition function on its lowest quantum state as the zero of energy.

Similarly, for the equilibrium concentration of activated complexes, $C_{\ddagger}$, we find

$$C_{\ddagger} = \frac{C_A C_B \cdots}{(Q_A/V)(Q_B/V) \cdots} \cdot \frac{Q_{activated}}{V} e^{-\Delta E_0^{\ddagger}/RT} \qquad (12.59)$$

where $\Delta E_0^{\ddagger}$ is the energy of activation from the lowest quantum state of the initial system to the lowest quantum state of the activated complex. Figure 12.4 shows $\Delta E_0^{\ddagger}$.

Our next problem is to calculate the partition function for the activated state. We apply exactly the principles used for ordinary molecules, including the normal coordinate method. There will be the usual three translational coordinates of the center of mass. For the linear A_3 system, there will be two rotational coordinates, but nonlinear systems would have three rotational coordinates. Then there will be a number of normal modes of vibration. The only difference is that along the reaction coordinate the derivative $\partial^2 V/\partial q_r^2$ will be negative. We will consider later the effect of this curvature; for the moment let us assume that the potential energy is constant for the short distance δ.

The factors in the partition function of the activated state for translation, rotation, and vibration are exactly the same as those for stable molecules, which have been given already. The factor for the reaction coordinate is just that for another translation, except that an appropriate reduced mass m^* replaces the total mass. Thus we have

$$\epsilon = p^2/2m^*$$

and

$$Q = \frac{1}{h} \int_0^{\delta} dq \int_{-\infty}^{+\infty} e^{-p^2/2m^*kT} \, dp$$

$$= \frac{\delta}{h} (2\pi m^* kT)^{1/2} \qquad (12.60)$$

Let us designate by $Q^{\ddagger}$ the product of all the remaining factors of the partition function for the activated state except the factor for the reaction coordinate, Eq. (12.60). Then the concentration of activated systems is

$$C_{\ddagger} = \frac{C_A C_B \cdots}{(Q_A/V)(Q_B/V) \cdots} \times \frac{\delta(2\pi m^* kT)^{1/2} Q^{\ddagger}}{hV} e^{-\Delta E_0^{\ddagger}/RT} \qquad (12.61)$$

Now we must calculate the rate at which molecular systems pass through the activated state, in terms of their concentration. The quantity we wish is $\bar{q}/\delta$. Here $\bar{q}$ is the average velocity in the reaction coordinate of those activated complexes moving only in the positive direction. Systems moving in the opposite direction are ignored except to count them in the total number. Since $\dot{q}$ is p/m^*, we have

$$\bar{q} = \frac{\int_0^\infty e^{-p^2/2m^*kT} p\, dp}{m^* \int_{-\infty}^{+\infty} e^{-p^2/2m^*kT}\, dp} = \left(\frac{kT}{2\pi m^*}\right)^{1/2} \qquad (12.62)$$

In Eq. (12.62) the limits of integration in the numerator are from zero to infinity in order to include only those complexes moving in the positive direction, whereas the limits of integration in the denominator are from minus to plus infinity in order to normalize the result on the concentration of all activated complexes which were included in the partition function in Eq. (12.60).

Now the rate of reaction, which is $-dC_A/dt$ or some equivalent quantity, is

$$\text{Rate} = \frac{C_{\pm}\bar{q}}{\delta} = k_R C_A C_B \ldots \qquad (12.63)$$

where the rate constant k_R is given the subscript to differentiate it from the Boltzmann constant. Combining our various results, we have

$$k_R = \frac{C_{\pm}\bar{q}}{\delta C_A C_B \ldots}$$

$$= \left(\frac{kT}{2\pi m^*}\right)^{1/2} \cdot \frac{1}{\delta} \cdot \frac{\delta(2\pi m^* kT)^{1/2}}{h} \frac{(Q^{\pm}/V)e^{-\Delta E_0^{\pm}/RT}}{(Q_A/V)(Q_B/V) \ldots} \qquad (12.64)$$

where the various factors have been written out in detail to emphasize how certain factors cancel and where other terms arise. The factor δ cancels because the concentration of activated complexes is proportional to δ, but the distance a reacting system must move to get across the activated state is also δ. Similarly, the reduced mass m^* cancels. With these simplifications one obtains

$$k_R = \frac{kT}{h} \frac{(Q^{\pm}/V)e^{-\Delta E_0^{\pm}/RT}}{(Q_A/V)(Q_B/V) \ldots} \qquad (12.65)$$

While the factor (kT/h) has the dimensions sec.$^{-1}$, it is important to realize that it did not arise directly but rather after combining the more complex factors. Also one should remember that $Q^{\ddagger}$ is not a complete partition function, and that the remaining factor besides $Q^{\ddagger}$ in a complete partition function for the activated state has been combined into the quantity kT/h.

Before adopting Eq. (12.65) as an adequate rate equation, we must reconsider some of our assumptions. We assumed the simple potential system of Figs. 12.3 and 12.4. It is also possible that there may be two or more potential summits of nearly equal height. Indeed, calculations for the very simple system $H_2 + H$ indicate that there are two equal maxima, as illustrated in Fig. 12.5.

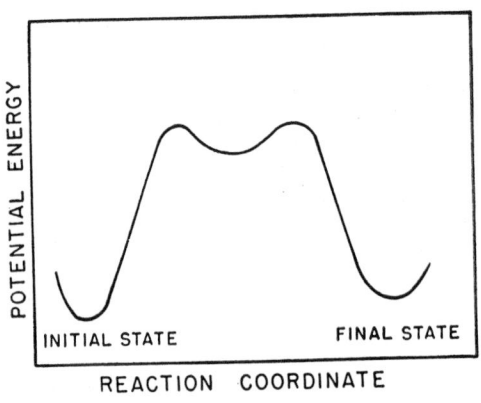

Fig. 12.5. The potential energy curve along the reaction path for a case where there are two potential maxima. Since the reaction coordinate is a complex coordinate, one cannot expect systems to be carried by their momentum across both summits in a single movement.

Now we may base our calculation on either the first or the second potential summit. If we choose the first, there will be the full number of activated complexes moving in the positive direction. However, our one-dimensional diagram is oversimplified, and we cannot expect an activated complex passing over the first summit to pass directly on over the second. Rather it will probably oscillate in its various coordinates in the high valley between the two summits. After several oscillations it may pass on over the second summit or back over the first. In this simple case of equal summits there will be equal chance for each process. Thus only half of the molecules passing the first summit in a positive direction will complete the reaction, and the actual rate will be half of that calculated by Eq. (12.65).

Alternatively, we may choose to consider the second summit for our activated state. Although we will have had our full concentration of activated complexes in the complete equilibrium state, half of those moving in the positive direction over the second summit will have actually started as products, passed the second summit to the left, oscillated in the high valley, and then passed out via the second summit to the right. Thus, when all the products are removed, the actual concentration of systems moving to the right in the activated state will drop to half of the equilibrium concentration. Thus, although every system passing the second summit moves on to the product state, the rate is only half of that calculated in Eq. (12.65).

To account for complications such as that just described, we introduce a factor κ, called the *transmission coefficient*. This factor is to allow for either a failure of systems passing the activated state to complete the reaction to products, or for a failure of the activated state to maintain its equilibrium concentration of systems moving in the desired direction. Our final equation is then

$$k_R = \kappa \, \frac{kT}{h} \, \frac{(Q^{\ddagger}/V)e^{-\Delta E_0^{\ddagger}/RT}}{(Q_A/V)(Q_B/V)\ldots} \tag{12.66}$$

If we ignore the absence of the factor for the reaction coordinate in $Q^{\ddagger}$, we may regard all the above expression to the right of the kT/h to be the equilibrium constant $K^{\ddagger}$ for the formation of the activated complex. Then the usual thermodynamic equations yield

$$\ln K^{\ddagger} = -\frac{\Delta F^{\ddagger}}{RT} = \frac{\Delta S^{\ddagger}}{R} - \frac{\Delta H^{\ddagger}}{RT} \tag{12.67}$$

and for the rate constant

$$k_R = \kappa \, \frac{kT}{h} \, e^{-\Delta F^{\ddagger}/RT} \tag{12.68}$$

$$= \kappa \, \frac{kT}{h} \, e^{\Delta S^{\ddagger}/R} e^{-\Delta H^{\ddagger}/RT} \tag{12.69}$$

The quantities $\Delta F^{\ddagger}$, $\Delta S^{\ddagger}$, and $\Delta H^{\ddagger}$ are called the free energy, entropy, and heat of activation, respectively. The heat of activation as defined above will be substantially the same as the energy of activation in the Arrhenius expression, but may differ by an amount such as RT, depending on the number of molecules entering the reaction, whether pressure or concentration units are used, etc.

It will be recalled that we assumed the top of the barrier to be flat for the distance δ. Actually it will have ordinarily a negative curvature. Thus for molecular systems below the top of the barrier in energy, there will be the possibility of penetrating the barrier in accordance with the principles discussed in Section 2g. If this penetration occurs near the top, the additional rate of reaction can be expressed in terms of the curvature of the energy surface. We take the usual equations for the harmonic oscillator (Section 2i), whereupon the force constant is negative, and when the square root is taken the frequency ν is imaginary. In terms of this imaginary frequency it has been shown[11] that the rate should be multiplied by the factor $[1 - (h\nu/kT)^2/24]$. This actually gives an increased rate because the factor ν^2 is negative. In practice this penetration of potential barriers has not been an important effect in ordinary chemical reactions.

It is beyond the scope of the present work to comment on any number of the particular reactions to which this statistical rate theory has been applied.[12]

In the very simple case of the hydrogen atom-molecule reactions such as

$$H + D_2 = HD + D$$

the completely theoretical calculations have been reasonably successful. In this case the potential energy surface may be calculated by methods related to the Heitler-London method for H_2 and the bond orbital method for larger molecules. The coulomb and exchange integrals may be evaluated empirically on certain assumptions. This theoretical potential surface not only yields the activation energy, but also the moment of inertia and the various vibration frequencies of the activated complex.

However, for the more general type of chemical reaction the theoretical calculation of the energy of activation is either impractical or is so approximate as to be little more than a rough estimate. Nevertheless, it is frequently possible to make a reasonably good calculation of the entropy of the activated complex for a proposed reaction mechanism. The moments of inertia are not very sensitive to the

[11] Wigner, E. P., Z. physik. Chem., B19, 203 (1932); Eckart, C., Phys. Rev., 35, 1303 (1930); Bell, R. P., Proc. Roy. Soc. (London), A139, 466 (1933).

[12] See, for example, Glasstone, S., Laidler, K. J., and Eyring, H., The Theory of Rate Processes, New York: McGraw-Hill Book Company, Inc., 1941.

exact atomic locations if the general pattern is fixed. Also, most of the vibration frequencies can be assigned values typical of the postulated bonds as observed in stable molecules.

There are many additional complications in chemical kinetics which are beyond the scope of this section. Our only aim here was to give the basic outline of a statistical rate theory which could be extended to meet more complex situations. The older collision theory can, of course, handle many of the same problems in different terms.

GENERAL REFERENCES

Biggs, H. F., *The Electromagnetic Field*, New York: Oxford University Press, 1934.

Fowler, R., and Guggenheim, E. A., *Statistical Thermodynamics*, London: Cambridge University Press, 1939.

Glasstone, S., Laidler, K. J., and Eyring, H., *The Theory of Rate Processes*, New York: McGraw-Hill Book Company, Inc., 1941.

Joos, G., *Theoretical Physics*, 2d ed., New York: Hafner Publishing Company, Inc., 1950.

Van Vleck, J. H., *Electric and Magnetic Susceptibilities*, New York: Oxford University Press, 1932.

Chapter 13

NUCLEAR PHENOMENA

13a. The general nature of nuclear theory. Nuclear phenomena and the forces within nuclei represent a subject of comparable breadth with that of atomic phenomena and forces within molecules, which has occupied our attention to this point. Thus it is obviously impossible to present more than a few introductory topics in this chapter. Also there are many topics whose treatment would require extensive additions to our basic theory.

There is one very basic difference between current nuclear theory and atomic and molecular theory. The latter is potentially all deductive. The fundamental theory appears to be complete, so that the insertion of the charges, masses, and spins of the electrons and of the various nuclei involved in a given problem is sufficient, in principle, to allow the computation of the properties of the resulting system. The theory of nuclear phenomena is in an entirely different state. The basic force law is one of short range. Therefore one has no chance of extrapolating from macroscopic distances as was done for the coulombic law for electric charges. Similarly, one can never be sure where quantum mechanics may break down on further extrapolation into unknown regions, just as Newtonian mechanics failed in the areas of both relativity (high velocities) and quantum mechanics (small energy-time or momentum-distance products). Consequently, nuclear theory is essentially inductive, and as often as not, speculative. Its final form may bear little resemblance to the components to be mentioned in this chapter.

There is another general idea which is important to the understanding of nuclear phenomena and which can be introduced best by an analogy. Let us assume for the moment that we are investigating hydrogen and helium, and that we have at our disposal energies only up to about 5 volts. At these low energies neither substance could be ionized or even raised to an excited electronic state. Thus one would never learn explicitly of the existence of electrons. One could study the dissociation of H_2 into atoms and the scattering of the various atoms by one another. All these phenomena could be described by potential functions for the interaction of H with H, He with He, H with He, H_2 with H, H_2 with He and H_2 with H_2. One would be inclined to think of the H and He atoms as the ultimate particles and to puzzle over the apparent lack of any simple relationship among their interaction potentials.

However, at higher energies both atoms are readily ionized, and a whole array of additional phenomena appear. Now the theory must be based on the nuclei and electrons, and the earlier theory for whole atoms appears as a limiting approximation for low energies.

Much of our present information with respect to the interactions of nuclei lies in this "low-energy" range. Thus in the bombardment of protons with protons only elastic collisions are found up to 350 Mev. (or half that energy in the "center of mass" coordinate system). We must remember that this does not prove that protons are ultimate, fundamental particles. Rather it indicates that we have not yet reached the energy of excitation or of dissociation of a proton. The complexity of the interactions of nuclear particles and particularly the discoveries of various types of mesons suggest that protons and neutrons are complex particles. However, just as it is easier to excite or ionize some heavy atoms than either hydrogen or helium, likewise it has been easier to excite or to dissociate heavy nuclei than either the proton or the neutron.

13b. The size of nuclei. While there is no method of determining the size of nuclei that does not make some interpretative assumptions, there are several quite independent methods that yield concordant results.

Probably the most direct method is that of fast neutron scattering. Neutrons have no long-distance interaction with nuclei, and if we raise their energy to the point that their wave length is short compared with nuclear distances, the scattering cross section should approximate the geometrical area πR^2. (Note that this limit of high energy is the opposite of that assumed in several of the equations of Appendix 23.) Actually there is an additional "shadow scattering" over very small angles which must be excluded. Also the neutron energy must not exceed the maximum interaction potential with the nucleus, or the neutrons might pass through the nucleus unscattered. These conditions are satisfied by neutrons of a few Mev. energy. Their scattering yields a cross section of about 3×10^{-24} cm.^{2} or 3 barns (where a barn $= 10^{-24}$ cm.^{2}) for heavy elements such as Pb or U. This corresponds to a radius of about 10^{-12} cm. Elements in the middle of the periodic table, such as Fe, show a radius of about 6×10^{-13} cm.

A somewhat less direct method concerns the electrostatic energy of so-called "mirror nuclei." These pairs of nuclei can be thought to consist of an equal number of protons and neutrons plus one neutron or one proton. Thus we have as examples

$$(_1H^3, \ _2He^3); \quad (_3Li^7, \ _4Be^7); \quad (_6C^{13}, \ _7N^{13}); \quad (_{14}Si^{29}, \ _{15}P^{29})$$

We examine the difference in energy between the two members of each pair. Although the neutron itself is slightly unstable as compared to a hydrogen atom, and H^3 similarly tends to change to He^3, the second member of these pairs becomes gradually the less stable as the total positive charge accumulates. While this might be explained in other ways, the simplest explanation is to attribute this shift in energy difference to the repulsive electric potential for the extra positive charge. In effect we are assuming equality of short range neutron-neutron and proton-proton interactions within the nucleus. This assumption is consistent with the presently favored theories of nuclear forces.

The assumption of a spherical shape for the nucleus with Z protons gives a potential at a radius R outside the nucleus for an additional proton of

$$\Phi = Ze^2/R \tag{13.1}$$

This is the energy necessary to bring the additional charge to the surface of the nucleus. The calculation is more complex for the process to place the extra charge within and uniformly distributed throughout the sphere, but it yields just a factor 1.2 times the result above. Actually we would expect the positive charge to concentrate somewhat on the surface, so that the correct result should lie between these two expressions.

On this basis, a number of radii have been calculated and the empirical equation

$$R = 1.5 \times 10^{-13}A^{1/3} \quad \text{cm.} \tag{13.2}$$

has been derived, where A is the atomic weight. Since the volume of a sphere is $4\pi R^3/3$, it is evident that the density of nuclei is approximately constant. If we define *nucleon* to be a term for either a neutron or proton, the volume per nucleon is about the same in all nuclei. This constant and definite density for various sizes of sample is also typical of ordinary solids and liquids, although there it is the force associated with the outer electrons which gives that result.

Another value of nuclear size can be obtained from the data on α-particle radioactivity which we shall discuss in the next section.

13c. α-Radioactivity. Many very heavy nuclei, and several of intermediate weight, undergo radioactive decay by the emission of an α-particle, a He^4 nucleus. It was found by Geiger and Nuttall in 1911 that the half life $t_{1/2}$ can be related to the energy of the emitted particle E by the equation

$$\log t_{1/2} = A - B \log E \qquad (13.3)$$

which holds for a group of similar radioactivities with given values of the empirical constants A and B. This behavior can be understood as a penetration of a potential barrier by the α-particle. In Fig. 13.1 we see the shape that this barrier must have. For the greater distance it is just that given by the electrostatic potential of an α-particle in the field of the remaining nucleus of charge $Z - 2$.

From our simple consideration of the penetration of potential barriers in Section 2g, it is clear that the probability of penetration

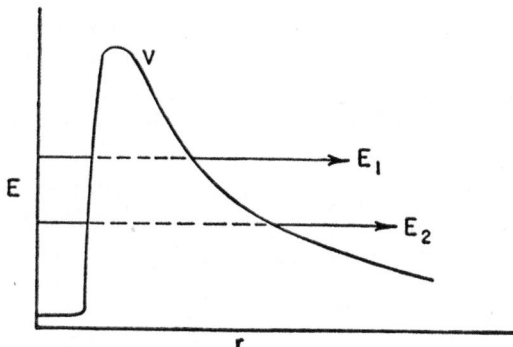

Fig. 13.1. The potential curve for an α particle near a nucleus. The height and thickness of the barrier which must be penetrated is shown for sample α particle energies.

depends exponentially on the thickness of the barrier and its height above the particle energy. The probability also depends on the particle mass, but this is constant for all α disintegrations.

The proper calculation for α-radioactivity differs from that of Section 2g in two respects: first, the shape of the barrier, and second, the extension from one dimension to three. We shall not give the details here but will point out that one of the essential features is the radius at which the coulombic repulsive potential stops and nuclear attractive forces become predominant. It is this radius which effectively gives the height of the barrier. Various investigators have found values near 9×10^{-13} cm. for the radius in heavy elements. This value is evidently in reasonable accord with the radius values quoted in the preceding section.

13d. Nuclear properties: spin, magnetic moment, and electric quadrupole moment. In addition to the well-known properties of mass and charge, we should give some attention to certain additional properties of nuclei. We have already noted the effect of nuclear spin on the rotational spectra of symmetrical molecules. Nuclear spin angular momentum manifests itself in a few other ways, but usually in connection with the magnetic moment of the nucleus. Spin, as before, is reported in units of $h/2\pi$, but nuclear magnetic moments are reported in terms of the *nuclear magneton*. This is $(eh/4\pi Mc)$, and differs from the Bohr magneton in the use of the proton mass M, in place of the electron mass.

In atomic spectra the magnetic moment of the nucleus interacts to give a *hyperfine structure*, just as the electron magnetic moment gives a fine structure. The number of hyperfine structure components indicates the spin. The magnetic moment influences the separation of the component lines.

Another general method of investigation is that of radiofrequency spectroscopy. Here we investigate directly transitions which merely reorient the nuclear spin. Under favorable conditions the magnetic moment of the nucleus can be calculated from the frequency of these lines and the magnetic field strength. For the very light nuclei, such as H and D, Rabi determined these properties in atomic or molecular beam experiments.

The neutron constituted a special problem, but it was found that a beam of neutrons passing through a magnetized block of iron became polarized. Then a second block of magnetized iron can be used as an analyzer, like a Nicol prism with polarized light.   Now one can investigate the frequency required to depolarize the neutron beam between the two iron blocks.   Thus the magnetic moment of the neutron was measured.

Finally, it is found that nuclei with a spin of one or greater show an electric quadrupole moment.   In Appendix 21 we discuss the energy of reorientation of this quadrupole moment in the unsymmetrical electric field arising from chemical bonds.   This moment is given a positive sign if the positive electric charge tends to be concentrated on the axis of spin, i.e., a prolate spheroid.   The opposite case of an oblate spheroid of positive charge is given a negative quadrupole moment.   In terms of the average values of $\overline{z^2}$ and $\overline{r^2}$ for all of the charged components of the nucleus, the quadrupole moment is

$$eQ = \sum_i e_i \overline{(3z_i^2 - r_i^2)} \qquad (13.4)$$

TABLE 13.1

PROPERTIES OF SEVERAL NUCLEI

Z	Isotope	M	Spin	μ (mag.)	Q (10^{-24} cm.^{2})
0	n	1.00899	$\frac{1}{2}$	-1.9128	0
1	H^1	1.00815	$\frac{1}{2}$	2.7926	0
	H^2	2.01474	1	0.8574	0.00273
2	He^3	3.0170	$\frac{1}{2}$	$(-)2.1274$	0
	He^4	4.0039	0	0	0
3	Li^6	6.0170	1	0.8219	$<10^{-3}$
	Li^7	7.0182	$\frac{3}{2}$	3.2559	(0.02)
4	Be^9	9.0150	$\frac{3}{2}$	-1.177	(0.02)
5	B^{10}	10.0162	3	1.800	0.06
	B^{11}	11.0128	$\frac{3}{2}$	2.6886	0.03
6	C^{12}	12.0038	0	0	0
	C^{13}	13.0075	$\frac{1}{2}$	0.7022	0
7	N^{14}	14.0075	1	0.4036	0.02
	N^{15}	15.0049	$\frac{1}{2}$	-0.2830	0
8	O^{16}	16.0000	0	0	0
	O^{17}	17.0045	$\frac{5}{2}$	-1.8935	-0.005
	O^{18}	18.005	0	0	0
17	Cl^{35}	34.979	$\frac{5}{2}$	0.8219	-0.0789
	Cl^{37}	36.977	$\frac{5}{2}$	0.6841	-0.0621
25	Mn^{55}	54.957	$\frac{5}{2}$	3.4681	?
45	Rh^{103}	102.941	$\frac{1}{2}$	$(-)0.11$	0
57	La^{139}	138.95	$\frac{7}{2}$	2.776	?
83	Bi^{209}	209.05	$\frac{9}{2}$	4.082	-0.4
90	Th^{232}	232.11	0	0	0

where the sum covers all charged particles (each of charge e_i), and the z axis is that of the spin angular momentum. The mean value implies the usual quantum mechanical average. It is customary to quote values of the ratio of the true moment to the proton charge. This is given the symbol Q.

We list in Table 13.1 these various properties of a number of nuclei. The isotopic weights M include the mass of the electrons to make the neutral atoms and are based on $O^{16} = 16.0000$. The mass number A is the integer near M.

13e. The deuteron and low-energy neutron-proton scattering. Let us turn now to the simplest example of the basic problem of nuclear structure, the formation of a deuteron from a proton and a neutron. This is analogous to the problem of the hydrogen molecule, which is fundamental to covalent chemical bonds generally. However, our mode of attack on the deuteron problem is quite different, because we do not know the cause of attraction between proton and neutron. Also, we were aided in the case of hydrogen by the multitude of vibrational and rotational energy levels, which allowed us to calculate the interatomic potential curve to high accuracy. So far as is now known, there are no excited states of the deuteron below the dissociation energy. Thus the energy of the deuteron provides just one datum. Additional information can be obtained from the scattering of neutrons by protons, but with all the data up to a few Mev. energy only two parameters, the width and depth, of the attractive potential can be evaluated. One still does not know the shape of the curve, nor does one know whether there is a repulsive region at shorter distances, such as is present for atomic interactions. Very recently, scattering data have become available in the energy range of a few hundred Mev. These data do give further information, but they have not yet been fully interpreted. Consequently, we shall first describe in this section the theory based upon the low-energy data, even though we know that the results will require modification to fit the higher energy results.

The deuteron is a two-particle system. Consequently, we can use all the preliminary work of Chapter 3 for the hydrogen atom and the diatomic molecule. Our major questions are, first, the applicability of nonrelativistic quantum mechanics, and second, the nature of the potential energy of proton-neutron interaction.

The net binding energy of the deuteron is represented in the masses in Table 13.1, although direct measurements of the dissociation energy are most accurate. The deuteron mass is less than the sum of the proton and neutron masses by 0.00240 atomic mass unit. This represents a decrease in internal energy according to the equation of relativity.

$$\Delta E = \Delta mc^2 = 3.57 \times 10^{-6} \text{ erg} = 2.23 \text{ Mev.} \qquad (13.5)$$

Since this mass change is a small fraction of a proton or neutron mass, it is at least plausible that the particle velocities within the deuteron are nonrelativistic. However, we shall have to check upon this conclusion later.

For our initial calculations we shall assume that the potential depends only on the distance between the proton and neutron, i.e., a central force. We realize that this is an oversimplification because it cannot explain the quadrupole moment of the deuteron. The single numerical value of the binding energy will allow us to fix only one parameter of the potential function. From various sources there is evidence that nuclear forces are of short range. The simplest potential of that nature is a vertical walled spherical potential well defined by the conditions

$$V = 0, \qquad r > r_0$$
$$V = -V_0, \qquad r < r_0 \qquad (13.6)$$

The binding energy W_B is then the energy below the level outside the well. In Appendix 22 we give the solution of the Schrödinger equation for this potential. It involves the fitting together of solutions for the two regions $r < r_0$ and $r > r_0$, and yields for states of zero orbital angular momentum (s states) the equation

$$\cot \frac{2\pi r_0}{h} \sqrt{M(V_0 - W_B)} = -\sqrt{W_B / (V_0 - W_B)} \qquad (13.7)$$

where M is the mean mass of proton and neutron.

Evidently we cannot solve Eq. (13.7) for both V_0 and r_0; we must have further information. Also we have no assurance that the potential has the assumed shape. An excited state for the deuteron would yield another datum, but no stable excited state has ever been found. Additional data can be obtained from the scattering of neutrons by protons.

To this point we have ignored the spin of the proton and the neu-

tron. Each have half unit spin; consequently the possible states are
a singlet of zero spin and a triplet of unit spin. The latter is the
stable state of the deuteron. Since the neutron and proton are different particles, the Pauli exclusion principle does not apply. Equation (13.7) is equally applicable to a singlet state. Hence the absence
of a singlet state of about the same energy as that of the normal
deuteron indicates that the potential depends in some way on the
relative spin orientation.

Since we cannot separate the neutron-proton scattering caused by
the singlet interaction from that caused by the triplet interaction, we
must handle the two effects simultaneously. The theory of scattering cross sections is discussed in Appendix 23. For low neutron
energies, say 1 Mev. or less, the wave length of the neutron in free
space is long compared with the range of the nuclear forces, r_0. Also
one needs to consider only collisions involving zero angular momentum, i.e., s states, because low-energy collisions with angular momentum never bring the particles close together. These assumptions
permit considerable simplification of the equation for scattering,
yielding for the total cross section σ the approximate formula[1]

$$\sigma = \frac{h^2}{4\pi M}\left[\frac{3}{E+W_t} + \frac{1}{E+|W_s|}\right] \tag{13.8}$$

where the subscripts s and t refer to the singlet and triplet interactions, respectively. E is the kinetic energy at $r > r_0$ in the "center
of mass" coordinate system. E is one-half of the bombarding neutron energy in this case where both particles have the same mass
(see Appendix 23). W_t is the binding energy of the normal deuteron
W_B, while W_s is the energy of the lowest singlet state of the deuteron.
The absolute magnitude sign indicates that the scattering effect is
the same for an unstable or "virtual" state of negative binding energy
as for a stable state of the same magnitude of W. The definition of
such a "virtual" energy level is necessarily arbitrary. For a potential
well of the type we have assumed, the definition consistent with
Eq. (13.8) is

$$\cot\left[\frac{2\pi r_0}{h}\sqrt{M(V_0+W_v)}\right] = +\sqrt{W_v/(V_0+W_v)}, \quad W_v > 0 \tag{13.9}$$

[1] Equation (13.8) also involves the assumption that $W \ll V_0$. See Appendix 23
for the corrections when this is not an adequate approximation.

One may note that this is similar, but not identical, to Eq. (13.7), with the sign of W reversed.

In Eq. (13.8) the factor 3 in the first term within the brackets arises from the three possible spin wave functions for the triplet state. This gives triple probability to the triplet scattering as compared with the singlet scattering.

Actually one cannot use free protons as a target; they will be chemically bonded in some manner. So long as the bombarding neutron energy is large compared with the bond energy, this does not matter. However, for very small neutron energies, corrections must be made for the binding of the protons and possibly for the total mass of the molecule in which they are bound.

In the formula for the cross section, the first term yields only about 2×10^{-24} cm.^{2}. At low neutron energies the observed σ is a little over 20×10^{-24}, when corrected to the basis of free protons. Thus one concludes that $|W_s|$ is very much smaller than W_t; indeed $|W_s|$ has been found to be about 0.064 Mev., while W_t was 2.23 Mev.

The range of the nuclear forces can be obtained from the deviation of the cross section from Eq. (13.8) as the bombarding energy is increased. For n-p scattering the singlet term predominates; hence this range value applies effectively to that state. The value obtained [2] is about 2.7×10^{-13} cm.

We have still to determine whether the singlet state is real or not. This is found from the scattering cross section of *para* hydrogen for very slow neutrons. The best measurements involve hydrogen at 20°K and neutrons of equivalent velocity, i.e., with energy equal to thermal energy at 20°K. These extremely slow neutrons have such a long wave length that they effectively interact with both protons of the H_2 molecule as if they were in the same location. In *ortho* hydrogen the protons have parallel spins, hence the neutron will interact in the same manner with each, i.e., either both singlet or both triplet. Thus the *ortho* hydrogen cross section should be related to that for free protons by factors accounting for the two protons present, the effective mass of the system, the velocity of the protons, etc.

It is the scattering from *para* hydrogen that yields new information. Since *para* H_2 has opposed proton spins, the interaction must be triplet with one proton and singlet with the other. However, the

[2] Lampi, E. E., Freier, G. D., and Williams, J. H., *Phys. Rev.*, **80**, 853 (1950).

net scattering probability arises from the interference of the two waves, one from the singlet interaction and one from the triplet interaction. Consequently, the phase difference between the two scattered waves is important, as well as their respective amplitudes. While we shall not attempt to give this theory in detail, it is found that the sign of W_s affects this phase difference. If the singlet state is a virtual state, the scattered waves very nearly cancel, while for a real singlet state the waves largely reinforce one another. Thus one predicts roughly equal cross sections for *ortho* and *para* hydrogen if the singlet state is stable, whereas the scattering of *para* hydrogen should be much less if the singlet state is a virtual state.

Experimentally it is found that the *para* cross section is only about 3% of the *ortho* cross section. This leads to the definite conclusion that the singlet state of the deuteron is a virtual state. The range of the potential well in the triplet state can also be calculated from the numerical value of the *para* hydrogen cross section. However, the result is quite sensitive to any errors in the other data or in the cross section value, because it arises effectively as a difference between larger quantities. Other experiments[3] of a more complex character have given the value 1.7×10^{-13} cm. for the range of the force in the triplet state.

The depth of the assumed square potential well can be calculated from the values of W and r_0 for the singlet and triplet interactions separately. The results are V_0 (triplet) $= 48$ Mev. and V_0 (singlet) $= 13$ Mev. However, it should be remembered that these values depend on both the assumption of the square well and the accuracy of the values of the range. Hence they do not have great significance.

Now that we have at least a tentative value of V_0 for the triplet state, we can verify that our nonrelativistic calculation was permissible. On the classical basis the value of (v^2/c^2) within the potential well is 0.2, where v is the relative velocity of the two particles. Thus our results are valid qualitatively, although some correction may be required for high accuracy.

It is appropriate to remark at this point that it would take a far larger attractive potential to confine an electron in a nucleus, than that assumed between neutrons and protons. If Eq. (13.7) applied, one can see that V_0 would have to increase in about the ratio of the proton to electron mass. However, at such energies relativistic me-

3 Burgy, M. T., Ringo, G. R., and Hughes, D. J., *Phys. Rev.*, **84**, 1160 (1951).

chanics would have to be used.   While current theories do not assume electrons in the nucleus, it is worth while to see the difficulties which would arise if any particle of electronic mass were confined within the nucleus.

The wave function for the normal state of the deuteron is shown in Fig. 13.2, along with the assumed potential well.   It is interesting

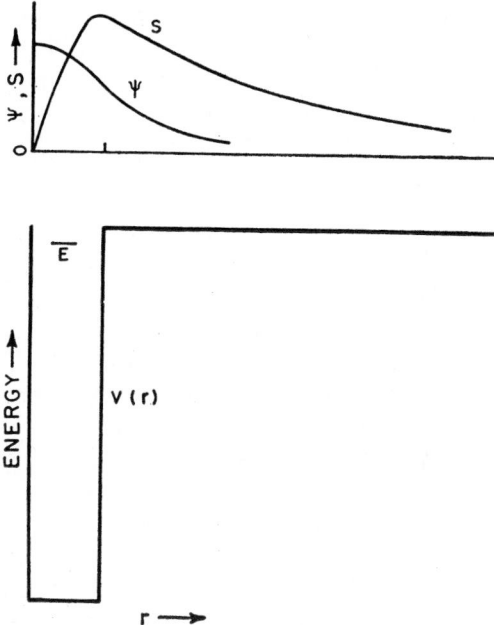

Fig. 13.2.   The spherical potential well assumed for the deuteron, the energy level at E, and the wave function.   The function S is $r\psi$, and its square gives the radial probability distribution.

to note from the function $S = r\psi$ the large probability of finding the particles outside of the potential well.   The precise shape of the potential well does not have much effect on the wave function and consequently on the experimental properties.   In particular the meson theory of Yukawa (Section 13f) leads to the function

$$V = -Ar^{-1}e^{-\eta r} \tag{13.10}$$

which gives a short range force.   Thus V approaches zero rapidly as

r exceeds η^{-1}. The properties calculated for a Yukawa potential[4] do not differ greatly from those for a square well.

To this point we have considered only central forces. Such a force law can never give the deuteron a quadrupole moment. However, we have assumed the force to be dependent on the relative orientation of proton and neutron spins. This is quite unlike the electrostatic force between an electron and a proton, which is assumed to be unaffected by the relative orientation of proton and electron spins. Thus, if we are to assume the potential to depend on the relative spin orientation, it is reasonable to assume also a dependence on the angle between the net spin vector and the line connecting the two particles. To yield the prolate or cigar-like shape required by the quadrupole moment, the potential function must favor small values of this angle.

Another effect of this sort of noncentral force is an interaction of spin and orbital angular momenta. This is an explanation of the fact that the magnetic moment of the deuteron is not exactly the algebraic sum of the proton and neutron moments. Both this deviation of magnetic moment and the electric quadrupole moment of the deuteron have been obtained from about a 4% contribution of an orbital with $l = 2$ (a d orbital) to the principal s orbital with $l = 0$.

In conclusion, it is possible to account for the properties of low-energy neutron-proton interactions, including the properties of the deuteron, in terms of nonrelativistic quantum mechanics, provided a sufficiently complex potential function is assumed. However, this potential function is not fully determined and is unlike the coulombic potential in that it depends on both the angles between the neutron and proton spins, and the angle of the net spin with the line connecting the particles, in addition to the distance between particles. Nevertheless, one can be quite certain that the nuclear potential has a short range of about 1.5 to 3×10^{-13} cm.

13f. Theory of interactions between nucleons; mesons. First let us include a comment on proton-proton interactions. Here the coulombic repulsion plays a major role. However, at energies of about 1 Mev. or more the presence of a short-range attractive force can be observed. The presence of the long-range coulomb force complicates the theory. Also one must take account of the symmetry of

[4] See Blatt, J. M. and Jackson, J. D., *Phys. Rev.*, **76**, 18 (1949); also Hulthen, L. and Laurikainen, K. V., *Revs. Modern Phys.*, **23**, 1 (1951).

the two protons. Consequently, one obtains only the singlet state potential from the scattering wave with $l = 0$. The data at moderate energies give the singlet potential for p-p interaction to be essentially the same as the singlet n-p potential (except for the coulombic term). If the p-p short range interaction is the same as the n-p interaction, it is a simple and reasonable assumption to take the n-n interaction to be the same as the other two. This is consistent with the treatment of "mirror" nuclei in Section 13b.

There has been a great deal of speculation as to the cause of these short-range forces between nucleons. One general plan has been to draw analogies from the electrostatic forces, which are in turn associated with the electromagnetic field and with photons. In 1935 Yukawa suggested that if the particles analogous to photons in the new system had a rest mass other than zero, the forces should have a short range. His equation for the potential was

$$V = - \frac{g_1 g_2}{r} e^{-(2\pi m_0 c/h)r} \tag{13.11}$$

where g_1 and g_2 are the effective "nucleonic" charges of the particles separated by the distance r, and m_0 is the rest mass of the particle analogous to the photon. It is apparent that this expression reduces to the electrostatic potential if m_0 is zero. For the ranges of nucleon forces m_0 must be 150–250 electron masses.

Shortly after Yukawa's theory was published, particles of such a mass were discovered in cosmic ray experiments and were named *mesons*. Now the particles analogous to photons should be neutral, whereas the early discoveries were of charged mesons, both positive and negative. Evidence was obtained later for neutral mesons. As further experiments have been completed, additional mesons of different masses have been discovered. It is now apparent that there is a complex array of new particles in the mass range between the electron and the nucleon mass.

We may propose also an analogy to chemical bonds. Suppose that the proton and neutron are systems of two or more particles each. One of these particles might be heavier and another lighter, like the proton and electron in a hydrogen atom. If the force of attraction between these particles were great enough, our present laboratory energies would not have been able to dissociate them or even raise them to an excited state. Yet when two protons or a proton and a neutron come close together, there might be an interplay of these lighter particles analogous to that of the electrons in chemical bonds. If these particles had half unit spin, the potential might become repulsive at very short distances, because of the usual effect of the Pauli exclusion principle.

At this time one cannot say whether theories of either of these general types will succeed or not.   However, it is surprising how far analogies of this type go in interpreting observed phenomena.

13g. High-energy neutron-proton interactions. In the preceding sections we considered various properties depending on neutron-proton and proton-proton interactions, and found these could be explained on the basis of potential wells of 10–50 Mev. depth and 1.5 to 3 × 10⁻¹³ cm. radius.   However, the scattering cross sections at energies of the order of 300 Mev. (or 150 Mev. in the center of mass system) are not consistent with predictions from these potential wells.   In particular, when the potential energy interaction is small compared with the kinetic energy, the interaction can only deflect the bombarding particle by a small angle.   Yet the differential p-p cross section is almost independent of angle and of bombarding energy in the ranges 30° to 90° (center of mass system) and 120–350 Mev. Such constancy is difficult to explain unless there is some interaction of energy large compared with 300 Mev.   Also from the magnitude of the cross section one may calculate that this force must have a range of the magnitude of 0.5 × 10⁻¹³ cm.

The results for the bombardment of heavy nuclei by protons of this energy also require some additional interaction of this type.   If the maximum interaction energy between a proton and another nucleon is of the magnitude of the 10–50 Mev. potential wells described above, protons of much higher energy should be able to pass right through nuclei.   Yet the cross sections are almost constant in the 150–350 Mev. range.

The only simple explanation of this effect is obtained[5] by assuming a hard repulsive core of 0.5 to 0.6 × 10⁻¹³ cm. radius in the potential interaction of the neutron-proton system.   This makes the neutron-proton potential similar to that between atoms, in that it is attractive at intermediate distances and repulsive at shorter distances.   With appropriate parameters, reasonable agreement with the experimental results can be obtained.

⁵ Jastrow, R., *Phys. Rev.*, **81**, 165, 636 (1951).

13h. Large nuclei; saturation of nuclear forces. We saw in Section 13b that the volume of nuclei is approximately proportional to the number of nucleons present. One can readily see from Fig. 13.3 that the binding energy per nucleon is also approximately constant for all large nuclei. Above an atomic weight of 20, the binding energy per nucleon lies within the range 7.5 to 8.8 Mev. The value for He⁴ is already 7.05 Mev. per nucleon.

These experimental binding energies are calculated from the isotopic masses and the values of the hydrogen and neutron masses, which are 1.00815 and 1.00899, respectively. The mass difference is converted to a value for the energy by the equation of relativity. Thus we have

$$E = c^2[1.00815Z + 1.00899(A - Z) - M] \qquad (13.12)$$

for a nucleus of mass M made up from Z protons and $(A - Z)$ neutrons.

These properties of nuclei are entirely similar to the properties of ordinary liquids and solids. Ordinary chemical forces yield an optimum interatomic distance at the potential minimum. Then the coordination number is limited by the geometry of packing, as in most

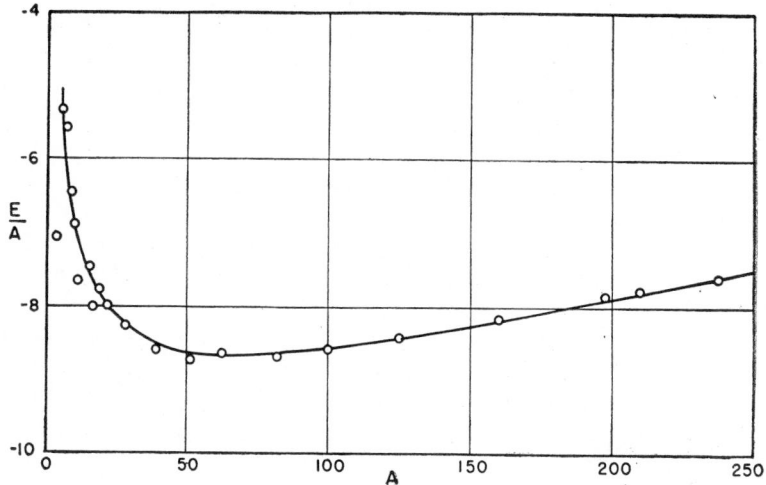

Fig. 13.3. The binding energy of nuclei per nucleon as a function of the atomic weight. The curve shows how these data may be fitted by Eq. 13.14.

molecular crystals and metals, or by the valence of the atoms, or by a combination of valence and geometry.   Thus if the forces are attractive for an unlimited number of neighbors, packing considerations limit the coordination number to twelve.   However, in an A^+B^- ionic crystal the repulsion between like ions eliminates such close packing.   Likewise, in a crystal such as diamond, the valence controls the packing.

For some time it was thought that the force between nucleons was attractive down to zero distance.   In that case the forces could be attractive between only a limited number of nucleons if the property of saturation was to be obtained.   This would be analogous to a limited chemical valence.   Now that the evidence favors repulsive interaction between nucleons at very short distances, it is less clear whether a limited valence in attraction is needed or not.   It may be that there can be attraction between an unlimited number of nucleons, analogous to the London forces between rare gas atoms.

We may consider the degree to which the translational motion of nucleons will be quantized.   In the n-p system for the deuteron, we found that the triplet spin state just barely had one stable energy level, while the singlet spin state just failed to have a stable level. Thus we have a situation very similar to that for a pair of helium atoms (Section 11c).   Since helium shows liquid properties down to the absolute zero, we may expect large nuclei to behave as quantum liquids.

Because the nucleon forces depend upon spin, one must hold reservations about the inferences concerning the nucleon potential which can be obtained by comparison with the properties of helium.   We may take Eq. (13.2) for the volume of "nucleon liquid."   The addition of a nucleon to a large nucleus of optimum n-p ratio releases an energy of about 8 Mev.   This value of 8 Mev. may be taken as the energy of vaporization.   Then we use the data of Table 11.4 and make comparisons with He^3 and He^4 separately.   The results from the He^3 comparison are: $\epsilon_0 = 16$ Mev. and $r_0 = 1.73 \times 10^{-13}$ cm.; from the He^4 comparison: $\epsilon_0 = 8$ Mev. and $r_0 = 1.96 \times 10^{-13}$ cm. Even though the inverse sixth and twelfth power potential for helium atom interactions may be quite different from that for nucleons, we see that these constants are of reasonable magnitude.   Also an evaluation of the parameter $(h/r_0\sqrt{m\epsilon_0})$ gives a higher value than that of

He^3. Thus we should extrapolate these results to a point equivalent to comparison with a helium isotope of mass less than 3.

We may add that nucleon liquid should follow Fermi statistics because nucleons have half unit spin. However, we have two types of nucleons, protons and neutrons. Consequently, the effect of Fermi statistics should be somewhat less marked than in the case of He^3.

Now that we have established the plausibility of a quantum liquid model for large nuclei, we can follow the effect of other liquid properties. In particular a liquid has surface tension because atoms on the surface are attracted by fewer neighbors than atoms in the interior.

The expression for the total energy of a nucleus should have a principal term, $-aA$, where a is the average binding energy from nuclear forces for a particle in the interior and A is the mass number, and hence the number of nucleons. The surface area will be proportional to R^2, and therefore, to $A^{2/3}$. The surface tension will raise the energy of the nucleus. Thus it will give a term $+bA^{2/3}$. Finally, we must remember the electrostatic repulsion of the positive charges. Equation (13.1) gave the electrostatic energy for the addition of one charge; hence its integral will yield the total electrostatic energy. This will be a term of the type, $+cZ^2A^{-1/3}$.

Let us now sum these terms and divide by A to give the binding energy per nucleon. We find

$$E/A = -a + bA^{-1/3} + cZ^2A^{-4/3} \qquad (13.13)$$

or, if we use the rough approximation $Z = A/2$, we obtain

$$E/A = -a + bA^{-1/3} + cA^{2/3}/4 \qquad (13.14)$$

We note that the surface tension term decreases with increasing A and eventually becomes negligible, while the electrical repulsion term increases with A. Consequently there should be a minimum in the energy curve for some intermediate value of the mass number. This is apparent in Fig. 13.3. The curve in that figure shows how Eq. (13.14) fits the energies of heavy nuclei quite well.

The properties of nuclei show no such marked periodic variation as those of atoms. However, significant points of greater stability are noted. These correspond to the completion of shells at 2, 8, 20, 28, 50, 82, or 128 of either neutrons or protons. Except for the first shell of 2, the numbers are different from those of the familiar periodic table. They have been explained in terms of two differences from the atomic model. First, the attraction to other nucleons yields a potential nearer to that of a spherical box than the modified coulombic potential of complex atoms. Second, the spin orbit coupling energies are very large for nucleon motion. This second suggestion, by Maria Geoppert Mayer and by Haxel, Jensen, and Suess in 1949, made possible the explanation of not only the shells mentioned above, but also the nuclear spin of many isotopes.[6]

13i. Other nuclear phenomena. Nuclear reactions in addition to those already discussed include β and γ decay, K electron capture and heavy element fission. The last is readily understood on the basis of the liquid drop model of heavy nuclei. Equation (13.13) included both a term for surface tension arising from nuclear forces and a term for electrostatic repulsion. Both terms were calculated for spherical shape. Actually a distortion of the sphere into an ellipsoid decreases the electrostatic term, but of course, increases the surface energy term. It is found that the magnitude of the former increases more rapidly with nuclear size than the latter. Consequently there is a size where the spherical shape would be unstable and the nucleus would fly apart. Isotopes such as Pu^{239} and U^{235} are still stable in this respect. However, these forces are so nearly in balance that the excitation by the binding energy of a single neutron is sufficient to start large oscillations in the shape of the liquid drop nucleus. Apparently at some phase of this motion, the nucleus is able to separate into two large fragments. The large release of energy arises, of course, from the electrostatic repulsion of the charges on these fragments, or in other words, from a decrease in the electrostatic potential energy of the final state as compared to the initial state.

The emission of γ rays is, of course, just the emission of photons or electromagnetic radiation. It is subject to the same principles we have discussed in earlier chapters. The principal topic to be added for nuclear processes is the relatively greater likelihood of emission by processes other than electric dipole. The next most probable processes are electric quadrupole and magnetic dipole.

As an example of this shift in relative probability let us consider electric and magnetic dipoles. Electric dipole transitions depend on the magnitude of μ^2 or e^2r^2. The charge will be of the magnitude of

[6] Klinkerberg, P. F. A., *Revs. Modern Phys.*, **24**, 63 (1952).

the electronic charge in either nuclear or atomic cases. Typical nuclear distances are of the magnitude 10^{-13} cm., while atomic distances are of the magnitude 10^{-8} cm. Thus at the same frequency, atomic transitions should be 10^{10} times as fast as nuclear transitions by the electric dipole process. According to Eq. (6.21), the probability of spontaneous emission depends also on the cube of the frequency. Thus nuclear processes are actually somewhat faster, because nuclear energies are in the million electron volt range, and atomic energies are typically a few e.v. We turn now to magnetic dipole processes. These depend on the square of a magnetic moment. The magnetic moments will be of the magnitude of a Bohr magneton in atomic cases and a nuclear magneton in nuclear cases. The ratio of the magnetons is the proton to electron mass ratio of 1836. Thus the ratio of rates of atomic to nuclear radiation processes (at equal frequencies) is reduced from 10^{10} in the electric dipole case to 1836^2, or about 4×10^6, in the magnetic dipole case.

We shall not continue this analysis further, but will merely remark that at about 2 Mev. electric dipole processes are only about 10^3 more probable than either magnetic dipole or electric quadrupole processes. Since electric dipole radiation is frequently forbidden in a given example, the other processes must be considered.

The emission of an electron or β particle from a nucleus involves the creation of the electron, since the nucleus does not contain it initially. The experimental evidence for β emission also indicates that some energy is carried away by another unidentified particle. This particle has been called the *neutrino*, and has been assumed to have properties such that it would have escaped detection. These include no charge and no rest mass, but probably half unit spin. Since we have not discussed basic theories for the creation of particles, we shall not attempt to discuss the theory of β decay in detail.

The reverse process to electron emission occurs when a nucleus can become more stable by decreasing its positive charge, instead of increasing it. Two possibilities exist, the emission of a positron or the absorption of an orbital electron. The former is called β^+ emission and is theoretically similar to regular β emission. The latter is called *K-capture* in the ordinary case, where it is a K shell or $1s$ electron that is captured. It is detected experimentally by the x-rays emitted by the resulting atom with a $1s$ electron missing.

The probability of electron capture depends on the electron probability at the nucleus. Thus in the case of Be^7, which decays by K-capture to Li^7, it is possible to affect the rate of the nuclear process by change of chemical state. Segrè suggested this effect in 1947 and proceeded to demonstrate[7] a difference in the rates of decay of Be^7 in Be (metal), BeO, and BeF_2. As might be expected, the most ionic compound, BeF_2, has the lowest electron density at the nucleus of the positive ion. The rate of decay of BeF_2 is 0.17% slower than Be (metal) and 0.14% slower than BeO.

  The percentage by which the electron density can be changed for a larger atom will be much less. Thus one cannot expect any general use of this rate of electron capture as a method of measuring changes in electron density. On the contrary, the principle that rates of radioactive processes are independent of chemical form will still hold for all practical purposes.

GENERAL REFERENCES

Brief discussions of nuclear phenomena are given in most books on atomic physics. An example is Born, M., *Atomic Physics*, which has been cited before.

The most complete work on nuclear theory, but one which is correspondingly difficult is Rosenfeld, L., *Nuclear Forces*, New York: Interscience Publishers, Inc., 1949.

An excellent treatise has been prepared from the lectures of E. Fermi, by Orear, J., Rosenfeld, A. H., and Schluter, R. A., *Nuclear Physics*, Chicago: The University of Chicago Press, 1950.

A more elementary text is Halliday, D., *Introductory Nuclear Physics*, New York: John Wiley & Sons, Inc., 1950.

Older but excellent books include Rasetti, F., *Elements of Nuclear Physics*, New York: Prentice-Hall, Inc., 1936; Bethe, H. A., *Elementary Nuclear Theory*, New York: John Wiley & Sons, Inc., 1947.

Other references of interest in this area include:
Bethe, H. A., Bacher, R. F., and Livingston, M. S., *Revs. Modern Phys.*, **8**, 82 (1936); **9**, 69, 245 (1937).
Friedlander, G. and Kennedy, J. W., *Introduction to Radiochemistry*, New York: John Wiley & Sons, Inc., 1949.
Glasstone, S., *Sourcebook on Atomic Energy*, New York: D. Van Nostrand Company, Inc., 1950.
Lapp, R. E. and Andrews, H. L., *Nuclear Radiation Physics*, New York: Prentice-Hall, Inc., 1948.

[7] Leininger, R. F., Segrè, E. and Wiegand, C., *Phys. Rev.*, **76**, 897 (1949).

THE ENERGY OF THE HELIUM ATOM

The calculation of an upper limit to the energy of the stable helium atom (or two-electron ion, Li^+, Be^{++}, . . .) will be given using as a variation function:

$$\psi = \frac{z^3}{\pi a_0^3} e^{-zr_1/a_0} e^{-zr_2/a_0} \qquad (A1\text{-}1)$$

where z is the effective atomic number. We can either assign z the atomic number of the atom, Z, to get a first approximation, or regard it as an adjustable parameter to obtain a second approximation.

The Hamiltonian operator is

$$H = \frac{-h^2}{8\pi^2 m} (\nabla_1^2 + \nabla_2^2) - Ze^2 \left(\frac{1}{r_1} + \frac{1}{r_2} \right) + \frac{e^2}{r_{12}}$$

where ∇^2 is the Laplacian operator $(\partial^2/\partial x^2 + \partial^2/\partial y^2 + \partial^2/\partial z^2)$. This expression may be rearranged by collecting the terms relative to a single electron.

$$H = \left(\frac{-h^2}{8\pi^2 m} \nabla_1^2 - \frac{Ze^2}{r_1} \right) + \left(\frac{-h^2}{8\pi^2 m} \nabla_2^2 - \frac{Ze^2}{r_2} \right) + \frac{e^2}{r_{12}} \qquad (A1\text{-}2)$$

Now except for the difference between z in ψ and Z in H, ψ is a solution of a Schrödinger equation based on the first two terms of H.

$$\left(\frac{-h^2}{8\pi^2 m} \nabla_1^2 - \frac{ze^2}{r_1} \right) \psi = z^2 E_H \psi \qquad (A1\text{-}3)$$

where E_H is the energy of the normal hydrogen atom, $-e^2/2a_0$. A similar relation holds for the terms for electron 2. The variation method energy may then be written

$$W = \int \psi \left[2z^2 E_H + e^2 \left(\frac{z-Z}{r_1} + \frac{z-Z}{r_2} + \frac{1}{r_{12}} \right) \right] \psi \, dv_1 \, dv_2$$

$$= 2z^2 E_H + 2e^2(z - Z) \int \frac{\psi^2}{r_1} \, dv_1 \, dv_2 + e^2 \int \frac{\psi^2}{r_{12}} \, dv_1 \, dv_2 \qquad (A1\text{-}4)$$

where the two equivalent terms involving $(z - Z)$ are combined in the first

415

integral. We must now evaluate the two integrals. The first is straightforward. The integration with respect to the second electron gives unity because of normalization.

$$\int \frac{\psi^2}{r_1} \, dv_1 \, dv_2 = \left(\frac{z^3}{\pi a_0^3}\right) 4\pi \int_0^\infty e^{-2zr_1/a_0} r_1 \, dr_1$$

$$= \left(\frac{4z^3}{a_0^3}\right)\left(\frac{a_0}{2z}\right)^2 \int_0^\infty e^{-y} y \, dy = \frac{z}{a_0} \qquad (A1\text{-}5)$$

The second integral in Eq. (A1-4) is more difficult. To evaluate it we note that it represents the mutual electrostatic energy of two spherically symmetrical distributions of electricity, each of density $(z^3/\pi a_0^3)e^{-2zr/a_0}$. Now it is a property of a spherical shell of charge that the potential is constant within the shell, and that the potential outside is the same as if an equal charge were at the center of the sphere. In this case the shell at radius r_1 and thickness dr_1 contains $(4z^3/a_0^3)e^{-2zr_1/a_0}r_1^2 \, dr_1$ charge and the potential at r_2 outside is

$$\left(\frac{4z^3}{a_0^3}\right) e^{-2zr_1/a_0} r_1^2 \, dr_1 \cdot \frac{1}{r_2} \qquad \text{for} \quad r_2 \geqslant r_1$$

The potential inside the shell is constant and equal to

$$\left(\frac{4z^3}{a_0^3}\right) e^{-2zr_1/a_0} r_1 \, dr_1 \qquad \text{for} \quad r_2 \leqslant r_1$$

One then obtains for the potential energy V at r_2

$$V(r_2) = \left(\frac{4z^3}{a_0^3}\right) \frac{1}{r_2} \int_0^{r_2} e^{-2zr_1/a_0} r_1^2 \, dr_1 + \left(\frac{4z^3}{a_0^3}\right) \int_{r_2}^\infty e^{-2zr_1/a_0} r_1 \, dr_1$$

$$= \frac{1}{2r_2} \int_0^{2zr_2/a_0} e^{-x} x^2 \, dx + \left(\frac{z}{a_0}\right) \int_{2zr_2/a_0}^\infty e^{-x} x \, dx$$

$$= \frac{1}{2r_2}\left[2 - e^{-2zr_2/a_0}\left(\frac{2zr_2}{a_0} + 2\right)\right] \qquad (A1\text{-}6)$$

The second integral in Eq. (A1-4), which is the total electrostatic interaction energy, is then

$$\int \frac{\psi^2}{r_{12}} \, dv_1 \, dv_2 = \left(\frac{4z^3}{a_0^3}\right) \int_0^\infty V(r_2) e^{-2zr_2/a_0} r_2^2 \, dr_2$$

$$= \left(\frac{z}{2a_0}\right) \int_0^\infty [2e^{-x} - e^{-2x}(x+2)]x \, dx = \frac{5z}{8a_0} \qquad (A1\text{-}7)$$

Now combining the results of Eq. (A1-4), (A1-5), and (A1-7), one obtains

$$W = 2z^2 E_H + (e^2/a_0)[2z(z - Z) + 5z/8]$$

or since $E_H = -e^2/2a_0$,

$$W = E_H[2z^2 - 4z(z - Z) - 5z/4] \qquad (A1\text{-}8)$$

For helium, the first approximation is obtained with both z and Z equal to 2, yielding

$$W = \tfrac{11}{2}E_H = -\tfrac{11}{4}e^2/a_0 \tag{A1-9}$$

which is the first result cited in Section 5b.

For a second approximation we differentiate Eq. (A1-8) with respect to z in order to obtain the minimum value of W

$$\frac{\partial W}{\partial z} = E_H(-4z + 4Z - \tfrac{5}{4}) = 0$$

$$z = Z - \tfrac{5}{16} \tag{A1-10}$$

Then substituting this value of z yields

$$W = 2E_H(Z - \tfrac{5}{16})^2 = -(e^2/a_0)(Z - \tfrac{5}{16})^2 \tag{A1-11}$$

as our final result for a two-electron atom with nuclear charge Z. In the following table are listed first the energy of the two-electron ion calculated from Eq. (A1-11), second the value calculated from more complicated variation functions by Hylleraas,[1] and third the experimental value. Strictly the value of a_0 must be adjusted in each case for the proper reduced mass of the electron with that nucleus.

ELECTRONIC ENERGIES OF TWO-ELECTRON ATOMS AND IONS
(Units: electron volts)

	$-W$ Eq. (A1-11)	$-W$ Hylleraas	$-E$ expl.
H⁻	12.848	14.311	
He	77.46	78.98	78.98
Li⁺	196.49	198.03	198.05
Be⁺⁺	369.93	371.12	371.10
B³⁺	597.78	599.32	599.4
C⁴⁺	880.02	881.57	881.5
N⁵⁺	1216.7	1218.2	
O⁶⁺	1607.8	1609.3	

Hylleraas' results may also be expressed by the following equation for the ionization potential of the two electron ion or atom.

$$I = \frac{R_\infty hc}{1 + \dfrac{m}{M}}\left(Z^2 - \frac{5}{4}Z + 0.31488 - \frac{0.01752}{Z} + \frac{0.00548}{Z^2}\right) \tag{A1-12}$$

Here R_∞ is the Rydberg constant for infinite nuclear mass ($2\pi^2 me^4/h^3c = 109737.32$ cm.$^{-1}$), m and M are the masses of electron and nucleus, respectively, and Z is again the nuclear charge. It is interesting to note that

[1] Hylleraas, E. A., Z. Physik, **65**, 209 (1930).

the first two terms in the parentheses are given correctly by the calculation of this Appendix, but that to this approximation the third term would be $25/128 \cong 0.2$. Thus the Hylleraas wave functions raised the third term by about 30% and added the last two terms. Since the important change was that in the third term, the error in Eq. (A1-11) values is almost constant at 1.5 e.v.

The value for H^-, which is particularly interesting for consideration of the character of hydrides, must be taken from theory, since no reliable experimental value has yet been obtained. In that case the 1.5 e.v. error of the approximate calculation is fatal, because the electron affinity of the hydrogen atom is only 0.718 e.v.

Appendix 2

EXCHANGE INTEGRALS BETWEEN
ORTHOGONAL FUNCTIONS

We are to show that the integral such as H_x in Eq. (5.9) is necessarily positive.

$$H_x = e^2 \int \frac{1s(1)2s(1)1s(2)2s(2)}{r_{12}} \, dv_1 \, dv_2 \geqslant 0$$

The corresponding integral without r_{12} is zero from the orthogonality of the $1s$ and $2s$ functions. This arises because there is a region where the $2s$ orbital is positive, and another region where it is negative. The integral over one region cancels that over the other. Considering the coordinates of both electrons, the integrand is positive if both electrons are in the same region, and negative if they are in different regions. Now r_{12} will be larger, on the average, if the electrons are in different regions than if they are in the same region. Hence as compared with the integral without r_{12}, the positive portions now contribute more (because r_{12} is smaller), and the negative portions contribute less. Thus the integral with r_{12} will be positive.

Since this argument did not depend in any essential way on the particular orbitals considered, we may assume it will hold generally.

DETAILS OF THE HEITLER AND LONDON
TREATMENT OF H

Three integrals are to be evaluated. Let us take first the nonorthogonality integral Δ from Eq. (8.6).

$$\Delta = \left[\frac{1}{\pi a_0^3} \int e^{-(r_{A1}+r_{B1})/a_0} \, dv_1 \right]^2 \tag{A3-1}$$

In the elliptical coordinates defined in Eqs. (8.11) to (8.14) this becomes

$$\Delta = \left\{ \frac{D^3}{8\pi} \int_1^\infty \int_{-1}^{+1} \int_0^{2\pi} e^{-D\xi}(\xi^2 - \eta^2) \, d\phi \, d\eta \, d\xi \right\}^2$$

$$= \left\{ \frac{D^3}{2} \int_1^\infty e^{-D\xi} \left(\xi^2 - \frac{1}{3} \right) d\xi \right\}^2$$

$$= \left\{ \frac{1}{2} \int_D^\infty e^{-x} \left(x^2 - \frac{D^2}{3} \right) dx \right\}^2$$

$$= \left\{ \frac{1}{2} \left[e^{-x} \left(-x^2 - 2x - 2 + \frac{D^2}{3} \right) \right]_D^\infty \right\}^2$$

$$= e^{-2D}(1 + D + D^2/3)^2 \tag{A3-2}$$

which is the result given in Eq. (8.7).

Next consider the integral H_c, which may be written

$$H_c' = \frac{e^2}{\pi^2 a_0^6} \int e^{-2r_{A1}/a_0} e^{-2r_{B2}/a_0} \left(-\frac{1}{r_{B1}} - \frac{1}{r_{A2}} + \frac{1}{r_{12}} + \frac{1}{r_{AB}} \right) dv$$

$$= -2e^2 C_1 + e^2 C_2 + e^2/r_{AB} \tag{A3-3}$$

$$C_1 = \frac{1}{\pi a_0^3} \int e^{-2r_{A1}/a_0} \left(\frac{1}{r_{B1}} \right) dv_1$$

$$C_2 = \frac{1}{\pi^2 a_0^6} \int e^{-2(r_{A1}+r_{B2})/a_0} \left(\frac{1}{r_{12}} \right) dv_1 \, dv_2$$

In these steps use has been made of the symmetry with respect to nuclei A and B, of electrons 1 and 2, and of the normalization relationship,

$$1 = \frac{1}{\pi a_0^3} \int e^{-2r_{A1}/a_0} \, dv_1$$

Proceeding with C_1, one notes that it is just the potential at nucleus B of the spherically symmetrical distribution of charge about A. Remembering that the contribution of shells inside B ($r_{A1} \leqslant r_{AB}$) is the same as if the charge were at A, and that the potential inside outer shells is constant, one has

$$C_1 = \frac{4}{r_{AB}a_0^3} \int_0^{r_{AB}} e^{-2r_{A1}/a_0} r_{A1}^2 \, dr_{A1} + \frac{4}{a_0^3} \int_{r_{AB}}^{\infty} e^{-2r_{A1}/a_0} r_{A1} \, dr_{A1}$$

$$C_1 = \frac{1}{2r_{AB}} \int_0^{2D} e^{-x} x^2 \, dx + \frac{1}{a_0} \int_{2D}^{\infty} e^{-x} x \, dx$$

$$= \frac{1}{a_0} \left[\frac{1}{D} - e^{-2D}\left(1 + \frac{1}{D}\right) \right] \tag{A3-4}$$

To evaluate C_2, note that it is the mutual electrostatic energy of the similar spherical charge distributions, one about A and one about B. To get the potential for the charge about A we need only replace r_{AB} in (A3-4) by r_{A2}, the distance of the second electron from the center of the first distribution

$$V = \frac{1}{a_0} \left[\frac{a_0}{r_{A2}} - e^{-2r_{A2}/a_0}\left(1 + \frac{a_0}{r_{A2}}\right) \right]$$

Then

$$C_2 = \frac{1}{\pi a_0^3} \int e^{-2r_{B2}/a_0} V \, dv_2$$

$$= \frac{1}{\pi a_0^3} \left[\int e^{-2r_{B2}/a_0} \frac{dv_2}{r_{A2}} - \int e^{-2(r_{A2}+r_{B2})/a_0}\left(\frac{1}{a_0} + \frac{1}{r_{A2}}\right) dv_2 \right]$$

Since $\quad 2r_B = (\xi - \eta)r_{AB}$ and $2r_A = (\xi + \eta)r_{AB}$, these become

$$C_2 = \frac{D^2}{2a_0} \left[\int_{-1}^{+1} \int_1^{\infty} e^{-D(\xi-\eta)} \frac{(\xi^2 - \eta^2)}{(\xi + \eta)} \, d\xi \, d\eta \right.$$

$$\left. - \int_{-1}^{+1} \int_1^{\infty} e^{-2D\xi}\left(\frac{D\xi^2}{2} - \frac{D\eta^2}{2} + \frac{\xi^2 - \eta^2}{\xi + \eta}\right) d\xi \, d\eta \right]$$

$$= \frac{D^2}{2a_0} \left[e^{-D} \int_{-1}^{+1} e^{D\eta}\left(\frac{1}{D^2} + \frac{1}{D} - \frac{\eta}{D}\right) d\eta \right.$$

$$\left. - e^{-2D} \int_{-1}^{+1}\left(\frac{1}{4} + \frac{3}{4D} + \frac{3}{8D^2} - \frac{\eta^2}{4} - \frac{\eta}{2D}\right) d\eta \right]$$

and finally

$$C_2 = \frac{1}{a_0} \left[\frac{1}{D} - e^{-2D}\left(\frac{D^2}{6} + \frac{3D}{4} + \frac{11}{8} + \frac{1}{D}\right) \right] \tag{A3-5}$$

which completes the evaluation of H_c'.

The third integral H_x' is

$$H_x' = \frac{e^2}{\pi^2 a_0^6} \int e^{-(r_{A1}+r_{A2}+r_{B1}+r_{B2})/a_0}\left(-\frac{e^2}{r_{A1}} - \frac{e^2}{r_{B2}} + \frac{e^2}{r_{12}} + \frac{e^2}{r_{AB}}\right) dv \tag{A3-6}$$

$$= -2e^2 \Delta^{1/2} C_3 + e^2 C_4 + \Delta e^2/r_{AB}$$

$$C_3 = \frac{1}{\pi a_0^3} \int e^{-(r_{A1}+r_{B1})/a_0} \frac{dv_1}{r_{A1}}$$

$$C_4 = \frac{1}{\pi^2 a_0^6} \int e^{-(r_{A1}+r_{A2}+r_{B1}+r_{B2})/a_0} \frac{dv}{r_{12}}$$

Of these quantities C_3 is easily evaluated in elliptical coordinates.

$$C_3 = \frac{D^2}{2a_0} \int_{-1}^{+1} \int_1^\infty e^{-\xi D} \frac{(\xi^2 - \eta^2)}{(\xi + \eta)} \, d\xi \, d\eta$$
$$= e^{-D}(1 + D)/a_0 \tag{A3-7}$$

However, C_4 is much more difficult. Heitler and London merely proved that

$$C_4 < \frac{5}{8a_0} e^{-2D} \left(1 + D + \frac{D^2}{3}\right) \tag{A3-8}$$

Later, Sugiura[1] obtained the following expression.

$$C_4 = \frac{1}{5a_0} \left\{ e^{-2D} \left(\frac{25}{8} - \frac{23D}{4} - 3D^2 - \frac{D^3}{3}\right) \right.$$
$$\left. + \frac{6}{D} \left[\Delta(0.5772 + \ln D) + \delta^2 Ei(-4D) - 2\delta\Delta^{1/2} Ei(-2D)\right] \right\} \tag{A3-9}$$

where $0.5772 \ldots$ is Euler's constant, Ei is a function called the integral logarithm,[2] and $\delta = e^D(1 - D + D^2/3)$.

[1] Sugiura, Y., *Z. Physik*, **45**, 484 (1927).
[2] See, for example, Jahnke, E. and Emde, F., *Tables of Functions*, 4th ed., New York: Dover Publications, 1945.

Appendix 4

OTHER VARIATION FUNCTIONS FOR H$_2$

In addition to the Heitler and London and the James and Coolidge treatments of H$_2$, a number of others are important primarily because of the indication they give of the importance of certain terms. We have already mentioned the treatment of Wang[1] who introduced the effective atomic number z analogous to our treatment of helium in Appendix 1. All the treatments here mentioned will similarly contain an adjustable z. Thus $1s_A$ may be taken to mean a $1s$ orbital about nucleus A with an effective atomic number z, etc.

The various functions (not normalized) follow.

A. WANG[1]

$$\psi = 1s_A(1)1s_B(2) + 1s_A(2)1s_B(1) \tag{A4-1}$$

$$z = 1.166, \quad r_e = 0.76 \text{ A}, \quad D_e = 3.78 \text{ e.v.}$$

B. MOLECULAR ORBITAL[2]

$$\psi = [1s_A(1) + 1s_B(1)][1s_A(2) + 1s_B(2)] \tag{A4-2}$$

$$= [1s_A(1)1s_B(2) + 1s_A(2)1s_B(1)] + [1s_A(1)1s_A(2) + 1s_B(1)1s_B(2)]$$

$$z = 1.193, \quad r_e = 0.73 \text{ A}, \quad D_e = 3.49$$

The first line illustrates the molecular orbital aspect in that the same orbital covering both nuclei is used for each electron. In the second line the function is rewritten to segregate the Heitler-London terms from those newly introduced. These new terms are commonly called *ionic terms* because they place both electrons in the orbital around a single nucleus, and hence correspond roughly to the states H$^-$ H$^+$ and H$^+$ H$^-$. In this function the ionic terms are given equal weight as compared with the Heitler-London terms. The resulting energy is poorer than the Wang value where the ionic terms are omitted.

[1] Wang, S. C., *Phys. Rev.*, **31**, 579 (1928).

[2] The numerical values are attributed to Weinbaum in Pauling, L. and Wilson, E. B. Jr., *Introduction to Quantum Mechanics*, New York: McGraw-Hill Book Company, Inc., 1935, p. 347.

C. WEINBAUM[3]

$$\psi = [1s_A(1)1s_B(2) + 1s_A(2)1s_B(1)] + c[1s_A(1)1s_A(2) + 1s_B(1)1s_B(2)] \quad \text{(A4-3)}$$
$$z = 1.193, \quad c = 0.256, \quad r_e = 0.77 \text{ A}, \quad D_e = 4.02 \text{ e.v.}$$

In this case we see that an adjustable parameter is used with the ionic terms. Its value is much lower than the value of one which corresponds to the molecular orbital treatment. However, it is significant and leads to appreciable improvement in the calculated energy from the Wang result.

D. ROSEN[4]

Replaced $1s$ in the Wang function by $1s + c2p$ with a double effective atomic number, $2z$, in the $2p$ function to obtain the same exponential factor as in the $1s$ function. Also the axis of the $2p$ function is taken as the internuclear axis and of the proper direction to increase the electron density between atoms. The effect of this change may be described as a polarization of the $1s$ orbital by the presence of the other nucleus (see Section 4i). Thus

$$\psi = u_A(1)u_B(2) + u_A(2)u_B(1)$$
$$u = 1s + c'2p \quad \text{(A4-4)}$$
$$z = 1.19, \quad c' = 0.10, \quad r_e = 0.77 \text{ A}, \quad D_e = 4.04 \text{ e.v.}$$

E. Weinbaum[3] added the polarization terms of Rosen to his partial ionic treatment, obtaining only slight further improvement to $D_e = 4.12$ e.v.

F. Gurnee and Magee[5] proposed a much simpler function which gives slightly better results than any of those mentioned so far. They use the Wang function, Eq. (A4-1), but offset the orbital centers a distance x from the nuclei. Thus there are only two parameters, z and x. These have the respective values 1.17 and $0.07a_0$ at the potential minimum, which lies at 1.45 a_0 or 0.77 A and gives a dissociation energy $D_e = 4.16$ e.v. The offset is in the direction that the orbital centers are closer together than the nuclei, which has the effect of further increasing the electron density between the nuclei.

Since the experimental value of the dissociation energy, 4.75 e.v., is considerably beyond any of these results and well beyond even the limit toward which they appear to be converging, it may be concluded that some essential factor has been omitted. This is the explicit dependence on the distance between the two electrons, which James and Coolidge included and which was found necessary in the helium calculations.

One further calculation deserves mention. Hirshfelder and Linnett[6]

[3] Weinbaum, S., *J. Chem. Phys.*, **1**, 593 (1933).
[4] Rosen, N., *Phys. Rev.*, **38**, 2099 (1931).
[5] Gurnee, E. F. and Magee, J. L., *J. Chem. Phys.*, **18**, 142 (1950).
[6] Hirshfelder, J. O. and Linnett, J. W., *J. Chem. Phys.*, **18**, 130 (1950).

took a function which includes essentially the London force terms of Eq. (8.54) in addition to the Weinbaum function (A4-3). The effect of the London force terms is to give some correlation with the actual distance between the electrons. Actually this complex function gives only a slightly better dissociation energy, 4.25 e.v., than the simple function of Gurnee and Magee. The importance of this treatment is that it contains the London force terms and therefore gives a good approximation also when the atoms are well separated. Of course, the James and Coolidge treatment would also give good results but it has not been extended into this range of interatomic distance.

It is doubtful how much can be concluded about the importance of the various types of terms introduced in these functions except for the introduction of the scale factor z, which is very important. The success of the Gurnee and Magee function suggests that the adjustment of the electron density midway between the nuclei is more important than the introduction of ionic terms. However, one should be cautious about drawing conclusions about small energy differences near 4.0 e.v. when the absence of the interelectronic coordinate has left the energy far above the true value of 4.75 e.v.

Appendix 5

THE VIRIAL THEOREM

The virial theorem in classical mechanics was originally deduced by Clausius and applied to imperfect gases. Newton's second law may be written

$$m_i \frac{d^2 x_i}{dt^2} = F_{x_i} \tag{A5-1}$$

where F_{x_i} is the x component of force acting on the ith particle. Multiplying by x, one obtains

$$x_i F_{x_i} = m_i x_i \frac{d^2 x_i}{dt^2} = \frac{d}{dt}\left(m_i x_i \frac{dx_i}{dt}\right) - m_i \left(\frac{dx_i}{dt}\right)^2 \tag{A5-2}$$

The last term is just twice the kinetic energy. Now we sum over all particles of the system and take the time average (indicated by a bar).

$$\sum_i \overline{x_i F_{x_i}} = \sum_i \overline{\frac{d}{dt}\left(m_i x_i \frac{dx_i}{dt}\right)} - 2\overline{T}$$

The total kinetic energy is indicated by T, and the sums must now cover also the y and z coordinates of every particle. The first term on the right is zero for the following reason. The time average of the time derivative is just the difference between the initial and final values divided by the elapsed time. Now m_i and dx_i/dt remain finite, as does x_i for any system we shall consider; hence the difference between initial and final values of this quantity will remain finite. Letting the elapsed time go to infinity will then yield the zero resulting average. (The result is also true for systems indefinitely expanding provided they do so by Brownian motion, which allows x to increase only as $t^{1/2}$). We have then the result

$$2\,\vec{\overline{T}} = -\sum_i \overline{x_i F_{x_i}} \tag{A5-3}$$

We now wish to prove this to be true in quantum mechanics, where we shall anticipate that the averages are of the usual quantum mechanical sort. The Schrödinger equation for a system of particles may be written

426

$$\sum_i -\frac{h^2}{8\pi^2 m_i}\frac{\partial^2 \psi}{\partial x_i^2} + (V - E)\psi = 0 \tag{A5-4}$$

where as before, the sum is to cover the x, y, and z coordinates of all particles. Now operate on Eq. (A5-4) by $x_j \psi^* \dfrac{\partial}{\partial x_j}$, obtaining

$$\sum_i -\frac{h^2}{8\pi^2 m_i} x_j \psi^* \frac{\partial^3 \psi}{\partial x_i^2\, \partial x_j} + x_j \psi^* \frac{\partial V}{\partial x_j}\psi + x_j \psi^*(V - E)\frac{\partial \psi}{\partial x_j} = 0 \tag{A5-5}$$

However, Eq. (A5-4) holds also for ψ^*, and multiplied by $x_j \dfrac{\partial \psi}{\partial x_j}$ yields

$$\sum_i -\frac{h^2}{8\pi^2 m_i} x_j \frac{\partial \psi}{\partial x_j}\frac{\partial^2 \psi^*}{\partial x_i^2} + x_j \frac{\partial \psi}{\partial x_j}\psi^*(V - E) = 0 \tag{A5-6}$$

Note that the last terms in Eqs. (A5-5) and (A5-6) are the same. Eliminating them by subtraction and summing over j yields

$$\sum_j \sum_i -\frac{h^2}{8\pi^2 m_i} x_j \left(\psi^* \frac{\partial^3 \psi}{\partial x_i^2\, \partial x_j} - \frac{\partial \psi}{\partial x_j}\frac{\partial^2 \psi^*}{\partial x_i^2}\right) + \sum_j x_j \psi^* \frac{\partial V}{\partial x_j}\psi = 0 \tag{A5-7}$$

We now integrate over space, but some manipulation of the first term is needed. Take the expression

$$\psi^{*2}\frac{\partial}{\partial x_i}\left(\frac{\sum_j x_j \dfrac{\partial \psi}{\partial x_j}}{\psi^*}\right) = \sum_j \left(\psi^* \frac{\partial x_j}{\partial x_i}\frac{\partial \psi}{\partial x_j} + \psi^* x_j \frac{\partial^2 \psi}{\partial x_i\, \partial x_j} - x_j \frac{\partial \psi}{\partial x_j}\frac{\partial \psi^*}{\partial x_i}\right)$$

$$= \psi^* \frac{\partial \psi}{\partial x_i} + \sum_j \left(\psi^* x_j \frac{\partial^2 \psi}{\partial x_i\, \partial x_j} - x_j \frac{\partial \psi}{\partial x_j}\frac{\partial \psi^*}{\partial x_i}\right)$$

Now differentiate this expression again with respect to x_i. After cancelling and collecting terms, one has

$$\frac{\partial}{\partial x_i}\left[\psi^{*2}\frac{\partial}{\partial x_i}\left(\frac{\sum_j x_j \dfrac{\partial \psi}{\partial x_j}}{\psi^*}\right)\right] = 2\psi^* \frac{\partial^2 \psi}{\partial x_i^2} + \sum_j x_j \left(\psi^* \frac{\partial^3 \psi}{\partial x_i^2\, \partial x_j} - \frac{\partial \psi}{\partial x_j}\frac{\partial^2 \psi^*}{\partial x_i^2}\right) \tag{A5-8}$$

The final sum is the quantity appearing in Eq. (A5-7). Solving for it and integrating with respect to x_i yields

$$\int \sum_j x_j \left(\psi^* \frac{\partial^3 \psi}{\partial x_i^2\, \partial x_j} - \frac{\partial \psi}{\partial x_j}\frac{\partial^2 \psi^*}{\partial x_i^2}\right) dx_i$$

$$= -2\int \psi^* \frac{\partial^2 \psi}{\partial x_i^2}\, dx_i + \left[\psi^{*2}\frac{\partial}{\partial x_i}\left(\frac{\sum_j x_j \dfrac{\partial \psi}{\partial x_j}}{\psi^*}\right)\right]_{-\infty}^{+\infty} \tag{A5-9}$$

where the last term is zero because ψ^* is zero at infinity. Substituting this result into Eq. (A5-7) and integrating over the remaining coordinates yields

$$2 \sum_i -\frac{h^2}{8\pi^2 m_i} \int \cdots \int \psi^* \frac{\partial^2 \psi}{\partial x_i^2} \, dv = \sum_j \int \cdots \int x_j \frac{\partial V}{\partial x_j} \psi^* \psi \, dv$$

This we may recognize as the virial theorem result, since the left side is $2\overline{T}$ and the right becomes $- \sum \overline{x_i F_{x_i}}$ on substitution of $-F_{x_i} = \partial V / \partial x_i$.

MOLECULAR ORBITALS FOR H₆ OR BENZENE

It is our problem here to use the symmetry of a plane regular hexagon to aid in finding the linear combinations of atomic orbitals which are appropriate for molecular orbitals in H_6 or benzene. The theory of symmetry groups will be employed.[1]

The full symmetry of a plane regular hexagon is that of the group D_{6h}; however, for the purpose of the present calculation the sixfold axis is the only essential element. Consequently we can simplify our calculations by the use of the group C_6, which is, of course, a subgroup of D_{6h}.

We label the atoms and their orbitals A, B, C, D, E, and F in order, and in Table A6-1 we present the results of applying the operations of C_6 to these orbitals. (The presentation is abbreviated by writing A for ϕ_A, etc.)

TABLE A6-1

```
          A
     F         B

       E       C
          D
```

	E	C_6	C_3	C_2	$C_3{}^2$	$C_6{}^5$
A	A	B	C	D	E	F
B	B	C	D	E	F	A
C	C	D	E	F	A	B
D	D	E	F	A	B	C
E	E	F	A	B	C	D
F	F	A	B	C	D	E
$\chi(\phi)$	6	0	0	0	0	0

C_6 means rotation by 60°, C_3 rotation by 120°, C_2 rotation by 180°, etc. Also in Table A6-1 in the last line is given the character of the reducible representation which these six orbitals constitute. To find the irreducible rep-

[1] Margenau, H. and Murphy, G. M., *The Mathematics of Physics and Chemistry*, New York: D. Van Nostrand Company, Inc., 1943, Chap. 15.

resentations included, we turn to the character table for C_6 as presented in Table A6-2.

TABLE A6-2

CHARACTER TABLE FOR C_6

		E	C_6	C_3	C_2	$C_3{}^2$	$C_6{}^5$
A	Γ_1	1	1	1	1	1	1
B	Γ_4	1	-1	1	-1	1	-1
$E_1\begin{cases}\\\\\end{cases}$	Γ_5	1	$-\epsilon^*$	$-\epsilon$	1	$-\epsilon^*$	$-\epsilon$
	Γ_3	1	$-\epsilon$	$-\epsilon^*$	1	$-\epsilon$	$-\epsilon^*$
$E_2\begin{cases}\\\\\end{cases}$	Γ_6	1	ϵ^*	$-\epsilon$	-1	$-\epsilon^*$	ϵ
	Γ_2	1	ϵ	$-\epsilon^*$	-1	$-\epsilon$	ϵ^*
$\chi(\phi)$		6	0	0	0	0	0

$\epsilon = e^{2\pi i/6} = \cos \pi/3 + i \sin \pi/3 = \tfrac{1}{2} + i\sqrt{3}/2$

One can derive from the usual formulas or verify by inspection that each of the irreducible representations occurs once.

$$\Gamma(\phi) = \Gamma_1 + \Gamma_2 + \Gamma_3 + \Gamma_4 + \Gamma_5 + \Gamma_6 = A + B + E_1 + E_2 \qquad \text{(A6-1)}$$

Next we must set up the linear combinations of the atomic orbitals which constitute each of these irreducible representations. Our task is simplified, as compared with a general case, by the fact that each irreducible representation occurs but once, and all representations are of dimension unity. Consequently, there will be only a single function ψ_i belonging to the ith irreducible representation. Any one of the atomic orbitals ϕ may then be expressed by

$$\phi = \sum_i c_i \psi_i \qquad \text{(A6-2)}$$

Performing any one operation of the group R, one has

$$R\phi = \sum_i c_i \Gamma_i(R) \psi_i = \sum_i c_i \chi_i(R) \psi_i \qquad \text{(A6-3)}$$

since the character is the representation if the dimension is one. Then multiplying by $\chi_j(R)$ and summing over all the operations of the group we have

$$\sum_R \chi_j(R) R\phi = \sum_i c_i \sum_R \chi_j(R)\chi_i(R) \psi_i$$

which because of orthogonality properties simplifies to

$$\sum_R \chi_j(R) R\phi = \sum_i c_i \delta_{ji}g\psi_i = c_j g\psi_j \qquad \text{(A6-4)}$$

where δ_{ji} has the usual value 1 if $i = j$, and zero otherwise, and g is the order of the group. It is usually simplest to note that $c_j g$ is a constant and to normalize ψ_j after its functional form is obtained. Applying equation (A6-4) to any one of the atomic orbitals with successive values of j yields the following.

$$\sum\chi_1(R)RA = A + B + C + D + E + F = (\text{const.})\,\psi_1$$
$$\sum\chi_2(R)RA = A + \epsilon B - \epsilon^*C - D - \epsilon E + \epsilon^*F = (\text{const.})\,\psi_2$$
$$\sum\chi_3(R)RA = A - \epsilon B - \epsilon^*C + D - \epsilon E - \epsilon^*F = (\text{const.})\,\psi_3$$
$$\sum\chi_4(R)RA = A - B + C - D + E - F = (\text{const.})\,\psi_4$$
$$\sum\chi_5(R)RA = A - \epsilon^*B - \epsilon C + D - \epsilon^*E - \epsilon F = (\text{const.})\,\psi_5$$
$$\sum\chi_6(R)RA = A + \epsilon^*B - \epsilon C - D - \epsilon^*E + \epsilon F = (\text{const.})\,\psi_6$$

in which it should be remembered that A indicates ϕ_A, etc. These molecular orbitals may be compactly expressed by

$$\psi_n = \frac{1}{\sqrt{6}} \sum_{k=1}^{6} e^{n\pi ik/3}\phi_k \qquad n = 0, \pm 1, \pm 2, 3 \qquad (A6\text{-}5)$$

where the k values 1 to 6 indicate the sequence $A, B, \ldots, F$, the n values have been reassigned for convenience, and the factor $1/\sqrt{6}$ normalizes the function if the ϕ's are orthogonal. The similarity to the imaginary exponential forms of rotational wave functions is striking, and it extends to the rearrangement of the ± 1 and ± 2 forms into pairs of real functions by taking the real and imaginary components, respectively. After renormalizing these are

$$\psi_{\pm 1} = \begin{cases} (2A + B - C - 2D - E + F)/\sqrt{12} \\ (B + C - E - F)/2 \end{cases}$$
$$\psi_{\pm 2} = \begin{cases} (2A - B - C + 2D - E - F)/\sqrt{12} \\ (B - C + E - F)/2 \end{cases} \qquad (A6\text{-}6)$$

The real forms in Eq. (A6-6), together with the $n = 0$ and $n = 3$ functions in (A6-5) have been renumbered in serial order, where they appear as Eq. (8.38) in the text. The bond energy values are readily computed to the simple molecular orbital approximation. Let us take as an example the totally symmetric orbital

$$\psi_1 = (\phi_A + \phi_B + \phi_C + \phi_D + \phi_E + \phi_F)/\sqrt{6}$$

and assume that the ϕ's are hydrogen $1s$ orbitals. Then

$$H = \frac{-h^2}{8\pi^2 m}\nabla^2 - \frac{e^2}{r_A} - \frac{e^2}{r_B} - \frac{e^2}{r_C} - \frac{e^2}{r_D} - \frac{e^2}{r_E} - \frac{e^2}{r_F}$$
$$W = \frac{\int \psi_1 H \psi_1 \, dv}{\int \psi_1^2 \, dv} = \frac{H_c + H_x + H_y}{1 + S_x + S_y} \qquad (A6\text{-}7)$$

whence by collecting all similar terms one finds

$$H_c = \int \phi_A H \phi_A \, dv = E_H - 2 \int \phi_A^2 \left(\frac{e^2}{r_B} + \frac{e^2}{r_C} + \frac{e^2}{2r_D} \right) dv$$

$$= E_H + 2H_c'$$

if we define H_c' so that its leading term is the same as in Eq. (8.35). Retaining the definitions of H_x and Δ exactly as in Eqs. (8.36) and (8.37), respectively, one has

$$H_x = 2 \int \phi_A H \phi_B \, dv = 2\Delta \, E_H + 2H_x'$$

$$S_x = 2\Delta$$

and

$$H_y = 2 \int \phi_A H \phi_C \, dv + \int \phi_A H \phi_D \, dv$$

$$S_y = 2 \int \phi_A \phi_C \, dv + \int \phi_A \phi_D \, dv$$

These last integrals between nonadjacent atoms will presumably be much smaller than those between adjacent atoms, and may be neglected. Then

$$W = \frac{E_H + 2H_c' + 2\Delta E_H + 2H_x'}{1 + 2\Delta}$$

$$= E_H + \frac{2H_c'}{1 + 2\Delta} + \frac{2H'}{1 + 2\Delta} \tag{A6-5}$$

and assuming as in Section 8h that the second term in (A6-8) compensates the repulsion between nuclei, and that Δ may be neglected in the third term, and writing β for H_x, one has finally

$$W_b = W - E_H = 2\beta \tag{A6-9}$$

The treatment is entirely applicable to the π electrons of benzene if one considers the p_z orbitals of the carbon atoms instead of $1s$ orbitals of hydrogen atoms. The p_z orbitals are, of course, antisymmetric to the plane of the benzene ring, which changes their symmetry in the full group D_{6h} but does not affect their relationships in the subgroup C_6 considered here.

BOND ORBITALS FOR H₄ AND FOR H₆ OR BENZENE

Since bond orbitals are many-electron functions, they are intrinsically more complicated than one-electron molecular orbitals. One must account for the exchange of identical electrons and for the fact that, although all spins are paired, nevertheless either orientation of spin is possible for the electron on any given atom.

Let us consider first the four-atom four-electron problem. Writing $a\alpha(1)$ for electron 1 in the orbital on atom A with spin oriented for $m_s = +\frac{1}{2}$, etc., $a\alpha(1)b\beta(2)c\alpha(3)d\beta(4)$ is evidently a satisfactory term in the complete wave function in that there is one electron on each atom and no net spin. One can account for electron interchange by writing the determinant

$$\phi_1 = \left(\frac{1}{4!}\right)^{1/2} \begin{vmatrix} a\alpha(1) & b\beta(1) & c\alpha(1) & d\beta(1) \\ a\alpha(2) & b\beta(2) & c\alpha(2) & d\beta(2) \\ a\alpha(3) & b\beta(3) & c\alpha(3) & d\beta(3) \\ a\alpha(4) & b\beta(4) & c\alpha(4) & d\beta(4) \end{vmatrix} \tag{A7-1}$$

Let us abbreviate this expression for ϕ_1 as $(a\alpha, b\beta, c\alpha, d\beta)$. Now if there are to be bonds A—B and C—D, the spins on A and B must be paired, and similarly for C and D. The function ϕ_1 meets this requirement, but there must also be included similar functions with the spins exchanged between the bonded atoms. The full array of functions is

$$\phi_1 = (a\alpha, \quad b\beta, \quad c\alpha, \quad d\beta)$$
$$\phi_2 = (a\beta, \quad b\alpha, \quad c\alpha, \quad d\beta)$$
$$\phi_3 = (a\beta, \quad b\alpha, \quad c\beta, \quad d\alpha)$$
$$\phi_4 = (a\alpha, \quad b\beta, \quad c\beta, \quad d\alpha)$$

By expanding examples and comparing with the simple bond orbital for one bond, it is found that the sign should be reversed for each spin exchange; hence the complete function for bonds A—B and C—D is

$$\psi_{AB,CD} = (\phi_1 - \phi_2 + \phi_3 - \phi_4)/2 \tag{A7-2}$$

For bonds in the B—C and D—A positions, one needs also

$$\phi_5 = (a\alpha, \quad b\alpha, \quad c\beta, \quad d\beta)$$
$$\phi_6 = (a\beta, \quad b\beta, \quad c\alpha, \quad d\alpha)$$

and the complete function is

$$\psi_{BC,DA} = (\phi_1 - \phi_5 + \phi_3 - \phi_6)/2 \qquad (A7\text{-}3)$$

The evaluation of the needed integrals for these functions is cumbersome but involves no new principles. The orthogonality of the spin functions makes many terms zero. If one neglects all integrals involving exchanges of more than a single pair of electrons, one obtains eventually the results stated in Section 8i. The rules given there for the coefficients of integrals were first derived by Pauling,[1] and were based on the system of bond diagrams introduced by Rumer.[2]

The lower energy solution for the variation method calculation with these two functions proves to be

$$\psi = (\psi_{AB,CD} + \psi_{BC,DA})/\sqrt{3}$$
$$= (2\phi_1 - \phi_2 + 2\phi_3 - \phi_4 - \phi_5 - \phi_6)/\sqrt{12} \qquad (A7\text{-}4)$$

This electronic wave function is unusual in that it is not symmetric to all the symmetry elements of the molecule, whereas the lowest energy wave function is usually totally symmetric. Consider the operation, C_4, rotation by 90°, which shifts nucleus A to B, B to C, C to D and D to A, respectively. Applying this to ϕ_1, Eq. (A7-1), we obtain

$$C_4\phi_1 = \left(\frac{1}{4!}\right)^{1/2} \begin{vmatrix} b\alpha(1) & c\beta(1) & d\alpha(1) & a\beta(1) \\ b\alpha(2) & c\beta(2) & d\alpha(2) & a\beta(2) \\ b\alpha(3) & c\beta(3) & d\alpha(3) & a\beta(3) \\ b\alpha(4) & c\beta(4) & d\alpha(4) & a\beta(4) \end{vmatrix}$$
$$= -\phi_3 \qquad (A7\text{-}5)$$

where the negative sign arises from the three interchanges of columns of the determinant needed to restore the original positions. The spin factors can be readily verified as corresponding to ϕ_3. Similarly one obtains

$$C_4\phi_2 = -\phi_6$$
$$C_4\phi_3 = -\phi_1$$
$$C_4\phi_4 = -\phi_5 \qquad (A7\text{-}6)$$
$$C_4\phi_5 = -\phi_2$$
$$C_4\phi_6 = -\phi_4$$

[1] Pauling, L., *J. Chem. Phys.*, **1**, 280 (1933).
[2] Rumer, G., *Nachr. Ges. Wiss. Gottingen, Math. physik. Klasse*, 1932, p. 337.

which, on substitution into Eq. (A7-4) shows that ψ is antisymmetric to the operation C_4. Application of the various symmetry operations of the group D_{4h} shows that ψ transforms as the representation B_{2g}.

Turning now to the six electron problems for six atoms in a planar regular hexagon, we consider first only structures I and II in Fig. 8.10. For these, with the same approximations as before, we obtain the secular equation

$$\begin{vmatrix} \frac{3}{2}\alpha - W_b & \frac{3}{2}\alpha - \frac{1}{4}W_b \\ \frac{3}{2}\alpha - \frac{1}{4}W_b & \frac{3}{2}\alpha - W_b \end{vmatrix} = 0 \tag{A7-7}$$

which has the solutions $W_b = 2.4\alpha$, $W_b = 0$.

Then if one wishes to include also the three structures III, IV, and V, one may either solve a fifth-order determinant or may use symmetry to select those combinations corresponding to the various irreducible representations. Following the latter method with the techniques of Appendix 6, one finds the appropriate symmetry functions and their corresponding energies to be as given in Table A7-1.

TABLE A7-1

CLASSIFICATION BY SYMMETRY OF THE BOND ORBITALS
FOR H₆ OR BENZENE

Representation	Wave function	W_b
A	$\begin{cases} \psi_1 = (\psi_I + \psi_{II})(\frac{2}{5})^{1/2} \\ \psi_2 = (\psi_{III} + \psi_{IV} + \psi_V)(\frac{2}{9})^{1/2} \end{cases}$	2.4α 2.0α
B	$\psi_3 = (\psi_I - \psi_{II})(\frac{2}{3})^{1/2}$	0
E_1	$\begin{cases} \psi_4 = (2\psi_{III} - \psi_{IV} - \psi_V)(\frac{2}{7})^{1/2} \\ \psi_5 = (\psi_{IV} - \psi_V)(\frac{2}{3})^{1/2} \end{cases}$	-2.0α

As an example of the method of finding W_b for these functions, let us work out ψ_2. The normalization factors in Table A7-1 were obtained as a result of these calculations also.

$$W_2 = \frac{H_{22}}{\Delta_{22}} = \frac{\frac{2}{9}(3H_{III,III} + 6H_{III,IV})}{\frac{2}{9}(3\Delta_{III,III} + 6\Delta_{III,IV})}$$
$$= \frac{\frac{2}{3}H_c + \frac{4}{3}(\frac{1}{4}H_c + \frac{3}{2}H_x)}{\frac{2}{3} + \frac{4}{3}(\frac{1}{4} + \frac{3}{2}\Delta)} \cong E_H + 2\alpha \tag{A7-8}$$

Only in the totally symmetric representation A is there more than one bond orbital function. Proceeding with the two functions ψ_1 and ψ_2, one obtains again the usual secular equation

$$\begin{vmatrix} H_{11} - \Delta_{11}W & H_{12} - \Delta_{12}W \\ H_{21} - \Delta_{21}W & H_{22} - \Delta_{22}W \end{vmatrix} = 0$$

which, on working out the various terms, becomes

$$\begin{vmatrix} \tfrac{12}{5}\alpha - W_b & \tfrac{6}{5}\alpha - \tfrac{2}{5}W_b \\ \tfrac{6}{5}\alpha - \tfrac{2}{5}W_b & 2\alpha - W_b \end{vmatrix} = 0 \qquad (A7\text{-}9)$$

This equation has the solutions $W_b = \alpha(-1 \pm \sqrt{13})$ or $W_b = +2.61\alpha$, -4.61α. The solution $+2.61\alpha$ is readily seen to represent the lowest energy state for the system, being 0.21α lower than the energy for the function ψ_1 and 1.11α lower than the energy for the simple bond functions represented by structures I and II in Fig. 8.10.

It will be noted that here the lowest energy function is totally symmetric, as is usually the case. Table A7-2 summarizes the energy levels for the six-electron problem. We have used here the symbols appropriate to the group D_{6h} to which a plane hexagon belongs.

TABLE A7-2

ELECTRONIC ENERGY LEVELS FOR H_6 OR BENZENE

Representation	W_b
A_{1g}	-4.61α
E_{2g}	-2.0α
B_{2u}	0
A_{1g}	$+2.61\alpha$

Appendix 8

ROTATIONAL ENERGY LEVELS OF AN UNSYMMETRICAL TOP

In order to discuss the energy levels of an unsymmetrical (or asymmetric) top, let us take the moments of inertia about the principal axes to be I_A, I_B, and I_C in increasing order, i.e., $I_C > I_B > I_A$. Let us also define the quantities

$$a = h^2/8\pi^2 I_A$$
$$b = h^2/8\pi^2 I_B \qquad \text{(A8-1)}$$
$$c = h^2/8\pi^2 I_C$$

The derivation of the energy levels is best done by matrix mechanics as is illustrated in Appendix 17.[1] However, the correct results have also been obtained in the Schrödinger method by using the wave functions for the symmetric top as a complete set of orthogonal functions to express in a series the functions for the asymmetric top.

The results for the energy levels may be expressed as

$$E(a,b,c) = J(J + 1)\left(\frac{a + c}{2}\right) + \left(\frac{a - c}{2}\right)E'(\kappa) \qquad \text{(A8-2)}$$

where κ is the parameter of asymmetry defined as

$$\kappa = \frac{2b - a - c}{a - c} \qquad \text{(A8-3)}$$

The quantity $E'(\kappa)$ is a separate function of κ for each energy level, i.e., each set of quantum numbers. The quantum number J carries over from the symmetric top with its relation for the square of the total angular momentum, $J(J + 1)h^2/4\pi^2$. However, the quantum number K from the symmetric case is useful only if the molecule approaches a symmetric top. Otherwise it is best to simply number the $(2J + 1)$ energy levels of a given J in order from the lowest to the highest. This is done with the quantity τ,

[1] See King, G. W., Hainer, R. M., and Cross, P. C., *J. Chem. Phys.*, **11**, 27 (1943) for a full derivation of the results presented here.

which is written as a subscript to $E'(\kappa)$ or J, and which takes the values $-J$, $-J + 1, \ldots, 0, \ldots, J - 1, J$ in order of increasing energy.

The particular form of expression given above is convenient because Ray[2] has proved that

$$E_\tau'^J(\kappa) = -E_{-\tau}'^J(-\kappa) \tag{A8-4}$$

Let us consider the two limiting cases where the unsymmetrical top approaches a symmetric top. If $I_B = I_A$, we have two small moments of inertia, hence an oblate symmetric top. Substitution in Eq. (A8-3) gives $\kappa = +1$. Similarly if $I_B = I_C$, one has a prolate symmetric top and $\kappa = -1$. Comparison with the symmetric top energy level equation yields for $E'(\kappa)$ the limiting expressions,

$$E'(+1) = J(J + 1) - 2K^2 \tag{A8-5a}$$
$$E'(-1) = 2K^2 - J(J + 1) \tag{A8-5b}$$

Before mentioning the quantitative values of $E'(\kappa)$ for the intermediate values of κ, it is helpful to get a qualitative picture of the energy level system. The levels up through $J = 4$ are plotted in Fig. A8-1 as a rough function of κ. The moments of inertia are selected rather close to one another in order to avoid overlapping of energy levels of different J. In actual examples, such overlapping is common.

One notes on the left side of Fig. A8-1 the levels for the prolate symmetric top ($\kappa = -1$), with the corresponding K values. On the right side are the levels for the oblate case ($\kappa = +1$), together with their K values. Since the K values have no meaning in the intermediate region of κ, there is no reason to expect the levels with the same K to join. However, since J retains its significance throughout, the levels with different J will remain distinct, even though in actual cases they may cross one another in energy. Within the set of levels of a given J it is found that the levels do not cross in the energy diagram. Thus the state with lowest energy has $K = 0$ on

Table A8-1

J_τ	$E'(\kappa)$	E
0_0	0	0
1_{-1}	$\kappa - 1$	$b + c$
1_0	0	$a + c$
1_1	$\kappa + 1$	$a + b$
2_{-2}	$2[\kappa - (\kappa^2 + 3)^{1/2}]$	$3(a + c) + (a - c)[\kappa - (\kappa^2 + 3)^{1/2}]$
2_{-1}	$\kappa - 3$	$a + b + 4c$
2_0	4κ	$a + 4b + c$
2_1	$\kappa + 3$	$4a + b + c$
2_2	$2[\kappa + (\kappa^2 + 3)^{1/2}]$	$3(a + c) + (a - c)[\kappa + (\kappa^2 + 3)^{1/2}]$

[2] Ray, B. S., Z. Physik, **78**, 74 (1932).

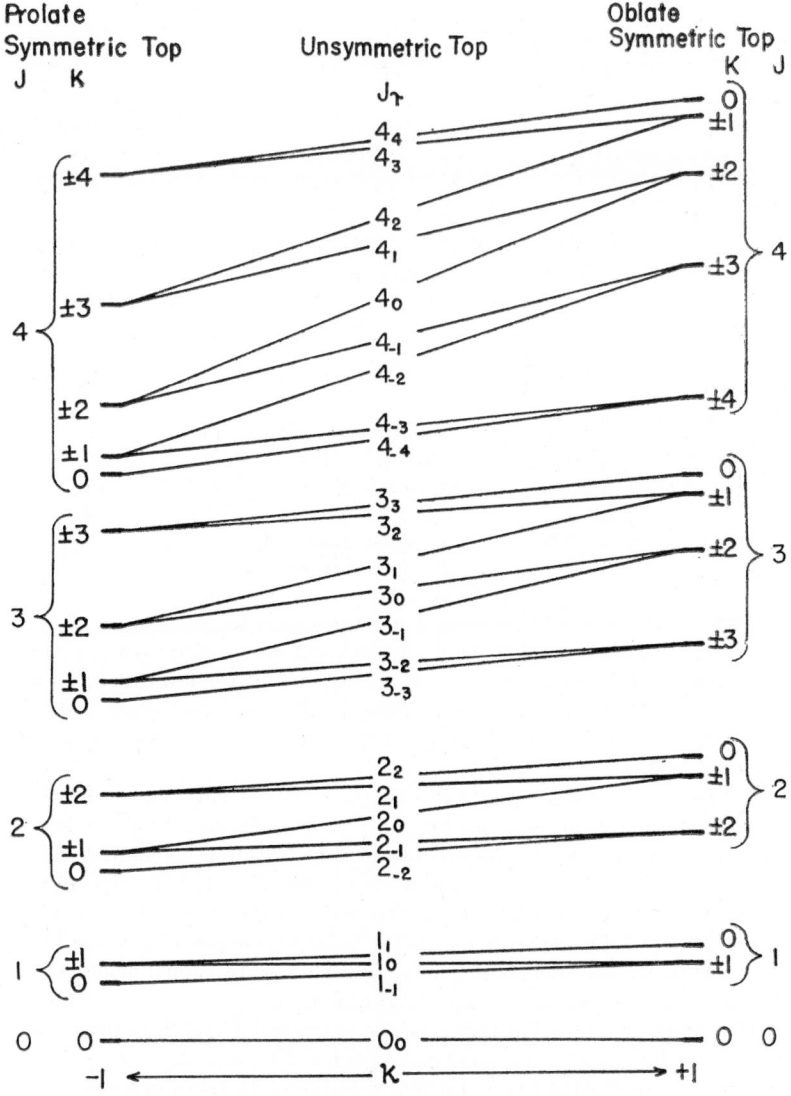

Fig. A8-1. The energy levels of an unsymmetrical top related to the limiting symmetrical tops.

the left, but has a maximum K value on the right.   In the middle of the diagram the τ values are given.

While it is impractical to give general expressions for all energy levels, the expressions for those up through $J = 2$ are simple, and are given in Table A8-1.   Except for the two involving the square root, the complete energy is readily expressed directly in the quantities a, b, and c.   These results in Table A8-1 are derived in Appendix 17.

Expressions for the energy levels for J greater than 2 are considerably more complex, since they are roots of secular equations of order about $\frac{1}{2}J$.   Those for $J = 3$ are given as $E'(\kappa)$ in Table A8-2.   Most of the higher levels cannot be expressed explicitly, but have been tabulated numerically for certain values of κ.

TABLE A8-2

$J\tau$	$E'(\kappa)$
3_{-3}	$5\kappa - 3 - 2(4\kappa^2 + 6\kappa + 6)^{1/2}$
3_{-2}	$2[\kappa - (\kappa^2 + 15)^{1/2}]$
3_{-1}	$5\kappa + 3 - 2(4\kappa^2 - 6\kappa + 6)^{1/2}$
3_0	4κ
3_1	$5\kappa - 3 + 2(4\kappa^2 + 6\kappa + 6)^{1/2}$
3_2	$2[\kappa + (\kappa^2 + 15)^{1/2}]$
3_3	$5\kappa + 3 + 2(4\kappa^2 - 6\kappa + 6)^{1/2}$

The expressions in Table A8-1 are sufficient to illustrate some of the properties of these energy levels.   The symmetry of the levels of $+\tau$ and $-\tau$ as required by Eq. (A8-4) is of course present, and this means that for $\kappa = 0$ the levels of a given J are symmetrically placed with respect to the one for $\tau = 0$.

The properties of the energy levels near $\kappa = \pm 1$ are important in relation to almost symmetrical tops.   In Fig. A8-1 we have shown the pairs of levels (where $K \neq 0$) as splitting immediately as κ deviates from its limiting value of ± 1.   However, this is correct only for the pair $K = 1, -1$.   The levels with higher K values separate only with a higher power of $(\kappa - 1)$ or $(\kappa + 1)$ as appropriate.   Furthermore the energy value for the pair of levels of high K is almost precisely that of a symmetric top whose two equal moments of inertia are the average of the nearly equal moments.

This behavior can be illustrated by the two levels 2_2 and 2_1 in the region near $\kappa = -1$ where $I_B = I_C$.   Taking a symmetric top with $I_X = (I_B + I_C)/2$ and $I_Z = I_A$, one obtains from Eq. (9.14) the energy level expression

$$E = \left(\frac{b + c}{2}\right) J(J + 1) + \left(a - \frac{b + c}{2}\right) K^2 \qquad (A8\text{-}6)$$

where we have used the quantities a, b, and c defined in Eq. (A8-1) and have made the additional approximation.

$$\frac{1}{2}\left(\frac{1}{I_B} + \frac{1}{I_C}\right) \cong \frac{2}{I_B + I_C} \qquad (A8\text{-}7)$$

Now substituting the value 2 for J and K, one has

$$E = 4a + b + c \qquad (A8\text{-}8)$$

for the symmetric top energy level, which is precisely that given in Table A8-1 for the 2_1 level. By expanding the square root in the expression for the 2_2 level, one obtains

$$E = 4a + b + c + 3(b - c)^2/4(a - c) + \ldots \qquad (A8\text{-}9)$$

where the last term is very small under the condition $b \cong c$.

Actually the levels with higher K values deviate from the symmetric top levels even less so that it has proved quite feasible to interpret the spectrum of such molecules as ethylene on the symmetric top formula for energy levels.

The rotational wave functions for the asymmetric top belong to a fourth-order symmetry group whose operations are the three mutually perpendicular twofold rotations and the identity operation. The various energy states are readily classified among the four irreducible representations of this group. The selection rules for light absorption or emission depend, of course, on the orientation of the dipole moment. An asymmetric top may have its dipole moment oriented along any principal axis, or in an arbitrary direction so that there are components on two or even all three principal axes. Consequently it is impossible to state briefly the selection rules for all these different cases. However, in any particular case it is not difficult to work out the expected spectrum. It should be noted that the line intensities change much more rapidly than the energies for small deviations from a symmetric top. Consequently, in analyzing the spectrum of an approximately symmetric top, one must consider the asymmetry in predicting intensities, even though it may be ignored in predicting the frequencies.

Just as in the symmetric top case, there is a quantum number which gives the component of angular momentum along an axis fixed in space. It has the $(2J + 1)$ values $-J$ to $+J$ and does not affect the energy unless perturbing fields are present. Recently the development of microwave spectroscopy has made it feasible to determine the Stark effect in the pure rotation spectrum. If the molecule has a permanent dipole moment, as it must to have a pure rotation spectrum, the energy levels will depend on the quantum number m. Since the maximum value of m is J, it is possible thereby to determine the J values corresponding to the lines in the spectrum.

King, Hainer, and Cross have given a very thorough treatment of unsymmetrical tops, including extensive numerical tables, in a series of papers in the *Journal of Chemical Physics.* The principal contents are indicated briefly below:

Calculation and symmetry classification of energy levels; numerical values through $J = 10$; *J. Chem. Phys.*, **11**, 27 (1943).

Extension of energy levels through $J = 12$ and discussion of calculation methods for higher levels; *J. Chem. Phys.*, **17**, 826 (1949).

Selection rules and dipole line intensities. *J. Chem. Phys.*, **12**, 210 (1944).

ROTATIONAL PARTITION FUNCTION
FOR AN UNSYMMETRICAL TOP

The kinetic energy, which is the total energy for the rotation of a rigid body, may be expressed as

$$2\epsilon = M_x^2/I_x + M_y^2/I_y + M_z^2/I_z \tag{A9-1}$$

where the M's are the instantaneous angular momenta about the three principal axes.

The phase integral expression for the partition function was given in Chapter 7 as

$$Q = \frac{1}{\sigma h^m} \int \cdots \int e^{-\epsilon/kT} \, dq_1 \ldots dq_m \, dp_1 \ldots dp_m \tag{7.58}$$

where the q's are coordinates and the p's their conjugate momenta. Since our expression for the energy is independent of the coordinates, the integrations with respect to coordinates and momenta may be carried out separately. Taking first the momenta, we find three integrals, each of the type

$$\int_{-\infty}^{+\infty} e^{-M_x^2/2I_xkT} dM_x = (2\pi I_x kT)^{1/2} \tag{A9-2}$$

The integration with respect to the angular coordinates is not convenient in the separate angles of rotation about each principal axis, since these are not independent. However, selecting any one axis in the molecule, the angle of rotation about that axis has the range 2π. Furthermore, the orientation of the selected axis in space covers the usual solid angle of 4π (which can be readily obtained from spherical polar coordinates). The triple integral over the angles of orientation of a solid body must therefore yield the product of these two factors, or $8\pi^2$.

Combining these results one obtains the final result which is given, with slight rearrangement, in the text as Eq. (9.16)

$$Q_r = \frac{8\pi^2}{\sigma h^3} (2\pi kT)^{3/2} (I_x I_y I_z)^{1/2} \tag{A9-3}$$

Stripp and Kirkwood[1] have verified this result by a more elaborate method which yields additional terms. Their expression is

$$Q_r = Q_r^\circ \left[1 + \frac{h^2}{96\pi^2 kT} \left(\frac{2}{I_x} + \frac{2}{I_y} + \frac{2}{I_z} - \frac{I_z}{I_x I_y} - \frac{I_x}{I_y I_z} - \frac{I_y}{I_z I_x} \right) + \cdots \right]$$

(A9-4)

where Q_r° is the first approximation given in Eq. (A9-3). These additional terms are negligible in most cases of practical interest.[2]

[1] Stripp, K. F. and Kirkwood, J. G., *J. Chem. Phys.*, **19**, 1131 (1951).
[2] Pitzer, K. S., *J. Chem. Phys.*, **7**, 251 (1939).

Appendix 10

LAGRANGIAN EQUATIONS OF MOTION

While elementary presentations of classical mechanics are commonly based on Newton's equations of motion, other mathematically more powerful methods exist. One is that due to Lagrange (1760–1788), which we shall now present. Its chief value is in connection with generalized coordinates. Thus we assume that these generalized coordinates $q_1, \ldots, q_j, \ldots$ are functions of the Cartesian coordinates of the particles x_i, and inversely that

$$x_i = x_i(q_1 \ldots q_j \ldots) \qquad (A10\text{-}1)$$

We also limit ourselves to conservative systems, which means that the forces can be derived from a potential energy

$$X_i = -\frac{\partial V}{\partial x_i}, \quad \text{etc.} \qquad (A10\text{-}2)$$

This potential energy V can also be expressed in terms of the generalized coordinates, q_i.

Newton's equations of motion are

$$m_i \ddot{x} = -\frac{\partial V}{\partial x_i}$$

Now multiply each by $\partial x_i / \partial q_j$ and sum over all coordinates of all particles, yielding

$$\sum_i m_i \ddot{x}_i \frac{\partial x_i}{\partial q_j} = -\sum_i \frac{\partial V}{\partial x_i} \frac{\partial x_i}{\partial q_j} = -\frac{\partial V}{\partial q_j} \qquad (A10\text{-}3)$$

The Lagrangian function is $L = T - V$, and the equations of motion are

$$\frac{d}{dt} \frac{\partial L}{\partial \dot{q}_j} - \frac{\partial L}{\partial q_j} = 0 \qquad (A10\text{-}4)$$

To prove that Eq. (A10-4) is equivalent to (A10-3), we set up L with T in Cartesian coordinates

$$L = \sum_i m_i \dot{x}_i^2 / 2 - V$$

445

Then
$$\frac{d}{dt} \sum_i m_i \dot{x}_i \frac{\partial \dot{x}_i}{\partial \dot{q}_j} - \sum_i m_i \dot{x}_i \frac{\partial \dot{x}_i}{\partial q_j} = -\frac{\partial V}{\partial q_j} \tag{A10-5}$$

At once we see that the right sides of Eqs. (A10-5) and (A10-3) are the same. Equating the left sides and taking the time derivative in (A10-5), we have

$$\sum_i m_i \ddot{x}_i \frac{\partial x_i}{\partial q_j} = \sum_i m_i \ddot{x}_i \frac{\partial \dot{x}_i}{\partial \dot{q}_j} + \sum_i m_i \dot{x}_i \left[\frac{d}{dt}\left(\frac{\partial \dot{x}_i}{\partial \dot{q}_j}\right) - \frac{\partial \dot{x}_i}{\partial q_j}\right] \tag{A10-6}$$

From the original definition of the coordinates,

$$\dot{x}_i = \sum_j \frac{\partial x_i}{\partial q_j} \dot{q}_j$$

Hence
$$\frac{\partial \dot{x}_i}{\partial \dot{q}_j} = \frac{\partial x_i}{\partial q_j} \tag{A10-7}$$

and differentiating the last with respect to time,

$$\frac{d}{dt}\left(\frac{\partial \dot{x}_i}{\partial \dot{q}_j}\right) = \sum_k \frac{\partial}{\partial q_k}\left(\frac{\partial x_i}{\partial q_j}\right)\dot{q}_k = \sum_k \frac{\partial^2 x_i}{\partial q_k \partial q_j}\dot{q}_k$$
$$= \frac{\partial}{\partial q_j} \sum_k \frac{\partial x_i}{\partial q_k}\dot{q}_k = \frac{\partial \dot{x}_i}{\partial q_j} \tag{A10-8}$$

Thus in Eq. (A10-6) the left side equals the first term on the right, and the second term is zero. This has established the equivalence of the Newtonian and Lagrangian equations of motion. However, the kinetic energy can be expressed equally well in terms of the generalized coordinates q_j. Then the equations of motion

$$\frac{d}{dt}\left(\frac{\partial L}{\partial \dot{q}_j}\right) - \frac{\partial L}{\partial q_j} = 0 \tag{A10-4}$$

can be solved directly in the generalized coordinates.

GENERALIZED MOMENTA IN CLASSICAL MECHANICS, HAMILTON'S EQUATIONS OF MOTION

The momentum in Newtonian mechanics is $m_i\dot{x}_i$, which one notes is equivalent to the derivative of the kinetic energy with respect to the velocity

$$\frac{\partial T}{\partial \dot{x}_i} = \frac{\partial}{\partial \dot{x}_i}\left(\sum_i \frac{1}{2}m_i\dot{x}_i^2\right) = m_i\dot{x}_i = p_{x_i}$$

Let us assume that this definition may be generalized to other coordinate systems,

$$p_k = \frac{\partial T}{\partial \dot{q}_k} \tag{A11-1}$$

where p_k is the momentum conjugate to the coordinate q_k.

For example, the kinetic energy of a single particle rotating about an axis is $\frac{1}{2}mr^2\dot{\phi}^2$, or $\frac{1}{2}I\dot{\phi}^2$, where mr^2 is the moment of inertia I. Then

$$p_\phi = mr^2\dot{\phi} = I\dot{\phi}$$

which one notes is the conventional angular momentum.

Recalling the Lagrangian function and equations of motion

$$L = T - V$$

$$\frac{d}{dt}\left(\frac{\partial L}{\partial \dot{q}_k}\right) - \frac{\partial L}{\partial q_k} = 0 \tag{A10-4}$$

one may write also

$$p_k = \frac{\partial L}{\partial \dot{q}_k} \quad \text{and} \quad \dot{p}_k = \frac{\partial L}{\partial q_k} \tag{A11-2}$$

because the potential energy is not a function of the velocities. Now define the Hamiltonian function,

$$H = \sum_k p_k\dot{q}_k - L = \sum_k p_k\dot{q}_k - T + V \tag{A11-3}$$

which we shall presently show to be equal to the total energy (kinetic plus potential) for systems of the type which interest us. The total differential of H is

$$dH = \sum_k \left(p_k \, d\dot{q}_k + \dot{q}_k \, dp_k - \frac{\partial L}{\partial q_k} \, dq_k - \frac{\partial L}{\partial \dot{q}_k} \, d\dot{q}_k \right) \tag{A11-4}$$

but using Eq. (A11-2) above, the first and last terms cancel, and the others become

$$dH = \sum_k (\dot{q}_k \, dp_k - \dot{p}_k \, dq_k) \tag{A11-5}$$

Up to this point L has been regarded as a function of q's and $\dot{q}$'s; however, it may readily be converted to a function of q's and p's. Assuming then that H is now a function of q's and p's, one obtains from Eq. (A11-5) the result

$$\frac{\partial H}{\partial p_k} = \dot{q}_k, \qquad \frac{\partial H}{\partial q_k} = -\dot{p}_k \tag{A11-6}$$

These are the equations of motion introduced by Hamilton in 1834, although anticipated in part by Poisson and Lagrange.

For any systems to be considered here the kinetic energy may be written as a homogeneous quadratic function of the velocities

$$2T = \sum_i \sum_j c_{ij} \dot{q}_i \dot{q}_j$$

Hence

$$p_k = \frac{\partial T}{\partial \dot{q}_k} = \sum_i c_{ik} \dot{q}_i$$

and

$$H = \sum_i \sum_k c_{ik} \dot{q}_i \dot{q}_k - L$$

$$= 2T - T + V = T + V \tag{A11-7}$$

Thus the Hamiltonian function may be taken as the total energy (kinetic and potential) expressed in terms of coordinates and conjugate momenta.

Appendix 12

SYMMETRY AND NORMAL VIBRATIONS

If a molecule has symmetry, it is most important to recognize the symmetry elements in treating the vibrations of the molecule. The use of proper symmetry coordinates factors the secular Eq. (9.39) into several smaller order equations. Furthermore, the selection rules are best given in terms of the irreducible representations of the symmetry group. In this appendix the method will be given for determining the number of normal modes of vibration of each symmetry type (irreducible representation) for a given molecule, together with the selection rules.

The basic theory of symmetry groups[1] will be assumed. In the usual symbolism C_n represents the operation of rotation about an axis by $2\pi/n$, S_n indicates rotation by $2\pi/n$, followed by reflection through a plane perpendicular to the axis of rotation, σ indicates a simple reflection, i indicates inversion through a point, and E is the identity operation which leaves everything unchanged. If there are different reflection planes, σ_h indicates a horizontal plane which is perpendicular to the principal (highest fold) rotation axis. This principal axis is always taken as vertical and as the z axis. Then σ_v is a vertical plane which contains this principal axis. In applying symmetry theory to a molecule, one first identifies all the symmetry elements present. Then one selects the point group which these elements constitute. Table 12-1 lists the more commonly needed point groups with various associated properties. The component operations are given in the top row of the table for each group. If there are classes containing more than one operation, these operations are indicated as $2C_3$ (for the rotations by $+2\pi/3$ and $-2\pi/3$) etc.

One wishes to obtain the number of normal modes of each symmetry type. While one can compute this quantity alone, it is almost as simple to obtain a complete itemized account of the translations, the rotations, and the normal modes of vibration contributed by each set of equivalent atoms in the molecule. By an equivalent set of atoms we mean the atoms

---

[1] Margenau, H. and Murphy, G. M., *The Mathematics of Physics and Chemistry*, New York: D. Van Nostrand Company, Inc., 1943, Chap. 15.

which are shifted into each other's positions by the symmetry operations. Thus the two carbon atoms form one set in ethylene, and the four hydrogens form another set.

We find the characters of the representation formed by the coordinates of all the atoms of one equivalent set. If $u^j(R)$ is the number of atoms of the jth set left unchanged by the symmetry operation R, the character $\chi^j(R)$ is given by the expressions[2]

$$\begin{aligned} \chi^j(R) &= u^j(R)(1 + 2 \cos \phi) \quad \text{for proper rotations} \\ \chi^j(R) &= u^j(R)(-1 + 2 \cos \phi) \quad \text{for improper rotations} \end{aligned} \tag{A12-1}$$

where ϕ is the angle of rotation in the operation. The operations C_n are proper rotations with $\phi = 2\pi/n$, while the operations S_n are improper rotations with the corresponding ϕ values. The identity operation E is a proper rotation with $\phi = 0$. A simple reflection through a plane, σ, is an improper rotation with $\phi = 0$, and an inversion through a point, i, is the same as S_2, i.e., an improper rotation with $\phi = \pi$.

Given the characters of the reducible representation formed by the coordinates of one set of atoms, one can proceed to calculate the number of modes of motion, vibrational, rotational, or translational, of each symmetry type. We write N_k^j for this number of modes of the kth symmetry type for the jth set of atoms.

$$N_k^j = \frac{1}{g} \sum_R \chi^j(R) \chi_k(R) \tag{A12-2}$$

where g is the order of the group, i.e., the total number of operations in the group, and $\chi_k(R)$ is the character of the kth irreducible representation, which is given in the tables at the end of this Appendix. The sum is over all operations of the group, and in particular, if there are several operations in any class, the corresponding term must be included the appropriate number of times.

The total number of normal modes of vibration of each symmetry type may be obtained by summing N_k^j over the various sets of atoms and subtracting the numbers of translations t_k and rotations r_k of that symmetry type.

$$N_k = \sum_j N_k^j - t_k - r_k \tag{A12-3}$$

In the character tables are also given the properties of translation and rotation. Translation is indicated simply by x, y, and z as appropriate, while rotation is indicated by R_x, R_y, R_z. Thus t_k and r_k are just the number of times x, ... or R_x, ... appears for that representation.

For the degenerate representations, the quantities N_k^j and N_k refer to the

[2] Rosenthal, J. E. and Murphy, G. M., *Revs. Modern Phys.*, **8**, 317 (1936).

number of degenerate pairs or triplets rather than to the total number of coordinates involved. Correspondingly, t_k and r_k must refer to the pairs or triplets of translational or rotational coordinates.

The selection rules for the absorption spectrum require the molecular vibration to change some component of the dipole moment. Thus only vibrations of the type of the irreducible representations of the components of a vector, i.e., x, y, and z, can be active. In the tables these representations are indicated by the same symbols x, y, and z as indicated translation.

Similarly the selection rules for the Raman effect involve the components of the polarizability tensor. Its components transform as x^2, y^2, z^2, xy, xz, yz, or equivalent linear combination of these. If the vibration is of the same representation as any of these components, it is Raman active. The representations corresponding to these components are similarly indicated in the left column of each table. As an example, let us take the molecule cyclopropane; it has the symmetry D_{3h}. The principal axis through the center of the ring and perpendicular to the plane of the three carbons is both C_3 and S_3. There is a symmetry plane through the three carbons, σ_h, and one through each CH$_2$ group, σ_v. There are also three twofold axes in the horizontal plane, one passing through each carbon atom.

There are two sets of atoms, the three carbons and the six hydrogens. We shall indicate these by the superscripts c and H. The calculation of $\chi^c(R)$, etc., proceeds as follows.

$$\chi^c(E) = 3(1 + 2) = 9 \qquad \chi^H(E) = 6(3) = 18$$
$$\chi^c(\sigma_h) = 3(-1 + 2) = 3 \qquad \chi^H(\sigma_h) = 0$$
$$\chi^c(C_3) = 0(1 - 1) = 0 \qquad \chi^H(C_3) = 0$$
$$\chi^c(S_3) = 0(-1 - 1) = 0 \qquad \chi^H(S_3) = 0$$
$$\chi^c(C_2) = 1(1 - 2) = -1 \qquad \chi^H(C_2) = 0$$
$$\chi^c(\sigma_v) = 1(-1 + 2) = 1 \qquad \chi^H(\sigma_v) = 2(1) = 2$$

Then taking the elements for the character table for D_{3h}, one obtains the values of N_j^c and N_j^H from Eq. (A12-2). The details are given only for N_j^c. The values of t_k and r_k other than zero are given also.

$$N_{A_{1'}}^c = \tfrac{1}{12}(9 + 3 - 3 + 3) = 1, \quad N_{A_{1'}}^H = 2$$
$$N_{A_{2'}}^c = \tfrac{1}{12}(9 + 3 + 3 - 3) = 1, \quad N_{A_{2'}}^H = 1, \quad r_{A_{2'}} = 1$$
$$N_{A_{1''}}^c = \tfrac{1}{12}(9 - 3 - 3 - 3) = 0, \quad N_{A_{1''}}^H = 1$$
$$N_{A_{2''}}^c = \tfrac{1}{12}(9 - 3 + 3 + 3) = 1, \quad N_{A_{2''}}^H = 2, \quad t_{A_{2''}} = 1$$
$$N_{E'}^c = \tfrac{1}{12}(18 + 6) = 2, \quad N_{E'}^H = 3, \quad t_{E'} = 1$$
$$N_{E''}^c = \tfrac{1}{12}(18 - 6) = 1, \quad N_{E''}^H = 3, \quad r_{E''} = 1$$

Thus we have all the data needed to obtain the N_k values.

Since there is some interest in the vibrations of the carbon skeleton separately, we remove the translations and rotations from the N_j^c values. Then the number of modes added by the hydrogens are just the N_k^H values.   These results are given in Table A12-1.

TABLE A12-1

VIBRATIONS OF CYCLOPROPANE

Symmetry type	Skeletal modes	H modes	Total modes	Selection rules
A_1'	1	2	3	$R(p)$
A_2'	0	1	1	inactive
A_1''	0	1	1	inactive
A_2''	0	2	2	$I(\|)$
E'	1	3	4	$R(d), I(\perp)$
E''	0	3	3	$R(d)$

The selection rules can be determined readily from the D_{3h} table, and are given in Table A12-1 also.   The A_2'' vibrations can generate a dipole moment in the z direction, and hence give the parallel bands of a symmetric top.   Similarly the E' vibrations affect the dipole moment in the x and y directions, and yield perpendicular bands.   Vibrations of types A_1', E', and E'' are all Raman active.   In accordance with the general statements in Section 9g, only the totally symmetric vibrations of type A_1' can give polarized lines.   All others must be fully depolarized.

Symmetry theory is also very important in connection with the effect of isotopic substitution on vibration frequencies.   The principal relationship here is the *product rule*, which is explained for a simple example in Section 9n.   A more general statement of the product rule follows here.

The product rule gives a separate equation for each irreducible representation, as follows.

$$\frac{\omega_1'\omega_2' \ldots \omega_N'}{\omega_1\omega_2 \ldots \omega_N} = \left[\left(\frac{M'}{M}\right)^t \left(\frac{I_x'}{I_x}\right)^{r_x} \left(\frac{I_y'}{I_y}\right)^{r_y} \left(\frac{I_z'}{I_z}\right)^{r_z} \prod_j \left(\frac{m_j}{m_j'}\right)^{N^j} \right]^{1/2} \quad \text{(A12-4)}$$

where the primed symbols refer to the isotopically substituted molecule throughout, and M is the total molecular weight.   The products on the left cover all the frequencies of the kth type, and the exponents t and N^j on the right are the quantities defined above for the kth irreducible representation. The quantities r_x, r_y, and r_z are zero unless that rotation falls in the irreducible representation being considered, in which case that r is 1.   For rotation in a degenerate representation, the I's are equal, and the ratio is used only once for the set of rotations.

Continuing with cyclopropane as an example, for the A_1' type and for deuterium substitution, one finds t and all r's zero, and

$$\left[\left(\frac{m_H}{m_D}\right)^2 \right]^{1/2} = 0.50039 = \frac{\omega_1'\omega_2'\omega_3'}{\omega_1\omega_2\omega_3}$$

Similarly for the E' type one has $t = 1$, all r's zero, and

$$\left[\left(\frac{M'}{M}\right)\left(\frac{m_{\mathrm{H}}}{m_{\mathrm{D}}}\right)^3\right]^{1/2} = 0.3785 = \frac{\omega_8'\omega_9'\omega_{10}'\omega_{11}'}{\omega_8\omega_9\omega_{10}\omega_{11}}$$

where the frequencies ω are those of the given symmetry type in each case.

TABLE A12-2

PROPERTIES OF SYMMETRY GROUPS

$C_{1h} = C_S$ (e.g.: propylene)			E	σ_h
x^2,y^2,z^2,xy	x,y,R_z	A'	1	1
xz,yz	z,R_x,R_y	A''	1	-1

C_{2v} (e.g.: H$_2$O)			E	C_2	σ_v	σ_v'
x^2,y^2,z^2	z	A_1	1	1	1	1
xy	R_z	A_2	1	1	-1	-1
xz	x,R_y	B_1	1	-1	1	-1
yz	y,R_x	B_2	1	-1	-1	1

C_{2h} (e.g.: trans C$_2$H$_2$Cl$_2$			E	C_2	σ_h	i
x^2,y^2,z^2,xy	R_z	A_g	1	1	1	1
	z	A_u	1	1	-1	-1
xz,yz	R_x,R_y	B_g	1	-1	-1	1
	x,y	B_u	1	-1	1	-1

C_{3v} (e.g.: NH$_3$)			E	$2C_3$	$3\sigma_v$
x^2+y^2,z^2	z	A_1	1	1	1
	R_z	A_2	1	1	-1
x^2-y^2,xy,xz,yz	x,y,R_x,R_y	E	2	-1	0

C_{4v} (e.g.: B$_5$H$_9$)			E	C_2	$2C_4$	$2\sigma_v$	$2\sigma_d$
x^2+y^2,z^2	z	A_1	1	1	1	1	1
	R_z	A_2	1	1	1	-1	-1
x^2-y^2		B_1	1	1	-1	1	-1
xy		B_2	1	1	-1	-1	1
xz,yz	x,y,R_x,R_y	E	2	-2	0	0	0

TABLE A12-2 (Continued)

D_{2d} (e.g.: allene)			E	C_2	$2S_4$	$2C_2'$	$2\sigma_d$
x^2+y^2,z^2		A_1	1	1	1	1	1
	R_z	A_2	1	1	1	-1	-1
x^2-y^2		B_1	1	1	-1	1	-1
xy	z	B_2	1	1	-1	-1	1
xz,yz	x,y,R_x,R_y	E	2	-2	0	0	0

D_{2h} (e.g.: ethylene)			E	C_2^z	C_2^y	C_2^x	i	σ_{xy}	σ_{xz}	σ_{yz}
x^2,y^2,z^2		A_{1g}	1	1	1	1	1	1	1	1
		A_{1u}	1	1	1	1	-1	-1	-1	-1
xy	R_z	B_{1g}	1	1	-1	-1	1	1	-1	-1
	z	B_{1u}	1	1	-1	-1	-1	-1	1	1
xz	R_y	B_{2g}	1	-1	1	-1	1	-1	1	-1
	y	B_{2u}	1	-1	1	-1	-1	1	-1	1
yz	R_x	B_{3g}	1	-1	-1	1	1	-1	-1	1
	x	B_{3u}	1	-1	-1	1	-1	1	1	-1

D_{3d} (e.g.: cyclohexane)			E	$2C_3$	$3C_2'$	i	$2S_6$	$3\sigma_d$
x^2+y^2,z^2		A_{1g}	1	1	1	1	1	1
		A_{1u}	1	1	1	-1	-1	-1
	R_z	A_{2g}	1	1	-1	1	1	-1
	z	A_{2u}	1	1	-1	-1	-1	1
x^2-y^2,xy,xz,yz	R_x,R_y	E_g	2	-1	0	2	-1	0
	x,y	E_u	2	-1	0	-2	1	0

D_{3h} (e.g.: cyclopropane)			E	σ_h	$2C_3$	$2S_3$	$3C_2'$	$3\sigma_v$
x^2+y^2,z^2		A_1'	1	1	1	1	1	1
	R_z	A_2'	1	1	1	1	-1	-1
		A_1''	1	-1	1	-1	1	-1
	z	A_2''	1	-1	1	-1	-1	1
x^2-y^2,xy	x,y	E'	2	2	-1	-1	0	0
xz,yz	R_x,R_y	E''	2	-2	-1	1	0	0

TABLE A12-2 (Continued)

D_{4h} (e.g.: cyclobutane)			E	C_2	$2C_4$	$2C_2'$	$2C_2''$	i	σ_h	$2S_4$	$2\sigma_v'$	$2\sigma_v''$
x^2+y^2,z^2		A_{1g}	1	1	1	1	1	1	1	1	1	1
		A_{1u}	1	1	1	1	1	-1	-1	-1	-1	-1
	R_z	A_{2g}	1	1	1	-1	-1	1	1	1	-1	-1
	z	A_{2u}	1	1	1	-1	-1	-1	-1	-1	1	1
x^2-y^2		B_{1g}	1	1	-1	1	-1	1	1	-1	1	-1
		B_{1u}	1	1	-1	1	-1	-1	-1	1	-1	1
xy		B_{2g}	1	1	-1	-1	1	1	1	-1	-1	1
		B_{2u}	1	1	-1	-1	1	-1	-1	1	1	-1
xz,yz	R_x,R_y	E_g	2	-2	0	0	0	2	-2	0	0	0
	x,y	E_u	2	-2	0	0	0	-2	2	0	0	0

D_{6h} (e.g.: benzene)			E	C_2	$2C_3$	$2C_6$	$3C_2'$	$3C_2''$	i	σ_h	$2S_6$	$2S_3$	$3\sigma_v'$	$3\sigma_v''$
x^2+y^2,z^2		A_{1g}	1	1	1	1	1	1	1	1	1	1	1	1
		A_{1u}	1	1	1	1	1	1	-1	-1	-1	-1	-1	-1
	R_z	A_{2g}	1	1	1	1	-1	-1	1	1	1	1	-1	-1
	z	A_{2u}	1	1	1	1	-1	-1	-1	-1	-1	-1	1	1
		B_{1g}	1	-1	1	-1	1	-1	1	-1	1	-1	1	-1
		B_{1u}	1	-1	1	-1	1	-1	-1	1	-1	1	-1	1
		B_{2g}	1	-1	1	-1	-1	1	1	-1	1	-1	-1	1
		B_{2u}	1	-1	1	-1	-1	1	-1	1	-1	1	1	-1
xz,yz	R_x,R_y	E_{1g}	2	-2	-1	1	0	0	2	-2	-1	1	0	0
	x,y	E_{1u}	2	-2	-1	1	0	0	-2	2	1	-1	0	0
x^2-y^2,xy		E_{2g}	2	2	-1	-1	0	0	2	2	-1	-1	0	0
		E_{2u}	2	2	-1	-1	0	0	-2	-2	1	1	0	0

T_d (e.g.: CH₄)			E	$8C_3$	$3C_2$	$6\sigma_d$	$6S_4$
$x^2+y^2+z^2$		A_1	1	1	1	1	1
		A_2	1	1	1	-1	-1
x^2-y^2, etc.		E	2	-1	2	0	0
	R_x,R_y,R_z	T_1	3	0	-1	-1	1
xy,xz,yz	x,y,z	T_2	3	0	-1	1	-1

Note: the symbol T is used for triply degenerate types of vibration, just as E is used for doubly degenerate types.

TABLE A12-2 (Continued)

O_h (e.g.: SF_6)			E	$8C_3$	$3C_2$	$6C_2$	$6C_4$	i	$8S_6$	3σ	6σ	$6S_4$
$x^2+y^2+z^2$		A_{1g}	1	1	1	1	1	1	1	1	1	1
		A_{1u}	1	1	1	1	1	-1	-1	-1	-1	-1
		A_{2g}	1	1	1	-1	-1	1	1	1	-1	-1
		A_{2u}	1	1	1	-1	-1	-1	-1	-1	1	1
x^2-y^2, etc.		E_g	2	-1	2	0	0	2	-1	2	0	0
		E_u	2	-1	2	0	0	-2	1	-2	0	0
	R_x,R_y,R_z	T_{1g}	3	0	-1	-1	1	3	0	-1	-1	1
	x,y,z	T_{1u}	3	0	-1	-1	1	-3	0	1	1	-1
xy,xz,yz		T_{2g}	3	0	-1	1	-1	3	0	-1	1	-1
		T_{2u}	3	0	-1	1	-1	-3	0	1	-1	1

$C_{\infty v}$ (e.g.: HCN)			E	$2C_{(\phi)}$	σ_v
x^2+y^2,z^2	z	A_1	1	1	1
	R_z	A_2	1	1	-1
xz,yz	x,y,R_x,R_y	E_1	2	$2\cos\phi$	0
x^2-y^2,xy		E_2	2	$2\cos 2\phi$	0
		—	—	—	—
		E_k	2	$2\cos k\phi$	0
		—	—	—	—

Note: the symbols Σ^+, Σ^-, Π, Δ, etc. are sometimes used instead of A_1, A_2, E_1, E_2, etc. for the groups $C_{\infty v}$ and $D_{\infty h}$.

$D_{\infty h}$ (e.g.: CO_2)			E	$2C_{(\phi)}$	C_2	i	$2S_{(\phi)}$	σ_v
x^2+y^2,z^2		A_{1g}	1	1	1	1	1	1
	z	A_{1u}	1	1	-1	-1	-1	1
	R_z	A_{2g}	1	1	-1	1	1	-1
		A_{2u}	1	1	1	-1	-1	-1
xz,yz	R_x,R_y	E_{1g}	2	$2\cos\phi$	0	2	$-2\cos\phi$	0
	x,y	E_{1u}	2	$2\cos\phi$	0	-2	$2\cos\phi$	0
x^2-y^2,xy		E_{2g}	2	$2\cos 2\phi$	0	2	$2\cos 2\phi$	0
		E_{2u}	2	$2\cos 2\phi$	0	-2	$-2\cos 2\phi$	0
		—	—	—	—	—	—	—

Appendix 13

THERMODYNAMIC FUNCTIONS FOR THE HARMONIC OSCILLATOR

These functions are defined by Eq. (9.49) and are given in the form of dimensionless ratios to avoid the need for revision of the body of the tables when the values of physical constants are changed. The present best values of physical constants give

$$R = 1.9872 \text{ cal./deg. mole}$$

$$u = \frac{hc\omega}{kT} = 1.4387 \frac{\omega}{T}$$

with ω in cm.$^{-1}$ and T in degrees Kelvin.

The present tables are an abridgment of those prepared by Johnston, Savedoff, and Belzer;[1] however, similar tables have been prepared by many different authors.

HARMONIC OSCILLATOR CONTRIBUTIONS

u	$\dfrac{C}{R}$	$\dfrac{H - H_0}{RT}$	$-\dfrac{F - H_0}{RT}$	$\dfrac{S}{R}$
0.00	1.0000	1.0000	∞	∞
.01	1.0000	0.9950	4.6102	5.6052
.02	1.0000	.9900	3.9220	4.9120
.03	0.9999	.9851	3.5215	4.5066
.04	.9999	.9801	3.2388	4.2189
0.05	0.9998	0.9752	3.0206	3.9958
.06	.9997	.9703	2.8433	3.8136
.07	.9996	.9654	2.6941	3.6595
.08	.9995	.9605	2.5655	3.5260
.09	.9993	.9557	2.4526	3.4083

[1] Johnston, H. L., Savedoff, L., and Belzer, J., *Contributions to the Thermodynamic Functions by a Planck-Einstein Oscillator in One Degree of Freedom:* Washington: Office of Naval Research, 1949.

457

u	$\dfrac{C}{R}$	$\dfrac{H - H_0}{RT}$	$-\dfrac{F - H_0}{RT}$	$\dfrac{S}{R}$
0.10	0.9992	0.9508	2.3522	3.3030
.11	.9990	.9460	2.2618	3.2078
.12	.9988	.9412	2.1797	3.1209
.13	.9986	.9364	2.1045	3.0409
.14	.9984	.9316	2.0353	2.9669
0.15	0.9981	0.9269	1.9712	2.8981
.16	.9979	.9221	1.9115	2.8336
.17	.9976	.9174	1.8558	2.7732
.18	.9973	.9127	1.8034	2.7161
.19	.9970	.9080	1.7542	2.6622
0.20	0.9967	0.9033	1.7078	2.6111
.21	.9963	.8987	1.6638	2.5625
.22	.9960	.8940	1.6221	2.5161
.23	.9956	.8894	1.5825	2.4719
.24	.9952	.8848	1.5447	2.4295
0.25	0.9948	0.8802	1.5087	2.3889
.26	.9944	.8756	1.4743	2.3499
.27	.9940	.8711	1.4413	2.3124
.28	.9935	.8665	1.4097	2.2762
.29	.9930	.8620	1.3794	2.2414
0.30	0.9925	0.8575	1.3502	2.2077
.31	.9920	.8530	1.3222	2.1752
.32	.9915	.8485	1.2952	2.1437
.33	.9910	.8441	1.2691	2.1132
.34	.9904	.8396	1.2440	2.0836
0.35	0.9898	0.8352	1.2197	2.0549
.36	.9893	.8308	1.1963	2.0271
.37	.9887	.8264	1.1736	2.0000
.38	.9880	.8220	1.1516	1.9736
.39	.9874	.8176	1.1303	1.9479
0.40	0.9868	0.8133	1.1096	1.9229
.41	.9861	.8090	1.0896	1.8986
.42	.9854	.8047	1.0702	1.8749
.43	.9847	.8004	1.0513	1.8517
.44	.9840	.7961	1.0329	1.8290
0.45	0.9833	0.7918	1.0151	1.8069
.46	.9826	.7876	0.9977	1.7853
.47	.9818	.7833	.9808	1.7641
.48	.9810	.7791	.9644	1.7435
.49	.9802	.7749	.9484	1.7233

u	$\dfrac{C}{R}$	$\dfrac{H - H_0}{RT}$	$-\dfrac{F - H_0}{RT}$	$\dfrac{S}{R}$
0.50	0.9794	0.7708	0.9328	1.7036
.51	.9786	.7666	.9175	1.6841
.52	.9778	.7624	.9027	1.6651
.53	.9769	.7583	.8882	1.6465
.54	.9760	.7542	.8741	1.6283
0.55	0.9752	0.7501	0.8603	1.6104
.56	.9743	.7460	.8468	1.5928
.57	.9734	.7419	.8336	1.5755
.58	.9724	.7379	.8208	1.5587
.59	.9715	.7338	.8082	1.5420
0.60	0.9705	0.7298	0.7959	1.5257
.61	.9696	.7258	.7838	1.5096
.62	.9686	.7218	.7721	1.4939
.63	.9676	.7179	.7606	1.4785
.64	.9666	.7139	.7493	1.4632
0.65	0.9655	0.7100	0.7382	1.4482
.66	.9645	.7060	.7274	1.4334
.67	.9634	.7021	.7168	1.4189
.68	.9623	.6982	.7065	1.4047
.69	.9612	.6944	.6963	1.3907
0.70	0.9602	0.6905	0.6863	1.3768
.71	.9590	.6867	.6766	1.3633
.72	.9579	.6828	.6670	1.3498
.73	.9568	.6790	.6576	1.3366
.74	.9556	.6752	.6484	1.3236
0.75	0.9544	0.6714	0.6394	1.3108
.76	.9532	.6677	.6305	1.2982
.77	.9520	.6639	.6218	1.2857
.78	.9508	.6602	.6132	1.2734
.79	.9496	.6565	.6048	1.2613
0.80	0.9483	0.6528	0.5966	1.2494
.81	.9471	.6491	.5885	1.2376
.82	.9458	.6454	.5806	1.2260
.83	.9445	.6418	.5728	1.2146
.84	.9432	.6381	.5651	1.2032
0.85	0.9419	0.6345	0.5576	1.1921
.86	.9406	.6309	.5502	1.1811
.87	.9392	.6273	.5429	1.1702
.88	.9379	.6237	.5358	1.1595
.89	.9365	.6202	.5288	1.1490

u	$\dfrac{C}{R}$	$\dfrac{H - H_0}{RT}$	$-\dfrac{F - H_0}{RT}$	$\dfrac{S}{R}$
0.90	0.9352	0.6166	0.5218	1.1384
.91	.9338	.6131	.5150	1.1281
.92	.9324	.6096	.5084	1.1180
.93	.9309	.6061	.5018	1.1079
.94	.9295	.6026	.4953	1.0979
0.95	0.9281	0.5991	0.4890	1.0881
.96	.9266	.5956	.4827	1.0783
.97	.9252	.5922	.4766	1.0688
.98	.9237	.5888	.4705	1.0593
.99	.9222	.5854	.4645	1.0499
1.00	0.9207	0.5820	0.4587	1.0407
.01	.9192	.5786	.4529	1.0315
.02	.9176	.5752	.4472	1.0224
.03	.9161	.5719	.4416	1.0135
.04	.9145	.5685	.4361	1.0046
1.05	0.9130	0.5652	0.4307	0.9959
.06	.9114	.5619	.4254	.9873
.07	.9098	.5586	.4201	.9787
.08	.9082	.5554	.4149	.9703
.09	.9066	.5521	.4098	.9619
1.10	0.9050	0.5489	0.4048	0.9537
.11	.9034	.5456	.3998	.9454
.12	.9017	.5424	.3949	.9373
.13	.9001	.5392	.3901	.9293
.14	.8984	.5360	.3854	.9214
1.15	0.8967	0.5328	0.3807	0.9135
.16	.8950	.5297	.3761	.9058
.17	.8933	.5266	.3716	.8982
.18	.8916	.5234	.3671	.8905
.19	.8899	.5203	.3627	.8830
1.20	0.8882	0.5172	0.3584	0.8756
.21	.8864	.5141	.3541	.8682
.22	.8847	.5111	.3499	.8610
.23	.8829	.5080	.3457	.8537
.24	.8812	.5050	.3416	.8466
1.25	0.8794	0.5019	0.3376	0.8395
.26	.8776	.4989	.3336	.8325
.27	.8758	.4959	.3297	.8256
.28	.8740	.4930	.3258	.8188
.29	.8721	.4900	.3220	.8120

u	$\dfrac{C}{R}$	$\dfrac{H - H_0}{RT}$	$-\dfrac{F - H_0}{RT}$	$\dfrac{S}{R}$
1.30	0.8703	0.4870	0.3182	0.8052
.31	.8685	.4841	.3145	.7986
.32	.8666	.4812	.3108	.7920
.33	.8648	.4782	.3072	.7854
.34	.8629	.4753	.3036	.7789
1.35	0.8610	0.4724	0.3001	0.7725
.36	.8591	.4696	.2966	.7662
.37	.8572	.4667	.2932	.7599
.38	.8553	.4639	.2898	.7537
.39	.8534	.4611	.2864	.7475
1.40	0.8515	0.4582	0.2832	0.7414
.41	.8496	.4554	.2799	.7353
.42	.8476	.4526	.2767	.7293
.43	.8457	.4499	.2735	.7234
.44	.8437	.4471	.2704	.7175
1.45	0.8418	0.4444	0.2673	0.7117
.46	.8398	.4416	.2643	.7059
.47	.8378	.4389	.2613	.7002
.48	.8358	.4362	.2583	.6945
.49	.8338	.4335	.2554	.6889
1.50	0.8318	0.4308	0.2525	0.6833
.51	.8298	.4282	.2496	.6778
.52	.8278	.4255	.2468	.6723
.53	.8258	.4229	.2440	.6669
.54	.8238	.4202	.2413	.6615
1.55	0.8217	0.4176	0.2386	0.6562
.56	.8197	.4150	.2359	.6509
.57	.8176	.4124	.2332	.6456
.58	.8156	.4099	.2306	.6405
.59	.8135	.4073	.2281	.6354
1.60	0.8114	0.4048	0.2255	0.6303
.61	.8094	.4022	.2230	.6252
.62	.8073	.3997	.2205	.6202
.63	.8052	.3972	.2181	.6153
.64	.8031	.3947	.2156	.6103
1.65	0.8010	0.3922	0.2132	0.6054
.66	.7988	.3897	.2109	.6006
.67	.7967	.3873	.2086	.5959
.68	.7946	.3848	.2063	.5911
.69	.7925	.3824	.2040	.5864

u	$\dfrac{C}{R}$	$\dfrac{H - H_0}{RT}$	$-\dfrac{F - H_0}{RT}$	$\dfrac{S}{R}$
1.70	0.7904	0.3800	0.2017	0.5817
.71	.7882	.3776	.1995	.5771
.72	.7861	.3752	.1973	.5725
.73	.7839	.3728	.1951	.5679
.74	.7818	.3704	.1930	.5634
1.75	0.7796	0.3681	0.1909	0.5590
.76	.7774	.3657	.1888	.5545
.77	.7752	.3634	.1867	.5501
.78	.7731	.3611	.1847	.5458
.79	.7709	.3588	.1827	.5415
1.80	0.7687	0.3565	0.1807	0.5372
.81	.7665	.3542	.1787	.5329
.82	.7643	.3519	.1768	.5287
.83	.7621	.3496	.1748	.5244
.84	.7599	.3474	.1730	.5204
1.85	0.7577	0.3452	0.1711	0.5162
.86	.7555	.3429	.1692	.5121
.87	.7532	.3407	.1674	.5081
.88	.7510	.3385	.1656	.5041
.89	.7488	.3363	.1638	.5001
1.90	0.7466	0.3342	0.1620	0.4962
.91	.7443	.3320	.1603	.4923
.92	.7421	.3298	.1585	.4883
.93	.7398	.3277	.1568	.4845
.94	.7376	.3256	.1551	.4807
1.95	0.7354	0.3234	0.1535	0.4769
.96	.7331	.3214	.1518	.4732
.97	.7308	.3192	.1502	.4694
.98	.7286	.3172	.1486	.4658
.99	.7263	.3151	.1470	.4621
2.00	0.7241	0.3130	0.1454	0.4584
.02	.7195	.3090	.1423	.4513
.04	.7150	.3049	.1393	.4442
.06	.7104	.3009	.1363	.4372
.08	.7058	.2970	.1334	.4304
2.10	0.7013	0.2930	0.1306	0.4236
.12	.6967	.2892	.1279	.4171
.14	.6921	.2854	.1252	.4106
.16	.6875	.2816	.1225	.4041
.18	.6829	.2778	.1200	.3978

u	$\dfrac{C}{R}$	$\dfrac{H - H_0}{RT}$	$-\dfrac{F - H_0}{RT}$	$\dfrac{S}{R}$
2.20	0.6783	0.2741	0.1174	0.3915
.22	.6736	.2705	.1150	.3855
.24	.6690	.2669	.1126	.3795
.26	.6644	.2633	.1102	.3735
.28	.6598	.2598	.1079	.3677
2.30	0.6552	0.2563	0.1056	0.3619
.32	.6505	.2528	.1034	.3562
.34	.6459	.2494	.1013	.3507
.36	.6413	.2461	.0992	.3453
.38	.6366	.2427	.0971	.3398
2.40	0.6320	0.2394	0.0951	0.3345
.42	.6274	.2362	.0931	.3293
.44	.6228	.2330	.0912	.3242
.46	.6181	.2298	.0893	.3191
.48	.6135	.2267	.0875	.3142
2.50	0.6089	0.2236	0.0856	0.3092
.52	.6043	.2205	.0839	.3044
.54	.5997	.2175	.0822	.2997
.56	.5951	.2145	.0805	.2950
.58	.5905	.2115	.0788	.2903
2.60	0.5859	0.2086	0.0772	0.2858
.62	.5813	.2057	.0756	.2813
.64	.5767	.2029	.0740	.2769
.66	.5722	.2001	.0725	.2726
.68	.5676	.1973	.0710	.2683
2.70	0.5631	0.1945	0.0696	0.2641
.72	.5585	.1918	.0682	.2600
.74	.5540	.1891	.0668	.2559
.76	.5495	.1865	.0654	.2519
.78	.5450	.1839	.0640	.2479
2.80	0.5405	0.1813	0.0627	0.2440
.82	.5360	.1787	.0615	.2402
.84	.5315	.1762	.0602	.2364
.86	.5271	.1737	.0590	.2327
.88	.5226	.1713	.0578	.2291
2.90	0.5182	0.1689	0.0566	0.2255
.92	.5138	.1665	.0554	.2219
.94	.5094	.1641	.0543	.2184
.96	.5050	.1618	.0532	.2150
.98	.5006	.1595	.0521	.2116

u	$\dfrac{C}{R}$	$\dfrac{H - H_0}{RT}$	$-\dfrac{F - H_0}{RT}$	$\dfrac{S}{R}$
3.00	0.4963	0.1572	0.0511	0.2083
.02	.4919	.1549	.0500	.2049
.04	.4876	.1527	.0490	.2017
.06	.4833	.1505	.0480	.1985
.08	.4790	.1484	.0471	.1955
3.10	0.4747	0.1462	0.0461	0.1923
.12	.4705	.1441	.0452	.1893
.14	.4662	.1421	.0442	.1863
.16	.4620	.1400	.0434	.1834
.18	.4578	.1380	.0425	.1805
3.20	0.4536	0.1360	0.0416	0.1776
.22	.4495	.1340	.0408	.1748
.24	.4453	.1321	.0400	.1721
.26	.4412	.1301	.0392	.1693
.28	.4371	.1282	.0384	.1666
3.30	0.4330	0.1264	0.0376	0.1640
.32	.4290	.1245	.0368	.1613
.34	.4249	.1227	.0361	.1588
.36	.4209	.1209	.0354	.1563
.38	.4169	.1191	.0346	.1537
3.40	0.4129	0.1174	0.0340	0.1514
.42	.4089	.1157	.0333	.1490
.44	.4050	.1140	.0326	.1466
.46	.4011	.1123	.0319	.1442
.48	.3972	.1106	.0313	.1419
3.50	0.3933	0.1090	0.0307	0.1397
.52	.3895	.1074	.0300	.1374
.54	.3856	.1058	.0294	.1352
.56	.3818	.1042	.0288	.1330
.58	.3780	.1027	.0283	.1310
3.60	0.3743	0.1011	0.0277	0.1288
.62	.3706	.0996	.0272	.1268
.64	.3668	.0981	.0266	.1247
.66	.3632	.0967	.0261	.1228
.68	.3595	.0945	.0253	.1198
3.70	0.3558	0.0938	0.0250	0.1188
.72	.3522	.0924	.0245	.1169
.74	.3486	.0910	.0240	.1150
.76	.3451	.0896	.0236	.1132
.78	.3415	.0883	.0231	.1114

u	$\dfrac{C}{R}$	$\dfrac{H - H_0}{RT}$	$-\dfrac{F - H_0}{RT}$	$\dfrac{S}{R}$
3.80	0.3380	0.0870	0.0226	0.1096
.82	.3345	.0856	.0222	.1078
.84	.3310	.0844	.0217	.1061
.86	.3276	.0831	.0213	.1044
.88	.3241	.0818	.0209	.1027
3.90	0.3207	0.0806	0.0204	0.1010
.92	.3174	.0794	.0200	.0994
.94	.3140	.0782	.0196	.0978
.96	.3107	.0770	.0192	.0962
.98	.3074	.0758	.0189	.0947
4.00	0.3041	0.0746	0.0185	0.0931
.05	.2960	.0718	.0176	.0894
.10	.2881	.0691	.0167	.0858
.15	.2803	.0665	.0159	.0824
.20	.2726	.0639	.0151	.0790
4.25	0.2652	0.0615	0.0144	0.0759
.30	.2578	.0592	.0137	.0729
.35	.2507	.0569	.0130	.0699
.40	.2436	.0547	.0124	.0671
.45	.2368	.0526	.0118	.0644
4.50	0.2300	0.0506	0.0112	0.0618
.55	.2235	.0486	.0106	.0592
.60	.2170	.0467	.0101	.0568
.65	.2108	.0449	.0096	.0545
.70	.2046	.0431	.0091	.0522
4.75	0.1986	0.0414	0.0087	0.0501
.80	.1928	.0398	.0083	.0481
.85	.1871	.0383	.0079	.0462
.90	.1815	.0368	.0075	.0443
.95	.1760	.0353	.0071	.0424
5.00	0.1707	0.0339	0.0068	0.0407
.05	.1656	.0326	.0064	.0390
.10	.1605	.0313	.0061	.0374
.15	.1556	.0300	.0058	.0358
.20	.1508	.0288	.0055	.0343
5.25	0.1462	0.0277	0.0053	0.0330
.30	.1416	.0266	.0050	.0316
.35	.1372	.0255	.0048	.0303
.40	.1329	.0245	.0045	.0290
.45	.1287	.0235	.0043	.0278

u	$\dfrac{C}{R}$	$\dfrac{H - H_0}{RT}$	$-\dfrac{F - H_0}{RT}$	$\dfrac{S}{R}$
5.50	0.1246	0.0226	0.0041	0.0267
.55	.1207	.0217	.0039	.0256
.60	.1168	.0208	.0037	.0245
.65	.1131	.0199	.0035	.0234
.70	.1094	.0191	.0034	.0225
5.75	0.1059	0.0184	0.0032	0.0216
.80	.1025	.0176	.0030	.0206
.85	.0991	.0169	.0029	.0198
.90	.0959	.0162	.0028	.0190
.95	.0927	.0155	.0026	.0181
6.00	0.08968	0.01491	0.00248	0.01739
.10	.08383	.01371	.00225	.01596
.20	.07833	.01261	.00203	.01464
.30	.07315	.01159	.00184	.01343
.40	.06828	.01065	.00167	.01232
6.50	0.06371	0.00979	0.00151	0.01130
.60	.05942	.00899	.00136	.01035
.70	.05539	.00826	.00123	.00949
.80	.05162	.00758	.00111	.00869
.90	.04808	.00696	.00101	.00797
7.00	0.04476	0.00639	0.00091	0.00730
.10	.04166	.00586	.00083	.00669
.20	.03876	.00538	.00075	.00613
.30	.03605	.00494	.00068	.00562
.40	.03351	.00453	.00061	.00514
7.50	0.03115	0.00415	0.00055	0.00470
.60	.02894	.00381	.00050	.00431
.70	.02687	.00349	.00045	.00394
.80	.02495	.00320	.00041	.00361
.90	.02316	.00293	.00037	.00330
8.00	0.02148	0.00269	0.00034	0.00303
.10	.01993	.00246	.00030	.00276
.20	.01848	.00225	.00027	.00252
.30	.01713	.00206	.00025	.00231
.40	.01587	.00189	.00022	.00211
8.50	0.01471	0.00173	0.00020	0.00193
.60	.01362	.00158	.00018	.00176
.70	.01261	.00145	.00017	.00162
.80	.01168	.00133	.00015	.00148
.90	.01081	.00121	.00014	.00135

u	$\dfrac{C}{R}$	$\dfrac{H - H_0}{RT}$	$-\dfrac{F - H_0}{RT}$	$\dfrac{S}{R}$
9.00	0.01000	0.00111	0.00012	0.00123
.10	.00925	.00102	.00011	.00113
.20	.00855	.00093	.00010	.00103
.30	.00791	.00085	.00009	.00094
.40	.00731	.00078	.00008	.00086
9.50	0.00676	0.00071	0.00007	0.00078
.60	.00624	.00065	.00007	.00072
.70	.00577	.00059	.00006	.00065
.80	.00533	.00054	.00006	.00060
.90	.00492	.00050	.00005	.00055

ADDITIONAL VALUES OF C/R FOR THE HARMONIC OSCILLATOR

u	0.0	0.2	0.4	0.6	0.8
10.0	0.00454	0.00387	0.00329	0.00280	0.00238
11.0	.00202	.00172	.00146	.00123	.00105
12.0	.00089	.00075	.00063	.00054	.00045
13.0	.00038	.00032	.00027	.00023	.00019
14.0	.00016	.00014	.00012	.00010	.00008

ANHARMONICITY AND ROTATIONAL STRETCHING EFFECTS ON ENERGY LEVELS AND THERMODYNAMIC PROPERTIES

The basic pattern of vibration-rotation energy levels is given by the harmonic oscillator and the rigid rotator formulas derived in the regular text. However, precise spectra can be fitted quantitatively only by recognizing the anharmonicity of the potential energy for vibration and the nonrigidity of the molecule in rotation. For diatomic molecules, Eq. (3.41) gives the next approximation, which is usually adequate. This equation includes the three types of correction terms which will be applied here to polyatomic molecules. However, for practical calculations of both spectral lines and thermodynamic functions a rearrangement of Eq. (3.41) is desirable.

$$\frac{\epsilon - \epsilon_0}{hc} = \omega_0 n - \omega_0 x n(n - 1) + J(J + 1)[B_0 - DJ(J + 1) - \alpha n] \quad \text{(A14-1)}$$

The three constants x, D, and α are exactly the same here as in Eq. (3.41), but the other constants are slightly transformed as follows.

$$\omega_0 = \omega_e - 2\omega_e x_e$$
$$B_0 = B_e - \tfrac{1}{2}\alpha$$

This expression has the practical advantage of using the actual separation of the first two vibrational levels ω_0, and the actual rotational constant for the lowest vibrational state B_0, rather than the constants for the hypothetical equilibrium state without zero point vibration.

Since the various correction terms are relatively small, one can calculate their effect on the partition function by approximate methods. We rearrange Eq. (A14-1) and bring in the temperature as follows:

$$\frac{\epsilon - \epsilon_0}{kT} = nu\,[1 - (n - 1)x] + J(J + 1)y[1 - J(J + 1)\beta - n\delta] \quad \text{(A14-2)}$$

where $u = hc\omega_0/kT$, $y = hcB_0/kT$, $\beta = D/B_0$, $\delta = \alpha/B_0$. The partition function is

$$Q = \sum_n \sum_j (2J + 1)e^{-nu[1-(n-1)x]-J(J+1)y[1-J(J+1)\beta-n\delta]} \quad \text{(A14-3)}$$

The sums over n and J would normally be from zero to infinity. Because the correction terms involve higher powers of n and J than the principal terms, the corrections will eventually predominate and, because of their sign, yield additional spurious low energy levels. Consequently it is necessary to break off the sums in (A14-3) as soon as the terms have become very small. Actually we shall introduce further approximations, which incidentally eliminate this problem and let us again use infinite upper limits for n and J.

To proceed with the evaluation we first consider J and expand the small terms involving β and δ.

$$e^{J(J+1)y[J(J+1)\beta+n\delta]} = 1 + J^2(J + 1)^2 y\beta + J(J + 1)yn\delta + \cdots$$

Taking only those terms of the exponential series written above, one has for the partition function,

$$Q = \sum_n e^{-nu[1-(n-1)x]} \int_0^\infty e^{-yz}(1 + z^2 y\beta + zyn\delta)\, dz \quad \text{(A14-4)}$$

where $z = J(J + 1)$ and $dz = (2J + 1)dJ$. Also we have replaced the sum in J by an integral, since we saw in Section 9b that this is a good approximation at high temperatures. The additional terms of Eq. (9.7) can be included if desired. After integrating, expanding the exponential for the correction term in x, and collecting terms to this same second approximation, one obtains

$$Q = \sum_{n=0}^\infty e^{-nu}\left[1 + n(n - 1)ux + n\delta + \frac{2\beta}{y}\right]\frac{1}{y} \quad \text{(A14-5)}$$

This expression must be summed exactly, since u is not necessarily small in the range of interest. We note that

$$\sum_{n=0}^\infty e^{-nu} = (1 - e^{-u})^{-1}$$

$$-\frac{d}{du}\sum e^{-nu} = \sum ne^{-nu} = e^{-u}(1 - e^{-u})^{-2}$$

$$\frac{d^2}{du^2}\sum e^{-nu} = \sum n^2 e^{-nu} = e^{-u}(1 - e^{-u})^{-2} + 2e^{-2u}(1 - e^{-u})^{-3}$$

Using these expressions, we obtain for the partition function,

$$Q = \frac{1}{y(1 - e^{-u})}\left[1 + \frac{2\beta}{y} + \frac{\delta}{e^u - 1} + \frac{2xu}{(e^u - 1)^2}\right] \quad \text{(A14-6)}$$

This expression should be divided by the symmetry number, if necessary, and the additional terms of Eq. (9.7) added within the bracket to correct for the replacement of the sum in J by the integral. Thus we finally have

$$Q = \frac{1}{\sigma y(1 - e^{-u})} \left[1 + \frac{2\beta}{y} + \frac{\delta}{e^u - 1} + \frac{2xu}{(e^u - 1)^2} + \frac{y}{3} + \frac{y^2}{15} \right] \quad \text{(A14-7)}$$

which will be valid as long as all the other terms in the bracket are small compared with unity. The fractional error will be of the order of magnitude of the square of the largest of the terms in β, δ, or x, or the cube of the term $y/3$.

Equation (A14-7) can be differentiated to yield the thermodynamic functions. Certain further approximations are usually appropriate at a given temperature in any particular problem, but these differ from case to case; consequently we will not give working equations for the thermodynamic functions. The usual harmonic oscillator and rigid rotator terms appear as the leading terms, of course, in any case.

The generalization of these expressions to polyatomic molecules is not too difficult, since the terms are all of the same general types. However, with degenerate vibrations, the complication arises that the multiplet overtone levels are not only shifted by anharmonicity but also separated to slightly different energies. This is most easily seen for the bending vibration of a linear molecule such as CO_2 (see ν_3 in Fig. 9.5). This vibration can take place in any direction perpendicular to the axis of the molecule. For the moment we will assume the vibration to be in either the x direction, with quantum number n_x or in the y direction with n_y. The lowest state then has $n_x = 0$, $n_y = 0$.

For the first excited state either $n_x = 1$, $n_y = 0$, or $n_x = 0$, $n_y = 1$. These two states have the same energy. The next state, $n_x + n_y = 2$, has three possibilities as follows: $n_x = 2$, $n_y = 0$; $n_x = 1$, $n_y = 1$; and $n_x = 0$, $n_y = 2$. All three states have the same energy to the harmonic oscillator approximation, but anharmonicity shifts two of the levels to an energy different from that of the third.

As is common in cases of degeneracy, there' is another representation, related by linear combinations of the degenerate wave functions, which has certain advantages. The transformation first involves the use of plane polar coordinates.

$$x = \rho \cos \phi, \qquad y = \rho \sin \phi \qquad \text{(A14-8)}$$

The wave function for a degenerate vibrational state is a product of the one dimensional functions of Eq. (2.67). We take the three states, $n_x + n_y = 2$, as an example, and transform by substituting (A14-8). Then taking the sum and difference combinations for the (0,2) and (2,0) function, one finally obtains

$$\psi_1 = \left(\frac{\alpha}{\pi}\right)^{1/2}(1 - \alpha\rho^2)e^{-\alpha\rho^2/2}$$

$$\psi_2 = \left(\frac{\alpha^3}{\pi}\right)^{1/2}\rho^2 e^{-\alpha\rho^2/2}\cos 2\phi \qquad (A14\text{-}9)$$

$$\psi_3 = \left(\frac{\alpha^3}{\pi}\right)^{1/2}\rho^2 e^{-\alpha\rho^2/2}\sin 2\phi$$

Here it is apparent that the first function is different from the other two. In particular it is axially symmetric since it has no dependence on ϕ. The angular factors in ψ_2 and ψ_3 can be rearranged further to the imaginary exponential form,

$$\psi_{2,3} = \left(\frac{\alpha^3}{2\pi}\right)^{1/2}\rho^2 e^{-\alpha\rho^2/2}\,e^{\pm 2i\phi} \qquad (A14\text{-}10)$$

One can now see that a new set of quantum numbers becomes appropriate for doubly degenerate vibrations. One is the coefficient of $i\phi$ in the exponent, called l, and the other is the total n. Then the angular factor is

$$e^{\pm il\phi}$$

and the harmonic oscillator energy (including zero point energy) is $\epsilon = (n + 1)h\nu$. The allowed values of l are $l = n,\ n - 2,\ n - 4, \ldots,$ 1, or 0.

The imaginary exponential form suggests an angular momentum to be associated with nonzero values of l, and this proves to be correct. The nuclei in the displaced configuration corresponding to ν_3 can be pictured as moving in circles about the molecular axis of CO_2 when $l = n$; in ellipses for $n > l > 0$; and oscillating linearly through the axis for $l = 0$. As for any classical model for a quantum mechanical phenomenon, this picture has only limited validity.

Anharmonicity has the effect of making the energy depend not only on higher powers of n but also on l. The usual expression, after conversion to spectroscopic units and extension to several vibrations, is

$$\frac{\epsilon}{hc} = \sum_i \omega_{ei}\left(n_i + \frac{d_i}{2}\right) + \sum_i \sum_{j \geq i} x_{ij}\left(n_i + \frac{d_i}{2}\right)\left(n_j + \frac{d_j}{2}\right) + \sum_i g_i l_i^2$$

$$(A14\text{-}11)$$

where ω_{ei} is a frequency for the potential minimum, as indicated by the subscript e, and d_i is the degree of degeneracy of the ith vibration. Note also that the sign of the x_{ij} term is positive here, which is the reverse of the convention for diatomic molecules. Presumably there should be some cross term in $l_i l_j$, but this question has never been adequately investigated. Such a term would arise only if there were more than one degenerate vibration of the same symmetry type. Hence it does not arise in molecules of the ABA, ABC, or $ABBA$ types, such as CO_2, OCS, or acetylene, which are the only types which have been investigated to this degree of detail.

Where accidental degeneracy and the consequent resonance phenomenon arise (see Section 9j), an additional term must be added to Eq. (A14-11). However, since the effect of this term is to raise one energy level slightly and lower an equivalent level by the same amount, it can be ignored in thermodynamic calculations unless extremely high accuracy is required.

The formula (A14-11) is equally applicable to nonlinear molecules, provided only doubly degenerate vibrations are involved. In nonlinear molecules the angular momentum associated with a given l_i value is smaller by a factor usually given the symbol ζ_i than for a linear molecule. The calculation of this quantity ζ and its complex effect on vibration-rotation levels is beyond the scope of this section. It can be said, nevertheless, that the complication is of a sort that raises some energy levels by the same amount that it lowers equivalent levels, so that it is of no thermodynamic consequence.

The complete description of overtones of triply degenerate vibrations has never been given. It would presumably involve an additional quantum number giving the component of the vibrational angular momentum along an axis in space. Numerous vibrational overtones have been observed in the spectrum of methane, but a complete assignment has never been made. Until further work is done in this area, one can only select such terms from Eq. (A14-11) as are clearly appropriate, and evaluate the corresponding constants from the spectrum as far as possible.

Before evaluating the partition function, it is desirable to transform Eq. (A14-11) to the basis of the actual separation of the ground and first excited states ω_0, as was done for the diatomic molecule.

$$\frac{\epsilon - \epsilon_0}{hc} = \sum_i \omega_{0i} n_i + \sum_i x_{ii}(n_i - 1)n_i + \sum_{i,j}' x_{ij}n_i n_j + \sum_i g_i l_i^2 \quad \text{(A14-12)}$$

Here the sum over x_{ij} is to include all terms with i different from j.

In addition to (A14-12) one must add the rotational energy. However, to write a completely general expression, including asymmetric tops, is impossible. Consequently, we will merely note that the moments of inertia in the usual rotational energy expressions are functions of the vibrational quantum numbers, and that there is a centrifugal stretching effect, analogous to the D term for the diatomic molecule, which depends on the fourth power of the rotational quantum numbers.

In any particular case, the appropriate expressions for the energy levels can be given. As mentioned above, the vibrational angular momentum associated with nonzero l values interacts with the rotational energy levels also.

For statistical-thermodynamic purposes, the classical rotational partition function is almost always adequate. Since this function depends in a simple manner on the moments of inertia, we can readily express it in terms of the vibrational quantum numbers. Any moment of inertia may be expressed as

$$I_x = I_x^\circ (1 + \sum_i \delta_{xi} n_i)$$

where I_x° is the moment of inertia in the ground vibrational state, and the sum covers all the normal modes of vibration of the molecule. The values of the quantities δ_{xi} can be obtained either from the rotational line spacing in excited vibrational states observed in spectra, or, theoretically, from the quantum mechanical average of the moment of inertia computed with wave functions expressed in terms of the true normal coordinates, and recognizing anharmonicity. The definition of δ_{xi} here reduces to that for the single quantity δ for the diatomic molecule given above.

Since the partition function for a nonlinear molecule always involves the product of the three moments of inertia, we have

$$I_x I_y I_z = I_x^\circ I_y^\circ I_z^\circ \left[1 + \sum_i n_i (\delta_{xi} + \delta_{yi} + \delta_{zi}) \right] \qquad \text{(A14-13)}$$

where only first-order correction terms have been retained. For a linear molecule one has the simpler expression

$$I = I_0 \left(1 + \sum_i n_i \delta_i \right) \qquad \text{(A14-14)}$$

In addition to the change in moment of inertia with vibration, we must consider the centrifugal stretching effect. This can be done by obtaining from the spectrum the terms in the fourth power of rotational quantum numbers, analogous to the term in D for the diatomic molecule. In such cases, the appropriate corrections to the partition function can be calculated by the method used for the diatomic molecule.

However, for many polyatomic molecules, the rotational spectrum has not been observed or analyzed to the detail necessary to establish these stretching terms. Since they are determined by the potential energy function for the molecule, which is known from the frequencies of the normal vibrations, a different method of evaluation is desirable. This was first given by Wilson,[1] whose methods we follow here. We will give the treatment in detail for the nonlinear molecule, and then in addition, state the much simpler result for the linear molecule.

The molecule is assumed to be in a vibrationless state, but to be flexible according to the potential energy function for vibration. Then the energy for rotation is

[1] Wilson, E. B., Jr., *J. Chem. Phys.*, **4**, 526 (1936).

$$\epsilon_r = \frac{1}{2} \sum_{\alpha,\beta} \mu_{\alpha\beta} M_\alpha M_\beta + V \tag{A14-15}$$

where α, $\beta = x$, y, or z, M_α is the instantaneous angular momentum about the α axis, and the potential energy V appears because the molecule may be stretched by centrifugal forces. The quantities $\mu_{\alpha\beta}$ are the components of the matrix which is the reciprocal of the matrix of inertia

$$\begin{bmatrix} I_x & I_{xy} & I_{xz} \\ I_{yx} & I_y & I_{yz} \\ I_{zx} & I_{zy} & I_z \end{bmatrix}$$

Here the moments and products of inertia are as defined in Eq. (9.12).

The potential energy will be taken as expressed in terms of normal coordinates

$$V = \frac{1}{2} \sum_i \lambda_i Q_i^2 \tag{9.35}$$

and the quantities $\mu_{\alpha\beta}$ expanded in terms of these same normal coordinates,

$$\mu_{\alpha\beta} = \overset{\circ}{\mu}_{\alpha\beta} + \sum_i \mu^i_{\alpha\beta} Q_i + \ldots \tag{A14-16}$$

with $\overset{\circ}{\mu}_{\alpha\beta}$ the equilibrium value in the absence of rotation, and

$$\mu^i_{\alpha\beta} = (\partial\mu_{\alpha\beta}/\partial Q_i)_0 \tag{A14-17}$$

In order to find the equilibrium value of Q_i in a rotating molecule, we use one of Hamilton's equations of motion,

$$\frac{\partial H}{\partial q_k} = -\dot{p}_k \tag{A11-6}$$

and identify the energy ϵ as a Hamiltonian function, since it is expressed in terms of momenta. The terms in ϵ for vibrational kinetic energy need not be included, because they would drop out for the vibrationless state being considered. Then

$$\frac{\partial\epsilon_r}{\partial Q_i} = \frac{1}{2} \sum_{\alpha,\beta} \frac{\partial\mu_{\alpha\beta}}{\partial Q_i} M_\alpha M_\beta + \frac{\partial V}{\partial Q_i} = -\dot{p}_i = 0$$

$$= \frac{1}{2} \sum_{\alpha,\beta} \mu^i_{\alpha\beta} M_\alpha M_\beta + \lambda_i Q_i = 0 \tag{A14-18}$$

where (A14-17) and the derivative of (9.35) have been substituted in the second line, and $\dot{p}_i$ is zero because the state is vibrationless. Solving for Q_i and substituting in (A14-16) we have

$$\mu_{\alpha\beta} = \overset{\circ}{\mu}_{\alpha\beta} - \sum_i \frac{\mu^i_{\alpha\beta}}{2\lambda_i} \sum_{\alpha',\beta'} \mu^i_{\alpha'\beta'} M_{\alpha'} M_{\beta'} \tag{A14-19}$$

Also the potential energy takes the value

$$V = \frac{1}{8} \sum_i \lambda_i^{-1} \left(\sum_{\alpha,\beta} \mu_{\alpha\beta}^i M_\alpha M_\beta \right)^2 \qquad (A14\text{-}20)$$

and the complete rotational energy becomes

$$\epsilon_r = \frac{1}{2} \sum_{\alpha,\beta} \mu_{\alpha\beta}^\circ M_\alpha M_\beta - \frac{1}{8} \sum_i \lambda_i^{-1} \left(\sum_{\alpha,\beta} \mu_{\alpha\beta}^i M_\alpha M_\beta \right)^2 \qquad (A14\text{-}21)$$

Proceeding to the partition function, we use the plan of calculation used in Appendix 9, but first expand the exponential for the small correction terms.

$$e^{-\epsilon_r/kT} = e^{-\epsilon_r^\circ/kT} \left[1 + \frac{1}{8kT} \sum_i \lambda_i^{-1} \left(\sum_{\alpha,\beta} \mu_{\alpha\beta}^i M_\alpha M_\beta \right)^2 + \ldots \right] \qquad (A14\text{-}22)$$

where ϵ_r° is just the first term in (A14-21) which is the same as the expression used in Appendix 9. Now any particular term in the sums in (A14-22) leads to a term in the partition function containing the product of integrals

$$\int_{-\infty}^{\infty} M_x^r e^{-M_x{}^2/2I_x{}^\circ kT} dM_x \cdot \int_{-\infty}^{\infty} M_y^s e^{-M_r{}^2/2I_y{}^\circ kT} dM_y \cdot \int_{-\infty}^{\infty} M_z^t e^{-M_r{}^2/2I_z{}^\circ kT} dM_z$$

where r, s, and t are positive integers (including zero) whose sum is 4. If r, s, or t is odd, that integral vanishes. By evaluating all the integrals with r, s, and t all even, one eventually obtains the result

$$Q_r = Q_r^\circ (1 + \rho T) \qquad (A14\text{-}23)$$

with

$$Q_r^\circ = \frac{8\pi^2}{\sigma h^3} (2\pi kT)^{3/2} (I_x^\circ I_y^\circ I_z^\circ)^{1/2} \qquad (A14\text{-}24)$$

as given above in Eq. (A9-3), including the symmetry number, which has been omitted in this derivation up to this point. Also

$$\rho = k \sum_i \left\{ \frac{3}{8} \sum_\alpha \left(\mu_{\alpha\alpha}^i I_\alpha^\circ \right)^2 + \frac{1}{4} \sum_{\alpha > \beta} \left[\mu_{\alpha\alpha}^i \mu_{\beta\beta}^i + 2 \left(\mu_{\alpha\beta}^i \right)^2 \right] I_\alpha^\circ I_\beta^\circ \right\} \lambda_i^{-1} \qquad (A14\text{-}25)$$

where it is to be noted that the sums are defined in a fashion to include each type of term only once.

It is not necessary to use normal coordinates for the calculation of ρ. The method is essentially the same for another coordinate system and can be carried through readily in any specific case.

Now if we introduce the effect of vibration on the moments of inertia, we have our final expression for the rotational partition function for the nonlinear molecule.

$$Q_r = Q_r^\circ \left[1 + \rho T + \frac{1}{2} \sum_i n_i (\delta_{xi} + \delta_{yi} + \delta_{zi}) \right] \qquad (A14\text{-}26)$$

The complete vibration-rotation partition function may now be summed by a more complex application of the same operations which were used in obtaining Eq. (A14-6). The result for the nonlinear molecule is

$$Q = Q_r^\circ \left[\prod_i (1 - e^{-u_i})^{-d_i} \right] \left[1 + \rho T + \sum_i \frac{d_i \delta_i}{e^{u_i} - 1} + \sum_{i,j} f_{ij} + \sum_i G_i \right]$$

(A14-27)

where

$$\delta_i = \tfrac{1}{2}(\delta_{xi} + \delta_{yi} + \delta_{zi})$$
$$f_{ii} = -d_i(d_i + 1)hcx_{ii}/kT(e^{u_i} - 1)^2$$
$$f_{ij} = -d_i d_j hcx_{ij}/kT(e^{u_i} - 1)(e^{u_j} - 1)$$
$$G_i = -hcg_i/kT(e^{u_i} - 1)(1 - e^{-u_i})$$
$$u_i = hc\omega_{0i}/kT$$

For the linear molecule, Eq. (A14-27) may be used, provided δ_i is taken from Eq. (A14-14), and ρ is taken as

$$\rho = kI_0^2 \sum_i \mu_i^2/\lambda_i = k \sum_i (\partial I/\partial Q_i)_0^2/I_0^2 \lambda_i$$

where the sum actually needs to cover only the parallel vibrations, since the perpendicular vibrations make no contribution.

Appendix 15

MATRIX MECHANICS APPLIED TO THE HARMONIC OSCILLATOR

Heisenberg proposed the matrix form of quantum mechanics in 1925, slightly earlier than the wave mechanics formulation of Schrödinger. As in the case of wave mechanics, Born helped in the formulation of some aspects of the matrix mechanics. Schrödinger proved the equivalence of the two formulations and in later years Dirac contributed to the logical unification of the whole of nonrelativistic quantum mechanics.

Because of its more familiar and generally convenient mathematical form, wave mechanics is the basis of the main text. However, the matrix formulation has advantages in some cases. In this Appendix the basic principles will be stated and applied to the familiar problem of the harmonic oscillator.

Heisenberg laid great stress on the importance of considering only observable quantities in a theory. The spectral frequency ν_{jk} is such a quantity and is related to the energies by the familiar expression of Bohr.

$$\nu_{jk} = \frac{E_j}{h} - \frac{E_k}{h} \tag{A15-1}$$

One may arrange the quantities ν_{jk} in a square array, where the order is arbitrary but may conveniently be taken to be that of increasing energy.

$$\nu = \begin{bmatrix} \nu_{11} = 0 & \nu_{12} & \nu_{13} & \nu_{14} & \cdots \\ \nu_{21} & \nu_{22} = 0 & \nu_{23} & \nu_{24} & \cdots \\ \nu_{31} & \nu_{32} & \nu_{33} = 0 & \nu_{34} & \cdots \\ \nu_{41} & \nu_{42} & \nu_{43} & \nu_{44} = 0 & \cdots \end{bmatrix} \tag{A15-2}$$

We now take the pattern of this array as fixed, i.e., the quantity in the jth row and the kth column is always associated with the transition from the jth to the kth quantum state. Such an array constitutes a matrix.

Similar matrices can be written for other observable quantities such as a coordinate, a momentum, the energy, or the transition probability which is equivalent to the intensity of the spectral lines.

In view of the uncertainty principle relationship between a coordinate

477

and its conjugate momentum, there must be some criterion in matrix mechanics analogous to the differential operator for momentum in wave mechanics. Here it takes the form of the commutation laws.

For the simple quantities in classical mechanics, the product is independent of the order of the factors, i.e., $pq = qp$. It is said that the product is commutative. However, for matrices, as for differential operators, multiplication is not necessarily commutative.

Let us take the momentum operators, as defined in Eqs. (2.8) to (2.10) and test their commutation properties with the coordinates. We find

$$p_x x \psi - x p_x \psi = \frac{h}{2\pi i} \left(\frac{\partial}{\partial x} x \psi - x \frac{\partial}{\partial x} \psi \right) = \frac{h}{2\pi i} \psi$$

$$p_x y \psi - y p_x \psi = 0$$

and similarly for the other possibilities. Thus it is consistent to take, as a postulate in matrix mechanics, the commutation laws

$$p_j q_j - q_j p_j = h/2\pi i$$

$$p_j q_k - q_k p_j = 0 \quad \text{if} \quad j \neq k \qquad (A15\text{-}3)$$

The rule for the multiplication of matrices in the algebra of determinants and matrices[1] was found appropriate for these quantum mechanical quantities. The element in the j'th row and the k'th column of the product ab is

$$(ab)_{jk} = \sum_n a_{jn} b_{nk} \qquad (A15\text{-}4)$$

With this brief formulation of the basic laws of matrix mechanics, let us turn to their application to the harmonic oscillator in one dimension.

We start with the classical Hamiltonian expression for the energy of the harmonic oscillator.

$$H = \frac{p^2}{2m} + \frac{kx^2}{2} \qquad (A15\text{-}5)$$

Application of Hamilton's equations of motion yield

$$\dot{p} = -kx, \qquad \dot{x} = p/m \qquad (A15\text{-}6)$$

and combining these, $\qquad \ddot{x} = -\frac{k}{m} x = -4\pi^2 \nu_0^2 x \qquad (A15\text{-}7)$

where ν_0 is the classical frequency $(k/m = 4\pi^2 \nu_0^2)$.

We assume that these classical equations apply to the matrices for the corresponding quantum mechanical properties. Thus for each element in the coordinate matrix,

---

[1] There are many books on matrix algebra. A brief account is given in Margenau, H. and Murphy, G. M., *The Mathematics of Physics and Chemistry*, New York: D. Van Nostrand Company, Inc., 1943, Chap. 10.

$$\ddot{x}_{jk} + 4\pi^2\nu_0^2 x_{jk} = 0$$

which has the solutions

$$x_{jk} = 0 \quad \text{and} \quad x_{jk} = x_{jk}^{\circ} e^{\pm 2\pi i \nu_0 t}$$

Since we are free to arrange the numbering of the matrix elements as we please, we shall anticipate that the exponent $(+2\pi i \nu_0 t)$ corresponds to the transition from the nth to the $(n-1)$th state (emission) and that the exponent $(-2\pi i \nu_0 t)$ corresponds to transition from the nth to the $(n+1)$th state (absorption). All other elements of the coordinate matrix are given the trivial solution 0, so that we have

$$x = \begin{bmatrix} 0 & x_{01} & 0 & 0 & \cdots \\ x_{10} & 0 & x_{12} & 0 & \cdots \\ 0 & x_{21} & 0 & x_{23} & \cdots \\ 0 & 0 & x_{32} & 0 & \cdots \\ \cdots & \cdots & \cdots & \cdots & \cdots \end{bmatrix} \tag{A15-8}$$

where the nonzero elements have the form

$$\begin{aligned} x_{j,j+1} &= x_{j,j+1}^{\circ} e^{-2\pi i \nu_0 t} \\ x_{j,j-1} &= x_{j,j-1}^{\circ} e^{2\pi i \nu_0 t} \end{aligned} \tag{A15-9}$$

where the x° quantities are constants.

Applying the equation, $p = m\dot{x}$, we find the momentum matrix

$$p = 2\pi i \nu_0 m \begin{bmatrix} 0 & -x_{01} & 0 & 0 & \cdots \\ x_{10} & 0 & -x_{12} & 0 & \cdots \\ 0 & x_{21} & 0 & -x_{23} & \cdots \\ 0 & 0 & x_{32} & 0 & \cdots \\ \cdots & \cdots & \cdots & \cdots & \cdots \end{bmatrix} \tag{A15-10}$$

We are now ready to apply the commutation law, which in matrix terms means that the difference of products, $pq - qp$, must equal $h/2\pi i$ times the unit matrix, which is

$$\begin{bmatrix} 1 & 0 & 0 & \cdots \\ 0 & 1 & 0 & \cdots \\ 0 & 0 & 1 & \cdots \\ \cdots & \cdots & \cdots & \cdots \end{bmatrix}$$

Applying the rule for matrix multiplication, we find

$$px - xp = -4\pi i \nu_0 m \begin{bmatrix} x_{10}x_{01} & 0 & 0 & \cdots \\ 0 & x_{21}x_{12} - x_{10}x_{01} & 0 & \cdots \\ 0 & 0 & x_{32}x_{23} - x_{21}x_{12} & \cdots \\ \cdots & \cdots & \cdots & \cdots \end{bmatrix} \tag{A15-11}$$

We note first that the arrangement of zero and nonzero elements in the coordinate matrix, which was assumed above, is consistent with the requirement of the commutation law. The elements in the last matrix can be found by applying the commutation law in sequence.

$$(x_{10}x_{01}) = h/8\pi^2\nu_0 m$$
$$(x_{21}x_{12} - x_{10}x_{01}) = h/8\pi^2\nu_0 m, \quad \text{etc.}$$

Consequently

$$x_{n+1,n}x_{n,n+1} = \frac{(n+1)h}{8\pi^2\nu_0 m} \tag{A15-12}$$

From Eq. (A15-9) one sees that the exponential factors cancel in these products.

We are now ready to find the energy by the use of Eq. (A15-5).

$$\frac{p^2}{2m} = 2\pi^2\nu_0^2 m \begin{bmatrix} x_{10}x_{01} & 0 & -x_{12}x_{01} & \cdots \\ 0 & x_{10}x_{01} + x_{21}x_{12} & 0 & \cdots \\ -x_{10}x_{21} & 0 & x_{21}x_{12} + x_{32}x_{23} \\ \cdots & \cdots & \cdots & \cdots \end{bmatrix}$$

$$\frac{kx^2}{2} = \frac{k}{2} \begin{bmatrix} x_{10}x_{01} & 0 & x_{12}x_{01} & \cdots \\ 0 & x_{10}x_{01} + x_{21}x_{12} & 0 & \cdots \\ x_{10}x_{21} & 0 & x_{21}x_{12} + x_{32}x_{23} \\ \cdots & \cdots & \cdots & \cdots \end{bmatrix}$$

but $k/2 = 2\pi^2\nu_0^2 m$, so the same factor multiplies each of these matrices. In adding matrices one merely adds the corresponding elements of each matrix. Hence the total energy is

$$E = H = 4\pi^2\nu_0^2 m \begin{bmatrix} x_{10}x_{01} & 0 & 0 & \cdots \\ 0 & x_{10}x_{01} + x_{21}x_{12} & 0 & \cdots \\ 0 & 0 & x_{21}x_{12} + x_{32}x_{23} \\ \cdots & \cdots & \cdots & \cdots \end{bmatrix} \tag{A15-13}$$

One notes that all elements off the main diagonal have vanished. Thus we have values only for the stationary states, which should be on the diagonal, since they correspond to the kth state remaining the kth state. By introducing the expressions of Eq. (A15-12), one finds for the diagonal elements

$$E_{n,n} = 4\pi^2\nu_0^2 m(x_{n,n-1}x_{n-1,n} + x_{n+1,n}x_{n,n+1})$$
$$= h\nu_0(n + \tfrac{1}{2}), \quad n = 0, 1, 2, \ldots \tag{A15-14}$$

This is exactly the expression given by wave mechanics in Section 2i.

If there is a charge e associated with the vibrating particle, the dipole moment is

$$\mu = ex$$

where x is the matrix in Eq. (A15-8).   The zero diagonal elements indicate zero dipole moment for all stationary states.   The off-diagonal elements, which are functions of time, indicate the transitions which can arise from the emission or absorption of radiation.   Thus only one unit change in the quantum number n is allowed, with the single frequency ν_0 for all such changes.

Appendix 16

CLASSICAL KINETIC ENERGY FOR A MOLECULE
WITH INTERNAL ROTATION

The expression for the kinetic energy of rotation (and of translation) will be derived for a molecule consisting of a rigid frame with two rigid rotating subgroups attached to the frame. Each subgroup is constrained to rotate about an axis fixed in the main frame, and will be assumed to be symmetrical with respect to the axis, such as a CH_3 group. This example will illustrate most of the typical terms which arise in rotational problems without all the complexity of the general case.[1] If one is interested only in the rotation of a rigid molecule, these equations may be simplified by dropping all terms involving the subgroups.

One assumes first a set of Cartesian axes fixed in space, which will be given the symbol (0). Next we fix in the main frame a set of axes (1) with the most convenient orientation. Finally we fix in each subgroup a set of axes (2a and 2b) with the z axis along the axis of rotation of the subgroup with respect to the main frame.

Each atom in the molecule is in a fixed position with respect to one set of axes. The instantaneous position in space of an atom of the main frame can then be described by the vector r_{10} from the origin of axes (0) to the origin of (1), the angular orientation of (0) with respect to (1), and the vector x_{1i} which locates atom i in axes (1). If the atom is located in a subgroup, one must also specify the vector $r_{2,1}$ from the origin of axes (1) to the origin of (2) and the angular orientation of (2) with respect to (1). Also the vector locating the atom will be written x_{2i} if the atom is in a subgroup.

The angular orientations are given by 3 by 3 matrices of direction cosines. Thus an arbitrary vector $\mathbf{R}$ has the components R_j^x, R_j^y, R_j^z in the jth axes and the components R_k^x, R_k^y, R_k^z in the kth axes. In expanded matrix form, these are related by

$$\begin{bmatrix} R_j^x \\ R_j^y \\ R_j^z \end{bmatrix} = \begin{bmatrix} \alpha_{jk}^{xx} & \alpha_{jk}^{xy} & \alpha_{jk}^{xz} \\ \alpha_{jk}^{yx} & \alpha_{jk}^{yy} & \alpha_{jk}^{yz} \\ \alpha_{jk}^{zx} & \alpha_{jk}^{zy} & \alpha_{jk}^{zz} \end{bmatrix} \begin{bmatrix} R_k^x \\ R_k^y \\ R_k^z \end{bmatrix}$$

[1] For the general case, see Kilpatrick, J. E. and Pitzer, K. S., *J. Chem. Phys.*, **11**, 1064 (1949).

where α_{jk}^{ab} is the cosine between the a axis of the jth set and the b axis of the kth set. In compact form this equation may be written

$$\mathbf{R}_j = \alpha_{jk}\mathbf{R}_k \qquad (A16\text{-}1)$$

If all sets of axes are right-handed Cartesian axes, the α's have certain properties. In particular the determinant of α is unity, its reciprocal is equal to its transpose $(\alpha^{-1} = \alpha')$, and any element is equal to its own cofactor.

Since we shall be calculating velocities, certain properties of the time derivatives are needed. The time derivative will be indicated by the dot, i.e., $\dot{x} = dx/dt$. It has been shown[2] that

$$\alpha_{jk}\dot{\alpha}_{jk}^{-1} = \begin{bmatrix} 0 & -\omega_j^z & \omega_j^y \\ \omega_j^z & 0 & -\omega_j^x \\ -\omega_j^y & \omega_j^x & 0 \end{bmatrix} = \Omega_j \qquad (A16\text{-}2)$$

where ω_j^x is the angular velocity of the other (k) axes about the x axis of the jth set, etc. By direct multiplication one can readily verify the identity,

$$\begin{bmatrix} 0 & -\omega_j^z & \omega_j^y \\ \omega_j^z & 0 & -\omega_j^x \\ -\omega_j^y & \omega_j^x & 0 \end{bmatrix}\begin{bmatrix} x_j \\ y_j \\ z_j \end{bmatrix} = -\begin{bmatrix} 0 & -z_j & y_j \\ z_j & 0 & -x_j \\ -y_j & x_j & 0 \end{bmatrix}\begin{bmatrix} \omega_j^x \\ \omega_j^y \\ \omega_j^z \end{bmatrix}$$

which can be written compactly if one adopts the symbol X_j for the right 3 by 3 matrix and uses, of course, the vectorial symbols $\mathbf{x}_j$ and $\boldsymbol{\omega}_j$ for the column matrices.

$$\Omega_j\mathbf{x}_j = -X_j\boldsymbol{\omega}_j \qquad (A16\text{-}3)$$

Now in order to obtain the kinetic energy, we need the linear velocity of each atom in terms of the various angular velocities. We first write the vector to an atom from the fixed origin, $\mathbf{x}_0$, in terms of quantities for the main frame.

$$\mathbf{x}_0 = \alpha_{01}\mathbf{x}_1 + \mathbf{r}_{10} = \alpha'_{10}\mathbf{x}_1 + \mathbf{r}_{10} \qquad (A16\text{-}4)$$

For an atom in a subgroup we must also use the equation

$$\mathbf{x}_1 = \alpha'_{21}\mathbf{x}_2 + \mathbf{r}_{21} \qquad (A16\text{-}5)$$

to give $\mathbf{x}_1$ in terms of the location of the atom in the subgroup, $\mathbf{x}_2$.

Now taking the time derivatives, we write $\mathbf{v}$ for $\dot{\mathbf{x}}_0$, the true velocity of a particular atom, and $\mathbf{u}$ for $\dot{\mathbf{r}}_{10}$, the linear velocity of the main frame.

$$\mathbf{v} = \dot{\alpha}'_{10}\mathbf{x}_1 + \alpha'_{10}\dot{\mathbf{x}}_1 + \mathbf{u}$$

But

$$\dot{\alpha}'_{10}\mathbf{x}_1 = \alpha'_{10}\Omega_1\mathbf{x}_1 = -\alpha'_{10}X_1\boldsymbol{\omega}_1$$

[2] Frazer, R. A., Duncan, W. J., and Collar, A. R., *Elementary Matrices*, London: Cambridge University Press, 1946, pp. 246–257.

Thus if the ith atom is fixed in the main frame, so that $\dot{\mathbf{x}}_1$ is zero, we have

$$\mathbf{v}_i = \mathbf{u} - \alpha'_{10}X_{1i}\omega_1 \tag{A16-6}$$

If the atom is fixed in one of the subgroups, one must use the time derivative of Eq. (A16-5) to obtain $\dot{\mathbf{x}}_1$, which is not zero. By the same methods just employed, one obtains

$$\mathbf{v}_i = \mathbf{u} - \alpha'_{10}X_{1i}\omega_1 - \alpha'_{10}\alpha'_{21}X_{2i}\omega_2 \tag{A16-7}$$

where the elements of X_{1i} refer to the location of the particle at some instant with respect to axes (1), while X_{2i} refers to the fixed location of the particle in a subgroup.

The kinetic energy is given by the expression

$$2T = \sum_i m_i \mathbf{v}'_i \mathbf{v}_i \tag{A16-8}$$

where the sum covers all atoms. In expanding this expression we will write all the terms for an atom in a subgroup. The terms to be omitted for atoms in the main frame are obvious. Here E is the unit matrix.

$$2T = (\mathbf{u}', \omega'_1, \omega'_2) \sum_i m_i \begin{bmatrix} E & -\alpha'_{10}X_{1i} & -\alpha'_{20}X_{2i} \\ -X'_{1i}\alpha_{10} & X'_{1i}X_{1i} & X'_{1i}\alpha'_{21}X_{2i} \\ -X'_{2i}\alpha_{20} & X'_{2i}\alpha_{21}X_{1i} & X'_{2i}X_{2i} \end{bmatrix} \begin{bmatrix} \mathbf{u} \\ \omega_1 \\ \omega_2 \end{bmatrix} \tag{A16-9}$$

The sum includes the square matrix and, after summation, yields a corresponding square matrix which is commonly called the *kinetic energy matrix* for the molecule. Since we assumed two subgroups, there will actually be rows and columns for each, but at this stage there will be no cross terms between the subgroups. Also, this matrix is of unnecessarily high order, since the subgroups are constrained to rotate about their z axes. Thus each ω_2 reduces to a single element ω_2^z.

We shall now discuss the blocks in the kinetic energy matrix. The first block, $\sum mE$ yields just a diagonal matrix with the total molecular weight M,

$$\begin{bmatrix} M & 0 & 0 \\ 0 & M & 0 \\ 0 & 0 & M \end{bmatrix}$$

The next diagonal block expands as follows.

$$\sum m \begin{bmatrix} 0 & z_1 & -y_1 \\ -z_1 & 0 & x_1 \\ y_1 & -x_1 & 0 \end{bmatrix} \begin{bmatrix} 0 & -z_1 & y_1 \\ z_1 & 0 & -x_1 \\ -y_1 & x_1 & 0 \end{bmatrix}$$

$$= \begin{bmatrix} \sum m(z^2 + y^2) & -\sum mxy & -\sum mxz \\ -\sum mxy & \sum m(z^2 + x^2) & -\sum myz \\ -\sum mxz & -\sum myz & \sum m(y^2 + x^2) \end{bmatrix}$$

$$= \begin{bmatrix} I_x & -I_{xy} & -I_{xz} \\ -I_{xy} & I_y & -I_{yz} \\ -I_{xz} & -I_{yz} & I_z \end{bmatrix}$$

This is just the matrix of moments and products of inertia with reference to the axes of the main frame (1). While the contributions of the subgroup atoms vary with the orientation of the subgroup, if the subgroup is symmetrical it can be shown to yield a constant sum.

The last diagonal block reduces to a single term

$$(0,0,\,\omega_2^z)\,\sum m X_2' X_2 \begin{bmatrix} 0 \\ 0 \\ \omega_2^z \end{bmatrix} = \omega_2^z \sum m(x_2^2 + y_2^2)\omega_2^z$$

$$= \omega_2^z A_2 \omega_2^z$$

where A_2 is the moment of inertia of the subgroup about its axis of internal rotation.

While we have made no assumption heretofore about the location of the axes (1) in the main frame, it is most convenient to place their origin at the center of mass of the molecule. If possible, one also selects the principal axes in advance, but we will not assume this.

The off-diagonal terms in the first row and column involve sums of the type

$$\sum m_i x_i$$

which vanish because of the selection of the origin as the center of mass or because of the symmetry of the subgroups. The final off-diagonal terms require a very lengthy sequence of manipulations, after which most of the terms vanish because of the symmetry of the subgroups. The details, as well as the complete expressions for the case of unsymmetrical subgroups has been given elsewhere.[1] The result is

$$\omega_1' \sum m X_1' \alpha_{21}' X_2 \omega_2 = \omega_1' \begin{bmatrix} \alpha_{21}^{xz} A_2 \\ \alpha_{21}^{zy} A_2 \\ \alpha_{21}^{zz} A_2 \end{bmatrix} \omega_2^z$$

We may now combine all these blocks to give the complete kinetic energy matrix. However, since there are no off-diagonal elements for the first three rows and columns, we shall omit that entire portion of the matrix which corresponds to the translational motion of the molecule. The complete rotational kinetic energy matrix is

$$(S) = \begin{bmatrix} I_x & -I_{xy} & -I_{xz} & \alpha_{2a}^x A_{2a} & \alpha_{2b}^x A_{2b} \\ -I_{xy} & I_y & -I_{yz} & \alpha_{2a}^y A_{2a} & \alpha_{2b}^y A_{2b} \\ -I_{xz} & -I_{yz} & I_z & \alpha_{2a}^z A_{2a} & \alpha_{2b}^z A_{2b} \\ \alpha_{2a}^x A_{2a} & \alpha_{2a}^y A_{2a} & \alpha_{2a}^z A_{2a} & A_{2a} & 0 \\ \alpha_{2b}^x A_{2b} & \alpha_{2b}^y A_{2b} & \alpha_{2b}^z A_{2b} & 0 & A_{2b} \end{bmatrix} \quad \text{(A16-10)}$$

and the rotational kinetic energy is

$$2T = (\omega_1', \omega_{2a}, \omega_{2b})(S) \begin{bmatrix} \omega_1 \\ \omega_{2a} \\ \omega_{2b} \end{bmatrix} \tag{A16-11}$$

The superscript z as applied to subgroup axes (2) has been omitted everywhere since it is the only subgroup axis remaining. Thus α_{2a}^z is the cosine of the angle between the z axis of the subgroup and the x axis of the main frame, etc.

While some results can be obtained from the matrix (S) in its present form, for most purposes it is necessary first to rotate the axes of the main frame to the principal axes, and second to diagonalize the matrix about the principal moments of inertia. The second step corresponds to the substitution of the average angular velocities ω_A for the angular velocities of the main frame itself.

$$\omega_A^x = \omega_1^x + (\alpha_{xa}^x A_{2a}\omega_{2a} + \alpha_{2b}^x A_{2b}\omega_{2b})/I_x, \quad \text{etc.}$$

We then obtain the expression,

$$2T = (\omega_A', \omega_{2a}, \omega_{2b})(S) \begin{bmatrix} \omega_A \\ \omega_{2a} \\ \omega_{2b} \end{bmatrix} \tag{A16-12}$$

with the matrix (S) now in the form

$$(S) = \begin{bmatrix} I_x & 0 & 0 & 0 & 0 \\ 0 & I_y & 0 & 0 & 0 \\ 0 & 0 & I_z & 0 & 0 \\ 0 & 0 & 0 & I_{2a} & -\Lambda_{2a,2b} \\ 0 & 0 & 0 & -\Lambda_{2b,2a} & I_{2b} \end{bmatrix} \tag{A16-13}$$

and

$$I_j = A_j \left[1 - A_j \sum_{i=x,y,z} \frac{(\alpha_j^i)^2}{I_i} \right] \tag{A16-14}$$

$$\Lambda_{jk} = \sum_{i=x,y,z} A_j A_k \alpha_j^i \alpha_k^i / I_i \tag{A16-15}$$

The kinetic energy of rotation of the entire molecule, whether there is internal rotation or not, is now separated into a simple expression which is easily put into the Hamiltonian form.

$$2H = 2T = \frac{M_x^2}{I_x} + \frac{M_y^2}{I_y} + \frac{M_z^2}{I_z} \tag{A16-16}$$

where M_x, M_y, and M_z are the components of angular momentum along the axes indicated.

The kinetic energy of internal rotation in terms of angular velocities is

$$2T = (\omega_{2a}\omega_{2b}) \begin{bmatrix} I_{2a} & -\Lambda_{2a,2b} \\ -\Lambda_{2a,2b} & I_{2b} \end{bmatrix} \begin{bmatrix} \omega_{2a} \\ \omega_{2b} \end{bmatrix}$$

$$= I_{2a}\omega_{2a}^2 + I_{2b}\omega_{2b}^2 - 2\Lambda_{2a,2b}\omega_{2a}\omega_{2b} \qquad \text{(A16-17)}$$

where the 2 by 2 matrix is commonly given the symbol (D). The conversion to the angular momenta M_{2a} and M_{2b} yields

$$2T = (M_{2a}, M_{2b})(D^{-1}) \begin{bmatrix} M_{2a} \\ M_{2b} \end{bmatrix}$$

$$= \frac{M_{2a}^2 I_{2b} + M_{2b}^2 I_{2a} + 2M_{2a}M_{2b}\Lambda_{2a,2b}}{I_{2a}I_{2b} - \Lambda_{2a,2b}^2} \qquad \text{(A16-18)}$$

but this is not ordinarily the complete Hamiltonian function, since a potential energy is normally associated with internal rotations.

Appendix 17

ROTATIONAL ENERGY LEVELS FROM MATRIX MECHANICS

In this Appendix we shall use matrix mechanics to derive the rotational energy levels for a nonlinear molecule. As shown in Appendix 16, the molecule may have internal rotations without affecting the results for the rotation of the whole molecule. The Hamiltonian function was given in Eq. (A16-16).

$$2H = \frac{M_x^2}{I_x} + \frac{M_y^2}{I_y} + \frac{M_z^2}{I_z} \tag{A16-16}$$

and the commutation properties of the angular momenta are

$$M_x M_y - M_y M_x = \frac{-h}{2\pi i} M_z$$

$$M_y M_z - M_z M_y = \frac{-h}{2\pi i} M_x \tag{A17-1}$$

$$M_z M_x - M_x M_z = \frac{-h}{2\pi i} M_y$$

These equations can be verified easily from the definitions of angular momenta in differential form in Eqs. (4.14).

A convenient solution of these commutation equations are matrices with elements as follows.

$$(M_y)_{J,K;J,K+1} = i(M_x)_{J,K;J,K+1} = \frac{h}{4\pi} [J(J+1) - K(K+1)]^{1/2}$$

$$(M_z)_{J,K;J,K} = \frac{h}{2\pi} K \tag{A17-2}$$

The inverse elements $(J, K + 1; J, K)$ can be obtained from the Hermitian property of these, and of any of the following matrices. Also $J \geqslant |K|$ throughout.

The squares of the angular momenta are then

$$(M_y^2)_{J,K;J,K} = (M_x^2)_{J,K;J,K} = \frac{h^2}{8\pi^2} [J(J+1) - K^2]$$

488

$$(M_y^2)_{J,K-1;J,K+1} = -(M_x^2)_{J,K-1;J,K+1} \tag{A17-3}$$

$$= \frac{h^2}{16\pi^2} \{[J(J+1) - K(K-1)][J(J+1) - K(K+1)]\}^{1/2}$$

$$(M_z^2)_{J,K;J,K} = \frac{h^2}{4\pi^2} K^2$$

and the square of the total angular momentum is

$$M^2 = M_x^2 + M_y^2 + M_z^2$$

$$(M^2)_{J,K;J,K} = \frac{h^2}{4\pi^2} J(J+1) \tag{A17-4}$$

We note that (M_z), (M_z^2), and (M^2) are all diagonal matrices.

If we now substitute the results of Eqs. (A17-3) into the equation for the Hamiltonian function, (A16-16), we obtain

$$(H)_{J,K;J,K} = \frac{h^2}{16\pi^2}\left[\left(\frac{1}{I_x} + \frac{1}{I_y}\right)J(J+1) + \left(\frac{2}{I_z} - \frac{1}{I_x} - \frac{1}{I_y}\right)K^2\right]$$

$$(H)_{J,K-1;J,K+1} = \frac{h^2}{32\pi^2}\left(\frac{1}{I_y} - \frac{1}{I_x}\right) \tag{A17-5}$$

$$\times \{[J(J+1) - K(K-1)][J(J+1) - K(K+1)]\}^{1/2}$$

In the case of the symmetrical top, where $I_x = I_y$, the off-diagonal terms in (H) vanish. Consequently, the diagonal terms may be adopted for the stationary state energy levels, yielding Eq. (9.14), which was given without proof in Section 9c.

$$E = \frac{h^2}{8\pi^2}\left[\frac{J(J+1)}{I_x} + K^2\left(\frac{1}{I_z} - \frac{1}{I_x}\right)\right] \tag{9.14}$$

With asymmetric tops, the (H) matrix must be diagonalized to obtain the energy levels. A general method is to form a secular determinant and set it equal to zero.

$$|H_{jk} - E\delta_{jk}| = 0 \tag{A17-6}$$

Here H_{jk} is an element from the nondiagonal (H) matrix; δ_{jk} has the usual values (1 if $j = k$, and 0 if $j \neq k$); and the solutions for E are the elements of a diagonal matrix, and therefore constitute the energy levels.

The complete secular determinant can be broken down into fairly small factors. First we note that there are no off-diagonal elements in J (such as for $J; J + 1$). Consequently the blocks for each J value are independent and may be treated separately. Even within a given J, we have off-diagonal terms only of the type $K - 1; K + 1$. Thus there is no interrelationship between the elements of even and odd K and these can be treated separately. It will be noted that the elements are unchanged by the substitution of $-K$ for K. This symmetry property can be used to factor the determinants even further, but we shall not use that property here.

In addition, one is free to assign the x, y, and z axes in the most convenient manner. This is particularly useful if two of the moments of inertia are nearly equal. By assigning these to the x and y axes, all the off-diagonal terms can be made relatively small.

The full development of these methods for the efficient calculation of the energy levels with high J values is beyond the scope of this Appendix but is given in the papers by King, Hainer, and Cross.[1] We shall merely derive a few of the lower energy levels. Let

$$a = h^2/8\pi^2 I_y$$
$$b = h^2/8\pi^2 I_z \qquad\qquad \text{(A17-7)}$$
$$c = h^2/8\pi^2 I_x$$

Then the elements of (H) become

$$(H)_{K,K} = \tfrac{1}{2}[(a + c)\,J(J + 1) + (2b - a - c)K^2] \qquad \text{(A17-8)}$$
$$(H)_{K-1,K+1} = \tfrac{1}{4}(a - c)$$
$$\times \{[J(J + 1) - K(K - 1)][J(J + 1) - K(K + 1)]\}^{1/2}$$

The solution for $J = K = 0$ is obviously $E = 0$. For $J = 1$, $K = 0$, one obtains the single term, $E = a + c$. In the case $J = 1$, $K = \pm1$, the secular determinant is

$$\begin{vmatrix} \dfrac{a}{2} + b + \dfrac{c}{2} - E & \dfrac{a}{2} - \dfrac{c}{2} \\[2ex] \dfrac{a}{2} - \dfrac{c}{2} & \dfrac{a}{2} + b + \dfrac{c}{2} - E \end{vmatrix} = 0$$

which has the solutions

$$E = (a + b), \quad (b + c)$$

For $J = 2$, one has a second-order determinant for the odd K values and a third-order determinant for even K values, as follows.

$$\begin{vmatrix} \dfrac{5a}{2} + b + \dfrac{5c}{2} - E & \dfrac{3}{2}(a - c) \\[2ex] \dfrac{3}{2}(a - c) & \dfrac{5a}{2} + b + \dfrac{5c}{2} - E \end{vmatrix} = 0$$
$$E = (4a + b + c), \quad (a + b + 4c)$$

---

[1] King, G. W., Hainer, R. M., and Cross, P. C., *J. Chem. Phys.*, **11**, 27 (1943); together with later papers listed at the end of Appendix 8.

and
$$\begin{vmatrix} a + 4b + c - E & \sqrt{3/2}(a - c) & 0 \\ \sqrt{3/2}(a - c) & 3a + 3c - E & \sqrt{3/2}(a - c) \\ 0 & \sqrt{3/2}(a - c) & a + 4b + c - E \end{vmatrix} = 0$$

$$E = (a + 4b + c), \quad 2(a + b + c) \pm [(2b - a - c)^2 + 3(a - c)^2]^{1/2}$$

One can readily identify these results with those given in Table A8-1.

Although certain levels would come from different determinants if a different assignment of the x, y, and z axes had been made in (A17-7), it can be shown that exactly the same array of levels would be obtained for each value of J.

INTERNAL ROTATION

The classical mechanical kinetic energy was derived in Appendix 16 for a molecule involving internal rotation, and the necessary transformation was made to separate the external rotation of the whole molecule from the internal rotation. The model was that of a rigid frame with two attached rotating subgroups. Each subgroup was taken to be symmetrical about its axis of internal rotation, such as a methyl group. Possible examples include *cis* and *trans* 2-butene, isobutene, and the three xylenes.

With some simplification of notation from Eq. (A16-17), the kinetic energy of internal rotation takes the form

$$2T = I_1\omega_1^2 + I_2\omega_2^2 - 2\Lambda_{12}\omega_1\omega_2$$

$$I_j = A_j(1 - A_j \sum_{i=1}^{3} \alpha_{ij}^2/I_i) \qquad \text{(A18-1)}$$

$$\Lambda_{jk} = \sum_{i=1}^{3} A_j A_k \alpha_{ij}\alpha_{ik}/I_i$$

where A_j is the moment of inertia of the jth subgroup about its axis of internal rotation, I_i is the moment of inertia of the whole molecule about the ith principal axis, and α_{ij} is the direction cosine between the ith principal axis and the axis of rotation of the jth subgroup.

If there is only one internal rotation, I_j is clearly the reduced moment of inertia I_r for internal rotation. The Hamiltonian function becomes

$$H = M_\phi^2/2I_r + V(\phi) \qquad \text{(A18-2)}$$

where M_ϕ is the angular momentum of internal rotation and $V(\phi)$ is the potential energy. Inserting the appropriate operator for a uniaxial angular momentum, one obtains Eq. (9.65),

$$\frac{d^2\psi}{d\phi^2} + \frac{8\pi^2 I_r}{h^2}[E - V(\phi)]\psi = 0 \qquad \text{(9.65)}$$

but with the more general definition of I_r,

$$I_r = A\left(1 - A \sum_{i=1}^{3} \alpha_i^2/I_i\right) \tag{A18-3}$$

This definition can be shown to reduce to Eq. (9.66) for the case of a pair of symmetrical, coaxial tops such as CH_3—CH_3. The further analysis for a single internal rotation proceeds as given in Section 9h, and yields the tables to be presented later in this Appendix.

Returning to the molecule with two rotating subgroups, one faces real difficulty in handling the interaction of the two rotations. In molecules such as *trans* 2-butene and *m*- and *p*-xylene it is probably a good approximation to assume separate potential energy functions,

$$V = V_1(\phi_1) + V_2(\phi_2)$$

Then any change of coordinates which might be introduced to eliminate the cross terms in the kinetic energy would only introduce similar cross terms into the potential energy.

In many cases it is found that the coefficient, Λ_{12}, of the interaction term is much smaller than either of the reduced moments of inertia. It is then best simply to ignore the cross term, and to handle the two internal rotations separately. If a second approximation is justified, the cross term can be introduced as a perturbation.

Another approach is the normal coordinate method, which can be used for the lowest energy levels if the potential function can be expressed as a quadratic with reasonable approximation up to that energy. We have

$$2V = b_1\phi_1^2 + b_2\phi_2^2 + 2b_{12}\phi_1\phi_2 \tag{A18-4}$$

where the potential constants b can be obtained from the second derivatives of a more general expression of the potential energy.

$$b_j = \left(\frac{\partial^2 V}{\partial \phi_j^2}\right)_e, \qquad b_{jk} = \left(\frac{\partial^2 V}{\partial \phi_j\, \partial \phi_k}\right)_e$$

The derivatives are evaluated at the equilibrium position.

From Eqs. (9.34) and (9.39) one can immediately write the secular equation,

$$\begin{vmatrix} b_1 - I_1\lambda & b_{12} + \Lambda_{12}\lambda \\ b_{12} + \Lambda_{12}\lambda & b_2 - I_2\lambda \end{vmatrix} = 0 \tag{A18-5}$$

$$\nu_i = \lambda_i^{1/2}/2\pi$$

from which the frequencies and corresponding harmonic oscillator energy levels can be calculated.

$$E = (n_1 + \tfrac{1}{2})h\nu_1 + (n_2 + \tfrac{1}{2})h\nu_2 \tag{A18-6}$$

The calculation of thermodynamic functions is based on the usual statistical equations of Section 7o. In some cases the classical partition function is a good approximation; in others the quantum effects predominate. The methods for treating various types of cases, including those with more than two rotating subgroups and those with unsymmetrical subgroups, have been presented in a series of papers by Pitzer, Gwinn, and Kilpatrick.[1] Only the simple case of a single internal rotation subject to a cosine potential function has proved to be of sufficiently wide usefulness to justify a full tabulation of thermodynamic functions. With the limitations stated, the results are more or less valid when applied to the more complex examples.

The tables are calculated for a single internal rotation, where one group is symmetrical about the axis of internal rotation but the other group need not be, and where the potential energy is

$$V = \tfrac{1}{2}V_0(1 - \cos n\phi) \tag{A18-7}$$

Here V_0 is the height of the potential peaks above the valleys, and n is the number of equivalent positions per complete turn, the symmetry number. The reduced moment of inertia I_r has been defined above in Eq. (A18-3).

The variables in the tables are the dimensionless quantities (V_0/RT) and Q_f, the partition function for a free rotation with the same I_r and n.

$$\begin{aligned} Q_f &= (8\pi^3 I_r kT)^{1/2}/nh \\ &= 2.7935(10^{38} I_r T)^{1/2}/n \end{aligned} \tag{A18-8}$$

The value of R used in computing the tables was 1.9869 cal./degree mole, while the present best value is 1.9872. Because of the limited accuracy of the tables, no revision would be justified for this small change except in the column $(1/Q_f) = 0$. Graphical interpolations are recommended if the maximum accuracy is desired.

Because the entropy and free energy approach infinity as $(1/Q_f)$ approaches zero, the difference from the value for free rotation is tabulated instead. The actual functions are then

$$\begin{aligned} -\frac{F}{T} &= R \ln Q_f - \frac{(F - F_f)}{T} \\ S &= R(\tfrac{1}{2} + \ln Q_f) - (S_f - S) \end{aligned} \tag{A18-9}$$

[1] Pitzer, K. S. and Gwinn, W. D., *J. Chem. Phys.*, **10**, 428 (1942); Pitzer, K. S., *J. Chem. Phys.*, **14**, 239 (1946); Kilpatrick, J. E. and Pitzer, K. S., *J. Chem. Phys.*, **17**, 1064 (1949); Pitzer, K. S., *J. Chem. Phys.*, **5**, 469 (1937).

TABLE A18-1

FREE ENERGY, $-F/T$ [cal./deg. mole]

V/RT \ $1/Q'$	0.25	0.30	0.35	0.40	0.45	0.50	0.55	0.60	0.65	0.70	0.75	0.80
0.0	2.754	2.392	2.086	1.821	1.587	1.377	1.188					
.2	2.710	2.359	2.061	1.803	1.574	1.368	1.182					
.4	2.623	2.296	2.014	1.765	1.543	1.342	1.160					
.6	2.518	2.208	1.944	1.708	1.498	1.309	1.134					
.8	2.406	2.106	1.856	1.636	1.442	1.266	1.100					
1.0	2.296	2.004	1.764	1.559	1.379	1.214	1.059					
1.5	2.040	1.770	1.548	1.370	1.210	1.069	.938					
2.0	1.819	1.563	1.360	1.193	1.052	.927	.817					
2.5	1.630	1.389	1.197	1.043	.912	.802	.709					
3.0	1.473	1.240	1.059	.914	.793	.695	.612	.53				
3.5	1.340	1.117	.943	.802	.694	.603	.528	.46				
4.0	1.225	1.013	.847	.713	.613	.527	.456	.40	.34			
4.5	1.133	.925	.764	.637	.543	.463	.397	.35	.29			
5.0	1.053	.849	.696	.577	.483	.408	.347	.30	.25	.22		
6	.919	.728	.586	.477	.393	.325	.272	.23	.19	.16	.14	
7	.819	.636	.503	.402	.325	.267	.218	.183	.15	.12	.10	.08
8	.735	.564	.440	.346	.275	.221	.178	.146	.119	.10	.08	.06
9	.667	.504	.388	.300	.235	.186	.149	.119	.096	.079	.06	.05
10	.610	.456	.345	.264	.203	.159	.125	.099	.079	.064	.051	.04
12	.521	.380	.280	.209	.157	.120	.092	.071	.055	.043	.033	.027
14	.452	.321	.232	.169	.124	.092	.069	.052	.038	.030	.022	.018
16	.396	.276	.195	.139	.100	.072	.053	.039	.028	.021	.016	.012
18	.351	.240	.166	.117	.082	.058	.042	.030	.022	.016	.012	.009
20	.315	.211	.144	.098	.068	.047	.033	.024	.017	.012	.009	.006

TABLE A18-2

FREE ENERGY INCREASE FROM FREE ROTATION, $(F - F_f)/T$ [cal./deg. mole]

V/RT \ 1/Q_f	0	0.05	0.10	0.15	0.20	0.25	0.30	0.35	0.40	0.45	0.50	0.55
0.0	0.0000	0.000	0.000	0.000	0.000	0.000	0.000	0.000	0.000	0.000	0.000	0.000
0.2	.1937	.154	.117	.085	.061	.044	.033	.025	.018	.013	.009	.005
0.4	.3776	.326	.274	.225	.176	.131	.096	.072	.056	.044	.035	.026
0.6	.5516	.489	.424	.361	.298	.236	.184	.142	.113	.089	.068	.054
0.8	.7161	.640	.566	.493	.420	.348	.286	.230	.185	.145	.111	.088
1.0	.8711	.784	.699	.617	.537	.461	.389	.322	.262	.208	.163	.129
1.5	1.2200	1.114	1.010	.909	.809	.714	.622	.538	.451	.375	.308	.250
2.0	1.5182	1.395	1.276	1.159	1.045	.935	.829	.726	.628	.535	.450	.371
2.5	1.7724	1.635	1.501	1.371	1.246	1.124	1.004	.889	.778	.675	.575	.479
3.0	1.9893	1.839	1.693	1.552	1.415	1.282	1.152	1.027	.907	.794	.682	.576
3.5	2.1756	2.013	1.856	1.704	1.557	1.414	1.275	1.143	1.019	.893	.774	.660
4.0	2.3366	2.163	1.996	1.833	1.676	1.525	1.379	1.239	1.108	.974	.850	.732
4.5	2.4772	2.293	2.117	1.945	1.780	1.621	1.467	1.322	1.184	1.044	.914	.791
5.0	2.6012	2.408	2.221	2.042	1.868	1.703	1.543	1.392	1.244	1.104	.969	.841
6.0	2.8108	2.599	2.396	2.202	2.015	1.836	1.664	1.500	1.344	1.194	1.052	.916
7.0	2.9833	2.755	2.537	2.328	2.129	1.936	1.757	1.583	1.418	1.262	1.111	.971
8.0	3.1294	2.886	2.653	2.432	2.220	2.020	1.828	1.646	1.474	1.312	1.157	1.011
9.0	3.2563	2.998	2.753	2.520	2.298	2.087	1.888	1.698	1.520	1.351	1.192	1.039
10.0	3.3686	3.097	2.839	2.594	2.362	2.144	1.936	1.741	1.557	1.383	1.219	1.063
12.0	3.5602	3.263	2.982	2.718	2.468	2.233	2.013	1.806	1.612	1.429	1.258	1.096
14.0	3.7205	3.400	3.099	2.816	2.551	2.303	2.071	1.854	1.651	1.462	1.285	1.119
16.0	3.8584	3.517	3.197	2.897	2.618	2.358	2.116	1.891	1.682	1.486	1.305	1.135
18.0	3.9793	3.618	3.280	2.965	2.674	2.403	2.152	1.920	1.704	1.505	1.319	1.146
20.0	4.0872	3.707	3.353	3.024	2.720	2.440	2.181	1.942	1.722	1.519	1.331	1.155

ENTROPY, S [cal./deg. mole]

V/RT \\ $1/Q_l$	0.25	0.30	0.35	0.40	0.45	0.50	0.55	0.60	0.65	0.70	0.75	0.80
0.0	3.748	3.386	3.079	2.814	2.580	2.371	2.181					
0.2	3.743	3.382	3.076	2.811	2.578	2.369	2.179					
0.4	3.730	3.370	3.065	2.801	2.568	2.359	2.171					
0.6	3.709	3.347	3.043	2.780	2.547	2.340	2.153					
0.8	3.679	3.318	3.013	2.750	2.519	2.315	2.128					
1.0	3.638	3.279	2.974	2.714	2.485	2.279	2.095					
1.5	3.512	3.156	2.854	2.600	2.376	2.173	1.992					
2.0	3.355	3.004	2.709	2.458	2.241	2.048	1.873					
2.5	3.180	2.836	2.548	2.303	2.091	1.907	1.741					
3.0	3.008	2.667	2.380	2.138	1.933	1.756	1.600	1.45				
3.5	2.838	2.500	2.218	1.978	1.782	1.610	1.459	1.34				
4.0	2.678	2.343	2.069	1.834	1.643	1.475	1.326	1.22	1.10			
4.5	2.528	2.199	1.926	1.698	1.511	1.348	1.204	1.10	1.00			
5.0	2.396	2.068	1.798	1.579	1.392	1.233	1.095	.97	.88	.81		
6.0	2.166	1.844	1.585	1.370	1.192	1.040	.913	.79	.70	.63	.56	.39
7.0	1.983	1.665	1.411	1.204	1.033	.891	.770	.665	.57	.50	.44	.31
8.0	1.830	1.519	1.272	1.071	.906	.770	.656	.564	.482	.41	.36	.25
9.0	1.703	1.397	1.156	.962	.804	.674	.569	.482	.411	.348	.29	.21
10.0	1.593	1.295	1.060	.872	.719	.596	.495	.418	.352	.295	.245	.143
12.0	1.417	1.125	.904	.728	.588	.476	.388	.315	.258	.212	.173	.102
14.0	1.275	.994	.783	.620	.492	.388	.309	.247	.196	.158	.126	.075
16.0	1.157	.890	.688	.533	.414	.322	.251	.196	.155	.120	.094	.056
18.0	1.058	.801	.609	.464	.353	.270	.205	.158	.121	.093	.072	.042
20.0	.975	.727	.542	.405	.303	.228	.170	.129	.097	.073	.056	

TABLE A18-4

ENTROPY DECREASE FROM FREE ROTATION, $(S_f - S)$ [cal./deg. mole]

V/RT \ $1/Q_f$	0.0	0.05	0.10	0.15	0.20	0.25	0.30	0.35	0.40	0.45	0.50	0.55
0.0	0.0000	0.000	0.000	0.000	0.000	0.000	0.000	0.000	0.000	0.000	0.000	0.000
0.2	.0049	.005	.004	.004	.004	.004	.004	.003	.003	.002	.002	.002
0.4	.0198	.020	.018	.018	.018	.018	.016	.014	.013	.012	.012	.010
0.6	.0440	.044	.043	.043	.040	.039	.039	.036	.034	.033	.031	.028
0.8	.0771	.077	.077	.075	.072	.069	.068	.066	.064	.061	.056	.053
1.0	.1185	.118	.117	.115	.112	.110	.107	.105	.100	.095	.092	.086
1.5	.2527	.252	.250	.248	.242	.236	.230	.225	.214	.204	.198	.189
2.0	.4182	.417	.415	.410	.402	.393	.382	.370	.356	.339	.323	.308
2.5	.6001	.599	.594	.585	.577	.568	.550	.531	.511	.489	.464	.440
3.0	.7856	.783	.777	.768	.757	.740	.719	.699	.676	.647	.615	.581
3.5	.9660	.964	.957	.944	.929	.910	.886	.861	.836	.798	.761	.722
4.0	1.1356	1.133	1.126	1.111	1.094	1.070	1.043	1.011	.980	.937	.896	.855
4.5	1.2918	1.289	1.280	1.265	1.244	1.220	1.187	1.153	1.116	1.069	1.023	.977
5.0	1.4339	1.431	1.421	1.404	1.380	1.352	1.318	1.281	1.235	1.188	1.138	1.086
6.0	1.6781	1.674	1.662	1.643	1.616	1.582	1.542	1.494	1.444	1.388	1.331	1.268
7.0	1.8783	1.874	1.860	1.837	1.807	1.765	1.721	1.668	1.610	1.547	1.480	1.411
8.0	2.0447	2.040	2.024	1.998	1.962	1.918	1.867	1.807	1.743	1.674	1.601	1.525
9.0	2.1864	2.180	2.163	2.134	2.095	2.045	1.989	1.923	1.852	1.776	1.697	1.612
10.0	2.3095	2.303	2.284	2.252	2.208	2.155	2.091	2.019	1.942	1.861	1.775	1.686
12.0	2.5155	2.508	2.485	2.447	2.394	2.331	2.261	2.175	2.086	1.992	1.895	1.793
14.0	2.6847	2.676	2.650	2.607	2.547	2.473	2.392	2.296	2.194	2.088	1.983	1.872
16.0	2.8289	2.819	2.788	2.740	2.674	2.591	2.496	2.391	2.281	2.166	2.049	1.930
18.0	2.9545	2.943	2.910	2.855	2.781	2.690	2.585	2.470	2.350	2.227	2.101	1.976
20.0	3.0659	3.054	3.017	2.956	2.872	2.773	2.659	2.537	2.409	2.277	2.143	2.011

Heat Content, H/T [cal./deg. mole]

V/RT \\ $1/Q_f$	0.0	0.05	0.10	0.15	0.20	0.25	0.30	0.35	0.40	0.45	0.50	0.55	0.60	0.65	0.70	0.75	0.80
0.0	0.9934	0.993	0.993	0.993	0.993	0.993	0.993	0.993	0.993	0.993	0.993	0.993					
0.2	1.1822	1.142	1.106	1.074	1.050	1.032	1.022	1.015	1.008	1.004	1.000	0.997					
0.4	1.3513	1.300	1.249	1.200	1.151	1.106	1.073	1.051	1.036	1.025	1.015	1.009					
0.6	1.5011	1.437	1.374	1.311	1.251	1.190	1.138	1.099	1.072	1.049	1.030	1.019					
0.8	1.6324	1.556	1.482	1.411	1.340	1.272	1.211	1.157	1.114	1.077	1.048	1.028					
1.0	1.7460	1.660	1.576	1.495	1.418	1.344	1.275	1.211	1.155	1.106	1.065	1.037					
1.5	1.9607	1.856	1.753	1.654	1.561	1.472	1.385	1.306	1.230	1.164	1.103	1.054					
2.0	2.0934	1.971	1.854	1.742	1.636	1.536	1.440	1.350	1.265	1.190	1.120	1.056					
2.5	2.1657	2.031	1.900	1.779	1.662	1.550	1.448	1.351	1.260	1.179	1.104	1.032					
3.0	2.1971	2.049	1.909	1.777	1.651	1.535	1.426	1.321	1.224	1.140	1.060	0.988	.92				
3.5	2.2030	2.043	1.893	1.753	1.621	1.497	1.382	1.275	1.176	1.088	1.006	0.931	.88				
4.0	2.1944	2.024	1.864	1.715	1.577	1.448	1.329	1.221	1.121	1.030	0.947	0.870	.82	.77			
4.5	2.1788	1.998	1.829	1.673	1.529	1.394	1.273	1.162	1.061	0.968	0.884	0.807	.75	.71			
5.0	2.1607	1.971	1.794	1.631	1.481	1.344	1.218	1.104	1.002	0.909	0.824	0.748	.67	.63	.59		
6.0	2.1261	1.918	1.727	1.552	1.392	1.247	1.115	0.999	0.893	0.799	0.714	0.641	.56	.51	.47	.42	
7.0	2.0984	1.875	1.670	1.484	1.315	1.164	1.029	0.908	0.802	0.708	0.624	0.553	.482	.42	.38	.34	.31
8.0	2.0781	1.840	1.623	1.427	1.251	1.095	0.955	0.833	0.725	0.631	0.549	0.479	.418	.363	.31	.28	.25
9.0	2.0634	1.811	1.583	1.379	1.196	1.035	0.892	0.768	0.661	0.569	0.488	0.420	.363	.315	.269	.23	.20
10.0	2.0526	1.787	1.548	1.335	1.147	0.982	0.838	0.715	0.608	0.515	0.437	0.371	.319	.273	.231	.194	.17
12.0	2.0382	1.749	1.492	1.264	1.067	0.896	0.745	0.624	0.519	0.431	0.356	0.296	.244	.203	.169	.140	.116
14.0	2.0292	1.717	1.441	1.202	0.997	0.823	0.672	0.551	0.450	0.367	0.295	0.240	.195	.158	.128	.104	.084
16.0	2.0229	1.690	1.401	1.150	0.937	0.760	0.613	0.493	0.394	0.314	0.249	0.198	.157	.127	.099	.078	.063
18.0	2.0182	1.666	1.363	1.102	0.886	0.707	0.561	0.443	0.347	0.271	0.211	0.164	.128	.099	.077	.060	.047
20.0	2.0147	1.646	1.329	1.061	0.841	0.660	0.515	0.399	0.307	0.236	0.181	0.138	.105	.080	.061	.047	.036

TABLE A18-6

HEAT CAPACITY, C [cal./deg. mole]

V/RT \ 1/Q	0.0	0.05	0.10	0.15	0.20	0.25	0.30	0.35	0.40	0.45	0.50	0.55	0.60	0.65	0.70	0.75	0.80
0.0	.9934	.993	.993	.993	.993	.993	.993	.993	.993	.993	.99	.99					
0.2	1.0033	1.003	1.003	1.002	1.001	1.000	.999	.998	.998	.998	1.00	1.00					
0.4	1.0326	1.033	1.032	1.030	1.028	1.025	1.024	1.021	1.019	1.017	1.02	1.01					
0.6	1.0799	1.080	1.079	1.076	1.073	1.068	1.065	1.060	1.056	1.051	1.05	1.04					
0.8	1.1433	1.143	1.141	1.138	1.133	1.128	1.121	1.114	1.106	1.099	1.09	1.08					
1.0	1.2201	1.219	1.217	1.212	1.206	1.199	1.190	1.180	1.169	1.157	1.14	1.13					
1.5	1.4506	1.449	1.444	1.435	1.423	1.408	1.391	1.370	1.348	1.324	1.30	1.27					
2.0	1.6975	1.695	1.687	1.673	1.655	1.632	1.606	1.574	1.541	1.505	1.469	1.43					
2.5	1.9211	1.917	1.908	1.888	1.866	1.840	1.801	1.756	1.717	1.670	1.623	1.58					
3.0	2.0986	2.095	2.082	2.062	2.033	1.996	1.952	1.900	1.846	1.794	1.738	1.68	1.7				
3.5	2.2223	2.218	2.204	2.180	2.146	2.106	2.054	1.995	1.934	1.869	1.803	1.74	1.7				
4.0	2.2986	2.294	2.276	2.249	2.213	2.168	2.110	2.048	1.980	1.907	1.832	1.76	1.69	1.6			
4.5	2.3354	2.330	2.312	2.280	2.238	2.190	2.129	2.062	1.990	1.911	1.834	1.75	1.67	1.6			
5.0	2.3443	2.338	2.318	2.285	2.241	2.186	2.120	2.056	1.972	1.890	1.808	1.719	1.62	1.55	1.4		
6.0	2.3155	2.307	2.283	2.245	2.192	2.130	2.059	1.979	1.893	1.803	1.711	1.616	1.51	1.43	1.33	1.2	
7.0	2.2647	2.256	2.228	2.185	2.126	2.055	1.973	1.883	1.787	1.688	1.588	1.491	1.394	1.30	1.21	1.12	1.0
8.0	2.2157	2.205	2.174	2.125	2.058	1.979	1.888	1.788	1.684	1.576	1.468	1.362	1.260	1.159	1.07	.99	.91
9.0	2.1759	2.164	2.130	2.074	1.999	1.909	1.808	1.699	1.587	1.474	1.362	1.252	1.149	1.049	.955	.86	.79
10.0	2.1454	2.133	2.094	2.033	1.951	1.854	1.745	1.630	1.507	1.382	1.262	1.151	1.047	.949	.853	.762	.68
12.0	2.1050	2.089	2.043	1.972	1.877	1.763	1.636	1.502	1.365	1.233	1.107	.989	.877	.774	.683	.600	.519
14.0	2.0810	2.063	2.009	1.923	1.814	1.686	1.546	1.400	1.254	1.112	.978	.855	.744	.644	.555	.476	.408
16.0	2.0654	2.044	1.983	1.887	1.764	1.622	1.468	1.311	1.156	1.009	.873	.749	.639	.542	.457	.384	.321
18.0	2.0544	2.031	1.961	1.853	1.717	1.562	1.397	1.232	1.070	.919	.780	.657	.549	.456	.378	.312	.256
20.0	2.0462	2.020	1.944	1.827	1.678	1.510	1.333	1.158	.991	.837	.701	.580	.477	.389	.316	.256	.207

DEBYE FUNCTIONS FOR THE THERMODYNAMIC PROPERTIES OF SOLIDS

These functions are defined by Eq. (10.42) and analogous equations for the other functions as follows.

$$\frac{C_v}{3R} = f_D\left(\frac{\theta_D}{T}\right) = 3\left(\frac{T}{\theta_D}\right)^3 \int_0^{\theta_D/T} \frac{u^4 e^u \, du}{(e^u - 1)^2} \tag{10.42}$$

$$\frac{E - E_0}{3RT} = 3\left(\frac{T}{\theta_D}\right)^3 \int_0^{\theta_D/T} \frac{u^3 \, du}{e^u - 1} \tag{A19-1}$$

$$\frac{A - E_0}{3RT} = 3\left(\frac{T}{\theta_D}\right)^3 \int_0^{\theta_D/T} \ln\left(1 - e^{-u}\right) u^2 \, du \tag{A19-2}$$

$$\frac{S}{3R} = \frac{E - E_0}{3RT} - \frac{F - A_0}{3RT} \tag{A19-3}$$

The numerical values for the first two integrals[1] are given in tables below. The free energy function and the entropy have also been tabulated elsewhere[2] but are not reproduced here.

[1] Beattie, J. A., *J. Math. Phys.* (Mass. Inst. Tech.), **6**, 1 (1926).
[2] Nernst, W., *The New Heat Theorem*, New York: E. P. Dutton & Co., Inc., 1926. Also *Landolt-Bornstein Tabellen.* The user is cautioned that these tables are given in a fashion to include the value of *R*, and that the values used are appreciably different from the present "best" value.

Table A19-1

Debye Heat Capacity Function, $C_v/3R$ as a function of θ_D/T

θ_D/T	0.0	0.1	0.2	0.3	0.4	0.5	0.6	0.7	0.8	0.9	1.0
0.0	1.0000	0.9995	0.9980	0.9955	0.9920	0.9876	0.9822	0.9759	0.9687	0.9606	0.9517
1.0	0.9517	0.9420	0.9315	0.9203	0.9085	0.8960	0.8828	0.8692	0.8550	0.8404	0.8254
2.0	0.8254	0.8100	0.7943	0.7784	0.7622	0.7459	0.7294	0.7128	0.6961	0.6794	0.6628
3.0	0.6628	0.6461	0.6296	0.6132	0.5968	0.5807	0.5647	0.5490	0.5334	0.5181	0.5031
4.0	0.5031	0.4883	0.4738	0.4595	0.4456	0.4320	0.4187	0.4057	0.3930	0.3807	0.3686
5.0	0.3686	0.3569	0.3455	0.3345	0.3237	0.3133	0.3031	0.2933	0.2838	0.2745	0.2656
6.0	0.2656	0.2569	0.2486	0.2405	0.2326	0.2251	0.2177	0.2107	0.2038	0.1972	0.1909
7.0	0.1909	0.1847	0.1788	0.1730	0.1675	0.1622	0.1570	0.1521	0.1473	0.1426	0.1382
8.0	0.1382	0.1339	0.1297	0.1257	0.1219	0.1182	0.1146	0.1111	0.1078	0.1046	0.1015
9.0	0.1015	0.09847	0.09558	0.09280	0.09011	0.08751	0.08500	0.08259	0.08025	0.07800	0.07582
10.0	0.07582	0.07372	0.07169	0.06973	0.06783	0.06600	0.06424	0.06253	0.06087	0.05928	0.05773
11.0	0.05773	0.05624	0.05479	0.05339	0.05204	0.05073	0.04946	0.04823	0.04705	0.04590	0.04478
12.0	0.04478	0.04370	0.04265	0.04164	0.04066	0.03970	0.03878	0.03788	0.03701	0.03617	0.03535
13.0	0.03535	0.03455	0.03378	0.03303	0.03230	0.03160	0.03091	0.03024	0.02959	0.02896	0.02835
14.0	0.02835	0.02776	0.02718	0.02661	0.02607	0.02553	0.02501	0.02451	0.02402	0.02354	0.02307
15.0	0.02307	0.02262	0.02218	0.02174	0.02132	0.02092	0.02052	0.02013	0.01975	0.01938	0.01902

when $\dfrac{\theta_D}{T} \geqslant 16$, $\dfrac{C_v}{3R} = 77.927 \left(\dfrac{T}{\theta_D}\right)^3$

Debye Function for Energy Content, $(E - E_0)/3RT$ as a function of θ_D/T

θ_D/T	0.0	0.1	0.2	0.3	0.4	0.5	0.6	0.7	0.8	0.9	1.0
0.0	1.0000	0.9630	0.9270	0.8920	0.8580	0.8250	0.7929	0.7619	0.7318	0.7026	0.6744
1.0	0.6744	0.6471	0.6208	0.5954	0.5708	0.5471	0.5243	0.5023	0.4811	0.4607	0.4411
2.0	0.4411	0.4223	0.4042	0.3868	0.3701	0.3541	0.3388	0.3241	0.3100	0.2965	0.2836
3.0	0.2836	0.2712	0.2594	0.2481	0.2373	0.2269	0.2170	0.2076	0.1986	0.1900	0.1817
4.0	0.1817	0.1739	0.1664	0.1592	0.1524	0.1459	0.1397	0.1338	0.1281	0.1227	0.1176
5.0	0.1176	0.1127	0.1080	0.1036	0.09930	0.09524	0.09137	0.08768	0.08415	0.08079	0.07758
6.0	0.07758	0.07452	0.07160	0.06881	0.06615	0.06360	0.06118	0.05886	0.05664	0.05453	0.05251
7.0	0.05251	0.05057	0.04873	0.04696	0.04527	0.04366	0.04211	0.04063	0.03921	0.03786	0.03656
8.0	0.03656	0.03532	0.03413	0.03298	0.03189	0.03084	0.02983	0.02887	0.02794	0.02705	0.02620
9.0	0.02620	0.02538	0.02459	0.02384	0.02311	0.02241	0.02174	0.02109	0.02047	0.01987	0.01930
10.0	0.01930	0.01874	0.01821	0.01769	0.01720	0.01672	0.01626	0.01581	0.01538	0.01497	0.01457
11.0	0.01457	0.01418	0.01381	0.01345	0.01311	0.01277	0.01245	0.01213	0.01183	0.01153	0.01125
12.0	0.01125	0.01098	0.01071	0.01045	0.01020	0.00996	0.00973	0.00950	0.00928	0.00907	0.00886
13.0	0.00886	0.00866	0.00846	0.00827	0.00809	0.00791	0.00774	0.00757	0.00741	0.00725	0.00710
14.0	0.00710	0.00695	0.00680	0.00666	0.00652	0.00639	0.00626	0.00613	0.00601	0.00589	0.00577
15.0	0.00577	0.00566	0.00555	0.00544	0.00533	0.00523	0.00513	0.00503	0.00494	0.00485	0.00476

when $\dfrac{\theta_D}{T} \geqslant 16$, $\quad \dfrac{E - E_s}{3RT} = 19.482 \left(\dfrac{T}{\theta_D}\right)^3$

Appendix 20

SECOND-ORDER PERTURBATION THEORY;
POLARIZABILITY

In Chapter 4 we indicated the general character of perturbation theory, and we found that first-order perturbation theory as applied to a normal hydrogen atom gave no energy change in an electric field. The polarizability was calculated by the variation method with a simple variation function. Second-order perturbation theory would have been appropriate also, but the equations are somewhat more complex. However, we shall now develop this perturbation theory and apply it to the problem of the polarizability of a general molecular system.

We assume that the Hamiltonian operation may be divided into a principal term H_0 and a perturbation $\lambda H^{(1)}$ which is assumed to be small and to include a parameter λ. We also assume that we have the wave functions for the unperturbed problem, ψ_n°, and their energy levels, E_n°.

Then we expand our solutions for the perturbed problem in series.

$$\psi_n = \psi_n^\circ + \lambda\psi_n^{(1)} + \lambda^2\psi_n^{(2)} + \ldots \qquad \text{(A20-1)}$$

$$E_n = E_n^\circ + \lambda E_n^{(1)} + \lambda^2 E_n^{(2)} + \ldots \qquad \text{(A20-2)}$$

and our complete Schrödinger equation is

$$H_0\psi_n + \lambda H^{(1)}\psi_n = E_n\psi_n \qquad \text{(A20-3)}$$

We substitute the expansions for the wave function and the energy level into the Schrödinger equation and collect terms of equal powers of λ. Each of these collections of terms must be zero up to the power of λ corresponding to the approximation desired. There result

$$(H_0 - E_n^\circ)\psi_n^\circ = 0 \qquad \text{(A20-4)}$$

$$(H_0 - E_n^\circ)\psi_n^{(1)} + (H^{(1)} - E_n^{(1)})\psi_n^\circ = 0 \qquad \text{(A20-5)}$$

$$(H_0 - E_n^\circ)\psi_n^{(2)} + (H^{(1)} - E_n^{(1)})\psi_n^{(1)} - E_n^{(2)}\psi_n^\circ = 0 \qquad \text{(A20-6)}$$

The first of these equations is already solved. In order to proceed further we expand $\psi_n^{(1)}$ in a series of the functions ψ_n°, which were shown in Section 4a to be orthogonal, and we shall assume to be normalized.

$$\psi_n^{(1)} = \sum_m a_m \psi_m^\circ \tag{A20-7}$$

Similarly, we may write

$$H^{(1)} \psi_n^\circ = \sum_m H_{m,n}^{(1)} \psi_m^\circ \tag{A20-8}$$

Where the quantities $H_{m,n}^{(1)}$ are constants. By multiplication of both sides of Eq. (A20-8) by $\psi_m^{\circ*}$ and integration over all space, we find

$$H_{m,n}^{(1)} = \int \psi_m^{\circ*} H^{(1)} \psi_n^\circ \, dv \tag{A20-9}$$

If we now substitute these last results into Eq. (A20-5), we obtain

$$\sum_m a_m (H_0 - E_n^\circ) \psi_m^\circ + \sum_m H_{m,n}^{(1)} \psi_m^\circ - E_n^{(1)} \psi_n^\circ = 0 \tag{A20-10}$$

By the further use of Eq. (A20-4) this becomes

$$\sum_m [a_m (E_m^\circ - E_n^\circ) + H_{m,n}^{(1)}] \psi_m^\circ - E_n^{(1)} \psi_n^\circ = 0 \tag{A20-11}$$

The coefficient of each ψ_i° must be zero. Hence we obtain from ψ_n°

$$E_n^{(1)} = H_{n,n}^{(1)} = \int \psi_n^{\circ*} H^{(1)} \psi_n^\circ \, dv \tag{A20-12}$$

which is the first-order perturbation energy.

From the ψ_m° functions other than ψ_n°, we obtain

$$a_m = H_{m,n}^{(1)} / (E_n^\circ - E_m^\circ) \tag{A20-13}$$

This gives us our first-order correction to the wave function except for a_n, which may be obtained by normalization. The value of a_n is found to be zero. This result breaks down if the nth state is degenerate, because the denominator of Eq. (A20-13) becomes zero for the other members of the degenerate set. As we stated in Section 4h, in this case one must constitute a linear function of all the degenerate wave functions and treat it just as a linear variation function with the perturbed Hamiltonian. If the off-diagonal quantities $H_{m,n}^{(1)}$ are not zero, one must solve the resulting secular equation and thereby obtain both the correct first-order energies and the correct zero-order wave functions. Now all $H_{m,n}^{(1)}$ and a_m quantities will be zero within the degenerate set. We shall assume this has been done, if necessary, before proceeding to the second order theory.

Our next step is to obtain the products of first-order terms which appear in Eq. (A20-6).

$$H^{(1)} \psi_n^{(1)} = \sum_m{}' \frac{H_{m,n}^{(1)}}{E_n^\circ - E_m^\circ} H^{(1)} \psi_m^\circ$$

$$= \sum_k \sum_m{}' \frac{H_{k,m}^{(1)} H_{m,n}^{(1)}}{E_n^\circ - E_m^\circ} \psi_k^\circ \tag{A20-14}$$

$$E_n^{(1)} \psi_n^{(1)} = \sum_m{}' \frac{H_{n,n}^{(1)} H_{m,n}^{(1)}}{E_n^\circ - E_m^\circ} \psi_m^\circ \qquad (A20\text{-}15)$$

where the prime on the summations indicates the omission of the term with $m = n$ (or for a degenerate set, the omission of the terms for all other members of the set containing the nth term).

We assume also that we may expand $\psi_n^{(2)}$ as we did $\psi_n^{(1)}$.

$$\psi_n^{(2)} = \sum_m b_m \psi_m^\circ \qquad (A20\text{-}16)$$

Now we insert all these results into Eq. (A20-6) and collect terms involving the same ψ_i°. The coefficient of each function must be zero, which yields

$$E_n^{(2)} = \sum_m{}' H_{n,m}^{(1)} H_{m,n}^{(1)} / (E_n^\circ - E_m^\circ) \qquad (A20\text{-}17)$$

$$b_k = \sum_m{}' \frac{H_{k,m}^{(1)} H_{m,n}^{(1)}}{(E_n^\circ - E_m^\circ)(E_n^\circ - E_k^\circ)} - \frac{H_{n,n}^{(1)} H_{k,n}^{(1)}}{(E_n^\circ - E_k^\circ)^2} \qquad (A20\text{-}18)$$

We have now our desired second-order energy and can construct the second-order wave function from Eqs. (A20-16) and (A20-18) if desired.

If the perturbation is that of an electric field, it is found that the first-order energy is zero unless the system contains a dipole moment with a fixed component along the field. A freely rotating dipole shows a second-order effect,[1] but since molecular rotation is effectively classical for most practical cases, we shall not pursue it further. Rather we shall turn to the polarizability contributed by higher frequency terms, such as molecular vibrations and electronic motions. These we may take as independent of temperature; specifically we calculate for just the lowest quantum state.

We take λ to be the electric field strength F, which we assume to be along the z axis, and the quantities $H_{m,n}^{(1)}$ become

$$H_{m,n}^{(1)} = \int \psi_m^{\circ *} \sum_i e_i z_i \psi_n^\circ \, dv = (\mu_z)_{mn} \qquad (A20\text{-}19)$$

Here we recognize the transition dipole integral which appeared in the theory of radiation induced transitions. Thus the energy of the lowest quantum state in the field is

$$E = E_0^\circ - F^2 \sum_m{}' (\mu_z)_{m0}^2 / (E_m^\circ - E_0^\circ) \qquad (A20\text{-}20)$$

The polarizability is the coefficient of F in the expression for the induced dipole moment.

[1] Eyring, H., Walter, J., and Kimball, G. E., *Quantum Chemistry*, New York: John Wiley & Sons, Inc., 1944, pp. 337–341.

$$\mu = -\frac{\partial E}{\partial F} = \alpha F$$

$$\alpha = 2 \sum_m{}' (\mu_z)^2_{m0}/(E^\circ_n - E^\circ_0) \tag{A20-21}$$

Usually we need the average of the polarizability for all orientations of the molecule. We then have

$$\alpha = \frac{2}{3} \sum_m{}' \frac{(\mu_x)^2_{m0} + (\mu_y)^2_{m0} + (\mu_z)^2_{m0}}{E^\circ_n - E^\circ_0} \tag{A20-22}$$

The application of this result is discussed in Section 12c.

NUCLEAR QUADRUPOLE COUPLING ENERGY IN RELATION TO BOND TYPE

Townes and Dailey[1] have pointed out that the coupling of nuclear quadrupole moments to the electric field of the electrons provides potentially very useful information about the type of bonds in molecules. Unfortunately, this method applies only to a limited group of isotopes—those with unit or higher nuclear spin. Nuclei with zero spin have neither magnetic nor electric moments of any order. Those with half unit spin have a magnetic dipole moment but no electric quadrupole moment. In some cases where none of the abundant isotopes of an element has the required nuclear spin, it will be possible to substitute an artificially enriched stable isotope or a long-lived radioisotope having the required property. Appropriate isotopes are abundant for Li, Be, B, N, Na, Al, Cl, and many heavier atoms, but for the particularly interesting case of carbon there is no suitable isotope.

The energy differences, which are detectable in radio spectrometry, arise from changes in the angular orientation of the nuclear quadrupole moment in the electrostatic field at the nucleus. Clearly, if the electron cloud of an atom is spherically symmetrical, there can be no energy change with orientation of the nucleus. Thus electrons in s orbitals make no contribution. However, a p orbital represents a charge density concentrated along one axis (or in the case of the imaginary exponential functions the charge is in a "doughnut" in the x, y plane). Consequently, a quadrupole in the field of a p electron has an energy minimum in the orientation indicated by A in Fig. A21-1.

The actual coupling of the nuclear moment to the field is quantized. The quadrupole moment is coaxial with the nuclear spin, and the number of quantum levels depends on the magnitude of the nuclear spin. Also this nuclear angular momentum will be coupled to the molecular rotation of a gas molecule. Thus the observed spectrum is subject to several complications, which will not be considered here in detail. The observable fre-

[1] Townes, C. H. and Dailey, B. P., *J. Chem. Phys.*, **17**, 782 (1949).

quency in any particular case can be related to the quadrupole coupling constant eQq, where e is the electronic charge, Q is the nuclear quadrupole moment, and q is the asymmetry of the electrostatic field.

The theory of the interaction of a quadrupole with an electric field involves the dyadic comprising the gradient of the vector field $\nabla \mathbf{E}$. We shall not attempt to give the theory[2] here but will merely describe the results.

In the most unsymmetrical cases, there are really several parameters involved in the field, but for linear molecules these reduce to the single quan-

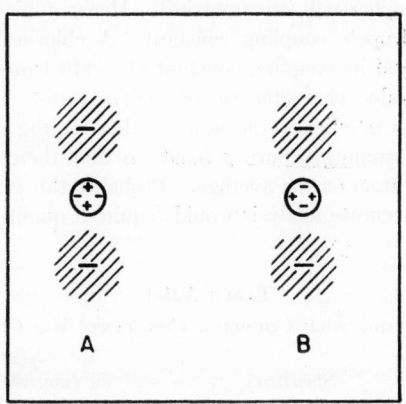

Fig. A21-1.   The stable orientation of a quadrupole in the field of a p orbital at A and the excited state of orientation at B.   An actual nucleus has a net positive charge, consequently the indicated regions of negative charge may be merely regions of decreased positive charge.

tity q.   This reduction to a single parameter holds also for atoms on the axis of a symmetric top molecule.   For atoms in less symmetrical locations it is found that a single asymmetry parameter suffices empirically, but that the orientation of the axis of the electric field may be different from that of lines connecting nuclei.

Let us consider further just the case where the field is symmetrical with respect to the x and y axes.   The z axis is then the axis of symmetry.   The Poisson equation is

$$\frac{\partial^2 V}{\partial x^2} + \frac{\partial^2 V}{\partial y^2} + \frac{\partial^2 V}{\partial z^2} = -4\pi\rho \tag{A21-1}$$

where ρ is the charge density and V is the electrostatic potential.   Hence if the system is spherically symmetrical at the nucleus,

[2] For this theory see Casimir, H. B. G., *On the Interaction between Atomic Nuclei and Electrons*, Haarlem: E. F. Bohn, 1936.

$$\frac{\partial^2 V}{\partial x^2} = \frac{\partial^2 V}{\partial y^2} = \frac{\partial^2 V}{\partial z^2} = -\frac{4}{3}\pi\rho \qquad \text{(A21-2)}$$

The difference in $(\partial^2 V/\partial z^2)$ from this symmetrical value is taken[3] for the quantity q.

$$q = \frac{\partial^2 V}{\partial z^2} + \frac{4}{3}\pi\rho \qquad \text{(A21-3)}$$

A series of chlorine compounds provides a particularly interesting set of data as given in Table A21-1. A chloride ion has a full shell of $3p$ electrons, and is therefore spherically symmetrical. Hence ionic chlorides should have a zero quadrupole coupling constant. A chlorine atom has one p electron missing, and its coupling constant of -110.4 megacycles/sec. may be taken as the value characteristic of such a state. The value for the chlorine molecule is practically the same as that for the atom. This could be explained by assuming a pure p bond, so that there is one p electron missing from each atom on the average. Probably this is an oversimplification, but a more accurate analysis would require a quantitative bond wave function.

TABLE A21-1

QUADRUPOLE COUPLING CONSTANTS FOR Cl^{35}

Molecule	Structures	$-eQq$ (mc./sec.)	$x_{Cl} - x_A$
Cl (atom)		110.4	...
Cl_2	Cl—Cl	108.5	0
ClF	Cl—F, Cl$^+$F$^-$	145.9	-1.0
ICl	I—Cl, I$^+$Cl$^-$	82.5	$+0.5$
CH_3Cl	H_3C—Cl, H_3C$^+$Cl$^-$	75.1	$+0.5$
GeH_3Cl	H_3Ge—Cl, H_3Ge$^+$Cl$^-$	43.2	$+1.3$
SiH_3Cl	H_3Si—Cl, H_3Si$^+$Cl$^-$	39.2	$+1.2$
TlCl	Tl—Cl, Tl$^+$Cl$^-$	15.8	?
NaCl	Na$^+$Cl$^-$	<1	2.1

In the various chlorine compounds there is a beautiful trend of eQq with the ionic bond character to the chlorine atom. In ClF, where the chlorine will tend to be positive, the constant indicates an average of more than one p electron vacancy in the orbital along the z axis. In the other compounds the average p orbital vacancy is less than one, indicating some negative character for the chlorine atom. The very small coupling constant

---

[3] Workers in this area have commonly defined q as the value of $\partial^2 V/\partial z^2$ at the nucleus produced by all molecular charges outside the nucleus. This is equivalent to the definition given above, but requires the arbitrary exclusion of the charge density of s electrons at the nucleus. It seems to the writer to be better to eliminate the effect of the electronic charge density at the nucleus by the subtraction indicated above.

for NaCl (gas molecule) indicates an almost purely ionic bond. The differences in electronegativity from Table 8.1 are also listed in Table A21-1 for comparison.

With other atoms this method could give information on the hybridization of the atomic orbitals in forming the bond orbitals. Thus in NH_3 the arrangement of an unshared pair in the $2s$ orbital and p orbital bonds would give a zero quadrupole coupling constant. In this case each of the three p orbitals must be equally occupied, yielding a symmetrical structure. However, if the orbital holding the unshared pair is a hybrid, the fact that its two electrons are both fully on the nitrogen will unbalance the p electron distribution. In the bond orbitals, roughly half of the electron probability will be associated with the attached atom, in this case hydrogen. Actually ammonia has a quadrupole coupling constant of ± 4.10 mc./sec., so that there must be some p character in the orbital for the unshared pair. However, as yet there are not enough data to yield an unambiguous value for a unit unbalance of one p electron. Consequently it is not possible to give a quantitative value for this hybridization ratio.

Appendix 22

THE PARTICLE IN A SPHERICAL BOX

In Section 2h we considered the one-dimensional problem of a particle in a box formed by vertical potential walls. Particularly for the discussion of the deuteron, we need the solutions to the similar problem involving three dimensions and a spherical box. Spherical polar coordinates are appropriate and we may go directly to Eqs. (3.19) and (3.35) of Chapter 3, where μ is either the mass of a single particle or the reduced mass of a two-particle system.

$$\psi = \Phi(\phi)\Theta(\theta)S(r)/r \qquad (A22\text{-}1)$$

$$\frac{d^2S}{dr^2} - \frac{l(l+1)}{r^2}S + \frac{8\pi^2\mu}{h^2}[E - V(r)]S = 0 \qquad (A22\text{-}2)$$

$$\begin{aligned} V &= -V_0 \quad \text{for} \quad r < r_0 \\ V &= 0 \quad \text{for} \quad r > r_0 \end{aligned} \qquad (A22\text{-}3)$$

Also let the binding energy of the system, $-E$, be W.

For the case of zero angular momentum $(l = 0)$ which is of principal interest, we may write directly

$$\begin{aligned} S &= A \sin \alpha r \quad \text{for} \quad r < r_0 \\ S &= Be^{-\beta r} \qquad \text{for} \quad r > r_0 \end{aligned} \qquad (A22\text{-}4)$$

with

$$\begin{aligned} \alpha &= [8\pi^2\mu(V_0 - W)/h^2]^{1/2} \\ \beta &= [8\pi^2\mu W/h^2]^{1/2} \end{aligned} \qquad (A22\text{-}5)$$

We have omitted the second mathematical solution in each region because it is unacceptable for a quantum mechanical wave function in the energy range $-V_0 < E < 0$ where both α and β are real.

Now we must make S and dS/dr continuous at $r = r_0$. This results in the condition

$$\cot \alpha r_0 = -\beta/\alpha \qquad (A22\text{-}6)$$

which may be solved for the energy levels.

For positive energies (negative W) we have no binding of the particles but only a scattering problem. Then in the region $r > r_0$ we have the solution with two constants

$$S = C \sin (kr + \delta_0)$$
$$k = (8\pi^2\mu E/h^2)^{1/2} \tag{A22-7}$$

Also we may now write

$$\alpha = [8\pi^2\mu(V_0 + E)/h^2]^{1/2}$$

Then the continuity conditions require that

$$\cot (kr_0 + \delta_0) = (\alpha/k) \cot \alpha r_0 \tag{A22-8}$$

The quantity δ_0 is called the *phase shift* for the $l = 0$ state and can be obtained from Eq. (A22-8). Any positive energy is allowable.

The solutions for l other than zero are similar in principle but do not yield such simple functions. In classical regions, i.e., where the apparent kinetic energy is positive, the wave function[1] can be expressed in Bessel functions of order $l + \frac{1}{2}$. The scattering effects have been worked out in terms of these functions.

[1] Schiff, L. I., *Quantum Mechanics*, New York: McGraw-Hill Book Company, Inc., 1949, pp. 76-80, 111-112.

Appendix 23

COLLISION THEORY; SCATTERING
CROSS SECTIONS[1]

In Chapter 2 we considered a number of one-dimensional problems involving collisions of free particles with potential barriers. We wish now to consider such problems in three dimensions. While our principal interest is connected with nuclear scattering phenomena, our results are equally applicable to atomic phenomena, upon introduction of appropriate potential functions.

The theory is most conveniently developed in terms of coordinates based on the center of mass as the origin. Let us now examine the relation between this *center of mass* system and the coordinates of the *laboratory experimental* system. This is most readily explained by reference to Fig. A23-1.

If particle one, of mass m_1, is initially at rest, then the velocity of the center of gravity is $v' = m_2 v/(m_1 + m_2)$, where v is the velocity of the bombarding particle. In the center of mass system, particle one has the center of mass velocity v' in the opposite direction, and the incident velocity of particle two is reduced to $v - v' = m_1 v/(m_1 + m_2)$, which we shall designate v''. Now if the collision is elastic, i.e., if there is no change in total kinetic energy, the final velocities in the center of mass system have the same magnitudes as the initial velocities. The vectorial relationship between the velocities and angles shown at the bottom of Fig. A23-1 may be expressed as follows.

$$v'' \cos \theta + v' = v_2 \cos \theta_0$$
$$v'' \sin \theta = v_2 \sin \theta_0 \qquad (A23\text{-}1)$$

We have also the relationship

$$\frac{v'}{v''} = \frac{m_2}{m_1} = \gamma \qquad (A23\text{-}2)$$

Then we obtain

$$\tan \theta_0 = \sin \theta/(\gamma + \cos \theta) \qquad (A23\text{-}3)$$

[1] General reference: Mott, N. F. and Massey, H. S. W., *The Theory of Atomic Collisions*, 2d ed., New York: Oxford University Press, 1949.

The somewhat more complex relationships may be derived for inelastic collisions where kinetic energy is converted to internal potential energy, or vice versa, and where the particles change mass in the collision.

We shall be particularly interested in collisions of two protons or of a proton and a neutron. In either case the two particles have at least approximately equal mass. Hence $\gamma = 1$ and $\theta = 2\theta_0$.

Scattering probabilities are expressed in terms of cross sections σ, defined in the following manner. One assumes n_1 particles or scattering centers per unit area and a parallel flux of n_2 bombarding particles per unit time and unit area. Then one measures the number of bombarding particles

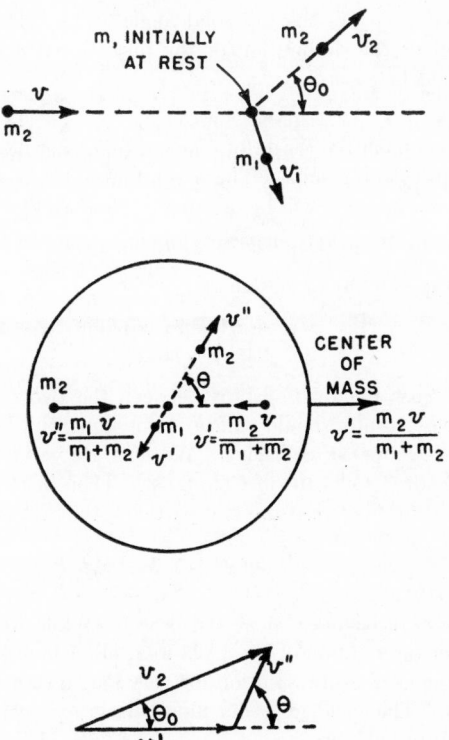

Fig. A23-1. At the top is the laboratory coordinate system for an elastic collision where the target particle of mass m_1 is initially at rest. In the center is the coordinate system where the center of mass is at rest. At the bottom there is the vector addition of the velocity of the scattered particles in the center of mass system, v'', to the velocity of the center of mass, v', to yield the velocity of the scattered particle in the laboratory system v_2.

that emerge within a solid angle $d\omega_0$ at a polar angle θ_0 (in the laboratory system) from the incident beam direction. This number of emerging particles can be written

$$n_1 n_2 \sigma_0(\theta_0, \phi_0) \, d\omega_0 \tag{A23-4}$$

where $\sigma_0(\theta_0, \phi_0)$ is the differential cross section. We have assumed the simplest case with no interference between individual collisions, no multiple collisions, etc. We have included the azimuthal angle ϕ_0, but it will not enter in simple examples.

The total scattering cross section σ_0 is

$$\sigma_0 = \int \sigma_0(\theta_0, \phi_0) \, d\omega_0 \tag{A23-5}$$

where the integral covers the full solid angle of 4π. The total scattering cross section gives the diminution of the unscattered emergent beam, n_2', from the incident beam, n_2,

$$n_2' = n_2(1 - n_1\sigma_0) \tag{A23-6}$$

The cross sections in the center of mass system must be defined in a manner to give equivalent results. The azimuthal angle is the same in both systems ($\phi_0 = \phi$), hence it will be omitted. Thus we have

$$\sigma(\theta) \sin\theta \, d\theta = \sigma_0(\theta_0) \sin\theta_0 \, d\theta_0 \tag{A23-7}$$

and by using Eq. (A23-3) we obtain

$$\sigma_0(\theta_0) = \frac{(1 + \gamma^2 + 2\gamma \cos\theta)^{3/2}}{|1 + \gamma \cos\theta|} \, \sigma(\theta) \tag{A23-8}$$

We could discuss the relationships between the two coordinate systems further, but these results should suffice. Consequently, let us turn now to the quantum mechanics of collisions. We separate variables in exactly the manner of Eqs. (3.1) to (3.10) in Chapter 3. Then in terms of the coordinates for the distance between the two particles, the Schrödinger equation is

$$-\frac{h^2}{8\pi^2\mu} \nabla^2\psi + V\psi = E\psi \tag{A23-9}$$

where μ is the reduced mass $m_1 m_2/(m_1 + m_2)$. While we shall eventually have to consider the solution of Eq. (A23-9) at all distances, for the moment we need only the asymptotic solution for very long distances where we shall assume $V = 0$. The incident beam along the z axis can be represented, with certain limitations, by

$$\psi = A_0 e^{ikz} \quad \text{with} \quad k = 2\pi\mu v/h \tag{A23-10}$$

where v is the relative velocity of the two particles.

This expression for the incident beam is the same as we have used in Chapter 2. However, we must keep in mind that we have in a typical laboratory experiment a collimated beam of finite cross sectional area and only approximately uniform in direction.   Equation (A23-10), by contrast, represents plane waves of infinite extent and exact uniformity of direction. The asymptotic solution for outgoing particles is

$$\psi = A[e^{ikz} + r^{-1}f(\theta, \phi)e^{ikr}] \tag{A23-11}$$

where the first term represents unscattered particles and the second term represents scattered particles. The transformation of Eq. (3.34) to (3.35) will help the reader check the acceptability of the second term in Eq. (A23-11). The constant A must be adjusted to conserve all particles, but since we assume only a small scattering, it will be only slightly less than A_0.

The intensity of scattered particles at large r and an angle θ, ϕ is obtained from $|\psi|^2 \, dv$ at that location. Here, however, we must remember the finite extent of the incident beam. Thus if we are outside the incident or the unscattered emergent beam, the first term in Eq. (A23-11) will disappear, and we obtain a scattered flux proportional to

$$|A|^2 r^{-2}|f(\theta, \phi)|^2 \, dv$$

The scattering cross section, $\sigma(\theta, \phi)$, is defined in terms of the scattered flux from a single scattering atom and the flux of the unscattered beam. Thus, with $d\omega$ an increment of solid angle, we have

$$\sigma(\theta, \phi) \, d\omega = \frac{|A|^2 r^{-2}|f(\theta, \phi)|^2 r^2 \, dr \, d\omega}{|A|^2 \, dz}$$

$$\sigma(\theta, \phi) = |f(\theta, \phi)|^2 \tag{A23-12}$$

Here it is appropriate to take equal increments of length along the path of the particle, $dz = dr$, because the velocities in the center of mass system are the same.

Let us now limit ourselves to a spherically symmetrical potential function $V(r)$. Then the wave equation can be separated in spherical polar coordinates. The angular functions will be those obtained in Section 3c, and the quantum number l will have the same significance. We also make the transformation of the radial equation shown in Eqs. (3.34) and (3.35), and obtain a general solution

$$\psi = r^{-1} \sum_{m,l} \Phi_m(\phi)\Theta_{l,m}(\theta)S_l(r) \tag{A23-13}$$

where $S_l(r)$ is a solution of the equation

$$\frac{d^2 S_l}{dr^2} + \left\{ -\frac{l(l+1)}{r^2} + \frac{8\pi^2\mu}{h^2}[E - V(r)] \right\} S_l = 0 \tag{A23-14}$$

and E is the energy in the center of mass system, which is $\frac{1}{2}\mu v^2$ rather than $\frac{1}{2}m_2 v^2$.

Again we consider the asymptotic behavior for large r. It is found that the expression of Eq. (A22-7) for the spherical potential well is generally valid as $r \to \infty$ provided the potential V approaches zero faster than $1/r$. Excepting coulomb fields, then, we have

$$S_0 = C_0 \sin (kr + \delta_0) \qquad \text{(A22-7)}$$

where δ_0 is the phase shift for the function with $l = 0$.

It is apparent that the effect of a nonzero value of l is the same as that of a short-range potential. Thus we may expect that the net effect on the asymptotic solution will be a phase shift. This shift is found to be $-\frac{1}{2}l\pi$; consequently we generalize Eq. (A22-7) to

$$S_l = C_l \sin (kr - \tfrac{1}{2}l\pi + \delta_l) \qquad \text{(A23-15)}$$

where δ_l is the phase shift caused by the potential energy for the lth state.

In the particular case of $l = 0$ and the spherical box potential, δ can be evaluated from Eq. (A22-8). In more general cases, the same principles are applied but the mathematics of the solution is more complex.

To complete our solution for the scattering cross section we must correlate our two asymptotic expressions for ψ, Eqs. (A23-11) and (A23-15). This is best done in terms of Legendre polynomials, which are essentially our θ functions of Section 3c, and Bessel functions.[2] Since we have not given heretofore the necessary properties of Legendre and Bessel functions, we shall omit the details of the next series of steps. The resulting differential cross section is

$$\sigma(\theta) = \frac{1}{k^2} \left| \sum_{l=0}^{\infty} (2l + 1)e^{i\delta_l} \sin \delta_l P_l (\cos \theta) \right|^2 \qquad \text{(A23-16)}$$

where P_l is the lth Legendre polynomial. If we write out the first few terms, the result is

$$\sigma(\theta) = k^{-2}[\sin^2 \delta_0 + 6 \sin \delta_0 \sin \delta_1 \cos (\delta_1 - \delta_0) \cos \theta + 9 \sin^2 \delta_1 \cos^2 \theta + \ldots]$$

The total cross section is the integral of the differential cross section over all angles. The orthogonality properties of the Legendre functions eliminate all the cross terms in Eq. (A23-16), hence the result is considerably simplified.

$$\sigma = \frac{4\pi}{k^2} \sum_l (2l + 1) \sin^2 \delta_l \qquad \text{(A23-17)}$$

The interesting conclusion arises from Eqs. (A23-16) and (A23-17) that if any δ is equal to a multiple of π, it contributes nothing to the total scattering.

A simple example to illustrate this theory is the scattering of rigid spheres of diameter r_0. Then we set $V = \infty$ for $r < r_0$ and $V = 0$ for $r > r_0$. The function S of Eq. (A22-7) must be zero at $r = r_0$, yielding

[2] Schiff, L. I., *Quantum Mechanics*, New York: McGraw-Hill Book Company, Inc., 1949, p. 105; Mott, N. F. and Massey, H. S. W., *The Theory of Atomic Collisions*, 2d ed., New York: Oxford University Press, 1949, Chap. 2.

$$\sin (kr_0 + \delta_0) = 0$$
$$\delta_0 = -kr_0 \tag{A23-18}$$

It is found that for low energies, where $kr_0 \ll 1$, only δ_0 is important. Hence we find

$$\sigma(\theta) \cong \frac{\sin^2 kr_0}{k^2} \cong r_0^2 \quad \text{and} \quad \sigma \cong 4\pi r_0^2 \tag{A23-19}$$

The scattering is spherically symmetrical in the center of mass system, and the cross section is four times the classical area of πr_0^2.

Another example, which is important in proton-neutron scattering, is the spherical box potential of Appendix 22. We take the limiting case of low energies and a short-range potential, so that the product kr_0 may be neglected. Then Eq. (A22-8) simplifies to

$$\cot \delta_0 = (\alpha_0/k) \cot \alpha_0 r_0 \tag{A23-20}$$
$$\alpha_0 = [8\pi^2 \mu V_0/h^2]^{1/2} \tag{A23-21}$$

Large cross sections are obtained for low-velocity particle scattering if there is an energy level very close to the dissociation energy. From Appendix 22 we have the relationship for a stable energy level

$$\alpha \cot \alpha r_0 = -\beta \tag{A22-6}$$

and if this is to be close to the dissociation energy, β must be small. Consequently, we find that αr_0 must be just slightly more than $(n + \frac{1}{2})\pi$, where n is an integer and α is very near the α_0 of Eq. (A23-21).

A first approximation is obtained by the substitution of $-\beta$ from Eq. (A22-6) as the value of $\alpha_0 \cot \alpha_0 r_0$ in Eq. (A23-20). Then one has

$$\sin^2 \delta_0 = (1 + \cot^2 \delta_0)^{-1} = (1 + \beta^2/k^2)^{-1}$$
$$\sigma(\theta) = \frac{1}{k^2 + \beta^2} = \frac{h^2}{8\pi^2 \mu(E + W)} \tag{A23-22}$$

or for the total cross section

$$\sigma = \frac{h^2}{2\pi\mu(E + W)} \tag{A23-23}$$

A second approximation may be obtained by considering the difference between α and α_0. The net result is to multiply Eqs. (A23-22) and (A23-23) by the factor $(1 + \beta r_0)$.

A stable energy just below the dissociation limit is given by Eq. (A22-6) if $\alpha_0 r_0$ is just over $(n + \frac{1}{2})\pi$. It is also of interest to consider the case when $\alpha_0 r_0$ is just a little less than $(n + \frac{1}{2})\pi$. We may then define a virtual energy level W_v by the equations

$$\alpha \cot \alpha r_0 = +\lambda$$
$$\alpha = [8\pi^2 \mu(V_0 + W_v)/h^2]^{1/2} \tag{A23-24}$$
$$\lambda = [8\pi^2 \mu W_v/h^2]^{1/2}$$

Then the substitution of λ for $\alpha_0 \cot \alpha_0 r_0$ yields exactly Eqs. (A23-22) and (A23-23) with W_v in place of W_1. Also the second approximation is found to introduce the factor $(1 - \lambda r_0)$ instead of $(1 + \beta r_0)$.

Where the particles have nuclear spin, the proper spin functions must be combined with the orbital functions. For neutron-proton scattering no symmetry is involved, and both singlet and triplet spin functions can be associated with any l value. However, if the potential function depends on the spin, one must apportion the right sides of Eqs. (A23-22) and (A23-23) in the ratio of the probability of the respective collisions, i.e., 25% singlet and 75% triplet.

There are further considerations when the bombarding and scattering particles are identical. Then the complete wave functions must be either symmetrical or antisymmetrical to the exchange of the particles. Thus for proton-proton scattering only the singlet spin function can be associated with the $l = 0$ orbital wave function for scattering. Similarly the $l = 1$ function is necessarily associated with the triplet spin state.

Another feature of the case of identical particles is that the experimental detector cannot possibly distinguish between the bombarding and scattering particle. Since the two particles leave in opposite directions in the center of mass system, we find

$$\sigma(\theta) = |f(\theta)|^2 + |f(\pi - \theta)|^2 \tag{A23-25}$$

where no dependence on ϕ is assumed. Then the scattering intensity is symmetrical about $\theta = \pi$ in the center of mass system, or $\theta_0 = \pi/2$ in the laboratory system.

Finally, we must add that we have not considered the treatment for electrostatic forces. Because of the long range of these forces, special methods are required which will not be given here. The results for coulomb forces alone or in combination with short range forces may be found elsewhere.[3]

---

[3] Mott, N. F. and Massey, H. S. W., *The Theory of Atomic Collisions*, 2d ed., New York: Oxford University Press, 1949, Chap. 3; Schiff, L. I., *Quantum Mechanics*, New York: McGraw-Hill Book Company, Inc., 1949, pp. 114–121.

VALUES OF PHYSICAL CONSTANTS AND CONVERSION FACTORS

PHYSICAL CONSTANTS

Avogadro number:

Chemical scale (O = 16.0000):

$$N_0 = (6.0238 \pm 0.0001) \times 10^{23} \text{ mole}^{-1}$$

Physical scale (O^{16} = 16.0000):

$$N_0' = (6.0254 \pm 0.0001) \times 10^{23} \text{ mole}^{-1}$$

Velocity of light:

$$c = (2.99790 \pm 0.00001) \times 10^{10} \text{ cm. sec.}^{-1}$$

Ice point (absolute scale):

$$T_0 = 273.16 \pm 0.01 ^\circ \text{K}$$

Planck constant:

$$h = (6.6238 \pm 0.0002) \times 10^{-27} \text{ erg sec.}$$

Boltzmann constant:

$$k = (1.38026 \pm 0.0001) \times 10^{-16} \text{ erg deg.}^{-1}$$

Gas constant per mole (chem.):

$$R = 8.3144 \pm 0.0004 \text{ abs. joule deg.}^{-1} \text{ mole}^{-1}$$
$$R = 1.9872 \pm 0.0001 \text{ defined cal. deg.}^{-1} \text{ mole}^{-1}$$

Second radiation constant:

$$hc/k = 1.4387 \pm 0.0001 \text{ cm. deg.}$$

Electron charge:

$$e = (4.8022 \pm 0.0001) \times 10^{-10} \text{ abs. e.s.u.}$$

Electron mass:

$$m = (9.1072 \pm 0.0003) \times 10^{-28} \text{ gm.}$$

Proton mass:

$$M_p = (1.6722 \pm 0.0001) \times 10^{-24} \text{ gm.}$$

Ratio mass proton to electron:

$$M_p/m = 1836.1 \pm 0.1$$

Radius of Bohr orbit (in H^1):

$$a_0(\text{H}) = (0.52942 \pm 0.00001) \times 10^{-8} \text{ cm.}$$

(for ∞ mass):

$$a_0(\infty) = (0.52915 \pm 0.00001) \times 10^{-8} \text{ cm.}$$

Rydberg constant for H^1:

$$R_\text{H} = 109677.59 \pm 0.01 \text{ cm.}^{-1}$$

Rydberg constant for infinite mass:
$$R_\infty = 109737.32 \pm 0.01 \text{ cm.}^{-1}$$
Energy of the normal hydrogen atom (H^1):
$$-E_H = 13.596 \pm 0.001 \text{ e.v.}$$
Magnetic moment of one Bohr magneton:
$$\mu_0 = (0.92712 \pm 0.00002) \times 10^{-20} \text{ erg gauss}^{-1}$$

ENERGY CONVERSION FACTORS

erg molecule^{-1}	e.v.	cm.$^{-1}$	cm.^{3} atm. mole^{-1}	joule mole^{-1}	defined cal. mole
1	6.243×10^{11}	5.036×10^{15}	5.945×10^{17}	6.024×10^{16}	1.4397×1
1.6019×10^{-12}	1	8067	9.523×10^5	96493	23062
1.9857×10^{-16}	1.2396×10^{-4}	1	118.05	11.962	2.8589
1.6821×10^{-18}	1.0501×10^{-6}	8.471×10^{-3}	1	0.10133	0.024217
1.6601×10^{-17}	1.0363×10^{-5}	8.360×10^{-2}	9.869	1	0.23901
6.946×10^{-17}	4.336×10^{-5}	0.3498	41.29	4.1840	1

The mole is on the chemical scale and all electrical units above are absolute units. 1 int. volt = 1.00033 abs. volt, and 1 int. joule = 1.00017 abs. joule.

The defined calorie is 4.1840 abs. joule by definition, or 4.1833 int. joule.

The sources of the above values are the Report of J. W. M. DuMond and E. R. Cohen to the National Research Council Committee on Constants and Conversion Factors of Physics, December 1950, and the Report of the Subcommittee on Physical Constants of the Committee on Physical Chemistry to the National Research Council of July 1951.

An attempt was made to make all data in the text consistent with the above values but certain small discrepancies probably remain.

AUTHOR INDEX

SUBJECT INDEX